Ku/Liepins

ELECTRICAL PROPERTIES
OF POLYMERS

CHEMICAL PRINCIPLES

ELECTRICAL PROPERTIES OF POLYMERS

CHEMICAL PRINCIPLES

by Chen C. Ku and Raimond Liepins

with 113 Figures and 47 Tables

Hanser Publishers, Munich – Vienna – New York

Distributed in the United States of America by
Macmillan Publishing Company, New York
and in Canada by
Collier Macmillan Canada, Inc., Ontario

Liepins – tel. (505) 471-6756

2301 North Ct, Santa Fe, NM 87505

raimond-liepins @ yahoo.c

Prof. Chen C. Ku
Shanghai Jiao Tong University, The People's Republic of China
Dr. Raimond Liepins
Los Alamos National Laboratory, Los Alamos, NM, USA

Distributed in USA by
Scientific and Technical Books
Macmillan Publishing Company
866 Third Avenue, New York, N. Y. 10022

Distributed in Canada by
Collier Macmillan Canada, Inc.
1200 Eglington Ave. E, Suite 200, Don Mills, Ontario M3C 3N1 Canada

Distributed in all other countries by
Carl Hanser Verlag
Kolbergerstrasse 22
D-8000 München 80

The use of general descriptive names, trademarks, etc., in this publication, even if the former are not especially identified, is not to be taken as a sign that such names, as understood by the Trade Marks and Merchandise Marks Act, may accordingly be used freely by anyone.

While the advice and information in this book are believed to be true and accurate at the date of going to press, neither the authors nor the editors nor the publisher can accept any legal responsibility for any errors or omissions that may be made. The publisher makes no warranty, express or implied, with respect to the material contained herein.

CIP-Kurztitelaufnahme der Deutschen Bibliothek

Ku, Chen C.:
Electrical properties of polymers : chem. principles /
by Chen C. Ku and Raimond Liepins. –
Munich ; Vienna ; New York : Hanser, 1987
    ISBN 3-446-14280-0
NE: Liepins, Raimond:

ISBN 3-446-14280-0 Hanser Publishers, Munich
ISBN 0-02-947631-3 Macmillan Publishing Company, New York
Library of Congress Catalog Card Number 86-63194

Printed in the Federal Republic of Germany by C. H. Beck'sche Buchdruckerei, Nördlingen

TO OUR FAMILIES

CONTENTS

PREFACE

This book treats polymeric materials from the most insulating to the most conducting and is an attempt to combine and correlate the vast experimental and theoretical literature in this field. We hope the book will be of predictive value in the control of the four fundamental parameters of electrical properties in polymers: dielectric constant, tangent of dielectric loss angle, dielectric breakdown, and electrical conduction.

The electrical properties of polymers make up an inherently interdisciplinary topic, being closely associated, on the one hand, with the mechanical properties of polymers (polarization and relaxation) and, on the other hand, with the semiconductive properties (conduction and breakdown). We have collated the relevant aspects of these contingent subjects to unify their treatment and then have analyzed them and related the available basic knowledge of structure to properties. At the end of each discussion of the fundamental parameters of electrical properties, we have shown how to use this knowledge: how to design materials with the dielectric constant low or high; how to prevent electrical and water treeing, and how to synthesize highly conductive polymers.

Except for the highly conducting polymers, these topics have long been the exclusive province of engineers. In our treatment, we have placed the emphasis on the interests of physical and synthesis chemists.

Thus, the book is primarily for chemists and technologists working with polymers for specific electrical and electronic engineering uses. We also have provided extensive tables of data on the fundamental parameters of electrical properties of polymers as well as the properties directly affecting them, along with the original references, to make the book a valuable reference source for specialists. At the same time, we have developed some of the material from first principles to make it useful to those entering the field of dielectrics and conductive and superconductive polymers. The emphasis on description and explanation in molecular and electronic terms of the observed phenomena provides a basic understanding of how polymers behave electrically and how to control this behavior chemically.

The authors are indebted to many persons for their help, discussions, comments, and suggestions. They are grateful to Edmund H. Immergut, Frank Karasz, Juergen Fuhrmann, Hans–Joerg Meyer–Christians, and Eli M. Pearce for reading the entire manuscript and excellent suggestions and to Alan Bishop, David Campbell, Mahmoud Aldissi, and David Duchane for reading sections and giving helpful comments and constructive criticism. One of the authors is grateful to the Los Alamos National Laboratory management, especially Siegfried Hecker, Eugene Wewerka, James Dickinson, Richard Mah, and Ainslie Young, for the permission and support in the writing of this book.

The authors are grateful to Janice Waskowiak and Maria J. Armijo for the care they showed in typing of the ever–changing text and to Cindy Boone for the highly professional and efficient work on all of the figures and graphs. For the contributions to clarity in presentation we are indebted to the eminently professional editorial staff, Barry Burton and Betty Leffler. The authors are also grateful to Mary Ann Martinez for lending help at a critical time, and to Otto Liepins for some of the Appendices. Last, but not least, we are grateful to our families for their patience with the turmoil that accompanies the preparation of a manuscript.

The book had its origins in some of the material presented in a series of lectures at the Xian and Shanghai Jiao Tong Universities by one of the authors (C. C. K.).

Shanghai, China and	Chen C. Ku
Los Alamos, New Mexico	Raimond Liepins
November 1985	

Some of the figures and tables which appear in this book have been previously published elsewhere and the authors are indebted to the many publishers, scientific societies and authors for granting permission to reproduce the copyrighted material. The individual sources are listed below:

Book or Journal	Publisher	Figure or Table (T)
Chem. Soc. Rev.	The Royal Society of Chemistry, London	1.1, 5.10
Thermal Conduction in Semiconductors	Pergamon Press, New York	1.2
Nature (London)	MacMillan and Co., Ltd., London	T 1.1
Ultrasonics	Butterworth Sci. Ltd. Guildford, Surrey, U.K.	1.3
Advances in Polymer Science, No. 33	Springer-Verlag, New York	1.4, 1.6, 1.7, 2.12, T 2.8
Electronic Properties of Polymers	John Wiley and Sons, New York	1.5
Polymer Science, A Materials Science Handbook, Vol. 2	North-Holland Physics Publ., Amsterdam	2.1, 2.2
Dielectrics and Waves	MIT Press, Cambridge	2.3, 2.5
Dielectric Spectroscopy of Polymers	Adam Hilger, Ltd., Bristol	T 2.6, 2.10, 2.11
Trans Faraday Soc.	The Royal Society of Chemistry, London	2.13
Dielectric Behavior and Structure	McGraw-Hill Book Co., New York	3.1
J. Am. Chem. Soc.	American Chemical Soc., Washington, DC	3.2, 3.18, 5.12, 5.20, T 5.4
J. Poly. Sci., Poly. Phys. Ed.	John Wiley and Sons, New York	3.5, 3.6, 3.13
J. Poly. Sci.	John Wiley and Sons, New York	3.7, 3.8
J. Materials Sci.	Chapman and Hall, London	3.9, 4.16, 4.28, 4.29, T 4.10, 4.32, T 4.11
Colloid and Polymer Science	Dr. Dietrich Steinkopff Verlag, Darmstadt	3.14, 3.17
1972 Annual Report, Conference on Electrical Insulation and Dielectric Phenomena	National Academy of Sciences, Washington, DC	4.1, 4.2, T 4.6
Engineering Dielectrics, IIA, Electrical Properties of Solid Insulating Materials: Molecular Structure and Electrical Behavior	ASTM, Philadelphia	4.4, 4.5, 4.14, 4.39, 4.41, T 4.22, T 4.23, 5.5, 5.6, 5.7, 5.8, 5.9
J. Applied Physics	American Institute of Physics, New York	4.6

1974 Annual Report, Conference on Electrical Insulation and Dielectric Phenomena	National Academy of Sciences, Washington, DC	4.7, 4.8, 4.9, 4.10
Proceedings of the Institution of Electrical Engineers	The Institute of Electrical Engineers, London	4.20, 4.40
IEEE Trans. Electrical Insul.	The Institute of Electrical and Electronics Engineers, Inc., New York	4.21, T 4.8, T 4.9, 4.22, T 4.21
Kirk-Othmer: Encyclopedia of Chemical Technology, Vol. 18	John Wiley and Sons, Inc., New York	5.13, 5.14
Quantum Chemistry of Polymers-Solid State Aspects	D. Reidel Publ. Co., Dordrecht, Holland	5.15, 5.16
J. Polym. Sci., Polym. Chem. Ed.	John Wiley and Sons, Inc., New York	T 5.2

SYMBOLS USED

Upper Case		*Lower Case*	*Greek*	
A	$N(E)$	a	α	σ_{eff}
A_0	$N(t)$	b	α_0	σ_s
A_1	P	c	α_α	τ
A_2	P_0	c_1	α_e	τ_{tr}
B	P_1	c_2	α_T	τ_r
C	P_t	c_3	β	Φ_{app}
C_T	$P(x)$	d	β_m	X
C_V	Q	d_0	β_s	Ψ
D	Q_m	d'	γ	$\Psi_\varkappa(x)$
D_0	Q_{exc}	e	$\dot{\gamma}$	ω
E,E	$Q_1(x)$	f	Γ	ω_m
E_0	$Q_2(x)$	f_m	Γ_c	
E_1	R	g	δ	
E_2	S	g_f	Δ	
E_3	ΔS	g_r	ε	
E_a	T	h,h	ε_0	
E_B	T_0	i	ε_g	
E_c	ΔT	j	ε_n	
E_d	T_c	k	ε_r	
E_F	T_g	k_0	ε_∞	
E_g	T_m	l_x	ε'	
E_m	T_p	m	ε''	
E_t	T_r	m_k	ε'_m	
E_σ	U	n	ε''_m	
E'	U_1	n_0	ε^*	
F	U_2	n_t	ζ	
ΔF	V	p	$[\eta]$	
$F(x)$	V_i	$p(t)$	η_0	
	V_m	q	Θ	
G	V_n	r	Θ_0	
ΔH	V_s	r_0	$\varkappa$	
I	V_{so}	s	λ	
I_0	$V(x)$	t	Λ	
J	W	t_1	μ	
J_b	W_0	t_f	μ_0	
J_c	W_g	t_i	μ_d	
$J_{cond.}$	W_p	t_s	μ_s	
$J_{diff.}$	W_{pr}	u	ν	
J_s	ΔW	$u_k(x)$	ξ	
K	W_{vap}	v	Ξ	
L	W_{cubic}	v_d	π	
M	$X_{A,B}$	v_{th}	ϱ	
$\bar{M}^2$	Y	v_{drift}	σ	
$\bar{M}$		w	σ_{00}	
N		w_1	σ_{++}	
N_0		x	σ_i	
N_c		z	σ_3	
N_t		z_c	σ_m	

A—Pit across which wood is placed. B—Forehearth. C—Ladle. D—Iron
mould. E—Cakes. F—Empty pot lined with stones in layers. G—Troughs.
H—Pits dug at the foot of the troughs. I—Small wood laid over the troughs.
K—Wind.

Chapter 1

THE FOUR FUNDAMENTAL PARAMETERS
OF ELECTRICAL PROPERTIES OF POLYMERS

1.1   INTRODUCTION

The people of ancient times classified the materials of their world as animal, plant, and mineral. One of the outstanding properties among these materials is their ability to serve as conductors of heat or other forms of energy. Although the animal and plant materials are generally covalently bonded organic compounds and therefore incapable of thermal conductivity, the reduction products of minerals–the metals–are excellent conductors of heat. After the discovery of electricity, the animal and plant materials were also found to be nonconductors of electric current, but the metals are in general excellent conductors. Today, much of our industrial progress is based on the use of organic materials such as polymers (polyethylene, polystyrene, and polyvinyl chloride) as insulators for both heat and electricity and on the use of metals as conductors for both.

However, our modern lifestyle increasingly demands more from the polymers than their traditional role of insulators for heat and electric current. For example, organic polymers are used commercially as conductors of electricity. The implantable cardiac pacemaker (Figure 1.1) uses a poly(2-vinylpyridine)-iodine complex as the cathode in the miniature Li-I_2 primary cell.[1] The complex serves a dual function: as a source of iodine for the cell reaction $2 \, Li + I_2 \rightarrow 2 \, LiI$ and as an electronic conductor carrying the current to the collector. The conductivity of the polymeric complex is constant at 10^{-3} $(ohm \cdot cm)^{-1}$. This solid-state cell with the LiI electrolyte formed *in situ* has an energy density of 120 whkg^{-1} compared with 30 whkg^{-1} for the best lead-acid battery. Furthermore, it has a service life of 10 years.

Thermal conductivity in polymeric materials is also being sought.[2,3] For example, the automobile industry is trying hard to use more and more plastic parts in automobiles to reduce weight and thereby increase energy efficiency. However, the industry is keyed to making parts in a fraction of a minute. In the process of forming the parts with conventional plastics, getting the heat in and then getting it out once the parts are formed requires much longer process cycles than with metals. Thus, making the same number of parts from plastics requires much more tooling, and one to two orders of magnitude greater thermal conductivity in plastics would be a very significant advance indeed.

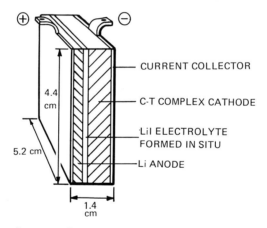

Fig. 1.1. Implantable cardiac pacemaker.

The conduction of heat in solids is a difficult and comparatively neglected subject. One reason for this is the great difficulty in making really accurate measurements of thermal conductivity, particularly at very high and very low temperatures. One of the more accurate techniques is that of Goldsmid.[4] It is used for materials with thermal conductivities ranging from below 0.02 W cm^{-1} °C^{-1} to greater than 0.1 W cm^{-1} °C^{-1} with an estimated accuracy of 3%. The apparatus used in the absolute determination of thermal conductivity is illustrated in Fig. 1.2.

Another reason is the major theoretical difficulty in dealing with the transport of heat by lattice vibrations. Still another reason is the generally variable purity and complex morphology of most solids manufactured outside the semiconductor industry. Because of the complexity of these problems and the slow progress that has been made in this field, it is far more significant at this time to understand the fundamental parameters of electrical properties of polymers than to discuss thermal conductivity.

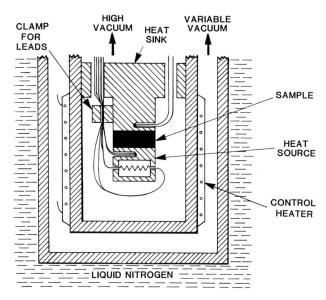

Fig. 1.2. Apparatus for the absolute determination of thermal conductivity of poor conductors.

Listed below for quick reference are more recent books and review articles that amplify the subject matter of the chapter.

1. R. B. Seymour, ed., *Conductive Polymers,* Plenum Press, New York (1981).
2. G. M. Sessler, *Electrets,* Springer-Verlag, New York (1980).
3. D. A. Seanor, ed., *Electrical Properties of Polymers*, Academic Press, New York (1982).
4. J. Mort and G. P. Fisher, eds., *Electronic Properties of Polymers*, John Wiley and Sons, New York (1982).
5. L. Brehmer, Acta Polymerica *34,* 278 (1983).
6. J. Lowell and A. C. Rose-Innes, Adv. in Physics *29,* 947 (1980).

1.2   ELECTRICAL PROPERTIES OF POLYMERS

1.2.1   Types of Electrical Responses

Electrical properties of polymers are their responses when an electric field is applied to them. The subject of electrical properties of polymers covers an extremely diverse range of molecular phenomena. In contrast to metals, in which the electrical field response is one of electronic conduction, polymers may respond in a more varied manner, and a whole set of delicate electrical effects may be observed. For example, polarization phenomena resulting from distortion and alignment of molecules under the influence of an applied field become apparent. Examination of various kinds of such polarization not only gives valuable insight into the nature of the electrical response itself, but it also provides an effective way to probe molecular dynamics. Hence, electrical studies form a desirable supplement to studies of purely mechanical properties aimed at reaching an understanding of the behavior of polymers on a molecular level. The study of electrical properties will also pave the way to a more fundamental understanding of the thermal and optical properties of polymers.

No known polymer is completely free of conduction processes, however small the quantity of charge carriers it may possess. Low-level conduction in essentially insulating polymers can take a variety of forms. Conduction may very often be contributed by impurities that provide a small concentration of charge carriers in the form of electrons or ions. At high fields, the electrodes may inject new carriers (holes and electrons) into the polymers. At very high fields, these and other processes will lead to complete breakdown of polymers as insulating materials.

The imposition of an electrical field upon a polymer will cause a redistribution of any charges in the polymer, provided they are mobile enough to respond in the time scale of the applied field. If some of the mobile charges are able to diffuse throughout the specimen and charge migration through the electrode sample interface is possible, then the charges will support a dc conductance. Alternatively, if the diffusion of mobile charges under the field is spatially limited, the polymers can be polarized by the field, but dc conductance will be absent.

1.2.2   Limitations to Charge Mobility

Limitations to charge mobility can be of two kinds. First, the charge may migrate to boundaries over which further transport is either restricted or totally inhibited. In this category, the boundary may (1) delineate the molecule as in the case for electronic and atomic polarizability; (2) extend further out as in the case for the ion atmosphere of a polyelectrolyte in solution; or (3) constitute a phase boundary that is semipermeable or impermeable to charge in a solid material. For the last example, the phenomenon is termed interfacial polarization.

The second kind of restricted mobility results when dipoles cause polarization by a redistribution of their inclinations relative to the field direction. Such orientation polarization need not involve complete rotatory diffusion of the dipole; even a restricted rotation or libration can affect polarization by this mechanism.

1.2.3   The Four Fundamental Parameters

In summary, the response of polymers to an electric field can be separated into two main parts:

    1. DIELECTRIC PROPERTIES and
    2. BULK CONDUCTIVE PROPERTIES.

Of the four fundamental parameters, those characterizing dielectric properties are the

    1A. DIELECTRIC CONSTANT,
        representing polarization, and
    1B. TANGENT OF DIELECTRIC LOSS ANGLE,
        representing relaxation phenomena.

Those parameters characterizing bulk conductive properties are

    2A. DIELECTRIC STRENGTH,
        representing breakdown phenomena and
    2B. CONDUCTIVITY,
        representing electrical conduction.

1.2.4 Special Electrical Properties

In addition to these four fundamental parameters, other electrical properties of polymers are being sought. An increasing number of polymeric materials with special electrical properties are being developed. These include piezoelectric, pyroelectric, ferroelectric, triboelectric, photovoltaic, and photoconducting materials.[5-7] A thorough summary of the varied electrical properties of polymers and the physical basis for them, as well as, applications of polymers based on the varied electrical properties has been compiled by Brehmer.[8] However, even though new special electrical properties are developed, they still can all be related to the four fundamental properties. Thus, a detailed study of the four electrical properties will not only permit one a better understanding of the macromolecular structure but also will allow one to specify how best to take full advantage of the desirable polymeric properties.

This can be illustrated with a historical example. Before 600 B. C., Thales of Miletus had already recognized that nonmetallic materials could store static charge. Amber could be made to acquire the property of attracting small particles by rubbing it with a piece of cloth, and the Greeks gave it the name "elektron", from which the term "electricity" evolved. This finding was expanded, and by the end of the sixteenth century scholars had identified a series of nonconductors that could be charged by this technique. However, systematic research into this topic was not undertaken until 1919 when Eguchi reported on some work with certain waxes.[9] This was then followed by studies in the 1940s on charge-storage phenomena in polymers. Later, studies were carried out on charge retention in thin polymer films, especially since the first report on the use of film electrets in microphones.[10, 11] The present-day uses of electrets are discussed in Section 1.5.2

1.2.5 Triboelectric Series

An early custom was to arrange such charged materials into a triboelectric series. The relative polarity of charge acquired on contact between any material in the series with another was predictable by its location (Table 1.1).[12]

This phenomenon of acquired charge through contact also accounts for the attraction of dust particles by plastic items, the accummulation of electrical charge in carpets in dry weather, and radio-frequency and electromagnetic interference (RFI and EMI) effects of plastic enclosures. Finally, it is also a key component in all xerographic processes.

The microscopic nature of the electronic states involved in triboelectricity is still under study. At present, only the molecular-ion model of bulk intrinsic states provides a microscopic description of the charge-transfer process.[6] Further advances in the understanding of this phenomenon will be made when new experiments probing the microscopic nature of the triboelectric charge are developed.

1.2.6 Electrostatic Charges

As a consequence of the characteristically insulating nature of most solid polymers, any electrostatic charges that they acquire may be retained for a long time. Since charges may be deposited by mere contact between different materials, charging of polymer materials is a common phenomenon. Although contact charges represent only a slight imbalance of charge compared with the total amount of positive and negative charge present in polymers, they can nevertheless give rise to electric fields strong enough to cause arcing in air. For instance, a surface charge density resulting from just one or two extra electronic charges per million surface atoms is sufficient to generate a field that exceeds the air breakdown value. The occurrence of arcing means that an insulating sample will often present a complex and confusing distribution of charge on its surface, reflecting a complicated history of charging and discharging events.

TABLE 1.1 Triboelectric Series

Material	Polarity
Silicone elastomer with silica filler	Positive
Borosilicate glass, fire polished	▲
Window glass	
Aniline-formal resin (acid catalyzed)	
Polyformaldehyde	
Poly(methyl methacrylate)	
Ethyl cellulose	
Polyamide II	
Polyamide 6–6	
Rock salt, NaCl	
Melamine formal	
Wool, knitted	
Silica, fire polished	
Silk, woven	
Poly(ethylene glycol succinate)	
Cellulose acetate	
Poly(ethylene glycol adipate)	
Poly(diallyl phthalate)	
Cellulose (regenerated) sponge	
Cotton, woven	
Polyurethane elastomer	
Styrene-acrylonitrile copolymer	
Styrene-butadiene copolymer	
Polystyrene	
Polyisobutylene	
Polyurethane flexible sponge	
Borosilicate glass, ground surface	
Poly(ethylene glycol terephthalate)	
Polyvinylbutyral	
Formaldehyde-phenol-hardened epoxy resin	
Polychlorobutadiene	
Butadiene-acrylonitrile copolymer	
Natural rubber	
Polyacrylonitrile	
Sulfur	
Polyethylene	
Poly(diphenylol propane carbonate)	
Chlorinated polyether	
Poly(vinyl chloride) with 25% DOP.	
Poly(vinyl chloride) without plasticizer	
Polytrifluorochloroethylene	▼
Polytetrafluoroethylene	Negative

The tendency for polymers to store electrostatic charge was overcome in the past by the addition of carbon black or acetylene black to rubber, the addition of metallic powders to plastics, and by the blending of metallic or metal-coated fibers with synthetic fibers.[13]

In recent years, there has been a resurgence of interest in electrostatics, and new experimental techniques have vastly improved the scope for scientific study. However, the foundation of the study of electrostatics of polymers and its prevention lie in a detailed knowledge of polarization, relaxation, conduction, and breakdown phenomena in polymers.

1.3 CHEMICAL ASPECTS OF ELECTRICAL PROPERTIES OF POLYMERS

1.3.1 Chemical and Structural Control

In the hands of synthetic chemists, polymers can be tailored to an amazing degree; even their electrical and electronic properties can be modified. Since a great diversity in polymers is possible, not only in their chemical composition but also in their structure and morphology, it is only natural to expect a great diversity in the electrical properties and an even greater variability in the reported numerical values for the fundamental parameters.

The chemical aspects of electrical properties of polymers therefore resolve into chemical and structural control of polymer composition. There are two major aspects to this control. The first is the design and synthesis of new polymers that will exhibit the desired electrical properties, such as high or low dielectric constant, low dielectric loss, high resistivity, high conductivity, high dielectric strength, or any other special electrical property. The second aspect is those polymer applications in which the electrical properties are not the chief concern, yet some small adjustment of electrical parameters is needed, such as the minimization of static charge accumulation.

To illustrate how both the chemical and structural control of polymer composition determines its electrical properties, examples of piezo- and pyroelectric polymers will be discussed.

1.3.2 Piezo- and Pyroelectric Polymers

Most piezo- and pyroelectric polymers are also polymer electrets. An electret is a dielectric material in which semipermanent polarization is related to semipermanent surface charge. Several recent reviews and proceedings provide background material on this subject.[14-16] The maximum piezoelectricity in various polymer electrets is roughly related to the dielectric constant (Fig. 1.3).[17] Dielectric constant in turn is determined basically by the chemical structure of the compound. However, this is no more than a necessary condition because the chain configuration and bulk morphology are equally important. Thus, poly(vinylidene fluoride), PVF_2, its highly polar carbon-fluorine bonds and a dipole moment μ_0 of 6.4×10^{-30} coulomb-meter (C·m), has the highest dielectric constant (8.0) and the highest piezoelectric constant d. Other fluoropolymers, such as polyvinyl fluoride (PVF),[18,19] copolymers of vinyl fluoride and vinylidene fluoride,[20] and copolymers of tetrafluoroethylene and vinylidene fluoride,[21] are also among the best piezoelectric polymers. Other polar groups that can be expected to lead to useful piezoelectric polymers include C-Cl, $\mu_0 = 7.0 \times 10^{-30}$ C·m, and C-CN, $\mu_0 = 12.9 \times 10^{-30}$ C·m. Typical polymers incorporating such groups are poly(vinylidene chloride), $(CH_2CCl_2)_n$ and poly(vinylidene cyanide), $[CH_2C(CN)_2]_n$. Poly(vinylidene chloride), although potentially similar in electrical activity to PVF_2, suffers from the presence of bulky chlorine atoms (van der Waals radii 1.80 Å compared with 1.35 Å for F-atoms and 1.2 Å for H-atoms), which prevent its chains from adopting the highly polar all-trans conformation. Among the cyanide-containing polymers, the poly(vinylidene cyanide-vinyl acetate) alternating copolymer was recently prepared and shown to exhibit a piezoelectric constant similar in magnitude to that of PVF_2:[22]

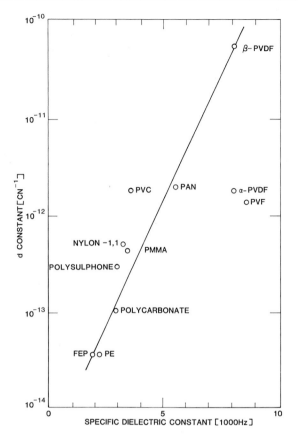

Fig. 1.3. Correlation between piezoelectricity and the dielectric constant in polymer electrets.

Polymer	Piezoelectric Constant pCN^{-1}	
	20°C	*100°C*
Poly V(CN)$_2$-VAC	5.0	10.0
PVF$_2$	7.0	10.5

Piezoelectricity of polymers increases rapidly near their glass-transition temperatures (Tg's) with an increase in electrostriction constant and a decrease in dynamic modulus. The above measurements were above the Tg for PVF$_2$ but below it for the copolymer. If both of the polymers are compared at temperatures below their Tg's, then the poly(vinylidene cyanide-vinyl acetate) copolymer is 10 times more active than the PVF$_2$.

This then illustrates how control of chemical structure is a contributing factor in achieving high piezoelectric activity. However, this may not be a sufficient condition. Appropriate polymer chain configuration and bulk morphology are equally important.

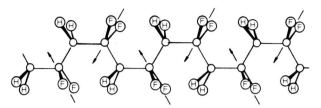

Fig. 1.4. The α-chain form of PVF$_2$.

Poly(vinylidene fluoride) is a highly crystalline (40–60%) material possessing at least three major crystal forms: α, β, and γ. Of these, the α-form (Fig. 1.4) is obtained when the polymer crystallizes from the melt below 150°C into spherulitic structures.[23] The structure of the α-form crystal (Fig. 1.5a) is monoclinic, β = 90°, with the chains taking on a glide-type TGTG conformation and possessing a dipole moment with components both normal and parallel to the chain axis.[24, 25] The dipole moments of two chains in the unit cell, however, are antiparallel, and the crystal therefore has no spontaneous polarization (antipolar crystal).

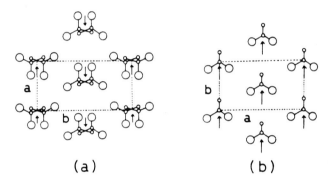

(a)   (b)

Fig. 1.5. Crystal structures of PVF$_2$: (a) α-form, (b) β-form.

When the film of PVF$_2$ is drawn at a temperature below 130°C to several times its original length, a new crystal form, the β-form, is produced (Fig. 1.6). This new crystal form has the orthorhombic structure illustrated in Fig. 1.5b, in which the chains take on a zigzag TTTT conformation.[24–26] The chain has a large dipole moment ($\mu_0 = 7.06 \times 10^{-30}$ C·m per monomeric unit) normal to the chain axis and is packed such that the crystal possesses a spontaneous polarization P_c (polar crystal). For an ideal crystal, P_c equals 0.23 C/m^2.

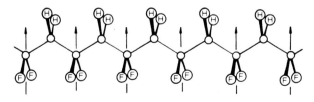

Fig. 1.6. The β-form of PVF$_2$.

In the real β-form crystal, P_c is smaller because of head-to-head and tail-to-tail defects.[27] Poly(vinylidene fluoride) with lower (3%) head-to-head and tail-to-tail defects has been synthesized; however, this destabilized the β-form and impeded its formation, and the α-form always formed preferentially.[28] Thus, the long-term stability of the β-form depends upon, among other factors, a certain minimum number of chain imperfections above 3%.

The conversion from the α-form to the β-form can be easily followed by infrared (IR) methods (from $530\,cm^{-1}$ for the α-form to $510\,cm^{-1}$ for the β-form), and the conversion fraction depends on the draw ratio and the draw temperature. The β-form crystal has the highest molecular packing among the various crystal forms of PVF_2. The separation between atoms belonging to neighboring chains is small compared with the sum of their van der Waals radii, and to avoid steric hindrances, the chain makes a statistical deflection of 7° about the c-axis.[25]

A third crystal form, the γ-form, is obtained by crystallization under atmospheric pressure at a temperature just below the melting point.[23,29,30] The γ-form crystal is also generated by melt crystallization under high pressure.[22] Lando, Hopfinger, and their coworkers proposed an orthorhombic unit cell of the γ-form crystal with chain conformation approximately TTTGTTTḠ.[31–35] Takahashi and Tadokoro prepared a highly oriented γ-form sample and proposed a monoclinic structure consisting of a TTTGTTTḠ conformation including some disorder.[36] The γ-form crystal readily transforms into the β-form by mechanical deformation.

The PVF_2 electret is prepared by annealing and poling the c-axis-oriented films containing β-form crystals. The induced surface charge is opposite in sign to the poling charge (heterocharge). Typical poling parameters are poling temperature $T_p \sim 80$–120°C, electric field of poling $E_p \sim 50$–$150\,MVm^{-1}$, and poling time $t_p \sim 30$ min. The resulting polarization is stable for heating cycles below T_p except for an irreversible part that vanishes on the first heating cycle. The mechanism inducing both reversible and irreversible polarization has been a subject of much discussion, and no agreement has been reached. The evidence is that the piezo- and pyroelectricity of PVF_2 together with its large polarization under a field are dependent on the number of crystallites in the β-form and the ease with which these can align during polarization. Another important point in the mechanism of polarization is the ability of dipole residues to move from amorphous regions and be incorporated into the crystallites, and to interconvert their orientation at grain-boundaries.

In summary, a combination of chemical and physical factors are responsible for the high polymer piezo- and pyroelectric properties: (1) the high electronegativities of fluorine and cyano groups resulting in large dipoles, (2) structural patterns for the fluorine that do not lead to symmetry, (3) the small bulk of fluorine atoms leading to easy conformational rearrangements, and (4) the presence of crystallites that stabilize the oriented dipoles (for example, β-form). Thus, both the chemical and physical factors for this particular electrical property of the polymer play key roles. This example also serves as an introduction to the next four chapters of this book, in which we will discuss in detail the control of each of the four fundamental parameters of electrical properties of polymers by chemical means.

1.4   REQUIREMENTS FOR POLYMERS AS ELECTRICAL INSULATING MATERIALS

The electrical insulating properties inherent in most polymers have long been exploited to constrain and protect currents flowing along chosen paths in conductors and to sustain high electric fields without breakdown. To achieve the optimum performance of electrical properties of polymers, we must completely understand the electrical insulation phenomena and the proper selection of polymers as electrical insulating materials. This requires an interdisciplinary approach including chemistry (synthesis and thermodynamics), physics (electromagnetics and quantum statistical mechanics), and electrical engineering. Continuing progress in the use of polymers in electrical insulation will require sophisticated analysis and computation coupled with careful experiments and materials preparation.

1.4.1   Insulating Materials and Their Uses

Polymeric materials for insulating early electrical equipment were made from natural products. For instance, the first Transatlantic telephone cable laid in the middle of last century was insulated with gutta-percha and natural rubber. As synthetic polymers became available, the quality of insulation was continually improved. The great value of synthetic polymers was in their combination of high quality of insulation with ease of fabrication. For example, polyethylene, which combines very low dielectric loss of insulating properties with moldability and a high degree of toughness and flexibility, became available just as the demand increased for insulation in coaxial cables for radar equipment and television devices.

More recently, demanding requirements for further low-dielectric-loss materials, such as those used in the insulation of transoceanic communications cables, have been met by polyolefins in general. Extremely low conductivity materials such as those used in electret microphones are represented by fluorinated polymers. High-performance thin polypropylene films have also been developed for various types of power capacitors. High-purity, pinhole-free, chemically inert poly(p-xylylene) and its chlorine-substituted ultrathin films have been developed as insulation barrier coatings for semiconductor surfaces.[37,38]

1.4.2   Current Trends

There are three major trends that demand polymeric insulation able to withstand increasingly higher voltages. The biggest single trend is in equipment/device miniaturization. The second trend is toward higher specific loading of equipment, that is, extracting the maximum output or throughput from power system components consistent with safety and reliability. The third trend is the increasing use of direct current for power transmission. Only a small fraction of the electric power generated is delivered by direct current; however, that fraction will almost certainly increase in the future. Hence, there is a great range in properties for insulating materials of higher dielectric strength.

1.4.3   Insulation for ac and dc

As far as the insulation is concerned several significant differences exist between ac and dc, for instance, voltage gradient across insulating systems if it is governed primarily by leakage rather than by capacitance, at least in the steady state. For this reason, some insulators for high-voltage dc applications have been formulated to include a small amount of conductivity. In other instances, semiconducting coatings have been used. There are also some special problems associated with high-voltage dc insulation. Many of these concern trapped charge, which can be particularly troublesome when a sudden polarity reversal is required.

1.4.4   Interfacial Phenomena

A scrutiny of the problem areas in high-voltage insulation systems reveals that most of them are associated with interfaces–solid to gas, solid to liquid, and solid to solid–for it is here that breakdown is often initiated or deterioration starts. The problems of voids in solid insulation, treeing from asperities on conductor surfaces or fissures in the adjacent insulation, contamination on surfaces, and trapping of surface charge are all examples of interface phenomena. Because of practical design consideration, such interfaces are often located at regions of high electric stress brought about by the geometry or a change in dielectric constant. It would seem therefore that the problem of interfaces should be a focus for special attention. The extraordinary complexity of the conduction processes and the breakdown mechanisms in solid, liquid, and gaseous dielectrics inevitably means that it may be a long time before a detailed understanding of all the processes is obtained. In the meantime, power equipment must continue to be built, preferably with an improved insulation design.

In high-voltage applications, polymeric materials require a high breakdown voltage or dielectric strength and often must mechanically support such structures as transformer windings and field-carrying conductors and must act as a heat-conducting medium. Such polymers must withstand thermal and mechanical as well as electrical stresses. The interface between the polymer and a metal then becomes critical, and the breakdown process must be inhibited there as well. Specially manufactured polyethylene resins are now most widely used in highvoltage polymeric insulation.

1.4.5   Summary of Requirements

The following are the typical requirements of an insulator:

1. An insulator must have a high enough dielectric strength to withstand an electrical field between the conductors.
2. An insulator must have high insulation resistance to prevent leakage of current across the conductors.
3. An insulator must possess good arc resistance to prevent damage in case of arcing.
4. Insulating materials must be mechanically strong enough to resist vibrations, shocks, and other mechanical forces.
5. An insulator must maintain integrity under a wide variety of environmental hazards such as humidity, temperature, and radiation.

The key electrical properties that have bearing on these requirements are dielectric constant, dielectric strength, dissipation factor, and volume and surface resistivity.

1.5   USE OF POLYMERS AS MATERIALS WITH SPECIAL ELECTRICAL PROPERTIES

The ability of metals to conduct so efficiently, both electrically and thermally, is the major reason for their uses in many applications. However, in addition to these properties, certain other special properties are frequently required or desired, for example, flexibility, low weight, the ability to form intricate shapes, and low manufacturing costs. Structures made from metals do not always meet these requirements. For this reason, conductive materials based on polymers are being developed to provide lightweight, flexible, and moldable parts having static bleed-off as well as EMI-shielding properties.

1.5.1 Insulators and Conductivity

Provision for the electrostatic protection and the EMI shielding that are so vital to the many solid-state components requires polymers with increased conductivity properties. These polymers must both drain the static charge and provide a barrier to the radiation generated when the static charge is dissipated as an arc to the ground. In part, the practice has been to incorporate a conducting filler into the polymers. However, a lightweight, readily processable, and intrinsically conductive polymer has long been recognized as a worthwhile goal, and considerable scientific research has been devoted to its development.[6, 39]

The permanency of storage of real and polarization charges in polymers depends on conductivity, carrier mobility, and dipolar relaxation. Insulating polymers may show a very good long-term real-charge storage capability because of the low conductivity and low carrier mobility. Examples of this type are poly(tetrafluoroethylene) (Teflon) and its fluoroethylene-propylene copolymers. An example of a polymer with a small dipolar relaxation frequency that can store a polarization for extended times is poly(vinylidene fluoride). Examples of polymers that can store both real and polarization charges are polyethylene and poly(ethylene terephthalate).

1.5.2 Applications of Electrets

Charge retention in thin polymer films has been extensively studied since the 1960s, when the first application of film electrets in electret microphones was reported.[38, 39] Since that time electrets have been used in many applications, Table 1.2.

TABLE 1.2 Electrets in Various Applications

Application	References
Absolute reflectivity detector	40
Accelerometer	41, 42
Acoustic emission sensor	43, 44, 45
Acoustic retina	46
Adaptive optics	47, 48, 49
Antifouling coating applications	50, 51, 52
Audio speakers	53, 54, 55, 56
Bearing-wear monitor	57
Blood-flow monitor	54, 58, 60
Bone healing implant	60, 61
Cartridge for disk records	53
Charge separator, filter	62
Coin sensors	63
Deformable mirror	47, 49
Displays	64, 65, 66, 67
Finger pressure sensor switches	17, 56, 68, 69, 70
Flexure-mode transducers	65, 66, 67, 71, 72, 73, 74, 75, 76, 77, 78
Fuze and detonator for explosives	79
Headphones	53
Heat exchanger membrane	80
Heat scanner	81
Hydrophones	56, 82, 83, 84, 85, 86, 87, 88

Application	References
Impact detector	89
Infrared detector	56, 90, 91
Intrusion alarm	92
Laser-beam profiling	56, 93
Light deflectors	65, 66, 67, 71, 72, 73, 74
Light detectors	10
Light modulation	10, 58, 94
Medical ultrasonic imaging	58, 74, 96, 97, 98, 99
Microphones	53, 56, 100, 101, 102, 103, 104, 105, 106
Nip pressure transducers	107, 108
Optical phase modulator	48
Optical scanners	71, 72, 73
Optical second harmonic generator	109, 110
Pacemaker	61
Personal verification device	111
Photocopying process	112, 113
Physiological implants	61
Position sensors	77
Radiometer	114, 115
Reflectometer	116
Shutters	72
Sonic beams	101
Spectral reference detector	117
Strain gauge	108
Stress gauge	118
Stress wave monitor	43, 89, 119, 120
Surface acoustic wave devices	121, 122
Telephone	100
Ultrasonic transmitters	10, 17, 58, 94, 95, 96, 97, 101, 123, 124, 125, 126
Variable-aperture diaphragm	72
Venetian blinds	78, 127
Vibrational fans	67, 74, 75, 76
Vibration damper	128
Vidicon target	56, 93, 129, 130, 131, 132, 133

An application of charge-storage phenomena of great practical importance is electrophotography. Initially, photoconducting materials used in the electrophotographic process were nonpolymeric. More recently the charge-transfer complex of the polymer-poly(N-vinyl carbazole), PNVC, and trinitrofluorenone, TNF- and other polymer-based systems have been used commercially as electrophotographic photoreceptors.[6]

The technique of electro-imaging or xerography for which PNVC/TNF or selenium are the photoactive elements is illustrated in Fig. 1.7. A corona discharge charges a photoconductive film that will only discharge significantly under illumination. The manuscript to be copied is illuminated, and light reflected from the print-free regions of the surface depolarizes these regions of the charged photoconductive film. The film now has a latent image of charge corresponding to the manuscript's text. Resin-encapsulated carbon particles that have been charged (usually self-charged *triboelectrically*) are then introduced and adhere electrostatically to the latent image. Transfer to paper is accomplished by charging of the paper. The image is set on the paper by heating so that the resin skin of the pigment is fused. The process is completed by mechanical removal of excess pigment from the photoconductive film and its total depolarization by illumination.

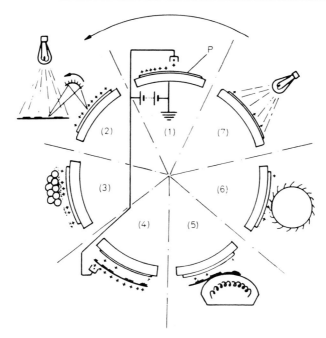

Fig. 1.7. Schematic illustration of the steps in xerography: (1) surface charging of photoconductive plate P; (2) copying of the document by scanning with light, thereby selectively discharging the plate; (3) selective addition of toner onto charged areas by carrier beads; (4) electrostatic transfer of toner onto paper;. (5) heat setting of image; (6) removal of excess toner from plate; and (7) re-illumination [same lamp as in (1)] to remove remaining charge on plate.

Related to electrophotography, but not depending on photographic methods, are electrostatic recording processes. These are used to record electrical signals, digital information, facsimiles, or alphanumeric characters on materials such as polymers or paper.[134] The recording is performed by an electron beam or electrical discharge from a needle electrode. The patterns may be read by a capacitive probe arrangement or by monitoring secondary emission from the sample with a low-current, low-energy scanning electron beam.[135]

1.5.3   Applications of Conducting Polymers

The metallic nature of polysulfur nitride, $(SN)_n$, has been exploited in the use of the polymer as an electrode in liquid electrolytes and in surface electrocatalysis.[136, 137]
Polysulfur nitride is also a prime example of a superconducting polymer material. It is not only a good electrical conductor along the direction of "fiber bundles" formed by large aggregates of individual polymer molecules, but it is also an anisotropic superconductor at 0.25 K.[138]
The prototype example of conducting polymers is polyacetylene. Metallically doped polyacetylene has been used as a Schottky-barrier contact to Si and GaAs.[139, 140] The near perfect match of the trans-polyacetylene band gap to the solar energy spectrum has also been exploited in photovoltaic devices by use of the Schottky-barrier configuration formed with inexpensive metals such as aluminum.[141–145] Polyacetylene can act either as an electron source or an electron sink according to whether it is, respectively, oxidized (p-type doped) or reduced (n-type doped). Because the doping can be carried out by electrochemical techni-

ques after synthesis and because the doping is reversible, it has been used in light-weight, high-power-density, rechargeable organic storage batteries.[146–148]

Exciting conceptual developments are under way in two areas: (1) the chemical computer based on molecular electronic devices constructed along a three-dimensional architecture in which molecular memory elements can be independently set and read;[149] and (2) organic, self-renewing biochips made from protein-based units that function like transistors and are triggered by enzymes. Again, the units, called Moletons, perform at the molecular level and potentially would be a billion times more powerful than today's 64K chips.[150]

1.6   REFERENCES

1. A. A. Schneider, W. Greatbatch, and R. Mead, 9th International Power Sources Symposium, paper No. 30, 1974.
2. N. F. Mott and E. A. Davis, *Electronic Processing in Non-Crystalline Materials*, Oxford University Press, New York (1979).
3. A. R. Blythe, *Electrical Properties of Polymers*, Cambridge University Press, London (1979).
4. H. J. Goldsmid, Proc. Phys. Soc. London *B69*, 203 (1956).
5. H. Block, Advances in Polymer Science *33*, 93 (1979).
6. J. Mort and G. Pfister, *Electronic Properties of Polymers*, Wiley-Interscience Pub., New York (1982).
7. P. J. Reucroft and H. S. Ullal, Solar Energy Mater. *2*, 217 (1979–1980).
8. L. Brehmer, Acta Polymerica *34*, 278 (1983).
9. M. Eguchi, Proc. Phys. Math. Soc. Jap. *1*, 320 (1919).
10. G. M. Sessler, *Electrets*, Springer Verlag, Berlin (1980).
11. G. M. Sessler and J. E. West, J. Acoust. Soc. Am. *34*, 1787 (1962).
12. J. Henniker, Nature (London) *196*, 474 (1962).
13. R. H. Norman, *Conductive Rubbers and Plastics*, Applied Science, London (1970).
14. H. J. Wintle, J. Acoust. Soc. Am. *53*, 1578 (1973).
15. G. M. Sessler and J. E. West, J. Acoust. Soc. Am. *53*, 1589 (1973).
16. M. M. Perlman, Ed., *Electrets, Charge Storage, and Transport in Dielectrics*, Electrochemical Society, Princeton, New Jersey (1973).
17. N. Murayama, K. Nakamura, H. Obara, and M. Segawa, Ultrasonics *14*, 15 (January, 1976).
18. R. J. Phelan, Jr., R. L. Peterson, C. A. Hamilton, and G. W. Day, Ferroelectrics *7*, 375 (1974).
19. J. Cohen and S. Edelman, J. Appl. Phys. *42*, 3072 (1971).
20. N. Murayama, T. Oikawa, T. Katto, and K. Nakamura, J. Polym. Sci., Polym. Phys. Edn. *13*, 1033 (1975).
21. A. I. Baise, H. Lee, B. Oh, R. E. Salomon, and M. M. Labes, Appl. Phys. Lett. *26*, 428 (1975).
22. S. Miyata, M. Yoshikawa, S. Tasaka, and M. Ko, Polym. J. *12*, 857 (1980).
23. W. M. Prest, Jr., and D. J. Luca, J. Appl. Phys. *46*, 4136 (1975).
24. R. Hasegawa, M. Kobayashi, and H. Tadokoro, Polym. J. *3*, 591 (1972).
25. R. Hasegawa, Y. Takahashi, Y. Chatani, and H. Tadokoro, Polym. J. *3*, 600 (1972).
26. J. B. Lando, H. L. Olf, and A. Peterlin, J. Polym. Sci. *A-1*, 941 (1966).
27. M. G. Broadhurst and G. T. Davis, *Topics in Applied Physics*, G. M. Sessler, Ed., Springer, Berlin, 1979, Vol. 33, p. 285.
28. R. Liepins, J. R. Surles, N. Morosoff, V. T. Stannett, M. L. Timmons, J. J. Wortman, J. Polym. Sci., Polym. Chem. Ed. *16*, 3039 (1978).
29. S. Osaki and Y. Ishida, J. Polym. Sci., Polym. Phys. Ed. *13*, 1071 (1975).
30. W. M. Prest, Jr. and D. J. Luca, J. Appl. Phys. *49*, 5042 (1978).
31. N. C. Banik, F. P. Boyle, T. J. Sluckin, P. L. Taylor, S. K. Tripathy, and A. J. Hopfinger, Phys. Rev. Lett. *43*, 456 (1979).
32. S. Weinhold, M. H. Litt, and J. B. Lando, J. Polym. Sci., Polym. Lett. Ed. *17*, 585 (1979).
33. M. A. Bachmann, W. L. Gordon, J. L. Koenig, and J. B. Lando, J. Appl. Phys. *50*, 6106 (1979).
34. N. C. Banik, P. L. Taylor, S. K. Tripathy, and A. J. Hopfinger, Macromolecules *12*, 1015 (1979).
35. S. Weinhold, M. H. Litt, and J. B. Lando, Macromolecules *13*, 1178 (1980).

36. Y. Takahashi and H. Tadokoro, Macromolecules *13*, 1317 (1980).
37. S. M. Lee, J. J. Licari, and I. Litant, Metallurgical Transactions *1*, 701 (1970).
38. E. A. Naga, Proceedings of International Microelectronic Symposium, Orlando, Florida, October 27–29, 1975, p. 207.
39. E. P. Goodings, Chem. Soc. Rev., p. 95 (1977).
40. W. R. Blevin and J. Geist, Appl. Opt. *13*, 2212 (1974).
41. S. Edelman, unpublished work.
42. S. Edelman, S. C. Roth, and J. F. Mayo-Wells, U.S. Pat. 3,970,862, July 20, 1976.
43. B. T. Brady, Nature *260*, 108 (1976).
44. W. M. McCabe, Proceedings Second Conference on Acoustical Emission/Microseismic Activity on Geological Structures and Materials, Pennsylvania State University, 1978.
45. W. R. Scott and J. Carlyle, Naval Development Center Report No. 3930 (1975).
46. A. S. DeReggi, S. Edelman, S. Roth, H. Warner, and J. Wynn, J. Acoust. Soc. Am. *61*, S17 (1977).
47. T. Sato, H. Ishida, and O. Ikeda, Appl. Opt. *19*, 1430 (1980).
48. T. Sato, Y. Ueda, and O. Ikeda, Appl. Opt. *20*, 343 (1981).
49. S. A. Kokorowski, J. Opt. Soc. Am. *69*, 181 (1979).
50. M. Latour, O. Gvelorget, and P. V. Murphy in Y. Wada, M. M. Perlman, and H. Kokado, Studies in Electrical and Electronic Engineering *2*, 175 (1979).
51. M. Latour, O. Gvelorget, and P. V. Murphy, Extended Abstracts of the 1978 International Workshop on Electric Charges in Dielectrics, Kyoto, Japan (1978).
52. B. Wooden and S. Edelman, patent application (1975).
53. M. Tamura, T. Yamaguchi, T. Oyaba, and T. Yoshimi, J. Audio Eng. Soc. *23*, 21 (1975).
54. S. Hunklinger, H. Sussner, and K. Dransfeld, *Advances in Solid State Physics*, J. Treusch, Ed., Vieweg, Braunschweig, (1976), Vol. XVI p. 267.
55. F. Micheron and C. Lemonon, J. Acoust. Soc. Am. *64*, 1720 (1978).
56. H. R. Gallantree and R. M. Quilliam, Marconi Rev. *39*, 189 (1976).
57. S. Edelman, J. M. Kenney, J. F. Mayo-Well, S. C. Roth, Proceedings 28th Meeting Mechanical Failures Prevention Group, T. R. Shives and W. A. Willard, Ed., Nat. Bur. Stds. Symp. Proceedings, No. 547 (1979).
58. H. Sussner, Ultrasonic Symposium Proceedings, p. 491 (1979).
59. H. Sussner and K. Dransfeld, Colloid Polym. Sci. *257*, 591 (1979).
60. E. Fukuda, private communication.
61. E. Hausler, H. Lang, and F. J. Shreiner, IEEE Frontiers of Engineering in Health Care *4*, 333 (1980).
62. A. L. Taylor, U.S. Pat. 4,035,164, July 12, 1977.
63. G. R. Crane, IEEE Trans. Sonics Ultrason. *SU-25*, 393 (1978).
64. M. Toda, Trans. IECE Jpn. *E61*, 5 (1978).
65. M. Toda and S. Osaka, Proc. SID (Soc. Inf. Disp.) *19*, 35 (1978).
66. M. Toda, S. Osaka, and S. Tosima, Ferroelectrics *23*, 115 (1980).
67. M. Toda, S. Osaka, and E. O. Johnson, RCA Engineer *25*, 24 (1979).
68. G. T. Pearman, J. L. Hokanson, and T. R. Meeker, Ferroelectrics Spec. Issue, Symposium on Appl. of Ferroelectrics, Minneapolis, June, 1979.
69. G. T. Pearman, J. L. Hokanson, and T. R. Meeker, Ferroelectrics *28*, 311 (1980).
70. M. Yoshida, M. Segawa, and H. Obara, U.S. Pat. 3,935,485, January 27, 1976.
71. J. K. Lee and M. A. Marcus, Ferroelectrics *32*, 93 (1981).
72. M. Toda, Trans. IECE Jpn. *61*, 507 (1978).
73. M. Toda, Trans. IECE Jpn. *61*, 513 (1978).
74. M. Toda and S. Osaka, IEEE Proc. *67*, 1171 (1979).
75. M. Toda, Ferroelectrics *22*, 911 (1979).
76. M. Toda, Ferroelectrics *22*, 919 (1979).
77. M. Toda, IEEE Trans. Electron. Devices *ED-26*, 815 (1979).
78. M. Toda and S. Osaka, U.S. Pat. 4,234,245, November 18, 1980.
79. P. E. Bloomfield, Nat. Bur. Stds. interagency report no. 75–724 (R) (1975).
80. S. Edelman and L. D. Ballard, U.S. Patent application Serial No. 30,966, April 17, 1979.
81. J. Cohen, S. Edelman, and C. Verretti, Nat. Bur. Stds. Tech. News Bull. *56*, 52 (1972).
82. J. M. Powers and T. D. Sullivan, J. Acoust. Soc. Am. *60*, S47 (1976).
83. S. Edelman, L. R. Grisham, S. C. Roth, and J. Cohen, J. Acoust. Soc. Am. *48*, 1040 (1970).

84. A. S. DeReggi, S. Roth, J. M. Kenney, S. Edelman, and G. R. Harris, J. Acoust. Soc. Am. *64*, S55 (1978).
85. S. Edelman, Proceedings of Workshop on Sonar Transducer Materials, P. L. Smith and R. C. Pohonka, Eds., Naval Res. Lab. (1975).
86. B. Woodward and R. C. Chandra, Electrocomponent Sci. Technol. *5*, 149 (1978).
87. A. S. DeReggi, S. C. Roth, J. M. Kenney, S. Edelman, and G. R. Harris, J. Acoust. Soc. Am. *69*, 853 (1981).
88. T. D. Sullivan and J. M. Powers, J. Acoust. Soc. Am. *63*, 1396 (1978).
89. A. S. DeReggi, S. Edelman, and S. C. Roth, Nat. Bur. Stds. interagency report 76–1078 (1976).
90. Nat. Bur. Stds. interagency report 75–728 (1975).
91. New England Research Center, Inc., Tech. Note PVF–B.
92. J. Stern and S. Edelman, Nat. Bur. Stds. Technical News Bull. *56*, No. 3, 52 (1972).
93. U. Korn, Z. Rav-Noy, and S. Shtrikman, Appl. Opt. *20*, 1980 (1981).
94. H. Ohigashi, R. Shigenari, and M. Yokota, J. Appl. Phys. Japan *14*, 1085 (1975).
95. R. G. Swartz and J. D. Plummer, IEEE Trans. Sonics Ultrason. *SU-27*, 295 (1980).
96. R. G. Swartz, Integrated Circuits Lab., Stanford Electronics Lab., technical rep. G561–1 (May, 1979).
97. J. G. Linvill, Integrated Circuits Lab. Stanford Electronics Lab., technical report 4834–3 (March, 1978).
98. R. G. Swartz and J. D. Plummer, IEEE Trans. Electron Devices *ED-26*, 1921 (1979).
99. R. G. Swartz and J. D. Plummer, in A. F. Metherall, *Acoustical Imaging*, Vol. 8, Ultrasonic Visualization and Characterization, Plenum Press, New York (1980), p. 69.
100. J. F. Sear, Electronics *49*, 36 (1976).
101. L. Bui, H. J. Shaw, and L. T. Zitelli, Electron. Lett. *12*, 393 (1976).
102. J. F. Sear and R. Carpenter, Electron. Lett. *11*, 532 (1975).
103. H. Naono, T. Gotch, M. Matsumoto, and S. Ibaraki, Audio Eng. Soc. preprint 1271(D–1) (1977).
104. R. Lerch and G.M. Sessler, J. Acoust. Soc. Am. *67*, 1379 (1980).
105. J. F. Guess, Audio Eng. Soc. preprint 1355(D–11) (1978).
106. R. Lerch, J. Acoust. Soc. Am. *66*, 952 (1979).
107. S. Edelman, S. C. Roth, A. S. DeReggi, and J. Kenney, 10th Annual Symposium on Paper and Pulp Technology, Miami Univ., Oxford, Ohio (1979).
108. M. G. Broadhurst, S. Edelman, and G. T. Davis, Am. Chem. Soc. Div. Org. Coat. Plast. Chem. *42*, 241 (1980).
109. J. H. McFee, J. G. Bergman, Jr., and G. R. Crane, Ferroelectrics *3*, 305 (1972).
110. J. G. Bergman, Jr., J. H. McFee, and G. R. Crane, Appl. Phys. Lett. *18*, 203 (1971).
111. P. R. Radice, UK Pat. GB–2,032,669A.
112. J. G. Bergman, G. R. Crane, A. A. Ballman, and H. M. O'Bryan, Jr., Appl. Phys. Lett. *21*, 497 (1972).
113. J. G. Bergman, Jr. and G. R. Crane, U.S. Pat. 3,824,098, July 16, 1974.
114. R. L. Peterson, G. W. Day, P. M. Gruzensky, and R. J. Phelan, Jr., J. Appl. Phys. *45*, 3296 (1974).
115. R. J. Phelan, Jr., C. A. Hamilton, and G. W. Day, SPIE *62*, 159 (1975).
116. W. R. Blevin and J. Geist, Appl. Opt. *13*, 2212 (1974).
117. G. W. Day, C. A. Hamilton, and K. W. Pyatt, Appl. Opt. *15*, 1865 (1976).
118. A. S. DeReggi and S. Edelman, U.S. Pat. 4,166,229, August 28, 1979.
119. S. Edelman, Air Force Weapons Laboratory tech. report AFWL- TR-73–186, (1973).
120. R. B. Bunker, Eighth Transducer Workshop, Telemetry Group, Range Commanders Council (1975).
121. R. S. Wagers, J. Appl. Phys. *51*, 5797 (1980).
122. M. Toda and K. Ikenohira, J. Appl. Phys. *51*, 5657 (1980).
123. C. Alquie, J. Lewiner, and C. Friedman, Appl. Phys. Lett. *29*, 69 (1976).
124. H. Kawai, J. Appl. Phys. Japan *8*, 975 (1969).
125. H. Sussner, D. Michas, A. Assfalg, S. Hunklinger, and K. Dransfeld, Phys. Lett. *A45*, 475 (1973).
126. H. Ohigashi, J. Appl. Phys. *47*, 949 (1976).
127. M. Toda, S. Osaka, and S. Tosima, Ferroelectrics *23*, 121 (1980).
128. S. Edelman, S. C. Roth, and L. R. Grisham, The Shock and Vibration Bulletin *39*, 1 (1969).
129. L. E. Garn and E. J. Sharp, IEEE Trans., Parts, Hybrids, and Packaging *PHP10*, 208 (1974).
130. W. R. Peters, Proc. Carnahan Crime Countermeas. *78*, 141 (1977).

131. J. E. Jacobs and S. A. Remily, Infrared Phys. *19*, 1 (1979).
132. Y. Hatanaka, S. Okamoto, and R. Nishida, Adv. Electron. Electron Phys. *52*, 31 (1979).
133. A. W. Stephens, A. W. Levine, J. Fech, Jr., T. J. Zrebiec, A. V. Cafiero, and A. M. Garofalo, Thin Solid Films *24*, 361 (1974).
134. U. Rothgordt, Philips Tech. Rdsch. *36*, 98 (1976/77).
135. J. Feder, J. Appl. Phys. *47*, 1741 (1976).
136. R. J. Nowak, H. B. Mark, Jr., A. G. MacDiarmid, and D. Weber, J. Chem. Soc. Comm. 9 (1977).
137. A. N. Voulgaropoulos, R. J. Nowak, W. Kutner, and H. B. Mark, Jr., J. Chem. Soc., Chem. Comm. 244 (1978).
138. K. H. Johnson, Syn. Metals *5*, 151 (1983).
139. M. Ozaki, D. Peebles, B. Weinberger, C. K. Chiang, S. C. Gan, A. J. Heeger, and A. G. MacDiarmid, Appl. Phys. Lett. *35*, 83 (1979).
140. M. Ozaki, D. Peebles, B. Weinberger, A. J. Heeger, and A. G. MacDiarmid, J. Appl. Phys. *51*, 4252 (1980).
141. T. Tani, P. M. Grant, W. D. Gill, G. B. Street, and T. C. Clarke, Solid State Commun. *33*, 499 (1980).
142. T. Tani, P. M. Grant, W. D. Gill, G. B. Street, and T. C. Clarke, Syn. Metals *1*, 301 (1980).
143. P. M. Grant, T. Tani, W. D. Gill, M. Krounbi, and T. C. Clarke, J. Appl. Phys. *52*, 869 (1981).
144. B. R. Weinberger, S. C. Gau, and Z. Kiss, Appl. Phys. Lett. *38*, 555 (1981).
145. B. R. Weinberger, M. Akhtar, and S. C. Gau, Syn. Metals *4*, 187 (1982).
146. P. J. Nigrey, A. G. MacDiarmid, and A. J. Heeger, J. Chem. Soc. Chem. Commun. p. 594 (1979).
147. P. J. Nigrey, D. McInnes, Jr., D. P. Nairns, A. G. MacDiarmid, and A. J. Heeger, J. Electrochem. Soc. *128*, 1651 (1981).
148. A. Feldblum, J. Kaufman, S. Etemad, A. J. Heeger, T. C. Chung, and A. G. MacDiarmid, Phys. Rev. B, Condensed Matter *26*(2) 815 (1982).
149. R. B. Fox, Naval Research Laboratory memorandum report 4335, Washington, DC, September 15, 1980.
150. J. B. Tucker, High Technology, p. 36, February, 1984.

Chapter 2

DIELECTRIC CONSTANT OF POLYMERS

2.1　INTRODUCTION

This chapter shows how, by chemical and structural control of polymer composition, it is possible to keep the dielectric constant of the composition either low or high. We discuss all the pertinent fundamental concepts first and, whenever possible, show the connection between theory and experimental results.

We start by giving a historical overview to the developments in this field. Next, having introduced the basic quantities used, we discuss polarization of polymers and how polarization phenomena contribute to the actual value of the dielectric constant. We then treat spontaneous polarization, interfacial polarization, and "hyperelectronic polarization" in detail and discuss the frequency and temperature dependence of the dielectric constant. With this as a background, we conclude by projecting the various correlations on how to keep the dielectric constant low or high.

Listed below for quick reference are more recent books and a symposium that amplify the subject matter of the chapter.

1. C. J. F. Böttcher, *Theory of Electric Polarization*, Vol. 1, Elsevier, Amsterdam (1973).
2. C. J. F. Böttcher and P. Bordewijk, *Theory of Electric Polarization*, Vol. 2, Elsevier, Amsterdam (1980).
3. R. Bartnikas and R. M. Eichhorn, *Engineering Dielectrics, Vol. IIA, Electrical Properties of Solid Insulating Materials: Molecular Structure and Electrical Behavior*, ASTM Special Technical Publication No. 783, Philadelphia (1983).
4. P. Hedvig, *Dielectric Spectroscopy of Polymers*, John Wiley & Sons, New York (1977).
5. I. Bunget and M. Popescu, *Physics of Solid Dielectrics*, Elsevier, Amsterdam (1984).
6. Brown University, *Symposium on Dielectric Phenomena*, IEEE, Electrical Insulation Society, New York (1985).

2.2   HISTORICAL OVERVIEW

Around the middle of the eighteenth century, it was discovered that large quantities of electric charge could be stored in a condenser. Cunaeus and Musschenbroek constructed one in 1745, and under the name Leyden jar, it became very popular for a variety of experimental purposes.[1]

Faraday and Cavendish were the first to perform experiments and publish numerical results on the properties of the insulating materials that Faraday called the dielectric.[2,3] Faraday's results indicated that the capacity of a condenser was dependent on the nature of the material separating the conducting surfaces. The ratio between the capacity of a condenser filled with a dielectric and the capacity of the same condenser when empty was termed by Faraday the *specific inductive capacity*, today known as the dielectric constant or permittivity.

In the middle of the nineteenth century, other electric and magnetic phenomena were studied. The results were summarized by Maxwell in his unified theory of electromagnetic phenomena in the middle of the1860s.[4,5] Since light was taken as a form of electromagnetic radiation, it followed that for most dielectrics the dielectric constant E should be equal to the square of the refractive index n. The simple relationship

$$E = n^2 \hspace{10cm} 2.1$$

is called the Maxwell relationship.

The subsequent experimental results showed that Maxwell's equation held reasonably well for many solids as well as for some liquids and gases. However, there were many other "associating" substances, for which the dielectric constant was considerably higher than the square of the refractive index measured in the visible region of the spectrum.

Later, after Hertz had discovered a way to generate electromagnetic waves of low frequency,[6] Drude used these frequencies to perform refractive index measurements on the associating substances and showed that the Maxwell relationship was also true for these substances at the low frequencies.[7] The first attempts to correlate the dielectric constant with the microscopic structure of matter were made by Mossotti in 1847, when he derived a relationship between the dielectric constant and the volume fraction occupied by the conducting particles in the dielectric.[8] However, this expression remained unknown until it was again derived in 1879 by Clausius.[9] At about this same time, Lorenz derived a corresponding expression for the square of the refractive index.[10] Furthermore, Lorentz showed the validity of the expression with n^2 for a medium built up of particles containing elastically bound electrons.[11,12] In his derivation, Lorenz introduced the concept of the internal field, that is, the average field working on an individual particle. This concept considerably advanced the theoretical understanding of the problem and contributed to the subsequent developments of the theory. By taking the number of particles per unit volume proportional to the density of the compound, he derived an equation that could easily be verified experimentally. This equation is known as the Lorenz-Lorentz equation.

For low frequencies, n^2 can be replaced by the dielectric constant, which transforms the Lorenz-Lorentz equation to a form equivalent to the expression derived by Mossotti and Clausius if in the latter expression the space filling of the conducting particles is taken proportional to the density. The resulting equation is used in this form and is generally called the Clausius-Mossotti equation.

The Clausius-Mossotti equation, however, failed to hold for the associating compounds. The deviations depended strongly on pressure, temperature, and the state of aggregation. Among the suggestions put forward to explain the discrepancy between the theory and the experimental results, attributing a permanent electric dipole moment to the molecules proved to be the most useful. In 1912, Debye published a quantitative theory and succeeded in deriving an extension of the Clausius-Mossotti equation: the Debye equation.[13] In this equation the dielectric constant depends not only on the molecular polarizability but also on the permanent moment of the molecules.

With the Debye equation, the temperature dependence of the dielectric constant could be elucidated, and the equation permitted calculation of molecular dipole moments from measurements of the dielectric constant. However, this capability was ahead of its time and did not create much interest until considerably later when the understanding of the structures of molecules was advanced to the point at which the value of the dipole moment could be connected with the geometrical arrangement of the atoms in the molecule.

Although the measurements of dipole moments in the gaseous phase and in dilute solutions of polar compounds agreed with the theory, it soon became apparent that the measurements on concentrated solutions and on pure polar liquids did not agree with the gas values. Nor did the temperature dependence of the dielectric constant agree with the theoretical predictions for these liquids.

In 1936, Onsager proposed a fundamental modification to Debye's method.[14] He pointed out that the internal field used by Debye included a part produced by the permanent moment of the molecule itself by means of the moments induced in it by the dielectric surrounding the molecule. This contribution to the internal field always has the direction of the permanent moment and therefore cannot produce a torque on the molecule. Consequently, the average component of the permanent moment in the direction of the internal field must be subtracted from the internal field to obtain one that tends to direct the permanent dipoles.

By considering the surroundings of a molecule as a continuum characterized by the macroscopic dielectric constant of the substance and by introducing some plausible approximations, Onsager derived a new relationship between the dielectric constant and the molecular dipole moment: the Onsager equation. Except for some specific classes of compounds, Onsager's theory accounted for most of the deviations from the Debye equation in the case of polar liquids.

The Onsager equation did not hold true for the liquid phase of compounds in which strong hydrogen bonding took place, such as carboxylic acids and alcohols. A few years after Onsager's work, Kirkwood developed a theory for hydrogen-bonded liquids relating the deviations from the Onsager equation to the orientation correlation of neighboring molecules, which was the result of short-range specific interactions.[15] On this basis it is possible to use the dielectric constant as a source for deriving information about specific interactions between the molecules and about the liquid structure.

It should be clear from this survey that progress is made by the development of new theories as well as from the availability of new experimental results.

2.3 BASIC RELATIONSHIPS

The dielectric constant or static relative permittivity ε of a material is the ratio of the capacitance of a condenser containing the material to that of the same condenser under vacuum. The capacitance of a condenser measures the extent to which it is able to store charge. For a nonpolar material, the increase in capacitance is due to the charges on the capacitor polarizing the molecules–attracting the positive charges in the molecules to one end and the negative charges to the other–with the result that increased charge appears on the surface, as indicated in Fig. 2.1.

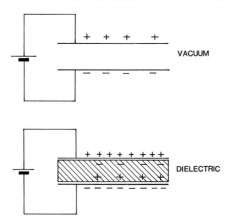

Fig. 2.1. Surface charge on a condenser.

Evidently, the greater the polarizability of the molecules, the higher the dielectric constant of the material will be. The polarizability of nonpolar molecules arises from two effects:

  a. electronic polarization, in which the applied electric field causes a displacement of the electrons relative to the nucleus in each atom; and
  b. atomic polarization, in which the applied field causes a displacement of the atomic nuclei relative to one another.

In polar molecules, a third process contributes to the total polarizability:

  c. orientation polarization, in which the applied field causes a net orientation of the dipoles parallel to the field.

A polar molecule has a permanent electric dipole moment; that is, although the molecule is electrically neutral, a distribution of charge exists such that the centers of positive and negative charge are separated by a distance of molecular dimensions. The dipole moment μ, which is equal to charge times distance, is measured in debyes. Historically, the debye has been taken as the order of magnitude of the electric charge (10^{-10} e.s.u.) multiplied by the order of magnitude of molecular dimensions (10^{-8} cm). Thus, 1 debye, or 1 D, equals 10^{-18} e.s.u.

The overall polarizability of a molecule, α_T, is the sum of three terms: $\alpha_T = \alpha_e + \alpha_a + \alpha_0$, where α_e, α_a, and α_0 are the electronic, atomic, and orientation polarizations, respectively.

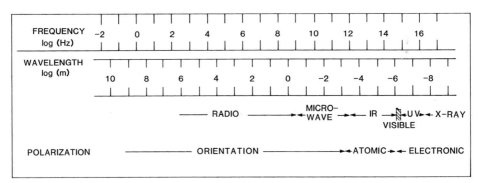

Fig. 2.2. Frequency spectrum showing the positions of the three main types of polarization, electronic, atomic, and orientation.

Each of the three types of polarization is a function of the frequency of the applied field (Fig. 2.2). At sufficiently low frequencies, all types of polarization can reach the values they would obtain in a steady field. As the frequency of the applied field is increased, the polarization no longer has time to reach its static field value. The orientation polarization is the first that fails to reach its equilibrium value, and the total polarizability falls from α_T to $(\alpha_T - \alpha_0)$. This fall in polarizability, its related fall in dielectric constant, and the occurrence of absorption constitute dielectric relaxation. The frequency at which the fall in orientation polarization occurs varies from very low frequencies for polymer chains (for example, approximately 100 Hz for polymer chain-backbone motion in polymethyl acrylate at room temperature) to 10^{10}–10^{12} Hz for small molecules. Both α_e and α_a remain unchanged at frequencies at which dielectric relaxation takes place, because the distortion polarization of a molecule reaches equilibrium with the applied field much sooner than does α_0. At frequencies comparable to the natural frequencies of vibration of the atoms in a molecule, however, α_a will fail to reach its equilibrium value, and further dispersion regions will appear in the infrared range of the spectrum. The dispersion caused by the fall-off of the electronic polarization occurs at still higher frequencies and corresponds to electronic transitions between different energy levels in the atom (visible, ultraviolet, and x-ray frequencies).

2.4   POLARIZATION OF POLYMERS

The difference between the dielectric constant of a polymer and that of free space is due to the restricted movements of charges within the polymer. Under the influence of the applied field, positive charges move with the electric field and an equal number of negative charges move against it, resulting in no net charge anywhere within the polymer. However, there is a net positive charge at the surface where the positive direction of the field emerges and a negative charge at the surface where the field enters. Thus, the field within the polymer is produced by a larger field outside it, and the normal components have the ratio given by the dielectric constant. This general process is called polarization. The charges are bound in the dielectric. They cannot move throughout it; otherwise they would produce conduction, not polarization. We now look in more detail at the fundamental components of molecular polarization: electronic, atomic, and orientation (Fig. 2.3).

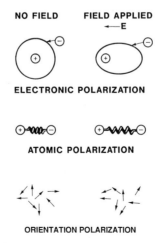

Fig. 2.3. Mechanisms of polarization.

2.4.1   Electronic Polarization

An electric field will cause a slight displacement of the electron cloud of any atom in the polymer molecule relative to its positive nucleus. As a result of relative movements of electron clouds from nuclei of atoms, the nuclei are no longer at the centers of the electron "orbits." This condition is called electronic polarization. However, the displacement resulting from this polarization is quite small because the applied electric field is usually very weak compared with the intra-atomic field at an electron, which is caused by the nucleus. This situation can be illustrated as follows. The charge on a proton is 1.6×10^{-19} C, and a typical atomic nucleus radius is 10^{-13} mm. Thus, the electric field on an electron will be about 10^8 V/mm, whereas externally applied electric fields even at the present level of high-voltage techniques seldom exceed 10^5 V/mm. Electronic polarization occurs in all materials and is responsible for the refraction of light.[16] Typically, the time required for electronic polarization is around 10^{-15} s and it produces a value of dielectric constant of about 2.

2.4.2   Atomic Polarization

An electric field can also distort the arrangement of atomic nuclei in a polymer molecule, a process called atomic polarization. The movement of heavy nuclei is more sluggish than that of electrons, so atomic polarization cannot occur at as high frequencies as electronic polarization, and the time required for atomic polarization is around 10^{-13} s. Atomic polarization is not observed above infrared frequencies. We know from infrared spectroscopy that for organic polymers, the force constants for bending or twisting of molecules, involving changes in angles between bonds, are generally much lower than those for bond stretching. This means that the major contribution to atomic polarization comes from bending and twisting motions. Usually the magnitude of atomic polarization for ordinary polymers is only one-tenth that of electronic polarization. However, where a particular mode of bending can produce a relatively large departure from the normally symmetric arrangements of positive and negative centers within the molecule, such as in the case of ionic or partially ionic crystallites, the magnitude of atomic polarization may even exceed that of electronic polarization. This is possible because the ionic or partially ionic nature of the bonds between atoms may produce a shift of charge distribution accompanying any relative movements of atoms, and an applied electric field will superpose on the thermal vibrations of the ions a slight average displacement of the positive charge center in one direction and of the negative charge center in the other direction. For example, the dielectric constant of insulating ceramics may reach a value of 5, of which a large part is due to atomic polarization.

Both electronic and atomic polarizations are displacements of positive and negative charge centers within the molecule, or alternatively, molecular deformation or molecular distortion. Thus, these processes may be also called displacement deformation or distortion polarization, and the dipole moment so produced is called an induced dipole moment.

2.4.3   Orientation Polarization

If the polymer molecules already possess a permanent dipole moment, the moment will tend to be aligned by the applied field to give a net polarization in that direction. This orientation polarization typically requires 10^{-9} s. In visualizing this process, we think of dipoles pointing in all directions and continually jumping from one orientation to another as a result of thermal agitation. The polarization that develops when the field is applied is a relatively small average of orientations favoring the direction of the applied field. The tendency to revert to random orientation opposes the tendency of the field to align the dipoles and thus allows for polarization to vary in proportion to the applied field. The orientation polarization produced by a field as high as 10^5 V/mm, nearly the highest used in engineering practice, results only in less than one-hundredth of the calculated polarization if all the dipoles were aligned.

2.4.4   Mechanics of Orientation Polarization

Electronic, and in many cases atomic, polarization takes place in times shorter than the period of oscillation of a 1-mm-wavelength radiation, and thus for the purposes of our discussion here are instantaneous. However, dipole rotation is very similar to molecular movements, giving rise to mechanical relaxation, and is thus subject to similar relaxation times.

To understand why the establishment of orientation polarization takes time, we can visualize a system that is similar to a springloaded rotary selector switch with a number of stable orientations. The switch is capable of being moved from one orientation to another when enough energy is available to overcome the potential energy barrier provided by the spring. In the case of the dipole, the barriers may be the hindrances from the neighboring parts of the molecule, electrostatic interactions, or other forms of restraint. To overcome the barrier between one orientation and the next, an energy W_0 has to be imparted, and the probability J of jumping is approximately proportional to the expression

$$J = \exp\left(\frac{-W_0}{kT}\right). \qquad\qquad 2.2$$

The average preference in favor of the direction of the field can only take effect when enough jumps have occurred.

If we apply an electric field E suddenly, the orientation polarization will grow to an equilibrium value at which the rate of polarization produced by the field is equal to the rate at which it is destroyed by thermal agitation. Suppose the equilibrium polarization is only a small fraction s of the polarization that would result if all the dipoles were aligned parallel to the field. The detailed theory[17] then shows that

$$s = \frac{\mu E_d}{3kT}, \qquad\qquad 2.3$$

where μ is the dipole moment and E_d is the average electric field acting on the dipoles themselves, which has about the same magnitude as the field E measured in the ordinary way but not equal to it.

The rate at which the electric field produces polarization from the nearly randomly oriented dipoles is practically independent of the polarization already created, whereas the rate at which polarization is destroyed by random thermal motion must be proportional to the polarization. In the latter case, if we write the constant of proportionality as $1/\tau$ (anticipating that τ will become the relaxation time of the orientation polarization), we get

$$\frac{dP}{dt} = -\frac{P}{\tau}, \qquad\qquad 2.4$$

where P is the instantaneous value of polarization. Integrating Eq. (2.4) with the condition that the final value of P is P_s (equilibrium polarization), we get[18]

$$P = P_s\left[1 - \exp\left(-\frac{t}{\tau}\right)\right]. \qquad\qquad 2.5$$

It is therefore the relaxation time of orientation polarization that varies for different kinds of polymer molecules because their potential energy barriers are different.

2.4.5   Polarizability

The three polarization mechanisms can also be expressed in terms of a molecular physical quantity called polarizability α. Polarizability is defined as the average molecular polarized dipole moment produced under the action of an electric field of unit strength. Suppose that under the action of the local electric field strength E' every molecule in the polymer produces an average polarized dipole moment m. Then for a general case, m is proportional to E', or

$$m = \alpha E', \qquad\qquad 2.6$$

where the proportionality constant α is the polarizability.

If a unit volume of a polymer contains n molecules (or n repeating units), then after polarization the total polarized dipole moment per unit volume is $n\bar{m}$, which is equal to the polarized charge density P. Thus,

$$P = n\bar{m}, \qquad\qquad 2.7$$

and from Eq. (2.6),

$$P = n\alpha E'. \qquad\qquad 2.8$$

This is the general expression of the value of polarization and it links the macroscopically measured dielectric constant to three molecular parameters: the number n of contributing elementary entities per unit volume, their polarizability α, and the local electric field E'. This field will normally differ from the applied field E because of the polarization of the surrounding dielectric medium.

2.5   POLARIZATION AND DIELECTRIC CONSTANT

The density of the neutralized surface charge is represented by the polarization vector:[19]

$$P = (\varepsilon' - \varepsilon_0)\, E = (\varepsilon - 1)\varepsilon_0 E. \qquad\qquad 2.9$$

Thus, Eqs. (2.8) and (2.9) give us two alternative expressions for polarization. Together they permit us to correlate polarizability with the dielectric constant. The dielectric constant ε is a macroscopic quantity, whereas polarizability α is a microscopic quantity, which is virtually related to the molecular structure. This correlation, therefore, will serve as the key for chemical control of the dielectric constant.

2.5.1   External and Local Electric Fields

Before we examine the correlation, we need to distinguish between E and E'. E refers to the external electrical field acting on a polymer, but E' refers to the local electrical field exerted on a polymer molecule. The difference between the local and external fields lies in the interactions of polymer molecules after polarization. Only in the case of gaseous dielectrics, where the intermolecular distance is rather large, can we say that $E \approx E'$. For polymers or more generally solid and liquid dielectrics, where the intermolecular distance is sufficiently small, induced dipole moments produced by the polarization of molecules will act on each other. Thus, E and E' are not equal, and their difference may even be large.

Let us look first at the local field E' in more detail. Suppose a solid dielectric contains a reference molecule A. To calculate the local field that A experiences, we have to consider the interactions of induced dipole moments of all the molecules on this molecule. For this purpose, we use a spherical model based on the postulates first proposed by Clausius[20] and Mossotti[21] (Fig. 2.4).

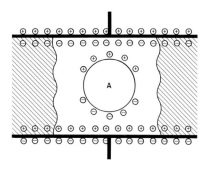

Fig. 2.4. Model for calculation of local field.

In their spherical model, reference molecule A is at the center of the sphere, which has a diameter much larger than that of the molecule, so that the region outside the sphere can be treated as a continuum. However, within the sphere the actual molecular structures of the dielectric material must be taken into account. Under these assumptions, the field within the sphere upon A is composed of the charge density contribution from the electrodes, E_0, from the induced charges at the electrode/dielectric interface resulting from polarization, E_1; from the charges induced at the spherical surface resulting from polarization, E_2; and from the molecular fields within the spherical region, E_3. Thus,

$$E' = E_0 + E_1 + E_2 + E_3. \qquad 2.10$$

According to the field analysis,

$$E_0 = \frac{D}{\varepsilon_0}. \qquad 2.11$$

where D is the electrical flux density of the external field and ε_0 is the dielectric constant of vacuum.
Then,

$$E_1 = -\frac{P}{\varepsilon_0}. \qquad 2.12$$

For E_2, Clausius and Mossotti calculated a value of

$$E_2 = \frac{P}{3\varepsilon_0} = \frac{E(\varepsilon - 1)}{3}. \qquad 2.13$$

To evaluate the field contribution E_3, which arises from the individual actions of the molecules inside the sphere, we need accurate information on the geometrical arrangement and polarizability of the contributing molecules. Even if this information were available, mathematical treatment would be prohibitively difficult. Hence, as an expedient, we consider a special case in which all the molecules are neutral and without a permanent dipole moment or in which they are arranged either in a complete disorder or in a cubic or similar highly symmetrical array. It can be shown that the additional individual field effects of the surrounding molecules on molecule A mutually cancel, and

$$E_3 = 0. \qquad 2.14$$

Thus, if $E_3 = 0$ for nonpolar or weakly polar polymer molecules, we can substitute all the known macroscopic parameters for the unknown molecular parameter E', and get

$$E' = \frac{D}{\varepsilon_0} - \frac{P}{\varepsilon_0} + \frac{(\varepsilon - 1)E}{3}$$

$$= \frac{\varepsilon_0 E + P}{\varepsilon_0} - \frac{P}{\varepsilon_0} + \frac{(\varepsilon - 1)E}{3} = \frac{(\varepsilon + 2)E}{3}. \tag{2.15}$$

This is known as the local *Mossotti* field.

2.5.2 Correlation of Polarization With Dielectric Constant

By substituting the local Mossotti field in Eq. (2.8), we obtain

$$P = n\,\alpha \left(\frac{\varepsilon + 2}{3}\right) E. \tag{2.16}$$

Now , if we equate Eq. (2.16) to Eq. (2.9),

$$n\,\alpha \left(\frac{\varepsilon + 2}{3}\right) E = (\varepsilon - 1)\,\varepsilon_0 E, \tag{2.17}$$

and then rearrange, we get

$$\frac{n\alpha}{3\varepsilon_0} = \frac{\varepsilon - 1}{\varepsilon + 2}. \tag{2.18}$$

Converting the relationship to molar basis,

$$\frac{N\alpha}{3\varepsilon_0} = \frac{\varepsilon - 1}{\varepsilon + 2} \cdot \frac{M}{\varrho}, \tag{2.19}$$

we obtain the Clausius-Mossotti equation. We have reached our goal of retaining the polarizability α as the only unknown molecular parameter.

Obviously, this is not a general equation for all polymers, because it applies only to nonpolar or weakly polar polymers. However, this equation and its derivation show the way for chemical control of the dielectric constant of polymers. From the relationship between ε and α so derived, it is clear that the way to reduce ε is to lower α and the way to increase ε is to raise α.

Table 2.1 summarizes the ranges of dielectric constants for various material classes that were measured at or near room temperature.

TABLE 2.1 Dielectric Constant Ranges

Material Class	Dielectric Constant (D)	Frequency Range (Hz)
Polymers and plastics	2.0–10.4	60–10^6
Filled polymers and plastics	2.50–170	10^3–3×10^9
Plastic and resin composites	2.24–150	60×10^7
Rubbers	2.25–9.53	60–10^6
Filled rubbers	2.66–17,900	10^3
Foamed plastics and rubbers	1.0–2.16	10^3–10^{10}

The dielectric constants for the polyacene quinone radical (PAQR) class of polymers have been reported to be as high as 300,000. More will be said about these materials in the section on "Hyperelectronic Polarization."[22]

In the use of polymers for electronic and electrical engineering applications, the range of dielectric constants is very wide. For example, polymers for insulation of high-frequency communication cables need ε lower than 2 and approaching 1 as near as possible. On the other hand, polymers as a dielectric in capacitors need ε as high as possible.

2.6   SPONTANEOUS POLARIZATION OR FERROELECTRICITY

When deriving the Clausius-Mossotti equation for the internal field in dielectrics, we said that the assumptions on which it was based could apply only to nonpolar molecules. However, if we can use the so-called Mossotti field in a dipolar material instead of the Lorentz field in a nonpolar material, the novel results allow for the possibility of generating novel materials.

The Clausius equation relates polarization and polarizability by

$$P = (\varepsilon - 1)\varepsilon_0 E = N\alpha E'. \qquad 2.20$$

If we assume an internal field of the Mossotti type,

$$E' = E + \frac{P}{3\varepsilon_0}, \qquad 2.21$$

then, by substituting in Eq. (2.20) we get

$$P = N\alpha E + \frac{N\alpha P}{3\varepsilon_0} \qquad 2.22$$

and

$$P = \frac{N\alpha E}{1 - (N\alpha/3\varepsilon_0)}. \qquad 2.23$$

But

$$P = (\varepsilon - 1)\varepsilon_0 E, \qquad 2.24$$

so

$$(\varepsilon - 1) = \frac{P}{\varepsilon_0 E}. \qquad 2.25$$

Substituting Eq. (2.23) into Eq. (2.25) we get

$$\varepsilon - 1 = \frac{N\alpha E/[1 - (N\alpha/3\varepsilon_0)]}{\varepsilon_0 E} \qquad 2.26$$

$$= \frac{N\alpha/\varepsilon_0}{1 - (N\alpha/3\varepsilon_0)}.$$

The right-hand sides of both Eqs. (2.23) and (2.26) will tend to infinity as

$$\frac{N\alpha}{3\varepsilon_0} \to 1 \text{ or } \alpha \to \frac{3\varepsilon_0}{N}.$$

Thus, both P and ε will also tend to infinity. From the standpoint of materials science, for the dielectric constant to approach infinity the necessary condition for α is

$$\alpha = \frac{3\varepsilon_0}{N}. \tag{2.27}$$

This type of a polarization, which would lead to materials with dielectric constants approaching infinity, had already been derived by the nineteenth century and is known as spontaneous polarization or ferroelectricity.

If we express the polarizability by the Debye equation,

$$\alpha = \alpha_e + \alpha_a + \frac{\mu^2}{3kT}, \tag{2.28}$$

then it can be seen that there may be a critical temperature T_c for which $N\alpha/3\varepsilon_0 = 1$:

$$N(\alpha_e + \alpha_a) + \frac{N\mu^2}{3kT_c} = 3\varepsilon_0. \tag{2.29}$$

Rearranging, we get

$$\frac{N\mu^2}{9\varepsilon_0 kT_c} = 1 - \frac{N(\alpha_e + \alpha_a)}{3\varepsilon_0} \tag{2.30}$$

and

$$T_c = \frac{N\mu^2}{9\varepsilon_0 K} \cdot \frac{1}{1 - [N(\alpha_e + \alpha_a)/3\varepsilon_0]}. \tag{2.31}$$

At this temperature, the expressions for both polarization and dielectric constant go to infinity. The same type of behavior is met in the theory of ferromagnetism, in which the critical temperature is the Curie temperature, below which the material becomes spontaneously magnetized. In this case, the dielectric will become spontaneously polarized below the Curie temperature. By analogy, a dielectric in which this occurs is called ferroelectric.

2.6.1 Mossotti Catastrophe

Since spontaneous polarization results predominantly from orientation polarization, the extraction of the dielectric constant can be further simplified if we neglect the deformation polarization, which is the actual case:

$$(\alpha_e + \alpha_a) \ll \frac{\mu^2}{3kT}. \tag{2.32}$$

Then Eq. (2.31) becomes

$$T_c = \frac{N\mu^2}{9\varepsilon_0 k}. \tag{2.33}$$

The dielectric constant of a ferroelectric at any temperature will then be

$$\varepsilon - 1 = \frac{(N/\varepsilon_0)\,(\mu^2/3kT)}{1 - [(N/3\varepsilon_0)\,(\mu^2/3kT)]}, \tag{2.34}$$

$$= \frac{3T_c}{T - T_c}$$

or

$$\varepsilon = \frac{T + 2T_c}{T - T_c} \qquad\qquad 2.35$$

Thus, a local field of the Mossotti type, in which the inner polarization supports the external field, should cause a spontaneous orientation of the dipoles at the critical temperature. This is known in the literature as the "Mossotti catastrophe." However, the tacit assumption in predicting such a "catastrophic event" is that the dipoles are free to orient, a situation generally not encountered in condensed phases.

Actually, a Mossotti-type catastrophe occurs only under very special conditions, and not at all as foreseen in the preceding derivation. The reason is that permanent electric dipole moments are anchored in molecular groups that tend to lose their freedom of orientation in a condensed phase through association and steric hindrance. Obviously, very special conditions must prevail if polar groups are to act as "free" dipoles in a solid.

2.6.2 Ferroelectric Polymers

Characteristic ferroelectric representatives among the polymers are poly(vinylidene fluoride), PVF_2, in the polar form[23–26] and its trifluoroethylene copolymers.[27] Although dipolar reorientation has been demonstrated[28–31] and ferroelectric hysteresis loops have been obtained between -100 and $140°C$,[31,32] convincing evidence regarding Curie transitions in PVF_2 has been lacking. Now a series of random copolymers of vinylidene fluoride and trifluoroethylene containing 52, 65, 73, and 78 mol% VF_2 has been shown by x-ray and dielectric techniques to undergo Curie transitions.[27] In their ferroelectric phase, the copolymer molecules assume structures analogous to the all-trans of β-PVF_2, whereas in the paraelectric phase, they are partly disordered through introduction of gauche$^{\pm}$ bonds. The Curie transitions extend over wide temperature ranges ($\sim 30°C$) and exhibit thermal hysteresis in that the ferroelectric $\rightarrow$ paraelectric transformation occurs at higher temperatures than does the reverse. Poled samples have higher Curie temperatures than do their unpoled counterparts, and for the 78-mol% copolymer, this causes thwarting of the Curie transition by the onset of melting. This suggests that the absence of a distinct Curie transition in β-PVF_2 may be due to prior melting. Extrapolation of the copolymer results to 100% PVF_2 leads to a hypothetical transition at $\sim 205°C$, which is $\sim 20°C$ above the melting point of β-PVF_2.

The structural prerequisites for the formation of ferroelectric polymers are: (1) a specific crystal form in a semicrystalline polymer, (2) hydrogen-bonded structures, (3) covalent bonds with strong ionicity, and (4) appropriate organometallic structures. For example, in n-primary alcohols the low-frequency absorption has been attributed to conducting filaments formed by hydrogen-bonded chains of hydroxyl groups.[33]

2.7   INTERFACIAL POLARIZATION

As early as 1892, Maxwell[34] pointed out that in heterogeneous dielectrics a type of polarization occurs as a result of the accumulation of virtual charge at the interface of two media having different dielectric constants, ε_1 and ε_2, and conductivities, σ_1 and σ_2, respectively, whenever

$$\varepsilon_1\sigma_2 = \varepsilon_2\sigma_1. \qquad\qquad 2.36$$

This polarization is now called interfacial polarization. Interfacial polarization is commonplace in electrical and electronic applications of polymers and is closely related to the breakdown of polymers. So far we have concerned ourselves with ideal specimens, which are entirely homogeneous and possess perfect interfaces with the electric fields. In practice, a material is always likely to have regions of nonuniformity, and second-phase materials may be present. For example, the stabilizers added to the polymers to prevent thermal and photodegradation are usually dispersed second-phase materials. Fillers and dyestuffs also form separate phases. Impurities such as traces of monomer, solvent, and water may also make the practical polymeric system heterogeneous. Complications can also arise at electrodes, where contact with the specimen may be incomplete and where species such as discharged ions may form spurious boundary layers. A common form of discontinuity occurs in a polymer having cracks or voids, especially if the polymer is old. It is important to be aware of such anomalous effects; they can give totally misleading results if they are not recognized or avoided.

2.7.1   Interfacial Behavior

When a dielectric material is composed of two or more phases, space-charge build-up occurs at the macroscopic interfaces as a result of the differences in the conductivities and dielectric constants of the materials at the interfaces. This accumulation of space charge then leads to field distortions and dielectric loss. Wagner first studied the interfacial behavior by considering the case of an equivalent circuit of a two-parallel-layer capacitor in which the layers were of different conducting and dielectric constants.[35] Figure 2.5 shows Wagner's two-layer capacitor system and its equivalent circuit.

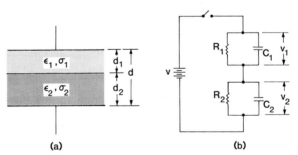

(a)   (b)

Fig. 2.5 (a) Maxwell-Wagner two-layer condenser; (b) equivalent circuit of two-layer condenser.

Wagner derived an equation for the dielectric constant as follows:

$$\varepsilon = \varepsilon_\infty \left(1 + \frac{K}{1 + \omega^2\tau^2}\right),$$

2.37

where

$$\varepsilon_\infty = \varepsilon_1 \left[1 + \frac{3f(\varepsilon_2 - \varepsilon_1)}{2\varepsilon_1 + \varepsilon_2}\right],$$

2.38

$$K = \frac{9f\varepsilon_1}{2\varepsilon_1 + \varepsilon_2},$$

2.39

and

$$\tau = \frac{\varepsilon_0(2\varepsilon_1 + \varepsilon_2)}{\sigma_2}.$$

2.40

Here ω is the frequency of the ac field and τ is the relaxation time of the interfacial polarization. A two-layer capacitor leads to a single relaxation time. If one were to consider a capacitor with n different layers, a dielectric spectrum of $(n-1)$ relaxation times would result. Wagner then showed that a dispersion of dielectric spheres (volume fraction f) in another dielectric medium would result in a behavior substantially similar to that of the two-layer capacitor. Eq. (2.37) shows that the frequency dependence of this dielectric constant is similar in form to those corresponding to orientation (dipole) polarization in homogeneous media.[36] The only difference is the appearance of the conductivity term. Equation (2.40) shows that the relaxation time decreases as the conductivity of the material of the spheres increases. To illustrate the approximate value of relaxation time of interfacial polarization, we may make the following assumptions: $\varepsilon_1 = \varepsilon_2 = 4$ and $\sigma_2 = 10^{-6}$ (ohm $\cdot$ cm)$^{-1}$, and we get a relaxation time of about 1 μs. Consequently, the effect can be very easily mistaken for one of dipole orientation.

Sillars extended the analysis to include ellipsoids and rods.[37] Since water is a common second phase in solid insulating materials, we would expect interfacial polarization effects to apply. Sillars has demonstrated that although the interfacial loss depends on the quantity of water present as well as on the geometrical shape of its dispersion, the magnitude of the interfacial loss is particularly susceptible to the length of the dispersed-phase geometry in the direction of the field.[18] In the cases of water trees or dendrites in polyethylene cables, water-filled channels or needles occur, and we would then expect the loss resulting from interfacial polarization at these locations to be appreciable.

2.7.2 Interfacial Polarization

Electronic, atomic, and orientation polarization are all due to charges that are locally bound in atoms, molecules, or the structures of solids and liquids. But in addition, charge carriers usually exist that can migrate for some distance through the dielectric. When the charge carriers are impeded in their motion, either because they become trapped in the material or at an interface or because they cannot be freely discharged or replaced at the electrodes, space charges and a macroscopic field distortion result. Such a distortion appears to an observer as an increase in the capacitance of the sample and may be indistinguishable from a real rise of the dielectric constant. For example, a polymer crystal inevitably has a large number of defects such as lattice vacancies, impurity centers, dislocations, and so on. Free charge carriers migrating through the crystal under the influence of an applied field may be trapped by, or pile up against, a defect. The effect of this will be the creation of a localized accumulation of charge that will induce its image charge on an electrode and give rise to a dipole moment. This constitutes a separate mechanism of polarization in the crystal and is given the name interfacial polarization.

2.7.3 Detection of Interfacial Polarization

Although it is not possible to detect the presence of interfacial polarization in homogeneous nonpolar polymers (for example, polyethylene, polypropylene, or polystyrene) by the usual dielectric techniques, it is possible to do so if low-frequency measurement techniques, such as dielectric depolarization, or very low frequency Fourier transformation methods are used.[38] The reason that interfacial polarization should be found in such polymers at all is that impurities in such polymers may cause some oxidation at the structural defects. This oxidation then leads to the formation of oxidized centers or regions that would then lead to interfacial polarization.

Generally, interfacial polarization may be detected in polymers having structural inhomogeneities even when there is no orientation polarization of the polar inclusions, or even if the inclusions are nonpolar. In any case, when structural inhomogeneities between materials of different dielectric constants and conductivities are present, interfacial polarization is expected to occur. This principally influences the low-frequency (10^{-5}- to 10^2-Hz) dielectric properties, because the interfacial polarization usually decreases with increasing frequency. Since even pure polymers are never homogeneous, the very low-frequency dielectric constants are expected (and found) to be much higher than the dielectric constants obtained from extrapolation of values measured at intermediate and high frequencies.

2.7.4   Conductive Fillers and Dielectric Constant

The effect of conductive filler on the dielectric constant of polymers is very instructive. For example, carbon-black-loaded rubber vulcanizates exhibit dielectric properties beyond those of the base material. Carbon-black-loaded rubber possesses high conductivity, whereas unloaded rubber is an insulator. At high carbon black loadings, it is possible to prepare electrically conductive rubber vulcanizates[39] exhibiting a σ of $10^{-3}-10^{-1}$ $(\Omega cm)^{-1}$. Usually the carbon black particles are separated by insulating polymer layers. In these systems, however, the interfacial polarization becomes extremely large. At high carbon black concentrations, 30–40%, the dielectric constant increases rapidly to reach values above 100.[40-42] Furthermore, the distribution of carbon black in rubber can be estimated from the ε and frequency correlation.

2.8   HYPERELECTRONIC POLARIZATION – A SPECIAL CASE OF INTERFACIAL POLARIZATION

The concept of hyperelectronic polarization is due exclusively to Pohl, Rosen, and Hartman.[43-47] The initial measurements of extraordinarily high dielectric constants (up to 900 at 300 Hz and 85°C) in the polyacene quinone radical (PAQR) class of polymers was reported by Pohl and Rosen in 1965.[43, 44] The proposed structures for typical PAQR polymers are illustrated in Fig. 2.6.

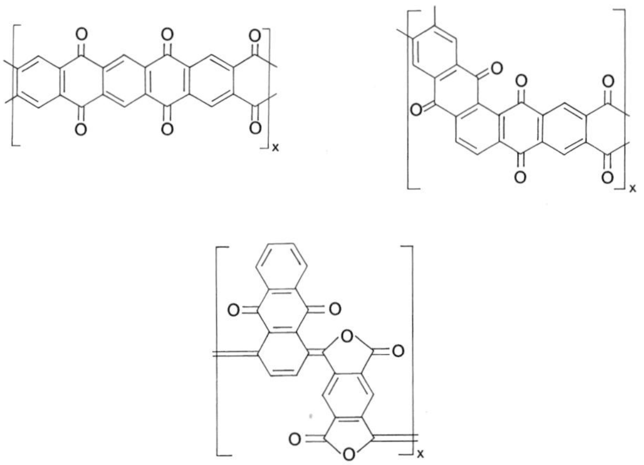

Fig. 2.6. PAQR class of polymers.

The polymers were obtained by reaction of pyromellitic dianhydride, with multinuclear aromatic compounds such as naphthalene, anthracene, and phenanthrene in the presence of $ZnCl_2$ as the catalyst at an elevated temperature (typically 300°C) for 24 h. The reaction residue was then powdered and purified by successive exhaustive extractions with hydrochloric acid, water, alcohol, and toluene at their respective boiling points.

The bulk materials contain potential carriers in the form of radicals or radical ions as evidenced by E.S.R. activity. For the PAQR polymers, relative dielectric constants approaching 300,000 were observed.[48] This can be understood in terms of enormous interfacial polarizations across the long conjugated domains in which the radical ions are mobile.

However, the proposal of "hyperelectronic polarization" was based on the following molecular view: mobile charges lie individually on extended regions of π-orbitals associated with near-zero resistance and their path is limited only by a molecular boundary. The mobile charges, arising from inherent and easily thermally excited intermolecular ionization levels of the long conjugated molecules, would form a collection of highly polarizable monopoles (such as excitons and ions) and thereby possibly exhibit a high bulk polarizability. This collection of highly field-sensitive monopoles would then exhibit what might be termed "hyperelectronic" polarization.

However, Rosen and Pohl[44] also stated that an alternative mechanism could not be eliminated. The polymers studied were polycrystalline semiconductors. It was possible that what was observed was the migration and accumulation of carriers at the crystallite boundaries in such a manner as to exhibit a similarly high dielectric constant. Thus, in a very real sense "hyperelectronic polarization" could also be regarded as interfacial polarization on a molecular or microscopic scale.

The authors admitted that this argument is very hard to refute. Therefore, there is no reason to dismiss it and propose a new mechanism. The authors also noted the discrepancy in relaxation times between the model of dielectric particles dispersed in a continuous medium, as developed by Takashima,[49] and the observed values. Hartman and Pohl then suggested that this anomaly may be removed if one uses the hyperelectronic polarization model in which the molecule is considered to be quite elongated and is treated as the *bulk grain*. This, however, disregards the earlier work of Pollack,[50] in which he showed that the discrepancy was removed when he developed an expression for relaxation times that is appropriate to the *interfacial polarization mechanism for highly elongated molecules*.

Finally, the described shearing experiments to disrupt the conductive grains wrapped in a layer of poorly conductive substance can hardly be taken as definitive evidence that the high polarizability is *not* due to interfacial polarization!

In conclusion we restate Rosen and Pohl's original surmise that the observed high dielectric constants in their materials could also be due to charge migration to the crystallite boundaries in such a manner as to exhibit high polarization. Molecular structure and the physical arrangement of molecules in solid polymers are not always precisely known, and certainly for the PAQR materials much more careful specification of the molecular arrangement is required before one can justify assigning a feature of dielectric behavior to a specific new feature of molecular structure.

2.9   HOW TO KEEP DIELECTRIC CONSTANT LOW

The dielectric behavior of a polymer is determined by the charge distribution and the statistical thermal motion of polar groups. It is therefore evident that the chemical structure should be the basic factor in the determination of the dielectric behavior. As shown in Appendix 1, polymers that have polar bonds in their chains would be expected *ab initio* to have high dielectric constants. This is, however, only a necessary condition. One polymer that has a low dielectric constant is polytetrafluoroethylene despite its strong polar C-F groups (1.39 D). The reason for this lies in the molecular configuration and morphology of the polymer, which makes the effective dipole moment small for the repeating units, which behave rigidly during thermal motion.

The guidance to low ε in polymers comes from two sources: (1) the basic structure properties correlation as expressed by total polarizability and the Clausius-Mossotti equation and (2) empirical considerations.

2.9.1   Polarization Considerations

a) *Total Polarizability*

Total polarizability was expressed in Sec. 2.3 as

$$\alpha_T = \alpha_e + \alpha_a + \alpha_0. \tag{2.41}$$

If we want to achieve as low ε as possible, then α_0 should be absent from the material. This leaves α_e as a parameter that can be structurally controlled quite readily. As for α_a one has less choice in its control for a given polymer.

b) *Electronic Polarizability*

Suppose an external electric field E causes a slight displacement x of the center of an electron cloud with a charge q on an atom in a polymer molecule. The induced dipole moment m is then

$$m = qx, \tag{2.42}$$

and electronic polarizability α_e is

$$\alpha_e = \frac{qx}{E}. \tag{2.43}$$

According to the model of elastically bound electrons, the charge displacement is in equilibrium with the interaction force between electrons and the positive nucleus which we can express as elastically bound, kx, then

$$kx = qE. \tag{2.44}$$

Substituting Eq. (2.44) into Eq. (2.43), we get

$$\alpha_e = \frac{q^2}{k}. \tag{2.45}$$

This means that electronic polarization will increase as the atomic radius increases because k decreases as the atomic radius increases. When this relationship is applied to polymers, those possessing repeating units with delocalized electrons will have a much larger α_e than will those with localized electrons only. This is one of the reasons why the dielectric constant of polystyrene is slightly larger than that of polyethylene or polypropylene.

c) *Clausius-Mossotti Equation*

The Clausius-Mossotti equation is applicable only to nonpolar or weakly polar polymers. However, the equation shows ways to control the dielectric constant. For example, it is clear that the way to reduce ε is to lower α. Likewise, decreasing the density of a material makes it possible to reduce its dielectric constant. For example, the electronic polarizability α_e of benzene is around 1.1×10^{-23} cm^3. The dielectric constant for benzene liquid is 2.25, whereas that for benzene vapor is only 1.0027. We can explain this difference in terms of density: the density of the former is 0.88 g/cm^3, and that for the latter is 0.0025 g/cm^3.

d) *Spontaneous and Interfacial Polarization*

Since spontaneous polarization results predominantly from orientation polarization, materials with polar groups are thus eliminated from this consideration. Interfacial polarization must also be eliminated if low ε is to be achieved. Thus, structural irregularities, polar impurities, or any second-phase materials are to be avoided.

2.9.2 Empirical Considerations

If we wish to keep the dielectric constant low, experience shows what we can do in every step, from the synthesis of the polymer to the final packaging of the plastic product. In the synthesis, use of a nonpolar comonomer will decrease the ε of the polar homopolymer. In the formulation of the plastic composition, ε will be decreased by the use of less polar or nonpolar plasticizers, antioxidants, stabilizers, and processing aids. In the processing (molding and extrusion) of the composition, avoidance of incipient degradation and oxidation will lead to lower ε.

In the generation of plastic foams the preferred foaming agent should decompose completely into gaseous components. If residue is left, it should be nonpolar and left in as low an amount as possible. For example, an excellent foaming agent is azodiformamide, which decomposes at around 185°C and leaves no residue:

$$3 \; H_2N\overset{\overset{O}{\|}}{C}-N=N-\overset{\overset{O}{\|}}{C}NH_2 \rightarrow 4N_2 \uparrow + 6CO \uparrow + 4NH_3 \uparrow.$$

A typical polyethylene foam containing about 50 vol% air has a density of 0.4–0.5 g/cm^3 and a dielectric constant of 1.5. Polyethylene foams of density as low as 0.03 g/cm^3 with a dielectric constant of 1.1 have been prepared.

Finally, once the plastic product has been manufactured, minimization of contact with moisture will maintain a low dielectric constant.

2.10 HOW TO KEEP DIELECTRIC CONSTANT HIGH

The dielectric constant of polymers has a lower limit of 1, but in principle no upper limit exists. In arriving at structures or materials with high dielectric constant, one may analyze the dielectric polarizability in more detail to gain knowledge about structures with high polarizability, and one may examine classical dielectric equations again to gain guidance in structure selection for high polarizability. One then uses this information in relating it to dielectric constant. Considerable empirical knowledge is available as to what materials and what processes lead to high dielectric constant.

Since for polar polymers both the atomic and electronic polarizations are often small compared with orientation polarization, these will not be considered further in this section. It will be profitable to examine the dipole moment of a molecule in some detail, because orientation polarization is due to the presence of permanent dipoles in a molecule.

2.10.1 Dipole Moment

Dipole moments originate from the asymmetry of the positive and negative charge densities of the system. Positive charges arise from the nuclei and are localized. Changes in the positive charge density result from structural transformations of the molecule (isomeric transitions, rotation of groups, or rotation of the solid, for example, recrystallization, local motions, or vibrations). Negative charge densities arise from the electronic system, which is delocalized. The extent of delocalization depends on the chemical structure.

In principle, it is possible to calculate the fractional electronic charge distribution of a molecule. If the equilibrium positions of the nuclei are known, the positive charge distribution is also known, and thus the dipole moment of the molecule can be calculated. In practice, such calculations are extremely difficult. This is the reason why the total dipole moment of a molecule is often calculated as the vectorial sum of the dipole moments of all the bonds in a molecule:

$$\mu_{mol.} = \sum_{i=1}^{N} \mu_i. \qquad 2.46$$

The absolute values of bond moments are approximately expressed as

$$\mu_i = 4.8RI, \qquad 2.47$$

where R is the bond distance and I is the ionicity of the bond. The ionicity of a bond between atoms A and B can be expressed in terms of the Pauling electronegativity values X_A and X_B as[51]

$$I(AB) = 1 - \exp\left[-\frac{(X_A - X_B)^2}{4}\right]. \qquad 2.48$$

The Pauling electronegativities are defined as

$$X_A - X_B = [0.18E_{AB} - (E_{AA}E_{BB})^{\frac{1}{2}}]^{\frac{1}{2}}, \qquad 2.49$$

where E_{AB} is the total binding energy of the bond and E_{AA} and E_{BB}, respectively, are the binding energies of the corresponding like atoms.

According to the type of the electron configuration, the following three main kinds of bond-dipole moments are distinguished:

1. *σ-moments*, defined by the ionic parts of the σ-bond eigenfunctions;
2. *mesomeric or π-moments*, caused by the deformation of the π-electronic density, which is due to the inductive effect of a substituent; and
3. *lone-pair moments*, resulting from nonbonding electrons.

Table 2.2 lists most of the common bond moments.[52] At least three other volumes of dipole moment data are available.[53-55]

These moments have been calculated from the measured values of the corresponding methyl compounds by assuming C^--H^+ polarization of the CH bonds and tetrahedral configuration. For chloromethane, for example, the tetrahedral angle is 109.5°. Correspondingly, the component of the C^--H^+ dipole moment along the C–Cl axis is μ(C–H) Cos

TABLE 2.2 Bond Dipole Moments[52]

Bond	Dipole Moment (D)	Bond	Dipole Moment (D)
+ − (polarization)		+ −	
C−F	1.39	C=N	1.4
C−Cl	1.47	C=O	2.4
C−N	0.45	C=S	2.0
C−O	0.7	C=N	3.1
C−S	0.9	H−O	1.5
C(sp^3)−C(sp^2)	0.69	H−N	1.3
C(sp^3)−C(sp)	1.48	H−S	0.7
C(sp^2)−C(sp)	1.15	Si−C	1.2
		Si−H	1.0
		Si−N	1.55

$180 - 109.5° = 1/3\ \mu(\text{C–H})$. Since there are three C–H bonds to contribute to the total moment along the C–Cl axis and $\mu(\text{C–H}) = 0.4\ \text{D}$, the total C–Cl bond moment is

$$\mu(\text{C–Cl}) = \mu(\text{CH}_3\text{Cl}) - \mu(\text{C–H}) = 1.87 - 0.4 = 1.47\ \text{D}.$$

The charge of the electron is 4.8×10^{-10} e.s.u., so to produce a dipole moment of 1 D, the positive and negative unit charge centers should be separated by 0.28 Å ($\sim 3 \times 10^{-9}$ cm).

To assume that the total dipole moment is a vectorial sum of the bond moments is, of course, an oversimplification. The charge density distribution of a bond is influenced by its neighbors through inductive effects and overlap of the electron densities. This is illustrated in Table 2.3 where the C–H, C–Cl, and C–F bond moments are shown by different halogen substitutions for chloro- and fluoromethanes.[53] We can see that the C–H bond moment is considerably increased by the halogen substitution, whereas the carbon-halogen bond moment is decreased.

TABLE 2.3 Inductive Effect of Halogen Substitution on the Bond Dipole Moments[53]

Compound	Bond Moment (D)		Total moment of the molecule (D)
	C–H − +	C–Cl + −	
CH$_3$Cl	0	1.86	1.87
CH$_2$Cl$_2$	0.16	1.25	1.62
CHCl$_3$	0.19	0.92	1.2
	CH − +	C–F + −	
CH$_3$F	0	1.81	1.79
CH$_2$F$_2$	0.23	1.45	1.96
CHF$_3$	0.32	1.22	1.64

This suggests that the dipole moment of a group or a molecule should be evaluated directly from the nuclear and electronic charge distributions, which can be calculated without assuming chemical bond structure. Such calculations are possible; however, they are complicated and require long computer time. The semiclassical method based on the Valence Bond Theory[51] is still useful, although quantitative agreement between theory and experiment is usually poor.

2.10.2 The Effective Dipole Moment

The shape of a polymer molecule and the total molecular dipole moment change as a result of thermal motion, and therefore the molecule cannot be treated as a rigid configuration. Correspondingly, the consequence of dipole orientation in macromolecular systems is that only parts of the molecule are considered, and thermal motion has no effect on the configuration. In calculating the effective dipole moment of the rigid parts, we must add the bond moments vectorially. If the molecule contains N polar groups having configurations that do not change during thermal motion, the effective dipole moment is expressed as

$$\mu_{eff} = \left[\sum_{i=1}^{N} \mu_{xi}^2 + \sum_{i=1}^{N} \mu_{yi}^2 + \sum_{i=1}^{N} \mu_{zi}^2 \right]^{1/2} , \qquad 2.50$$

where μ_{xi}, μ_{yi}, and μ_{zi} are the bond moment components along the coordinate axes x, y, and z. The effect of thermal motions on polymer molecules is that the effective dipole moment depends upon the temperature.

a) Group Moments

In considering effective dipole moments, it is easier to use group moments instead of bond moments. Group moments are the dipole moments of chemical groups that have stable configurations during thermal motion. Table 2.4 lists some group dipole moments.[52] Two main types are illustrated: (1) the polar group attached to a phenyl ring and (2) the polar group attached to a methyl group. The angles listed are the angles of the dipole moment with the phenyl-X and methyl-X bond.

b) Stereochemical Structure

The effective dipole moments of polymer molecules also depend on their stereochemical structure. One would expect the highest effective dipole moment for isotactic polymers, in which the monomer units, and correspondingly the same moments, are oriented regularly the same way (Fig. 2.7).

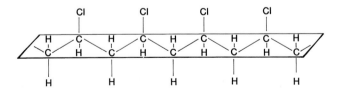

Fig. 2.7. Isotactic form of polyvinyl chloride.

TABLE 2.4 Group Dipole Moments[52]

Group Ph−X	Direction of the Moment	Angle of the Group Moment	Dipole Moment, (D)	Group CH$_3$=X	Angle of the Group Moment	Dipole Moment (D)
Ph−CH$_3$	←	0	0.37	H$_3$C−CH$_3$	0	0
Ph−CF$_3$	→	0	− 2.54	H$_3$C−CF$_3$	0	− 2.32
Ph−CCl$_3$	→	0	− 2.04	H$_3$C−CCl$_3$ + ← −	0	− 1.57
Ph−CN	→	0	− 4.05	H$_3$C−CN + ← −	0	− 3.47
Ph−CHO	146°	146	− 2.96	H$_3$C−CHO + ← −	125	− 2.49
Ph−COCH$_3$	132°	132	− 2.96	H$_3$C−COCH$_3$ + ← −	120	− 2.75
−	−	−	−	H$_3$C−COOH + ← −	106	− 1.63
Ph−COOCH$_3$ + −	120°	110	− 1.83	−	−	−
Ph−COOC$_2$H$_5$	118°	118	− 1.9	H$_3$C−COOC$_2$H$_5$ − → +	89	1.8
Ph−F	→	0	− 1.47	H$_3$C−F + ← −	0	− 1.79
Ph−Cl	→	0	− 1.59	H$_3$C−Cl + ← −	0	− 1.87
Ph−OH	↑	90	1.55	−	−	−
Ph−OCH$_3$ − → +	72°	72	1.28	H$_3$C−OCH$_3$ − → +	124	1.28
Ph−OCF$_3$ − → +	160°	160	− 2.36	−	−	−
Ph−OCOCH$_3$ − → +	66°	66	1.69	−	−	−
Ph−NO + ← −	149°	149	− 3.09	−	−	−
Ph−NO$_2$ + ← −	→	0	− 4.01	H$_3$C−NO$_2$ + ← −	0	− 3.10

The next highest effective dipole moment results from atactic followed by syndiotactic placement of the groups, in which the polar groups are arranged at random or opposite one another (Fig. 2.8).

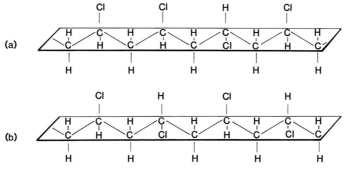

Fig. 2.8. (a) Atactic and (b) syndiotactic forms of polyvinyl chloride.

The individual bond moments are more likely to be cancelled in these placements, resulting in effective dipole moment smaller than that in isotactic polymers. Table 2.5 lists effective dipole moment data of some polymers of different tacticities in dilute solution. Isotactic placement of the groups possesses higher effective dipole moments than both the atactic and syndiotactic placements.

TABLE 2.5 Effective Dipole Moments vs Stereoregularity

Polymer	Tacticity			Ref.
	Isotactic	Atactic	Syndiotactic	
Polystyrene in toluene, 311 K	0.44	0.36	–	56
Polymethyl methacrylate in benzene, 303 K	1.42	1.28	1.26	57
Polybutyl methacrylate in benzene, 293 K	1.52	1.45	1.45	57, 58
Polyvinyl isobutyrate in benzene, 298 K	1.16	1.07	–	59
Poly-tert-butyl-methacrylate in benzene, 293 K	1.73	1.54	–	60

c) *Reduction Factors*

In the condensed phase, the dipole moments of the molecules or groups interact strongly, resulting in a decrease of the total dipole moment. This reduction was defined by Kirkwood[15] as

$$g_r = \frac{\mu_{eff}^2(\text{condensed})}{\mu_0^2(\text{gas})} \, , \qquad\qquad 2.51$$

where μ_0 is the total dipole moment of the group or molecule and μ_{eff} is the effective dipole moment measured in the condensed phase. The value of the reduction factor is determined by the number and distances of the nearest polar neighbors to the group considered. The Kirkwood reduction factor is significantly different from unity because of the intramolecular interactions of the polar units of a polymer molecule. Table 2.6 lists the effective dipole moments and the reduction factors for some polymers as well as calculated dipole moments for the monomer units.

d) *Inductive and Resonance Effects*

Effective dipole moments of polymers are usually determined from the measured values of the static (relaxed) dielectric constant ε and the high-frequency optical (unrelaxed) dielectric constant ε_∞. We can assume that the interactions affecting the reduction factor g extend to a few repeat units both within a chain and between chains. Thus, according to this model, the static dielectric constant should not depend on the molecular weight of the polymer. This has been experimentally observed.

When we consider molecules with delocalized electrons, the vectorial summation rule meets another challenge. For example, a look at the organic compounds in Fig. 2.9 will show that p-nitrotoluene obeys the vectorial summation rule, whereas p-hydroxytoluene does not.

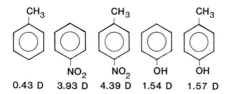

Fig. 2.9. Dipole moments of some compounds.[61]

TABLE 2.6 Effective Dipole Moments and Reduction Factors of Some Polymers

Polymer	Polymers		Monomers	
	μ_{eff}	$\mu_0\,g_r$	μ_0	g_r
Polymethyl methacrylate	1.6–1.7	1.33	1.79	0.55
atactic	1.6			
isotactic	1.7			
Polypropyl methacrylate		1.41	1.89	0.56
Polyisopropyl methacrylate		1.45	1.87	0.61
Polybutyl methacrylate	1.4–1.5	2.38	1.88	0.55
atactic	1.4			
isotactic	1.5			
Poly-tert-butyl methacrylate				
atactic	1.5			
isotactic	1.7			
Polyphenyl methacrylate				
atactic	1.4			
isotactic	1.6			
Polymethyl acrylate		1.37	1.75	0.68
Polyethyl acrylate		1.58	1.82	0.76
Polypropyl acrylate		1.58	1.83	0.75
Polybutyl acrylate		1.52	1.85	0.67
Polyvinyl acetate		1.66	1.83	0.82
Polyvinyl propionate		1.71	1.82	0.82
Polyvinyl butyrate		1.63	1.77	0.81
Polyethyl methacrylate		1.35	1.85	0.53

This difference cannot be explained by inductive effects because both nitro and hydroxyl groups are electron withdrawing groups. We now have to consider resonance effects. In p-hydroxytoluene, the electron density of one unshared lone pair in the OH group does not reside entirely on the oxygen but is spread over the benzene ring. This is called the electron-donating resonance effect (+M). In p-nitrotoluene, the nitro group has multiply bonded electronegative atoms connected directly to a delocalized electron system. Thus, electrons have been removed from the benzene ring and attached to the nitro group. This is called the electron-withdrawing resonance effect (−M). Table 2.7 lists some +M and −M groups. Here CH_3 and OH are both +M groups, but NO_2 is a −M group; hence they exhibit different behavior toward resonance.

Of course, both inductive and resonance effects can be expressed in a quantitative way. By putting the inductive and resonance effects as correction terms in the vectorial summation rule, it is possible to predict the dipole moment of the whole molecule within certain limits.

TABLE 2.7 Resonance Effect of Some Groups

+ M	OH, O^-, S^-, NR_2, NHR, NH_2, OR, Cl, Br, F, CH_3
− M	NO_2, CN, $COOH$, $CONH_2$, CHO, SO_2R

e) *Mean Square Dipole Moment*

Since the real molecular structure of a polymer is complicated by its chain conformations, we must consider the conformations of chains in predicting its dipole moment. Only for very few cases, such as in the rigid molecular chain polymer polytetrafluoroethylene, is the conformation frozen in only one configuration, and we can apply the vectorial summation rule to the repeating units to estimate the dipole moment of the whole polymer. In general, since polymers are never fixed in one configuration, the polarity of a polymer molecule must be characterized by its mean square dipole moment. At each instant, the total dipole moment of the whole molecule M is the vectorial sum of the dipole moments of all the chain segments m_k:

$$\vec{M} = \sum_{k=1}^{n} \vec{m}_k \tag{2.52}$$

The mean square dipole moment of this polymer molecule is defined as

$$\overline{M^2} = \sum_{i=1}^{n} \left(\sum_{j=1}^{n} \overline{\vec{m}_i \, \vec{m}_j} \right) =$$

$$= m^2 \left(n + \sum_{\substack{i=1 \\ (i \neq j)}}^{n} \sum_{j=1}^{n} \overline{\cos \theta_{ij}} \right), \tag{2.53}$$

where $\overline{\cos \theta_{ij}}$ is the mean value of the cosine of the angle θ_{ij} formed between two dipoles of repeating units i and j. Using Eq. (2.53), we can express the effective mean square dipole moment of each repeating unit as

$$\frac{\overline{M^2}}{n} = m^2 \left(1 - \frac{1}{n} \sum_{\substack{i=1 \\ (i \neq j)}}^{n} \sum_{j=1}^{n} \overline{\cos \theta_{ij}} \right) = g_r m^2. \tag{2.54}$$

where g_r is the correlation factor of polymer segments. This correlation factor characterizes the steric hindrance of neighboring parts of the chain, the limitation of chemical bond orientation between different segments, and the interaction between dipoles along the chain.

f) *Physical State of Polymers*

The physical state of polymers may also influence their polarity. This factor can be best illustrated indirectly by the values of dielectric constants (Appendix 1). For example, although polyvinyl chloride is more polar than poly(chloroprene), at room temperature the dielectric constant of the former is around 3.2, whereas that for the latter is around 10. The reason lies in the fact that at room temperature poly(chloroprene) is in the rubbery state. Its chain segments can move freely, and the high value comes from the dipole orientation polarization of the chain segments. Polyvinyl chloride at room temperature is in the glassy state, its chain segment movement is forbidden, and the dipole orientation polarization comes only from the movement of the polar group itself. At sufficiently high temperatures (for example, above the Tg) polyvinyl chloride will transform to the rubbery state, and its dielectric constant will be very large indeed, around 15.

The effect of physical state is therefore due to the different behavior of thermal motions of polar groups in different physical states. The nature of thermal motion influences the nature of dipole polarization; hence, it is as important as the effect of charge distribution. Thus, we may say that the nature of thermal motion of polar groups also affects the value of effective dipole moment.

Similarly, if the same polar group is present in two polymers of different chemical structure, with one on the main chain and the other on the side group, then the polar group in the former case is far less mobile than in the latter case and the effective dipole moment of the former group is smaller than that of the latter group. A flexible polar group will have a still larger effective dipole moment.

Symmetry, cross linking, and stretching all tend to decrease the effective dipole moment caused by thermal motion of polar groups. Branching, on the other hand, tends to increase the effective dipole moment.

2.10.3 Defect Dipole Moments

a) *Frenkel Approximation*

Permanent dipole moments of the polar bonds do not determine dielectric behavior alone. In solids moments associated with structural inhomogeneities are also effective. Some electrons in the solid are shared by many molecules, so the electronic state of such a system cannot be described solely in terms of individual molecular obitals; rather, we must consider combinations of molecular or crystal orbitals. Crystal orbitals can be constructed on the basis of molecular orbitals by assuming that intermolecular interactions are weak. This is referred to as the weak-binding or Frenkel approximation.[62]

In this approach, the molecular orbital excited to some state is referred to as the exciton state. It means that an excitation travels through the crystal as a wave over all sites. Exciton states are not only effective in the excited state of the solid but also in the ground state. The ground state of the solid cannot be constructed purely by a combination of the ground-state molecular orbitals; some excited states will be mixed in by configurational interaction. Such an intermixing of higher energy orbitals to the ground state is often encountered in molecules.

b) *Wannier Approximation*

In another approximation the intermolecular interactions are considered strong; charge transfer between subsequent sites is regarded possible. This approach is referred to as the tight-binding or Wannier approximation.[63] Wannier constructed crystal orbitals in terms of electron-hole pair eigenfunctions. The situation is similar to that of considering the ionicity of bonds; in this case, transfer of an electron from one atom to another is considered. In the Wannier case, electron-hole pairs can move correlated, resulting in transfer of excitation energy. The Wannier exciton energies are only valid for semiconductors, in which the intermolecular interactions are very strong. The radius of the electron-hole combination may be as large as 100 Å. For usual polymeric solids, the situation falls between the Frenkel and Wannier cases. In the Frenkel approximation, the electron-hole distance is about 1 Å.

c) *Conclusions*

From the exciton picture, some important conclusions about the polarization of a bulk polymers can be drawn:

Case I. The binding energy and correspondingly the radius of the electron-hole pair depend on the regularity of the structure. At structural defects, the binding energy is decreased and the radius is increased. In the presence of an external electric field, a dipole is therefore formed at structural defects. This will be referred to as defect dipole. A structural defect can be a missing lattice site, a dislocation or an interface of a crystallite. A defect dipole formed by the polarization of a Wannier exciton state at a missing lattice point is schematically illustrated in Fig. 2.10. Note that a periodical crystalline structure is not necessary for formation of a defect dipole.

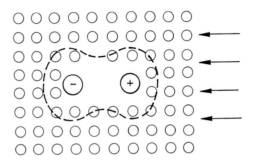

Fig. 2.10. Defect dipole formed at a missing lattice site in a solid.

Case II. Since the radius and binding energy of the exciton are dependent on the dielectric constant of the medium, any inhomogeneity in the dielectric constant should result in a corresponding change in the formation of dipoles in the presence of an external field. This phenomenon has long been known as the Maxwell-Wagner-Sillars (MWS) effect. If the sample contains regions of different dielectric constants, in an external electric field interfacial dipole polarization builds up. The build-up of dipole polarization at an interface of two media of different dielectric constants is schematically illustrated in Fig. 2.11.

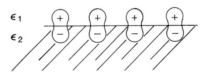

Fig. 2.11. Defect dipoles formed at the interface of two media.

It is seen that, in addition to the permanent dipole moments of the molecules or groups, induced dipole moments can be present either from the physical (Case I) or chemical (Case II) inhomogeneities or defects of the solid. The defect dipole moments formed this way can be extremely large. For an electron-hole formation 5 Å apart, the dipole moment would be about 20 D, which is an order of magnitude higher than the bond moments.

2.10.4 Classical Dielectric Equations

In a review of some of the classical dielectric equations, it may be instructive to look at water in some detail. A water molecule contains two OH dipoles, has a molecular dipole moment of 1.85 D, and a dielectric constant of 81. Why is ε so high?

a) *Debye Equation*

The first classical equation to be considered is that of Debye.[13] Debye assumed E_3 to be zero, which holds true for polar gases because in the gaseous state, every polar molecule is sufficiently separated from every other to justify the assumption. From studies of the permanent dipole moment μ and dipole polarizability α_0, Debye derived

$$\alpha_0 = \frac{\mu^2}{3kT},$$
2.55

where k is the Boltzmann constant. The corresponding Clausius-Mosotti equation is then

$$\frac{N}{3\varepsilon_0}\left(\alpha_e + \alpha_a + \frac{\mu^2}{3kT}\right) = \frac{\varepsilon - 1}{\varepsilon + 2} \cdot \frac{M}{\varrho}.$$
2.56

Debye showed that polarization can be divided into two parts: (1) distortion polarization, which is independent of temperature, and (2) dipole polarization, which varies with the reciprocal of temperature. Thus, Eq. (2.56) can be written as

$$\left(\frac{\varepsilon - 1}{\varepsilon + 2} - \frac{\varepsilon_\infty - 1}{\varepsilon_\infty + 2}\right)\frac{M}{\varrho} = \frac{N}{3\varepsilon_0} \cdot \frac{\mu^2}{3kT}.$$
2.57

Of course, this equation does not hold true for water and other polar liquids because for them $E_3 \neq 0$.

b) *Onsager Equation*

The re-examination by Onsager of the problem of the internal field led to an advance in the Debye equation. Onsager limited his treatment to spherical polar molecules. He took care of the so-called counteraction field and calculated the effective energy of interaction between the molecule and the field, and the resulting average orientation of the molecule. The final form of the Onsager equation is[64]

$$\left(\frac{\varepsilon - 1}{\varepsilon + 2} - \frac{\varepsilon_\infty - 1}{\varepsilon_\infty + 2}\right)\frac{M}{\varrho} = \frac{3\varepsilon(\varepsilon_\infty + 2)\mu^2 N}{(2\varepsilon + \varepsilon_\infty)(\varepsilon + 2)9kT}.$$
2.58

The Onsager equation differs from Debye's by the factor

$$\frac{3\varepsilon(\varepsilon_\infty + 2)}{(2\varepsilon + \varepsilon_\infty)(\varepsilon + 2)}$$

on the right hand side of the equation. As ε approaches ε_∞ this factor approaches 1, that is, the difference between the two equations approaches zero. For polar gases at or below atmospheric pressure, ε and ε_∞ are so close to 1 that the factor becomes indistinguishable from 1, and the two equations become identical. Only when $\mu = 0$, $\varepsilon = \varepsilon_\infty$ does the Onsager equation reduce to the Clausius-Mosotti equation.

When ε is large compared with ε_∞ (which is always small), the Onsager equation can be written as

$$\frac{2\varepsilon}{(\varepsilon + 2)^2} \approx \frac{N\mu^2}{9kT}.$$
2.59

This equation is useful in making the following correlations: (1) dielectric constant directly proportional to the number of polar molecules per unit volume, (2) dielectric constant proportional to the square of the permanent dipole moments, and (3) dielectric constant proportional to the reciprocal of the absolute temperature. For liquids with not very strong polarity, this equation holds true. However, for strong polar liquids with hydrogen bonds (for example, water or alcohols) the Onsager equation is still not sufficient. Its failure to apply to water is due to the neglect of the molecular structure within the hollow sphere, the assumption of spherical molecules, and the treatment of the surrounding medium as a continuous dielectric.

c) *Kirkwood Generalization*

Kirkwood has pointed out that hindered rotation must play a part in the dipole polarization of polar liquids, that it must be responsible for large departures from the Lorentz field, and that it should be introduced not to supplement, but to correct, the Lorentz field.[65, 66] He generalized the Onsager theory by eliminating the approximation of a uniform local dielectric constant, identical with the macroscopic dielectric constant of the medium, and obtained

$$\frac{(\varepsilon - 1)(2\varepsilon + 1)}{9\varepsilon} \cdot \frac{M}{\varrho} = \frac{N}{3\varepsilon}\alpha_e + \alpha_a + \frac{\mu_0^2(1 + z\,\overline{\cos\gamma})}{3\,kT}, \qquad 2.60$$

where γ is the angle between the dipole moments of neighboring pairs of molecules; $\mu_0^2(1 + \cos\gamma)$ can be expressed as

$$\mu^2 = \mu_0^2(1 + z\,\overline{\cos\gamma}) = g\mu_0^2, \qquad 2.61$$

where μ_0 is the intrinsic molecular dipole moment in the liquid state and corresponds to the dipole moment in the gaseous state when the molecular interactions are neglected; μ is the effective molecular dipole moment in the condensed state; and g is the Kirkwood coefficient, which is the ratio of μ^2 to μ_0^2.

The precise calculation of the correlation parameter g is possible, in principle, by statistical mechanics methods but is usually prevented by insufficient knowledge about the liquid structure. Positive deviations of g from unity result when short-range hindering torques favor parallel orientation of the dipoles of neighboring molecules, and negative deviations result when the hindering torques favor antiparallel orientation. The above equation is based upon a rough quasi-crystalline model of local liquid structure, in which each molecule is surrounded by a shell of z nearest neighbors beyond which orientational effects do not extend. This model gives

$$g = 1 + \overline{\cos\gamma} \qquad 2.62$$

and

$$\overline{\cos\gamma} = \int \cos\gamma \; e^{-W/kT} \; dw. \qquad 2.63$$

This integral defining $\overline{\cos\gamma}$ extends over all relative orientations of the pair, and W is the potential of average torque hindering their relative rotation, with a constant term adjusted to normalize the integral of $e^{-W/kT}$ to unity.

In the case of water, Kirkwood obtained

$$g = 1 + z\,\cos^2\frac{\theta}{2}, \qquad 2.64$$

where θ is the H–O–H bond angle, taken as 105°, and z differs slightly from 4 because of superposition on the tetrahedral structure of contributions from more closely packed structures. The dielectric constant of liquid water calculated from the molecular dipole moment by means of Eq. (2.60) differs only 0.4% from the observed value at 25°C. The unmodified Onsager equation leads to a value of 31 for the dielectric constant of water.

Like the Onsager equation, the Kirkwood equation contains the approximation involved in treating the polar molecules as spherical. But it is evident that the Kirkwood equation represents a theoretical advance in that it takes into account the hindrance of molecular orientation by neighboring molecules. However, since the g-factor can be estimated only roughly from the knowledge of the liquid structure, which is usually imprecise, the equation is still empirical.

To extend the use of Kirkwood equation to polymers, the following can be said: "normal" liquids show values of g that do not depart much from unity, whereas "abnormal" or "associated" liquids show values that depart significantly from unity. For polymers, g-values are usually significantly smaller than 1. This is due to the mutual influence of dipoles between different segments of the chain so that the effective dipole moment is decreased.

In summary of the more detailed examinations of the dielectric polarizability and classical dielectric equation approaches to the control of ε, it can be said that many factors affecting ε were identified; however, few hard suggestions could be made for the synthesis of materials with high dielectric constant. Thus, the synthetics chemist is still left pretty much by himself to come up with innovative structures or morphologies of materials to obtain a high dielectric constant.

2.10.5 Empirical Considerations

The accumulated empirical knowledge is only a little more helpful. In the synthesis, avoiding nonpolar monomers in the copolymers will maintain a high dielectric constant. In the formulation of the plastic composition, use of polar plasticizers, antioxidants, stabilizers, and processing aids will increase the ε of the composition. In general, addition of a material with high dipolar or ionic polarizability to a nonpolar polymer will increase its ε. In the formulation of filled polymer compositions, carbon black is one of the most effective fillers to raise the ε to very high values. For example, a bis(2-chloroethyl)formal and ethylene dichloride copolymer filled with 60 pts of carbon black had a dielectric constant of 17,900 at 25°C and 1000 Hz. Other fillers with high dielectric constant, such as TiO_2, $SrTiO_3$, and $BaTiO_3$, are also effective.

In poly(vinylidine fluoride), PVF_2, uniaxial or biaxial orientation increases the dielectric constant. Poling of PVF_2 and its copolymers also increases the dielectric constant. In this family of polymers, the isotactic stereoisomer possesses the highest ε.

As we have seen, a polar material is a dielectric material that may possess a spontaneous polarization and thus lead to high ε. The phenomenon of interfacial polarization caused by inhomogenity in the material also leads to high ε.

2.11 FREQUENCY DEPENDENCE OF DIELECTRIC CONSTANT

The dielectric constant of insulators varies with frequency. Spectra are obtained that are indicative of relaxation processes or resonances, and to account for these, it is necessary to propose models that will describe the atomic and molecular processes of polarization.

A pair of opposite charges, separated by a small distance, forms an electric dipole. This dipole may be imagined as free to rotate to align itself with a field. If the field is an alternating one, the dipole will continue to rotate in sympathy with it; a resonance will occur when the applied field has a frequency equal to the natural rotational frequency of the dipole. If the dipole is imagined to be in a medium presenting heavy frictional damping on its rotation, its response to the field will be of the relaxation type, the rotation falling further and further in phase behind the applied field.

Rotation is only one of the possible modes of vibration that may be imagined for the dipole. It may also act as a linear harmonic oscillator in which the distance between the charges varies under the influence of an applied field. Again, resonance or relaxation behavior is possible depending on the nature of the damping present. The study of the frequency dependence of dielectric constant provides insight into these processes.[67-71]

In polymers, dipole orientation is highly correlated. The very essence of a polymer chain generally renders independent orientation of a main-chain dipole component impossible, and coupling between side-chain and main-chain modes is frequently involved. For a rigid chain polymer in solution, dipole orientation requires rotatory diffusion of a macromolecule as a whole, in which no component caused by local modes is involved. However, this situation is the exception. Flexible polymers permit polarization by local mode motions as well as by rotary diffusion as illustrated in Fig. 2.12.

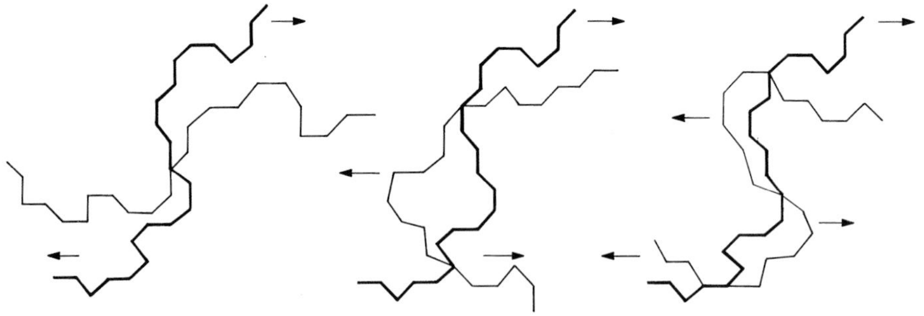

FIRST MODE   SECOND MODE   THIRD MODE

Fig. 2.12. Schematic illustration of some normal modes of motion of a polymer chain; first mode corresponds to rotational diffusion.

2.11.1 Dielectric Relaxation of Polymers

The situation for polymer molecules in solution, discussed by Stockmayer,[67] is based on the normal mode analysis of Zimm[72] and Rouse.[73] Certain generalizations about the dielectric relaxation of polymers can be made from these studies. Dipole components attached to the chain differ in possible relaxation behavior when they are of the parallel or perpendicular type, and side-chain components with more independent movement form a third category. For a parallel component, relaxation requires odd-numbered modes, including the first mode (whole-molecule rotation), which is often dominant in solution. The auto correlation functions for such dipole vectors ensemble-average as the chain bond vectors, and in consequence the decay function strongly depends on molecular weight. In such cases the relaxation frequency for maximum loss takes the form $f_m \propto M[\eta]\eta_0/T$, where M is the molecular weight, $[\eta]$ is the intrinsic viscosity, η_0 is the solvent viscosity, and T is the temperature. The constant of proportionality depends on the model (free draining[73] or nondraining[72]) and involves the orders (all odd) of the contributing modes. Since $[\eta]$ is itself a function of M, the exponent of M in f_m is greater than 1. For perpendicular components, the situation is much more complex to model theoretically because the extent of correlation along a sequence of dipoles is reduced and depends on local structure. The Rouse-Zimm model becomes unsuitable for such local "high-order" modes. At one extreme, as pointed out by Bueche,[74] for a very flexible chain, f_m for such a process should be independent of M and governed only by the rate of change from one local conformer to another. At the other extreme if the chain is sufficiently rigid, rotatory diffusion must be the relaxing mode (as pointed out by Kuhn[75]),

TABLE 2.8 The Dielectric Relaxation of Selected Polymers in Solution

Polymer	Solvent	T/K	f_m	$\mu \times 10^{-4}$	Dipole type/mode[a]	Ref.
Poly(vinyl acetate)	Toluene	235	5–8 MHz	1.5–200	(n + s)/Is	76,77
Poly(methyl methacrylate)	Toluene	263	8–13 MHz	1.4–180	(n + s)/Is	78
Poly(butyl methacrylate)	Toluene	260–266	6–10 MHz	6.1–35	(n + s)/Is	79
Poly(vinyl bromide)	Various	Various	~30 MHz	1.3–9.2	n/I	80
Poly(p-chlorostyrene)	Various	Various	i) 43 MHz ii) 141–43 MHz	2–100 0.2–2	n/I n/II	81,82,83
Poly(p-fluorostyrene)	Benzene	298	i) 38.9–37.2 MHz ii) 97.7–38.9 MHz	2.7–15.7 0.2–2.7	n/I n/II	83
Poly(ethylene oxide)	Toluene	293	16 GHz	0.02–2.9	n/I	82,84
Poly(propylene oxide) (liquid)	None	253	0.63 MHz } and 2–32 kHz	0.09–0.37	p/III	85
Poly(N-vinylcarbazole)	Toluene	298	60–0.9 MHz	0.166–4.57	n/II to n/I	86
Poly(hexene-1-sulphone)	Benzene	298	0.12 MHz – 1 kHz	70–1000	n/II to n/I	87
Poly(n-butyl isocyanate)	Various	Various	1.6 MHz–30 Hz	0.32–230	n/II	88,89,90
Poly(ε-caprolactone)	1,4-dioxane	303	0.2 MHz–28 kHz } and 10 GHz	3.4–8.7	p/III n/I	91,92
Poly(γ-benzyl-L-glutamate)	Various	Various	0.2 MHz–1 kHz	2.8–50	(n + p)/III	93,94,95

[a] *Codes:* n, normal (perpendicular); p, parallel; s, side chain; I, local segmental modes;
Is, I cooperative with side chain; II, correlated segmental modes;
III, whole molecule rotation relaxing dipole.

and f_m must be M dependent. Both situations are well documented (Table 2.8). The expected range of behavior is found for polymers with perpendicular dipoles. In some of these polymers, relaxation frequency appears independent of molecular weight, and in others, such as poly(n-butyl isocyanate), relaxation frequency is strongly dependent on the molecular weight. In some polymers, [for example, poly(p-chlorostyrene), poly(p-fluorostyrene), and poly(N-vinylcarbazole)], relaxation behavior changes from being molecular weight independent to being molecular weight dependent as the molecular weight is reduced. This constitutes what must be a characteristic of all perpendicular dipole polymers since at sufficiently low molecular weight, the whole molecule rotational mode must become dominant, while for sufficiently long polymer molecules, a sequence of links (analogous to a Kuhn equivalent segment) will partake in a local model relaxation process. In this latter situation, further increase in molecular weight does not influence f_m because the relaxation involves localized motions of equivalent segments.

2.12 TEMPERATURE DEPENDENCE OF DIELECTRIC CONSTANT

In addition to polymers with low or high dielectric constant, the electrical and electronic practice also requires materials with dielectric constant that is unvarying within the working temperature range.

2.12.1 Nonpolar Polymers

As discussed earlier, the polarization in response to the applied external electric field is different for nonpolar and polar polymers. In nonpolar polymers, in which the polarization is mainly electronic, the Clausius-Mossotti equation written as

$$\frac{N\alpha_e}{3\varepsilon_0} = \frac{\varepsilon - 1}{\varepsilon + 2} \cdot \frac{M}{\varrho} \qquad \qquad 2.65$$

can be roughly used to relate polarizability to dielectric constant. It seems that the dielectric constant is independent of the temperature. However, since the density is temperature dependent (it decreases as the temperature increases), then ε is indirectly related to temperature. The dielectric constant decreases slightly with the temperature.

2.12.2 Polar Polymers

The Clausius-Mossotti equation no longer holds true for polar polymers. No satisfactory equation exists to relate ε and T: we can only use some of the equations, which are themselves approximations for polar liquids. We can use the Kirkwood equation for polymers as a very rough approximation:

$$\left[\frac{(\varepsilon - 1)(2\varepsilon + 1)}{9\varepsilon}\right] \frac{M}{\varrho} = \frac{N}{3\varepsilon_0}\left(\alpha_e + \alpha_a + \frac{g\mu_0^2}{3kT}\right). \qquad \qquad 2.66$$

When neglecting distortion polarizability, we can use

$$\left[\frac{(\varepsilon - 1)(2\varepsilon + 1)}{\varepsilon}\right] \frac{M}{\varrho} = \frac{N}{\varepsilon_0 kT}g\mu_0^2. \qquad \qquad 2.67$$

For polymers in solution, N is the concentration of the repeating units, μ_0 is the intrinsic dipole moment, and g is the Kirkwood coefficient (g-factor), which is expressed as an average of the spatial orientations within the sphere. In dilute solutions where the polymer molecules are not entangled, the Kirkwood coefficient is expressed as[96]

$$g = 1 + \sum_{i=1}^{K} (\text{Cos } \gamma_{0i})_{av}, \qquad\qquad 2.68$$

where γ_{0i} is the angle between one repeating unit o of the chain and another i within the same chain. In concentrated solutions or in bulk, where entanglements also occur,

$$g = 1 + \sum_{i} \sum_{k} \text{Cos } \gamma_{0i}^{k}, \qquad\qquad 2.69$$

where k refers to a different molecule. It can be assumed that the interactions affecting the Kirkwood coefficient g are extended to a few repeating units within the same chain as well as between chains. This means that according to this model the dielectric constant should not depend on the molecular weight of the polymer. This has been experimentally observed.

Based upon the Kirkwood equation, the temperature dependence of the dielectric constant is also determined by the 1/T factor. But the dielectric constant depends more upon temperature indirectly through the temperature dependence of the Kirkwood coefficient g and the intrinsic dipole moment μ_0.

The intrinsic dipole moment depends on the temperature only if the configuration of the molecule is changed. The Kirkwood coefficient is highly temperature dependent because it is a measure of the intra- and intermolecular interactions; by definition,

$$g = \frac{\mu^2}{\mu_0^2}, \qquad\qquad 2.70$$

where μ can be called the effective dipole moment.

If the molecular configuration μ_0 and the intra- and intermolecular interactions g are not changed in the working temperature range, then the dielectric constant should decrease with increasing temperature. This is the case for dilute solutions or for some polymers in the molten state. However, the dielectric constant of practically all polar polymers increases with increasing temperature, indicating that the dependence is mainly governed by the change in the intra- and intermolecular interactions.

2.12.3 Temperature Independence

By means of proper selection of nonpolar and polar monomers, it is then possible to synthesize a suitable copolymer in which the temperature effects on the dielectric constant can be just cancelled out. For example, polystyrene is a nonpolar polymer, whose dielectric constant decreases slightly with temperature, whereas polymethyl methacrylate is a polar polymer whose dielectric constant increases with temperature. The copolymer of styrene and methyl methacrylate in proper proportion possesses a dielectric constant that is independent of temperature within a certain temperature range.

2.13 DIELECTRIC CONSTANT AS A FUNCTION OF FREQUENCY AND TEMPERATURE

Poly(ethylene terephthalate) is a particularly beautiful example of how ε varies with frequency and temperature. It was studied by Reddish[97] and is illustrated in Fig. 2.13. This three-dimensional surfaces map shows that ε increases with temperature and decreases with frequency in general. However, in certain frequency and temperature ranges, plateaus appear in the ε surface. The molecular relaxation processes in polymers that give rise to dielectric relaxation also, in general, give rise to mechanical relaxation. Similar surface maps can be prepared for the mechanical quantities, and if the dynamic modulus surface were plotted, it would give a map that is the reciprocal of the dielectric constant map.

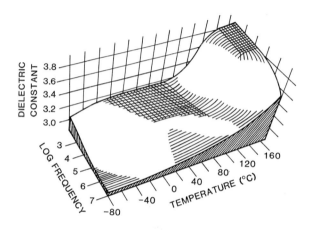

Figure 2.13. Dielectric constant as functions of frequency and temperature.

2.14 REFERENCES

1. P. van Musschenbroek, *Introduction ad Philosophiam Naturalem*, Luchtmans, Leiden, 1762.
2. M. Faraday, Phil. Trans. *128*, 1, 79, 265 (1837/38).
3. J. C. Maxwell, Ed., *The Electric Researches of the Honorable Henry Cavendish*, J. C. Maxwell, Cambridge (1879).
4. J. C. Maxwell, Phil. Trans. *155*, 459 (1865).
5. J. C. Maxwell, Phil. Trans. *158*, 643 (1868).
6. H. Hertz, Ann. Phys. *31*, 421 (1887).
7. P. Drude, Z. Phys. Chem. *23*, 267 (1897).
8. P. F. Mossotti, Bibl. Univ. Modena *6*, 193 (1847).
9. R. Clausius, *Die Mechanische Wärmetheorie*, Vol. II, Vieweg Verlag, Braunschweig (1879).
10. L. Lorenz, Am. Phys. Chem. *11*, 70 (1880).
11. H. A. Lorentz, *Verh. Kon. Acad. van Wetenschappen*, Amsterdam (1879).
12. H. A. Lorentz, Ann. Phys. *9*, 641 (1880).
13. P. Debye, Phys. Z. *13*, 97 (1912).
14. L. Onsager, J. Am. Chem. Soc. *58*, 1486 (1936).
15. J. G. Kirkwood, J. Chem. Phys. *7*, 911 (1939).
16. A. R. Blythe, *Electrical Properties of Polymers*, University of Cambridge, Cambridge (1979).

17. C. J. F. Böttcher, O. C. van Belle, P. Bordewijk, and A. Rip, *Theory of Electric Polarization*, second ed., Elsevier, New York (1973).

18. R.W. Sillars, *Electrical Insulating Materials and Their Applications*, Peter Peregrinus, Stevenage (1973).

19. A. von Hippel, Ed., *Dielectric Materials and Applications*, The Technology Press of MIT and John Wiley & Sons, New York (1958).

20. R. Clausius, *Die Mechanische Wärmetheorie*, Vieweg Verlag, Braunschweig (1879).

21. P. F. Mossotti, *Memoria di Mathematica e di Fisica in Modena 24*, 49 (1850).

22. H. A. Pohl, 1974 Annual Report Conference on Electrical Insulation and Dielectric Phenomena, National Academy of Sciences – National Research Council, Washington, D.C., 1975, p. 621.

23. K. Nakamura, Y. Wada, J. Polym. Sci. A-2 *9*, 161 (1971).

24. J. H. McFee, J. G. Bergman, Jr., R. R. Crane, Ferroelectrics *3*, 305 (1972).

25. P. Buchman, Ferroelectics *5*, 39 (1973).

26. M. G. Broadhurst, Ferroelectrics *49*, 159 (1983).

27. A. J. Lovinger, T. Furukawa, G. T. Davis, and M. G. Broadhurst, Ferroelectrics *50*, 227 (1983).

28. R. G. Kepler and R. A. Anderson, J. Appl. Phys. *49*, 1232 (1978).

29. D. Naegele and D. Y. Yoon, Appl. Phys. Lett. *33*, 132 (1978).

30. T. Takahashi, M. Date, and E. Fukada, Appl. Phys. Lett. *37*, 791 (1980).

31. T. Furukawa, M. Date, and E. Fukada, J. Appl. Phys. *51*, 1135 (1980).

32. J. C. Hicks, T. E. Jones, M. L. Burgener, and R. B. Olsen, Ferroelectrics *44*, 89 (1982).

33. B. V. Hamon and R. J. Meakins, Australian J. Sci. Res. A *5*, 671 (1952).

34. J. C. Maxwell, *Electricity and Magnetism*, Oxford University Press, Oxford (1892).

35. K. W. Wagner, Archiv für Electrotechnik *2*, 371 (1914).

36. L. K. H. van Beck, in *Progress in Dielectrics*, J. B. Birks and J. Hard, Eds., Vol. 7, p. 69, Heywood Books, London (1967).

37. R. W. Sillars, IEE Journal *80*, 378 (1937).

38. P. Hedvig, *Electrical Conductivity and Polarization in Plastics*, Akademiai Kiado, Budapest (1969) (in Hungarian).

39. V. E. Goul, L. N. Tzarsky, N. S. Maisel, L. Z. Schenfi, V.S. Zhurovlev, and N. G. Tzibrya, *Electrically Conductive Polymeric Materials*, Izv. Khimia, Moscow (1968) (in Russian).

40. W. C. Carter, M. Magat, W. G. Schmieder, and C. P. Smyth, Trans. Faraday Soc. *42A*, 213 (1946).

41. P. Thirion, and P. Chasset, Trans. Inst. Rubber Ind. *27*, 364 (1951).

42. A. I. Lukomskaya, B. A. Dogadkin, Kolloidnyi Zhurnal *22*, 576 (1960) (in Russian).

43. H. A. Pohl and R. Rosen, Bull. Am. Phys. Soc. *10*, 396 (1965).

44. R. Rosen and H. A. Pohl, J. Polym. Sci. A-1 *4*, 1135 (1966).

45. R. D. Hartman and H. A. Pohl, Bull. Am. Phys. Soc. *12*, 409 (1967).

46. R. D. Hartman, *Hyperelectronic Polarization and Related Electronic Properties of Macromolecular Solids: Organic Semiconductors*, Oklahoma State Univ., Stillwater (1968).

47. R. D. Hartman and H.A. Pohl, J. Polym. Sci. A-1, *6*, 1135 (1968).

48. J. W. Mason, H. A. Pohl, and R. D. Hartman, J. Polym. Sci., Part C, No. 17, 187 (1967).

49. S. Takashima, J. Mol. Biol. *7*, 455 (1963).

50. M. Pollak, J. Chem. Phys. *43*, 908 (1965).

51. L. Pauling, *The Nature of the Chemical Bond*, third ed., Cornell Univ. Press, New York (1960).

52. V. I. Minkin, O. A. Osipov, and Y. A. Zhdanov, *Dipole Moments in Organic Chemistry*, Izv. Khimia, Leningrad (1968) (in Russian).

53. J. W. Smith, *Electric Dipole Moments*, Butterworth, London (1955).

54. M. McClellan, *Tables of Experimental Dipole Moments*, Freeman, San Francisco (1963).

55. O. A. Osipov, V. I. Minkin, *Dipole Moments*, Izv. Vys. Skola, Moscow (1965) (in Russian).

56. W. R. Kriegbaum, and A. Roig, J. Chem. Phys. *31*, 544 (1959).

57. G. P. Mikhailov, L. V. Krasnev, Vysokomol. Soed. *A9*, 1346 (1967).

58. T. I. Borisova, L. C. Burshtein, and G. P. Mikhailov, Vysokomol. Soed. *4*, 1479 (1962).

59. M. Takeda, J. Imamura, S. Okamura, and T. Higoshimura, J. Chem. Phys. *33*, 631 (1960).

60. G. P. Mikhailov, and L. L. Burshtein, Vysokomol. Soed. *6*, 1713 (1964).

61. E. V. Goode, and D. A. Ibbitson, J. Chem. Soc. 4265 (1960).

62. J. Frenkel, Phys. Rev. *37*, 1276 (1931).

63. G. H. Wannier, Phys. Rev. *52*, 191 (1937).

64. L. Onsager, J. Am. Chem. Soc. *58*, 1486 (1936).

65. J. G. Kirkwood, J. Chem. Phys. *7*, 911 (1939).
66. J. G. Kirkwood, Trans. Faraday Soc. *42A*, 7 (1946).
67. W. H. Stockmayer, Pure Appl. Chem. *15*, 539 (1967).
68. H. Block, and A. M. North, Adv. of Mol. Relax. Processes *1*, 309 (1970).
69. L. de Brouckere, and M. Mandel, Adv. Chem. Phys. *1*, 77 (1958).
70. A. M. North, Chem. Soc. Rev. *1*, 49 (1972).
71. A. M. North, Pure Appl. Chem. *39*, 265 (1974).
72. B. H. Zimm, J. Chem. Phys. *24*, 269 (1956).
73. P. E. Rouse, J. Chem. Phys. *21*, 1272 (1953).
74. F. Bueche, J. Polym. Sci. *54*, 597 (1961).
75. W. Kuhn, Helv. Chem. Acta *33*, 2057 (1950).
76. B. L. Funt, and S. G. Mason, Can. J. Res., Sect. B *28*, 182 (1950).
77. L. de Brouckere, and L. K. H. van Beek, Recl. Trav. Chim. Pays-Bas *75*, 355 (1956).
78. L. de Brouckere, D. Buess, J. de Bock, and J. Versheys, Bull. Soc. Chim. Belg. *64*, 669 (1955).
79. L. de Brouckere, and A. Lecocq-Robert, Bull. Soc. Chim. Belg. *70*, 549 (1961).
80. M. Kryszewski, and J. Marchal, J. Polym. Sci. *29*, 103 (1958).
81. B. Baysal, B. A. Lawry, H. Yu, and W. H. Stockmayer, in *Dielectric Properties of Polymers*, F. E. Karasz, Ed., Plenum Press, New York, 1972, p. 329.
82. W. H. Stockmayer, H. Yu, and J. E. Davies, Am. Chem. Soc. Div. Polym. Chem. Prepr. *4*, 132 (1963).
83. W. H. Stockmayer, and K. Matsuo, Macromolecules *5*, 766 (1972).
84. M. Davies, G. Williams, and G. D. Loveluck, Z. Elektrochem. *64*, 575 (1960).
85. M. E. Baur, and W. H. Stockmayer, J. Chem. Phys. *43*, 4319 (1965).
86. A. M. North, and P. J. Phillips, Chem. Commun. 1340 (1968).
87. T. W. Bates, K. J. Ivin, and G. Williams, Trans. Faraday Soc. *63*, 1964 (1967).
88. H. Yu, A. J. Bur, and L. J. Fetters, J. Chem. Phys. *44*, 2568 (1966).
89. A. J. Bur, and D. E. Roberts, J. Chem. Phys. *51*, 406 (1969).
90. V. N. Tsvetkov, E. I. Ryumtsev, F. M. Aliyev, and I. N. Shtennikova, Eur. Polym. J. *10*, 55 (1974).
91. A. A. Jones, G. A. Brehm, and W. H. Stockmayer, J. Polym. Sci., Polym. Symp. *46*, 149 (1974).
92. A. A. Jones, W. H. Stockmayer, and R. J. Molinori, J. Polym. Sci., Polym. Symp. *54*, 227 (1976).
93. A. Wada, in *Polyamino Acids, Polypeptides and Proteins*, M. A. Stahlmann, Ed., Univ. of Wisconsin Press, Madison, 1961, p. 131.
94. E. Marchal, C. Hornick, and H. Benoit, J. Chim. Phys. *64*, 514 (1967).
95. H. Block, E. F. Hayes, and A. M. North, Trans. Faraday Soc. *66*, 1095 (1969).
96. P. Hedvig, *Dielectric Spectroscopy of Polymers*, John Wiley & Sons, New York (1977).
97. W. Reddish, Trans. Faraday Soc. *46*, 459 (1950).

Chapter 3

TANGENT OF DIELECTRIC LOSS ANGLE OF POLYMERS

3.1   INTRODUCTION

In this Chapter we show what can be done to keep the tangent of the dielectric loss low and then how to prepare polymers of low tangent but high dielectric constant. To do this in a reasonably detailed manner, we examine in some depth the mechanism of relaxation loss, how this relates to the tangent of dielectric loss angle, and how the latter is affected by plasticization, molecular weight, and supermolecular structure.

We also include a discussion on dielectric spectroscopy and how it contributes to the study of dielectric loss and then conclude with a modern interpretation of relaxation phenomena-that of soliton models of dielectric relaxation in crystalline polymers. Appendix 2 contains dielectric loss angle data for more than 280 polymers, plastics, rubbers, foams, and composites.

Listed below for quick reference are more recent books that amplify the subject matter of the chapter.

1. C. J. F. Böttcher, *Theory of Electric Polarization*, Vol. 1, Elsevier, Amsterdam (1973).
2. C. J. F. Böttcher and P. Bordewijk, *Theory of Electric Polarization*, Vol. 2, Elsevier, Amsterdam (1980).
3. R. Bartnikas and R. M. Eichhorn, *Engineering Dielectrics, Vol. IIA, Electrical Properties of Solid Insulating Materials: Molecular Structure and Electrical Behavior*, ASTM Special Technical Publication No. 783, Philadelphia (1983).
4. P. Hedvig, *Dielectric Spectroscopy of Polymers*, John Wiley & Sons, New York (1977).

3.2   HISTORICAL OVERVIEW

In 1864, Siemens observed that a capacitor's ac conductivity was several times its measured dc value.[1] Later, Pellet derived a set of equations describing the dielectric loss and dielectric constant as functions of the frequency of the applied field.[2,3] By 1907, von Schweidler had already realized that the dielectric relaxation process could not be described by a single relaxation time and proposed a theory for the distribution of relaxation times.[4] Later, Wagner showed that depending on the number of perturbations on the original relaxation time of the loss process, there will be a Gaussian distribution of relaxation times.[5] This then explained the difference between the reduced dielectric loss peak found in practical insulating materials and that predicted from theory in terms of a single relaxation time. Wagner also explained the dielectric loss behavior of composite insulating systems in terms of equivalent resistance-capacitance circuits based on the multiple-sheet-layer capacitor systems.[6]

Debye made a major contribution to the field by relating the effect of the molecular structure to the resulting dielectric loss.[7,8] He obtained the dielectric loss equations using a molecular model based on a molecular dipole sphere rotating in a viscous medium under the action of an external electrical field.

A more recent development is that of Fröhlich, who proposed a model of dielectric loss based on a potential barrier concept.[9] The molecular dipoles or ions were postulated to jump between two equilibrium positions separated by a potential barrier. Various refinements and improvements to the basic concept of Debye and Fröhlich have been worked out by Böttcher et al.[10,11]

Although the dielectric loss behavior of solid molecules as a function of temperature and frequency is relatively well understood, under high electric gradients, complications result from space charge and other nonlinear effects, with the result that the dielectric loss behavior cannot be readily predicted as a function of the electric field.

3.3   BASIC CONSIDERATIONS

3.3.1   Relaxation of Polarization

In Chapter 2 we considered the static or low-frequency dielectric constant that is observed when the dielectric is in equilibrium with the externally applied field. Now we will discuss dielectric behavior when the frequency of the externally applied alternating field causes an observable lag in the attainment of equilibrium. This lag is commonly referred to as relaxation, which in general may be defined as the lag in the response of a system to a change in the forces to which it is subjected.[12] The existence of relaxation becomes apparent when its rate is near the same order of magnitude as that of the change of the applied forces. Since we are concerned with the polarization of matter, as in the case of the static dielectric constant, it is desirable to classify the various types of polarization according to the time required for the polarization process.

a)   *Rapidly Forming Polarization*

The polarization process may involve both rapidly forming and slowly forming polarization.[13] Rapidly forming polarization consists in part, and often in large part, of electronic polarization caused by the displacement of the electrons in the atoms relative to the positive nuclei, a process requiring about 10^{-16} s and corresponding approximately to the frequency of ultraviolet light. A relatively small atomic polarization arises from the displacement of atoms relative to one another in the molecule, a process requiring about $10^{-12}-10^{-14}$ s and corresponding to the frequency of infrared light. In ionic crystals, a similar but usually larger polarization arises from the displacement in the lattice of the ions of one sign relative to those of the opposite sign, a process requiring about 10^{-12} s and corresponding to the frequency of the far infrared region. The time required for the dipole or orientation-polarization process depends on the frictional resistance of the medium to the change in molecular orientation. For a gas, the time required is about 10^{-12} s. Resonance absorption to changes in rotational energy levels may occur in the microwave region to give rise to microwave spectra, but the energy loss is normally small. For small molecules in liquids of low viscosity, the time required is about $10^{-11}-10^{-10}$ s, corresponding to the frequency of the microwave region. For large molecules or viscous liquids, the time required is about 10^{-6} s, corresponding to radio frequencies.

b) *Slowly Forming Polarization*

The high internal frictional resistance of very viscous liquids, glasses, and solids may lengthen the time required for the polarization process to seconds, minutes, or longer so that it may not make itself evident during observation. In a heterogeneous material, an additional type of polarization-interfacial polarization-arises from the accumulation of charge at the interfaces between phases. It arises only in two situations: (1) when two phases differ in dielectric constant and conductivity, and (2) for a two-layer dielectric in particular, when the product of the dielectric constant σ_1 of one phase and the conductivity σ_2 of the second phase is not equal to the product of the dielectric constant ε_2 of the second phase and the conductivity σ_1 of the first phase:

$$\varepsilon_1\sigma_2 \neq \varepsilon_2\sigma_1. \qquad\qquad 3.1$$

This accumulation of charge requires a flow of current through the dielectric phases, a process that may require seconds or minutes so that it may be observed only at very low frequencies. However, if one phase has a high conductivity, the polarization may occur so rapidly that it is observed in the radiofrequency range.[13]

3.3.2   Dielectric Relaxation

Dielectric relaxation, also known as dielectric dispersion and dielectric loss, is the exponential decay with time of the polarization in a dielectric when an externally applied field is removed. The relaxation time may be defined as the time in which this polarization is reduced to 1/e times its original value, where e is the natural logarithmic base. Dielectric relaxation is the cause of anomalous dispersion in which the dielectric constant decreases with increasing frequency. From a structural point of view, the most interesting dielectric relaxation is that involving orientation polarization, which depends on the internal structures of the molecules and on the molecular arrangement or structure of the dielectric.

In terms of the theory of this phenomenon as developed by Debye,[8] dielectric relaxation is the lag in dipole orientation behind an alternating electric field. Under the influence of such a field, the polar molecules of a system rotate toward an equilibrium distribution in molecular orientation with a corresponding dielectric polarization.[14] For example, a dipole attached to a flexible chain can reorient more easily than one attached to a stiff chain. A dipole in a crystal will find it more difficult to orient than one in an amorphous phase. When the polar molecules are very large, or the frequency of the alternating field is very high, or the viscosity of the medium is very great, the rotatory motion of the molecules is not sufficiently rapid for the attainment of equilibrium with the field. The polarization then acquires a component out of phase with the field, and the displacement current acquires a conductance component in phase with the field, resulting in thermal dissipation of energy. When this occurs, dielectric losses will be generated. Therefore, depending on the molecular and morphological structure of a polymer, there will be several loss regions determined by the effect of each local environment on the inherent ability of a dipole to reorient.

3.3.3 Tangent of Dielectric Loss Angle

In an ideal condenser of geometrical capacitance C_0, in which the polarization is instantaneous, the charging or capacitive current $E\omega\varepsilon'C_0$ is 90° out of phase with the alternating potential (Fig. 3.1). In a condenser in which absorptive polarization occurs, the current also has a component $E\omega\varepsilon''C_0$ in phase with the potential and determined by Ohm's law. This ohmic or loss current, which measures the absorption, is due to the dissipation of part of the energy of the field as heat. In vector notation, the total current is the sum of the charging current and the loss current. The angle δ between the vector for the amplitude of the total current and that for the amplitude of the charging current is the loss angle, and the tangent of this angle is the loss tangent or tangent of dielectric loss angle:

$$\tan \delta = \frac{\text{loss current}}{\text{charging current}} = \frac{\varepsilon''}{\varepsilon'}, \qquad\qquad 3.2$$

where ε' is the measured dielectric constant of the dielectric material in the condenser and ε'' is the imaginary part of the dielectric constant, commonly known as the loss factor or loss index.

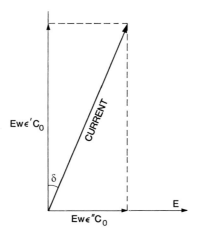

Fig. 3.1. Current-voltage diagram of a dielectric with loss.

The ratio of the imaginary to the real dielectric constants, $\varepsilon''/\varepsilon'$, or tangent of the dielectric loss angle, is commonly employed as a direct measure of the dielectric loss.

To evaluate the structure-property relationship between the values of the tangent of dielectric loss angles of polymers and their chemical and morphological structures, we must examine the relationships among dielectric constant, dielectric loss, frequency, dipole moment, molecular size, and viscosity of the polymers.

The classical development of these relationships is due to Debye,[8] but the simplified version shown here is by Fröhlich.[9] In response to the alternating electric field E, the electric displacement D is also periodic in time and will normally be out of phase with E, the phase shift being δ, so that

$$D - D_0\cos(\omega t - \delta) = D_1\cos \omega t - D_2\sin \omega t, \qquad 3.3$$

where

$$D_1 = D_0\cos \delta \qquad 3.4$$

and

$$D_2 = D_0\sin \delta. \qquad 3.5$$

Two different dielectric constants may be written:

$$\varepsilon' = D_1/E_0 \qquad 3.6$$

and

$$\varepsilon'' = D_2/E_0. \qquad 3.7$$

It follows then from Eqs. (3.4) and (3.5) that

$$\tan \delta = \frac{D_2}{D_1} = \frac{\varepsilon''}{\varepsilon'}, \qquad 3.8$$

which is the same as Eq. (3.2). As the frequency approaches zero, ε'' approaches zero, and ε' approaches the static dielectric constant ε_0, represented in Chapter 2 by ε. As the frequency approaches infinity, ε' approaches ε_∞, the optical dielectric constant. With the quantities and equations of Chapter 2, ε_0 and ε_∞ can be defined by

$$\frac{\varepsilon_\infty - 1}{\varepsilon_\infty + 2} \cdot \frac{M}{\varrho} = \frac{N\alpha_e}{3\varepsilon_0} \qquad 3.9$$

and

$$\frac{\varepsilon_0 - 1}{\varepsilon_0 + 2} \cdot \frac{M}{\varrho} = \frac{N}{3\varepsilon_0}\left(\alpha_e + \alpha_a + \frac{\mu^2}{3kT}\right). \qquad 3.10$$

Assuming an electric field E(t), which is dependent on time, a field E(u), which is applied during a time interval between u and u + du, and a corresponding electric displacement D(t), we may write

$$D(t) = \varepsilon_\infty E(t) + \int_{-\infty}^{t} E(u)f(t - u)du. \qquad 3.11$$

The first term on the right of Eq. (3.11) is the instantaneous displacement, and the second is the absorptive term. It is convenient to assume that the attainment of equilibrium is exponential with time and has the decay function

$$f(t) \approx e^{-t/\tau}, \qquad 3.12$$

where τ is the relaxation time, which is independent of time but dependent on temperature. Differentiating Eqs. (3.11) and (3.12) with respect to time, combining the results, and multipolying by τ, we obtain

$$\tau\frac{dD(t)}{dt} = \varepsilon_\infty \tau\frac{dE(t)}{dt} + \tau f(0)E(t) - \int_{-\infty}^{t} E(u)f(t - u)du, \qquad 3.13$$

where the constant f(0) is the value of the decay function when the field is constant. Addition of Eqs. (3.11) and (3.13) gives

$$\tau\frac{d}{dt}(D - \varepsilon_\infty E) + (D - \varepsilon_\infty E) = \tau f(0)E. \qquad 3.14$$

When the field is constant,

$$\frac{d}{dt}(D - \varepsilon_\infty E) = 0 \tag{3.15}$$

and

$$D = \varepsilon_0 E. \tag{3.16}$$

Substituting Eqs. (3.15) and (3.16) into Eq. (3.14), we obtain

$$\tau f(0) = \varepsilon_0 - \varepsilon_\infty. \tag{3.17}$$

Inserting Eq. (3.17) into Eq. (3.14) gives

$$\tau\frac{d}{dt}(D - \varepsilon_\infty E) + (D - \varepsilon_\infty E) = (\varepsilon_0 - \varepsilon_\infty)E. \tag{3.18}$$

Since

$$E = E_0 e^{j\omega t}, \tag{3.19}$$

differentiating E with respect to time gives

$$\frac{dE}{dt} = E_0 e^{j\omega t} j\omega = j\omega E. \tag{3.20}$$

Also, since

$$D = \varepsilon^* E, \tag{3.21}$$

where ε^* is a complex dielectric constant defined as

$$\varepsilon^* = \varepsilon' - j\varepsilon'', \tag{3.22}$$

where

$$j = \sqrt{-1},$$

then

$$\frac{dD}{dt} = \varepsilon^* \frac{dE}{dt} = j\omega\varepsilon^* E. \tag{3.23}$$

Substituting Eqs. (3.20) and (3.21) into Eq. (3.18) and rearranging, we get

$$\varepsilon^* = \varepsilon_\infty + \frac{\varepsilon_0 - \varepsilon_\infty}{1 + j\omega\tau}. \tag{3.24}$$

Then

$$\varepsilon' - j\varepsilon'' = \varepsilon_\infty + \frac{(\varepsilon_0 - \varepsilon_\infty)(1 - j\omega\tau)}{1 + \omega^2\tau^2}. \tag{3.25}$$

Separating real and imaginary parts, we obtain

$$\varepsilon' = \varepsilon_\infty + \frac{\varepsilon_0 - \varepsilon_\infty}{1 + \omega^2\tau^2} \tag{3.26}$$

and

$$\varepsilon'' = \frac{(\varepsilon_0 - \varepsilon_\infty)\omega\tau}{1 + \omega^2\tau^2}. \tag{3.27}$$

Examination of Eq. (3.27) shows that ε'' approaches zero for both small and large values of $\omega\tau$, whereas it is maximum for

$$\omega\tau = 1.$$ 3.28

For this value of $\omega\tau$, Eq. (3.27), becomes

$$\varepsilon''_m = \frac{\varepsilon_0 - \varepsilon_\infty}{2}$$ 3.29

and Eq. (3.26) becomes

$$\varepsilon' = \frac{\varepsilon_0 + \varepsilon_\infty}{2}.$$ 3.30

Equation (3.26) requires that ε' decrease from ε_0 to ε_∞ with increasing frequency. For polar liquids this decrease may occur within a 100-fold frequency range as shown for isobutyl bromide in Fig. 3.2. In this same range, Eq. (3.27) requires that ε'' change from a small value through a maximum to a small value again.[15] Although polar liquids may conform to the behavior demanded by these equations, for polymers the dispersion commonly occurs over a wider frequency range with a maximum value of ε'' lower than that predicted by Eq. (3.27). This effect has been attributed to a distribution of relaxation times.

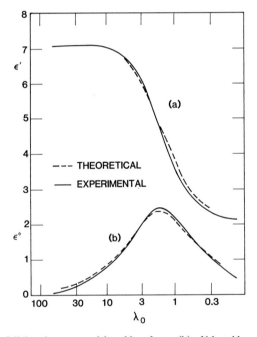

Fig. 3.2. Dependence of dielectric constant (a) and loss factor (b) of i-butyl bromide on the logarithm of the wavelength (in centimeters). Source is Ref. 15.

3.3.4   Distribution of Relaxation Times.

If we are to have a chemical control over the loss tangent of polymers, we must understand the phenomenon of relaxation times in more detail. Equation (3.12) shows that, when $t = \tau$,

$$f(t) \approx 1/e;$$ 3.31

that is, during the time τ, the polarization has decayed to $1/e$ of its original value, which is just the definition of the relaxation time. This is an experimentally observable quantity for the macroscopic relaxation process. A directly measurable value of τ is given by Eq. (3.28), which requires that the value ω_m of the angular frequency for which the loss factor is a maximum, called the critical frequency, should be

$$\omega_m = \frac{1}{\tau}.$$ 3.32

When we divide Eq. (3.27) by Eq. (3.26) in rearranged form, we obtain

$$\frac{\varepsilon''}{\varepsilon' - \varepsilon_\infty} = \omega\tau$$ 3.33

That means when $\varepsilon''/(\varepsilon' - \varepsilon_\infty)$ is plotted against the angular frequency, it should give a straight line with slope τ passing through the origin. In examining the experimental data, it may be more convenient for one to use the critical frequency instead of ω_m:

$$f_m = \frac{\omega_m}{2\pi} = \frac{1}{2\pi\tau},$$ 3.34

where f_m is the frequency of the alternating field for which the loss factor is a maximum.

3.3.5   Friction Factor

According to the assumption of dominating friction, we must picture the polar molecules as rotating under the torque T of the electric field with an angular velocity dP/dt proportional to the torque, or

$$T = \zeta \frac{d\theta}{dt}.$$ 3.35

The friction factor ζ will depend on the shape of the molecule and on the type of interaction it encounters. To interpret the relaxation time τ molecularly, we can consider the simplest case, in which a molecule is regarded as a sphere with radius a rotating in a liquid with viscosity η. According to Stokes Law,[16] classical hydrodynamics leads to the value

$$\zeta = 8\pi a^3 \eta.$$ 3.36

In a static field, the spherical dipole carriers will have a slight preferential orientation parallel to this field and thus contribute to the average dipole moment μ_d as

$$\overline{\mu}_d = \frac{\mu^2}{3kT} E',$$ 3.37

which is a statistical compromise between the torque action of the electric field and the randomizing thermal agitation. A sudden removal of the external field will cause an exponential decay of this ordered state because of the randomizing agitation of the Brownian movement. The relaxation time τ measures the time required to reduce the order to $1/e$ of its original value. Debye calculated this time statistically by deriving the space orientation under the counteracting influence of the Brownian motion and of a time-dependent electrical field and found that

$$\tau = \frac{\zeta}{2kT}.$$ 3.38

Combining Eqs. (3.36) and (3.38), Debye obtained for a spherical molecule, if it behaved like a ball rotating in oil, the relaxation time

$$\tau = \frac{4\pi a^3 \eta}{kT} = V \frac{3\eta}{kT}.$$

3.39

Therefore, for this particular case, the relaxation time was proportional to the volume V of the sphere and the macroscopic viscosity of the medium.

Obviously, this is not a universal equation. Even for small molecules, the value estimated by Eq. (3.39) agrees poorly with the experimental value. For example, water at room temperature has a viscosity $\eta = 0.01$ poise with a radius of 2 Å for the water molecule. The relaxation time calculated by Eq. (3.39) is around 0.25×10^{-10} s, whereas the actual measurement of the relaxation time of water is located near the frequency of 10^{10} Hz (or a wavelength of 2 cm). However, agreement is not that good when we realize that the experimentally determined macroscopic relaxation time for water should be 20 times the molecular relaxation time. The essence of Debye's approach was to postulate that the orientation of polar molecules in liquids, solids, and polymers leads spectroscopically to a simple relaxation spectrum, but in those cases in which molecule is not a sphere, the process of orientation by rotation about different axes requires a distribution of relaxations.[17]

3.3.6   Relaxation Mechanisms

Most polymers exhibit more than one region of dielectric loss.[18] Usually a minimum of two regions occurs for amorphous polymers, whereas in crystalline polymers loss regions can be expected to arise from both phases. Invariably the glass-rubber transition T_g will give rise to a major dispersion. Other, shorter range motions such as side-group rotations or local mode motions will give rise to small to moderate dispersions, usually in the low-temperature range. Dispersions arising from the crystalline phases may originate from the surfaces of the crystals or be vibrational modes, such as the onset of torsional chain oscillations. Phase transformations, involving a change of crystal structure, may also produce dispersions. Most crystalline dispersion modes occur between the glass transition temperature and the melting point. Crystalline contributions to low-temperature dispersions have also been noted.

Conventionally, when a new polymer is studied, the peaks observed are labeled with Greek letters. The highest temperature process is always α with the remaining peaks being labeled in order of decreasing temperature (Fig. 3.3). Often a particular peak is a composite of several peaks. When this occurs the component peaks are labeled α', α'', and so on.

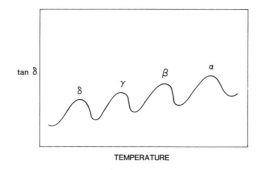

Fig. 3.3. Relationship between tan δ and temperature at constant frequency.

In the tan δ-temperature plot, the α-peak is usually slightly higher than the "conventional" glass transition temperature for that polymer. According to the literature, the secondary relaxations may occur in the glassy state[19-25] and the α-relaxation may occur in the rubbery state.[26-30] But this may not always be the case because the higher the frequency used in a measurement, the more the peak is shifted to a higher temperature. The converse is also true. To avoid such confusion, we shall call the α-peak temperature to be the glass transition temperature of that polymer as measured by the dielectric method. Since the dielectric method uses alternating voltage at a certain frequency, the glass transition temperature measured by the dielectric method will always be higher than that measured by a static method.

a) *Crystalline Polymers*

Polyethylene. One of the most studied polymers, largely because of its importance to electrical insulation, is polyethylene. This polymer is available in various forms. Low-density polyethylene (LDPE) contains a significant proportion of branches and generally has a relatively low crystallinity, usually 50–65% depending on the amount of branching. High-density polyethylene (HDPE) and linear or Phillips polyethylene (LPE) are very similar despite the different modes of synthesis, and both grades have little branching. The result is a polymer having crystallinity 75% or more depending on the conditions of crystallization. LDPE exhibits higher losses associated with amorphous phase relaxations, whereas HDPE and LPE exhibit large crystalline phase dispersions.[31-33] Figure 3.4 presents curves for HDPE and LDPE derived from the work of Mikhailov and coworkers.[31] The highest temperature peak, centered between 60 and 90°C, is the α-loss peak; arising from the crystalline phase it is naturally enhanced in HDPE. The second peak, β, is generally accepted as being associated with glass transition and is the largest in quenched LDPE. The third and lowest temperature peak, γ, is sizable in all polyethylenes and is now believed to arise from local mode motions in the amorphous phase. Additional but minor peaks at cryogenic temperatures have received considerable attention. Because of low activation energies, the losses are appreciable at ambient temperature for microwave frequencies.[34-36] The lowest

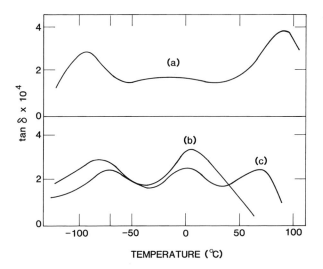

Fig. 3.4. Dielectric loss spectra of oxidized polyethylene at 10 kHz: (a) high density; (b) low density, quenched; (c) low density, annealed. Source is Ref. 31.

temperature peaks are probably due to inherent defects of the polyethylene hydrocarbon chain rather than oxidation effects or initiator fragments.

The magnitudes of the three major loss peaks in polyethylenes are of course dependent on the number of active dipoles present. Oxidation, either deliberate or adventitious, is usually the source of the dipoles. Infrared spectroscopy has identified hydroperoxy, hydroxyl, and carboxyl groups in addition to the widely assumed carbonyl groups.[37,38] This may not seem important at first glance; however, only the carbonyl group is easily accepted by the polyethylene crystal. Hydroxyl groups can be accepted but produce more distortion. The result is that the amorphous peaks are disproportionately visible in oxidized polyethylene.

Dipoles may also be placed in polyethylene through the use of chlorination. Careful chlorination increases loss levels without greatly disturbing the crystal structure.[39] The most thorough study of the dielectric behavior of oxidized and chlorinated polyethylenes is that of Ashcraft and Boyd, which is the only study that has considered all types of polyethylene in a consistent manner.[39] Their analyses clearly demonstrated that both the β- and γ-processes are amorpohous in origin and that the α-process arises from the crystalline phase. Not only is the intensity of the α-process linearly dependent on crystallinity (Fig. 3.5), but any isochronal frequency maximum decreases as lamellar thickness increases (Fig. 3.6). This effect indicates that the motion occurring is more likely to be a combination of a rotation and twist of the chain than a simple rotation. Ashcraft and Boyd clearly identified the β-process as the glass-rubber transition and regard the γ-process as a purely local mode in amorphous regions. Orientation in polymers is another important variable. The vast majority of dielectric studies carried out have considered only isotropic materials. The effect of stretching on the loss behavior of a copolymer of ethylene and carbon monoxide has been determined in the α- and β-regions.[40] During elongation of crystalline polymers, individual crystals or crystalline blocks are reoriented so that the sections of chain within the crystal become aligned in the direction of the applied stress. Since the dipoles in an ethylene-carbon monoxide copolymer are perpendicular to the chain direction, they become oriented across the thickness, that is, in the direction of a field applied when parallel plate electrodes are used.

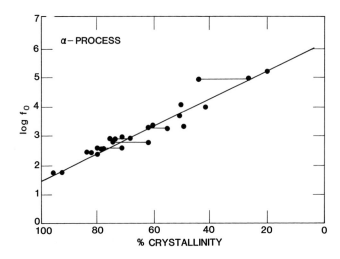

Fig. 3.5. Variation of the logarithm of the frequency maximum at 70°C with crystallinity for several polyethylenes. Source is Ref. 39.

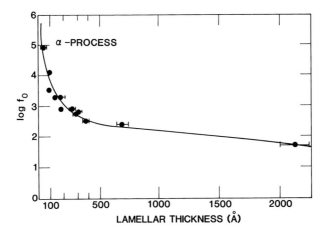

Fig. 3.6. Variation of the logarithm of the frequency maximum at 70°C with lamellar thickness for several polyethylenes. Source is Ref. 39.

The result is that the dielectric loss across the film is enhanced (Fig. 3.7), whereas losses along the stretch direction are decreased.[40, 41]

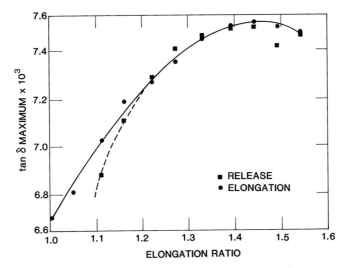

Fig. 3.7. Variation of maximum value of tan δ with elongation ratios at 43°C for an ethylene-carbon monoxide copolymer. Source is Ref. 40.

Polychlorotrifluoroethylene. A second crystalline polymer that has been extensively investigated is polychlorotrifluoroethylene (Kel-F). The advantages of this polymer for diagnostic study lie in the occurrence of a dipole in each monomer unit together with a controllable range of crystallinity between 12 and 80%.[42, 43] It may therefore be regarded generally as a prototype dipolar crystalline polymer, whereas polyethylene is a nonpolar crystalline polymer. Specimens crystallized under different conditions showed quite different loss behavior, Fig. 3.8. The α-loss peak was associated with the crystalline phase, the β-loss peak with the glass transition, and the γ-loss peak with a complex peak with contributions from both phases. The crystalline α-process was the subject of thorough modeling studies involving possible mechanisms. Models were constructed for both extended-chain crystals and chain-folded crystals. The models for the chain-folded systems included both complex and independent motions in the chain fold and crystal interior chains. The authors concluded that the α-loss, consisting of two overlapping mechanisms, was a result of motions of chain folds and reorientation (with translation) of interior chains. The crystalline γ-relaxation was interpreted as a result of chain reorientation in a chain-end-induced defect in the polymer crystal.

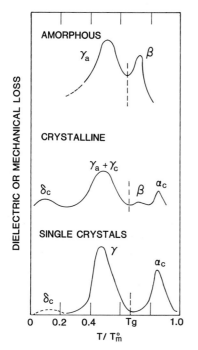

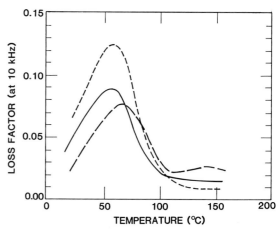

▲

Fig. 3.9. Loss factor vs temperature for isotropic (−) and drawn specimens of polychlorotrifluoroethylene with draw direction perpendicular (---) and parallel (--) to the applied field. Source is Ref. 45.

Fig. 3.8. Dielectric or mechanical loss factor at 1 Hz vs reduced temperature, T/T_m^0, for a linear polymer with no independently rotatable side groups. Source is Ref. 43.

To investigate the relative contributions of fold surfaces and interior regions of the crystal, Baird and Blackburn studied a series of drawn specimens.[44] Both the α- and γ-loss peaks were enhanced with the draw direction perpendicular to the field direction. As with copolymers of ethylene and carbon monoxide, the dominant contribution came from interior dipoles (Fig. 3.9). Studies of specimens of various lamellar thicknesses were also carried out.[45] The temperature of the maximum loss and of the activation energy increased with increasing lamellar thickness, confirming the assignment of the loss to interior chains. No systematic changes were observed for the γ-loss because of its complex nature.

Not all polar crystalline polymers will show a loss peak arising from the crystalline phase. Two conditions must be met for a crystalline α-process to occur: (a) the motion of the chain must be such that the polymer chain attains a final position indistinguishable from the original position, and (b) the activation energy of the process must not be too high. In polyethylene and polychlorotrifluoroethylene, the translation-rotational unit is only two bonds long. In polyester and polyamides, the unit can be very large because the distances separating identical functional groups may be 10–20 bond lengths (Fig. 3.10).

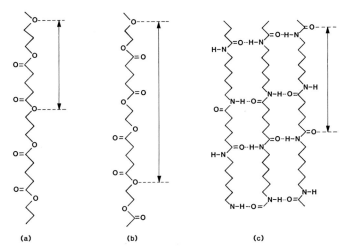

Fig. 3.10. Crystallographic repeat distances for (a) an odd-odd polyester, (b) an even-odd polyester, and (c) a polyamide (Nylon 66).

The activation energy for such a large translation is prohibitive. If the distance separating identical functional groups becomes comparable to the lamellar thickness, then the polyethylene α-process can reappear, and the functional groups act as impurity units in the predominantly polyethylene chain.

Neither polyamides nor polyethylene terephthalate exhibit crystalline loss regions; however, crystallinity does affect the loss peaks arising from the amorphous phase. In polyethylene terephthalate,[46] the magnitudes of α- and β-loss peaks are depressed by increasing crystallinity (Fig. 3.11). Simply, fewer amphorous dipoles are available to enter into the relaxation processes. From the diagnostic point of view, studies of single crystals can be of considerable assistance. Because of their small size, it is impossible to study isolated single

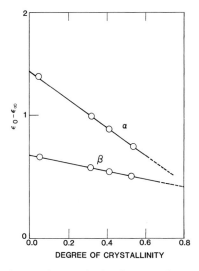

Fig. 3.11. Effect of crystallization on the magnitude of $\varepsilon_0 - \varepsilon_\infty$ for polyethylene terephthalate: α at 100°C; β at −25°C. Source is Ref. 46.

crystals, so mats are collected; hence, the experiments are carried out on specimens containing hundreds or thousands of crystals. A good example is polyethylene oxide (Fig. 3.12).

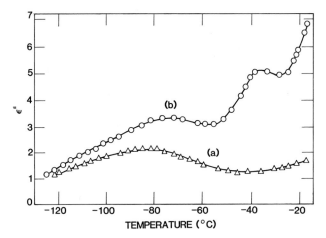

Fig. 3.12. Temperature dependence of ε'' for (a) single-crystal mat and (b) melt-crystallized film of polyethylene oxide at 12.8 kHz. Source is Ref. 46.

It has been reported for poly(vinylidene fluoride) in the α-crystalline form that loss magnitudes vary with crystallization conditions even though the bulk density remains constant.[47] Ascribed at the time to changes in spherulite size, the effect is much more likely to be caused by changes in lamellar thickness similar to those observed in polychlorotrifluoroethylene.[45]

b) *Amorphous Polymers*

For noncrystalline polymers the situation is much simpler because the complication of potential vibrational modes within the crystal no longer exists. Dielectric loss peaks are those associated with either the glass transition or local reorientational processes. The largest loss peak usually occurs at the highest temperature and is associated with the glass transition.[18] In identifying the mechanism responsible for lower temperature peaks, a rule of thumb is to classify the polymer on the basis of whether or not the active dipole is rigidly attached to the polymer backbone[48] (Fig. 3.13).

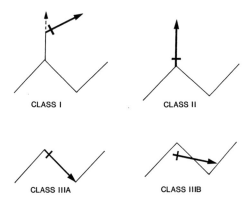

Fig. 3.13. Classification of dipoles in relation to their chain locations. Source is Ref. 48.

The most quoted examples of the two major classifications are poly(vinyl chloride), PVC, (dipole rigidly attached to the backbone) and poly(methyl methacrylate), PMMA, (dipole in a flexible side chain). Very few examples exist of a polymer with the dipole in the backbone direction, the best known being polypropylene oxide and polyphenylene oxide. In both PVC and PMMA, a relaxation is associated with the glass transition; however, both show prominent secondary relaxation peaks (Figs. 3.14 and 3.15).

For acrylic polyesters such as PMMA, the mechanism of the secondary relaxation is well established.[18,49,50] The molecular motion is a rotation of the ester side groups. This fact has been demonstrated quite convincingly in studies of several methacrylate polymers in which the size of the side-chain alkyl group was varied systematically. The glass transition temperature was affected significantly in these studies, whereas the side-group motion remained essentially unchanged. The nature of the secondary relaxation in PMMA was recently confirmed by nuclear magnetic resonance studies.[51] Increasing the side-chain size (if flexible) decreased the glass transition temperature because of internal plasticization. This effect is very similar to that of deliberately added diluents or plasticizers[49] (Fig. 3.15).

For polymers such as PVC, which have this dipole rigidly attached to the backbone, the nature of the secondary relaxation is still something of an enigma. Although the peaks are easily detected (Fig. 3.14)[52] and must be associated with some type of local mode motion, the detailed mechanism has never been established. Several models have, however, been

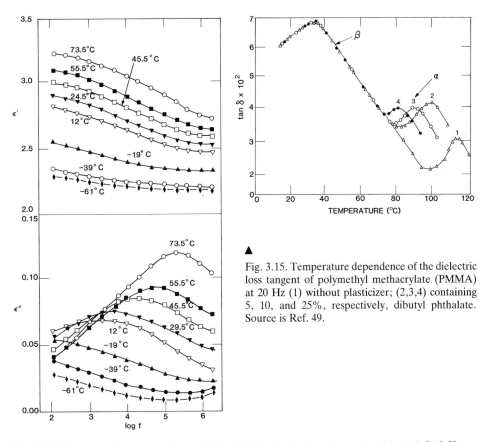

Fig. 3.15. Temperature dependence of the dielectric loss tangent of polymethyl methacrylate (PMMA) at 20 Hz (1) without plasticizer; (2,3,4) containing 5, 10, and 25%, respectively, dibutyl phthalate. Source is Ref. 49.

Fig. 3.14. Frequency dependence of ε' and ε'' for PVC in the β-relaxation region. Source is Ref. 52.

proposed.[18] As with all other glassy polymers, plasticization, since it decreases the glass temperature, decreases the temperature at which the α-loss peak occurs.

The effects of elevated pressures on the dielectric relaxation spectra have been thoroughly studied for several noncrystalline polymers, mainly by Williams and co-workers.[53-58] Pressure tends to separate overlapping peaks and assist in resolution and identification. It causes all peaks to shift to higher temperatures, the amount of shift varying with the nature of the operative relaxation process.

3.4   INFLUENCE OF PLASTICIZATION ON DIELECTRIC LOSS

Plasticization is widely used in industry for the modification of polymers to change their physicochemical properties and to extend their fields of application. The distribution of the plasticizer molecules in polymers varies with the types of plasticizers and polymers. Plasticization may be roughly classified into two types: (1) molecular and (2) structural.

Using the cooperative segment motion idea, Bueche[59-61] suggested that because of the shielding effect of the plasticizer molecules, the cooperative movement range of the polymer molecules is reduced and the relaxation process of polymers is modified. Thus, it was found that the tan δ peak and the glass transition temperature of rubber, polystyrene, PMMA, and PVC are all shifted to lower temperatures after plasticization. This shift is closely related to the nature, kind, and quantity of plasticizer material used.

3.4.1   Molecular and Structural Plasticizers

The cooperative segment movement model can be used to interpret not only the effects of molecular plasticizers but also those of structural plasticizers. The difference between these plasticizers is that the former is able to form an associative bond with the polymer, whereas the latter is not or at the most forms only a weak association. For practical reasons an ideal structural plasticizer is one that would cause no change in the T_g, τ, and ΔH of the polymer. However, no such plasticizer has yet been discovered. The effect of the two plasticizers on T_g is illustrated in Fig. 3.16. An example of a structural plasticizer is glycerine, which when added to polyvinyl alcohol[62] or polycarbonate,[63] initially decreases the T_g of the polymers but has no further effect at higher concentrations. In this sense, glycerin is a nearly ideal plasticizer for those two polymers.

The influence of the polarity of structural plasticizers on the peak value of tan δ is the same as that of molecular plasticizers. Thus, the addition of a transformer oil to polystyrene produces a molecular plasticizer because the polarities of both are nearly the same and plasticization has practically no influence on the peak value of tan δ. Moreover, adding a vegetable oil with dipole moment of 3.96 D to polystyrene leads to a structural plasticization. Since the effective dipole moment μ_{eff} and concentration N_0 of dipoles per unit volume both increase, the peak value of tan δ increases too. When the content of vegetable oil is less than 1%, it is weakly bonded with polystyrene, and its diffusion into the polymer reduces the dimensions of cooperative segment movement regions, thus decreasing the values of T_g, τ, and ΔH. Again, at small levels the structural plasticizer is very effective, but because it tends to stay at the boundary layers of cooperative segment movement regions, further addition has minimal effect. Water also behaves as a structural plasticizer in most polymers.

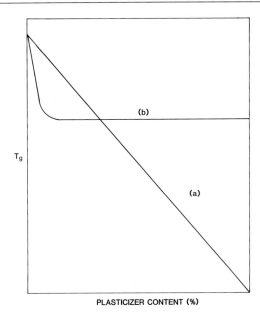

Fig. 3.16. The effect of (a) molecular and (b) structural plasticizers on Tg.

When the plasticizer added to the polymer is a molecular plasticizer of different polarity, the variation of the tan δ peak value is due to the original supermolecular structure of the polymer being altered by the plasticizer molecules: they diffuse into the interior of the polymer and associate with the polymer chains. When the plasticizer is more polar than the polymer, the cooperative segment motion of the polymer segments with associating plasticizer molecules will increase the effective dipole moment and thus the dielectric loss of the system. If there is no plasticizer diffusion and/or association, the consequence will be just the opposite.

3.4.2   Polarity and tan δ Level

Early investigations had already established that addition of a polar plasticizer to nonpolar polymers will increase the tan δ level.[64-67] For example, the tan δ levels of dichloro-diphenyl-polystyrene and diphenyl-polydichlorostryene systems are nearly equal. In this particular case, the value depended mostly on the chlorine content of the system, whether in the plasticizer or in the polymer. Similarly, for poly(vinyl chloride)-diphenyl[65] and polyvinyl acetate-diphenylmethane systems,[68] the dipole moments are determined only by the quantity of the nonpolar plasticizers added, which in turn then determines the values of the tan δ.

3.4.3   Other Polarity Effects

The use of polar plasticizers actually leads to more complicated effects. The rather detailed studies of Würstlin[69,70] and Dyson[71] showed that the effect consisted of the initial appearance of two peaks as tricresyl phosphate concentration increased but returned to a single low-temperature peak at very high concentrations (Fig. 3.17). The effects were first explained in terms of dipolar interactions between polymer and plasticizer.[70] The situation is

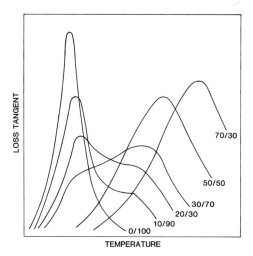

Fig. 3.17. Loss tangent of plasticized PVC at 10^7 Hz as a function of tricresyl phosphate content. Source is Ref. 70.

not clear, however, since the dielectric constants of polar plasticizers influence the degree of compatibility, and it is possible that a microphase separation occurs.[71]

For polar polymers, plasticizers not only affect α-relaxation, but they also affect secondary relaxations.[72] For example, when 22.5 wt% benzyl acetate is added to nitrocellulose, both α- and β-loss peaks are shifted to lower temperatures, 135 and 18°C, respectively. In contrast, when naphthalene is added as a plasticizer to polyvinyl acetate, it has no influence on the β-peak. Generally, the stronger the polarity of the plasticizer, the stronger its effect on the β-relaxation process. This has been most clearly shown in the plasticization of PVC.[73] The effect is due to the fact that the C−Cl bond is rather rigid, and its β-relaxation depends not only on the arrangement of polar groups in the polymer chain but also on the arrangement of neighboring polymer chain segments relative to the polar group. Plasticization helps the movement of chain segments and enhances the movement of polar groups.

3.4.4   Plasticization and Activation Energy

Plasticization influences not only the relaxation times of α- and β-processes, but also their respective activation energies. For example, the addition of 10–20 wt% of a plasticizer to poly(vinyl chloride) decreases the activation energy to the α-peak, and with further addition, the decrease gradually slows down until it approaches a constant value as a limit.[68, 72, 74] After a certain quantity of plasticizer has been added, full shielding has been established, and further addition has no effect.

The effect of the quantity of plasticizer on ε'' for PVC plasticized with diphenyl is illustrated in Fig. 3.18. It decreases the temperature at which the α-loss peak occurs just as it decreases the T_g.[75] This means that the relaxation time decreased as the quantity of the plasticizer was increased. Furthermore, if for each quantity of plasticizer, one plots the logarithm of peak frequency against the reciprocal of the corresponding temperature (Fig. 3.19) or plots the logarithm of frequency against the reciprocal of the corresponding peak temperature a straight line is obtained. This means that the activation energy ΔH is generally different for different contents of plasticizer, decreasing as the content of the plasticizer increases.[76] If we extrapolate these $\ln f_m$ vs $1/T$ straight lines to $f_m = 1$ Hz (that is, $\ln f_m = 0$),

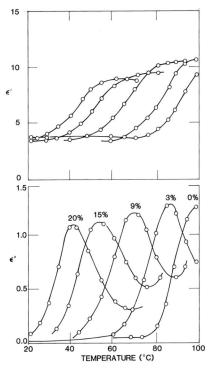

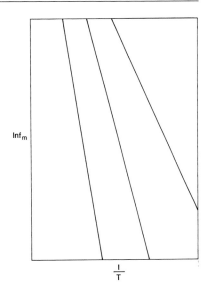

Fig. 3.19. Schematic diagram of $\ln f_m$ vs $1/T$ for different plasticizer contents in a polymer.

Fig. 3.18. Temperature dependence of ε' and ε'' at 60 Hz for PVC plasticized with percentage of diphenyl as a parameter. Source is Ref. 75.

we obtain the glass transition temperature (determined dielectrically) of that polymer with a specific quantity of plasticizer.

The relationship between T_g and the quantity of plasticizer is linear for styrene-plasticized polystyrene, but for many other cases the relationship is seldom linear. The decrease in T_g as a consequence of molecular plasticization clearly shows that the active segments in the polymer chains are shielded by the plasticizer molecules.[77,78]

When toluene is used as the plasticizer of polystyrene, the tan δ (α-peak) is shifted to higher frequency under constant temperature or lower temperature at constant frequency.[72]

3.4.5   The Effects of Conduction

To properly interpret the increase in the tan δ value by plasticization, one also has to take into account any changes in conduction.[79,80] For example, the percentage increases of the tan δ value in polystyrene caused by the addition of the monomer styrene is different for different temperature regions. For temperatures far below T_g, addition of 1% of styrene will increase its tan δ value appreciably. Addition of 10–20% of styrene will increase the tan δ value as much as tenfold. This indicates that the conduction loss predominates over the tangent loss at these temperatures because the relaxation loss at these temperatures is much smaller than the conduction loss. However, in the vicinity of the tan δ peak temperature, the relaxation loss increases. In this temperature region, the tan δ value may increase too, but it is still a relatively small increase.

This increase of the tan δ peak value is mainly due to the polarity of the monomer, which is higher than that of the polymer: 0.30–0.37 D for styrene[81] vs 0.2 D polystyrene.[82] As derived by Mikhailov[83] from the dipole polarization theory, the peak value of the loss factor can be estimated from

$$\varepsilon''_m = A \cdot \frac{n^2 + 2}{2 + \dfrac{n^2}{\varepsilon'^2_m + \varepsilon''^2_m}} \cdot \mu_{eff} \frac{N_0 \alpha}{T}, \qquad\qquad 3.40$$

where μ_{eff} is the effective dipole moment of the system, N_0 is the concentration of dipoles per unit volume, α is a parameter to characterize the distribution of relaxation time, and n is the refractive index. The effective dipole moment of the polystyrene-styrene system is greater than that of polystyrene or styrene alone only when the styrene content in the system is over 40%. For practical purpose, Eq. (3.39) is useful for estimating the tan δ variation of polystyrene as it ages thermally as well as optically.

3.5   INFLUENCE OF MOLECULAR WEIGHT ON DIELECTRIC LOSS, RELAXATION TIME, AND ACTIVATION ENERGY

Electrical properties and polymer aging are both related to molecular weight and its distribution. Thus, generation of materials with desired electrical properties and optimum long-term properties are very much dependent upon the knowledge of molecular weight characteristics.

Generally, the tan δ_{max} decreases as the molecular weight increases. For thermosetting polymers, for example, the tan δ_{max} of epoxy resins decreases with increasing degree of cure.[84] Therefore, it is also usually possible to establish some correlation between the tan δ value and the degree of polymerization for linear polymers and the cross-linking density for cross-linked polymers.[85] However, in the course of polymerization as well as curing, the possibility of introducing oxygen-containing groups has to be considered. These groups may then lead to an increased effective dipole moment and thus increase dielectric loss. As a result, the determination of the degree of polymerization or molecular weight by dielectric measurements is a less effective and rather complicated procedure.

3.5.1   Polystyrene and Polyvinyl Acetate

Experiments on carefully dried polymer samples with narrow molecular weight distributions have been done for molecular weights of 263 to 4.71×10^5 for polystyrene and 172 to 8.4×10^4 for polyvinyl acetate.[86] In the measurement of tan δ, the frequency used was $10^2–10^5$ Hz, and temperatures were from −50 to 160°C for polystyrene and from 0 to 100°C for polyvinyl acetate. It was found that tan δ_{max} and tan δ at temperatures $T << T_c$ decreased with increasing molecular weight. The rate of decrease with the low-molecular-weight samples was rather large at first. When the molecular weight of polystyrene reached 7×10^4, and that of polyvinyl acetate reached 4×10^4, the tan δ values became rather insensitive to the molecular weight. Further increases in molecular weight had practically no effect on tan δ_{max}.

a) *Molecular Weight Dispersity Effects*

For another set of polystyrene and polyisobutylene samples with high dispersity of molecular weight, the same results were obtained when the relationship between tan δ and molecular weight was determined at a fixed set of values for frequency and temperature.[87,88] However, the difference caused by the high dispersity of molecular weight was that even at the very high weights, the tan δ values continued to decrease (Table 3.1). No doubt, the low-molecular-weight fractions provided some plasticization in these samples.

TABLE 3.1 The tan δ of Polystyrene and Polyisobutylene with High Dispersity of Molecular Weight*

Polymers, Frequency, and Temperature	Average Molecular Weight	tan δ
Polystyrene	18×10^3	0.00220
3×10^3 Hz	27×10^3	0.00144
25°C	33×10^3	0.00127
	41×10^3	0.00124
	54×10^3	0.00078
	96×10^3	0.00051
	240×10^3	0.00043
Polyisobutylene	3×10^3	0.00420
800 Hz	15×10^3	0.00260
20°C	50×10^3	0.00220
	100×10^3	0.00155
	200×10^3	0.00150

* Source is Refs. 87 and 88.

b) *Dynamic Mechanical Loss tan δ*

The dynamic mechanical loss tan δ of polystyrene also decreases with increasing molecular weight from 1.71 to 3.70×10^5 (Ref. 89). This is only one of many examples of analogy between the mechanical and electrical properties of polymers. Both properties are affected by the physical process of relaxation of molecules or chain segments, but each has its own emphasis.

3.5.2 Polyethylene

Considerable detail is available on how various molecular parameters of polyethylene affect tan δ. For a low-density polyethylene with a molecular weight of 1.5×10^3 to 3.7×10^4 and for a high-density polyethylene with a molecular weight of 3.0×10^3 to 6.13×10^5 at frequencies of 10^3 to 10^5 Hz and temperatures of -120 to 150°C, the tan δ values obtained could be correlated with the heterogeneity index or molecular weight distribution, density, crystallinity, branching, and spherulite size.[90] At room temperature, the value of tan δ of polyethylene decreases with molecular weight, but when the molecular weight is larger than 10^5, tan δ gradually approaches a constant value. Simultaneously, the spherulite diameter also decreases with increasing molecular weight, in parallel with the change in tan δ. As the molecular weight increases, the interspherulite space becomes more dense and the packing density of spherulites increases. This then leads to a decrease of conduction currents and a relaxation loss from the α-relaxation process and hence to a tan δ decrease.

Molecular Weight Dispersity Effects

The influence of the molecular weight distribution on tan δ of high-density polyethylene has been evaluated[91] on a sample with an average molecular weight of 6.2×10^4. The relationship between heterogeneity index, density, spherulite index, branching, and tan δ is shown in Table 3.2. As the heterogeneity index increases, the branching of the polyethylene chain also increases, but the spherulite diameter and tan δ decrease. The decrease in tan δ is primarily due to an increase in density of the interspherulite space.

TABLE 3.2 Relationship of tan δ of High-Density Polyethylene to Some of its Physicochemical Parameters[91]

Heterogeneity Index	Density (g/cm³)	Spherulite Diameter (μm)	Branching CH₃/1000C	tan δ at 10⁴ Hz and 30°C
1.1	0.9585	13–20	5.68	0.00022
2.5	0.9530	8–13	6.20	0.00018
3.7	0.9530	5–8	6.70	0.00018

3.5.3   Polar Polymers

For polymers that are polar, the influence of the molecular weight of polyhydroxyacid ester on its α- and β-relaxation processes has also been investigated.[92] The range of molecular weights was from 10^3 to 7×10^4, and the frequency used was from 60 to 2×10^5 Hz; the temperature was from −70 to 250°C. It was found that as the molecular weight increased, the tan δ peak value for the α-loss decreased, whereas that of the β-loss remained unchanged. This showed that the effect of molecular weight was important in the cooperative segment movement although less so for movement of the polar groups. In other words, the effect of molecular weight is more limited to the mobility of the movement of larger units. The decrease of the tan δ value with increasing molecular weight above T_g is due to the decrease of mobility of macromolecules, but below T_g it is due to the decrease of conduction currents. As the dimensions of polymer molecules increase, the tan δ peak value of the α-loss decreases. When the molecular weight has reached a certain value, tan δ eventually approaches a constant value.

3.5.4   Molecular Weight and Relaxation Time

For most polymers the relaxation time for α-relaxation increases with increasing molecular weight. For example, Girard et al. studied polyvinyl chloride with 2% lead stearate and found that the relaxation time for α-relaxation increased with increasing molecular weight.[93] But in this case, the presence of lead stearate may have influenced the relaxation time too. For polystyrene, the relaxation time also increased with increasing molecular weight.[89] For both low- and high-density polyethylene, the relaxation time of all relaxations (α, β, and γ) increased as the molecular weight increased.[90]

However, some polymers behave differently. For example, although the most probable relaxation time for α-relaxation of polyethylene and polypropylene oxides increased with increasing molecular weight, after the maximum time had been reached, the most probable relaxation time then began to decrease.[94, 95] For poly(methyl methacrylate), no evidence exists that the relaxation time of its α-relaxation is dependent on molecular weight.[96]

The increase of τ as a consequence of increasing molecular weight may be due to the effect of increasing density.[94, 95, 97] Because the densities of polystyrene[98, 99] and polyethylene[100] increase with increasing molecular weight, the density of interspherulite space increases also. More dense means that it is more difficult for segmental motion to occur. This idea comes from the following work. When external pressure was imposed on a polymer, the τ increased along with an increase in density.[101] Therefore, the increase of τ is due to an increase in molecular packing, which then generates more steric hindrance for the cooperative segment movement.

3.5.5   Molecular Weight and Activation Energy

The investigation of the relationship between the activation energy ΔH_α and molecular weight and temperature will give further insight into the nature of the dielectric relaxation of polymers. For example, ΔH decreases with increasing temperature because the kinetic energy of polymer chains is sufficiently high to overcome intermolecular association and thus facilitate internal rotation and chain flexibility.[22, 102] The picture is less clear on the relationship between ΔH_α and molecular weight. For example, ΔH_α for polyvinyl acetate is independent of molecular weight.[73] However, Würstlin showed that ΔH_α increased as the molecular weight increased at low molecular weight averages and became constant at 2×10^4 (Refs. 70, 103, 104).

Another unusual example is polytetrafluoroethylene. Although its relaxation time increased with increasing molecular weight, its ΔH_α decreased.[98]

Many contradictory results can be explained once care has been taken in preparing and purifying the polymer samples. The activation energy is very sensitive to the presence of low-molecular-weight species. Even trace amounts of the low-molecular-weight fraction of the polymer, plasticizer, solvent, or water will decrease the ΔH_α significantly. Thus, reproducible results can be obtained only on carefully purified, fractioned, and dried samples.

When carefully prepared samples of polystyrene and polyvinyl acetate of very narrow molecular weight were studied, it was found that at first ΔH_α increased with increasing molecular weight.[105] The ΔH_α reached a maximum value for polystyrene with a molecular weight of 2.5×10^3 and for polyvinyl acetate with a molecular weight of 1.5×10^3. After the maxima were reached, ΔH_α then decreased with further increase in molecular weight until a constant value was achieved at molecular weight of 10^5 for polystyrene and 7×10^4 for polyvinyl acetate, respectively.

These changes in ΔH_α may be understood as follows: In the very low molecular weight region, intermolecular interactions increase with increasing molecular weight, and relaxations have to overcome an increasing energy barrier with increasing molecular weight; hence, the activation energy is proportional to the molecular weight. After the molecular weight has reached a certain value, the movement of polymer chains turns into segmental motions. The α-loss peak usually occurs at higher temperatures, which means increased kinetic energy for the chain segments, which in turn translates into a smaller cooperative segment movement region and a decreasing activation energy.

3.6   INFLUENCE OF SUPERMOLECULAR STRUCTURE ON DIELECTIC LOSS

3.6.1   The Nature of Supermolecular Structure

A real polymeric solid is usually a mixture of crystalline and amorphous phases, that is, its physical structure is heterogeneous. However, even in purely amorphous polymers, structural heterogeneity has been discovered by electron microscopy and electron diffraction techniques.[106–110] Polymer molecules form aggregates of different shape and size depending on the preparation and thermal history of the material. This aggregate structure is also referred to as supermolecular structure.[111] Further refinements of the supermolecular structure have been made by Yeh et al.[112–114]

The supermolecular structure of polymers may change with plasticization, molecular weight, crystallization, and stretch orientation. We have already discussed how plasticization and molecular weight can affect dielectric loss through changes in the supermolecular structure. Supermolecular structure is also largely determined by the property of the polymer to crystallize and by uni- or biaxial orientation. We now consider these two variables.

3.6.2   The Effect of Stretch Orientation

When a semicrystalline polymer is stretched, the unit cell of the crystal contracts perpendicular to the direction of stretching, and some of the supermolecular secondary and tertiary structures may be destroyed.[115–117] This may also, for example, decrease the peak value of $\tan \delta_m$ of α-relaxation, and the peak may be shifted to a lower frequency.[118] Stretching of amorphous polymers produces little change in α-relaxation,[119] and the correlation between $\tan \delta_m$ and orientation in amorphous polymers is generally weak.

After stretch orientation of a polymer the dielectric properties exhibit anisotropy. In the α-relaxation region, the value of $\tan \delta_m$ is largest perpendicular to the draw direction, smallest parallel to the draw direction, and intermediate in unoriented polymers.[120] A more detailed study of this anisotropy phenomenon showed that the distribution of relaxation times remained the same; only the most probable relaxation time changed.[121] Of course, the anisotropy in dielectric properties is most pronounced for polar polymers.

3.6.3   The Effect of Crystallinity

The crystallinity, especially of polar polymers, affects not only the values of $\tan \delta$ but also the most probable relaxation times of both the α- and β-relaxation processes.[83, 121–123] As crystallinity increases, ε''_m (or $\tan \delta_m$) of α- and β-relaxation processes decreases, and their peaks are shifted to higher temperature or lower frequency, that is, their relaxation times increase. The change in crystallinity especially affects the α-relaxation process. When the crystallinity of a polymer is larger than 70%, the dipole segment polarization may sometimes be completely suppressed so that there is no longer any α-dielectric loss. But the influence of crystallinity on the relaxation time of α-loss is a rather complicated process. Some observations are very difficult to explain. For example, when polytrifluorochloroethylene is crystallized, the peak position of the α-relaxation process is shifted to a lower temperature and its relaxation time decreases.

The increase in relaxation time caused by increased crystallinity can be rationalized as follows: Since the relaxation loss, especially at higher temperatures, comes chiefly from the cooperative segment movement in the amorphous phase of the polymer, the increasing crystallinity results in decreasing number of dipoles per unit volume that enter the relaxation processes. Hence, the relaxation time increases.

On the other hand, in the process of crystallization of an amorphous polymer, which usually takes place near the melting point of the crystalline phase, the original relaxation in the amorphous phase is suppressed because its cooperative segment motion is obstructed by the appearance of the crystalline phase. At the same time, for the newly formed crystalline phase, a new characteristic loss peak may occur, with a value that increases as the crystallization process proceeds. The temperature of this peak corresponds to the melting point of the crystalline phase of the polymer.[124] Often this characteristic loss peak disappears upon annealing of the polymer. For example, low-density polyethylene loses its α-loss peak after annealing, but when the same sample is heated again at 90°C, this loss peak reappears.[125] This relaxation is usually called the α_c process or crystalline α process. Its activation energy is similar to those of α-relaxation. If this relaxation process is examined at a very high frequency, the peak temperature position shifts to a higher temperature, which may be higher than the melting point of the crystalline phase of the polymer, and identification of its existence may become problematic. There have been other cases in which the peak temperature of α_c-loss corresponded to the transition temperature of one crystalline phase to another one.[126, 127]

The occurrence of the α_c-process of dielectric and mechanical losses is closely related to the supermolecular structure of the polymers, especially their spherulite content.[128] The α_c-relaxation process has been observed in polyethylene, polypropylene, and polytrifluorochloroethylene only when spherulites are present. If no spherulites are present after annealing, the α_c-relaxation process is also absent. The nature of this α_c-process is now considered to be caused by supermolecular structure acting as a new unit for relaxation, which may be thought of as a kind of interfacial polarization. This polarization can be detected by dielectric spectroscopy.

3.7 DIELECTRIC SPECTROSCOPY OF POLYMERS

Dielectric spectroscopy is based on the interaction of electromagnetic radiation with the electric dipole moments of the material tested. The frequency of the radiation is between 10^{-6} and 10^{10} Hz. Above 10^{10} Hz, in the infrared, optical, and ultraviolet regions, the absorption and emission of radiation is due to changes in the induced dipole moments, which depend on the polarizability of the atoms or molecules. At lower frequencies the contribution of the induced dipole moments becomes small compared with that of the permanent dipole moments of the system. Dielectric spectroscopy is especially useful for studying polar molecules in the gaseous or in solution phases.

In the condensed phase the situation is more complicated because the electronic states of the system cannot be described in terms of molecular orbits. Rather, collective crystal states or excitons must be considered. Dielectric behavior of a solid can be rigorously interpreted only in terms of exciton states.[129] Consequently, induced dipole moments may contribute appreciably to the absorption of radiation even at low frequencies. Moreover, the dipole moments of molecules or groups are strongly influenced by intermolecular interactions that can also be described in terms of exciton states.

In polymeric solids and viscoelastic liquids, the contribution of the exciton states to the permanent dipole moments is not very large; at least it is weak enough that one can consider certain groups of atoms or bonds individually. As a further assumption, in the ground state one can regard polymeric solids containing certain polar groups as a system of not very strongly interacting electrical dipoles. With these assumptions dielectric spectroscopy has been applied with more or less accuracy to polymeric solids. The response of a material to an external electrical field is essentially a statistical effect. It is not possible to observe the orientation of the individual moments; only the bulk polarization of the assembly can be measured. This means that dielectric spectroscopy is based on statistical thermodynamic considerations.

3.7.1   Technical and Practical Considerations

For technical reasons it would be desirable to record spectra as a function of the frequency at different, fixed, temperatures, that is, using the frequency as a variable and the temperature as a parameter. Because of instrumental difficulties, in practice the frequency is often used as a parameter and the temperature as a variable. This method has the advantage that the dielectric spectra can easily be compared with mechanical, dilatometric, and differential scanning calorimetric curves, which are essentially recorded as a function of the temperature.

The use of temperature as a variable has the disadvantage that the shape of the spectrum bands is difficult to interpret because, especially at structural transitions, the oscillator strength $\varepsilon_0 - \varepsilon_\infty$ changes abruptly at the transition temperature.

However, in practical use of polymers for electrical and electronic engineering purposes, the dielectric spectrum data as a whole are far more important than a single value of tan δ at a certain frequency and temperature. For example, in the preparation of PVC cable insulation or in the preparation and aging study of epoxy resin insulation, a value of tan δ at a definite temperature and frequency is not sufficient. We must know the dielectric spectrum with temperature at the operating frequency of the cable because in operation the temperature of the cable insulation may vary widely.

The addition of plasticizer will also change the shape of the spectrum. Hence, dielectric spectroscopy can also help in the selection of suitable plasticizers qualitatively and quantitatively.

In general, the molecular weight and molecular weight distribution of epoxy resins are subject to change during long-term use because of aging. Dielectric spectroscopy can help monitor the effects of aging over long periods.

In practice, polymers are seldom used in the pure state. Stabilizers are added to lengthen their useful life, and when a plastic is too brittle, plasticizers are often used to make them more flexible. A practical polymeric material often contains organic or inorganic fillers and dyes as well. Polymer and copolymer blends are used to improve specific properties such as toughness. Consequently, a practical polymeric material is a multicomponent system. It is important to study how the physical structure and macroscopic properties of the polymer are changed by low molecular weight or polymeric additions. Dielectric spectroscopy offers a very efficient method for studying such problems.

The effect of plasticizers on the dielectric properties of polymers is very important from the practical point of view because so many plasticized polymers are used in the electrical industry. From the dielectric behavior of the polymer, it is often possible to deduce information about the mechanism of plasticization. One may even be able to understand a plasticization problem should one occur.

3.7.2   Plasticized PVC

Since plasticized PVC is one of the most used plastics in the world, its characterization by dielectric spectroscopy will be illustrated in some detail.[70,73] The effect of the quantity of the plasticizer di-2-ethylhexyl phthalate (DOP) on tan δ is illustrated in Fig. 3.20. As the quantity of DOP increases and the α-peak is shifted to a lower temperature, the peak value decreases, and the half-width of the curve becomes wider, which flattens the curve and decreases the value of tan δ.

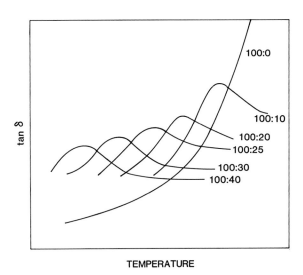

TEMPERATURE

Fig. 3.20 Effect of plasticizer (DOP) quantity on the tan δ of PVC.

The effect of different kinds of plasticizers on the tan δ value of PVC is shown in Fig. 3.21.[73] The ratio of plasticizer to polymer was fixed at 40:100, yet the effect on the dielectric spectrum differed greatly. Dioctyl sebacate is sufficiently effective that the α-peak temperature is shifted to very low temperatures; the tan δ shown in Fig. 3.21 is merely the conduction loss. The flattening effect of tricresyl phosphate is far less than that of dioctyl phthalate. The different plasticizing effects of each plasticizer are mainly due to their chemical structural differences. However, other physicochemical properties of each plasticizer such as the compatibility, α-peak temperature, viscosity, and temperature coefficient of viscosity also have a significant effect. The α-peak temperature of dioctyl sebacate is very low; hence, it has the ability to shift the α-peak temperature of the PVC polymer to a very low level. The α-peak temperatures of some plasticizers are shown in Table 3.3.[73] The temperature coefficient of viscosity of dioctyl phthalate is relatively small, so its spectrum in Fig. 3.21 is more flat.

a) *Estimation of α-Peak Temperature*

The α-peak temperature T_m of a PVC polymer can be estimated by the following empirical equation:

$$\frac{1}{T_m} = \frac{a}{a+b}\left(\frac{1}{T_p}\right) + \frac{b}{a+b}\left(\frac{1}{T_r}\right), \qquad\qquad 3.41$$

where T_p and T_r are the α-peak temperatures (Kelvin) of plasticizer and polyvinyl chloride (with a stabilizer), respectively, and a and b are the volume ratios of the two, respectively.

This empirical formula is based on the following assumptions: (1) relaxation time is related to viscosity, (2) plasticization is mainly a volume effect, and (3) the plasticizer must be completely compatible with the resin.

The temperature estimated from Eq. (3.41) is usually in reasonable agreement with the measured values. For plasticizers with poor compatibility with PVC, the differences become significant.

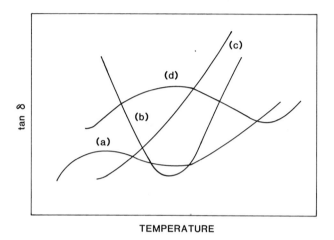

Fig. 3.21 Effect of different kinds of plasticizers on the tan δ of PVC: (a) dioctyl phthalate, (b) dibutyl phthalate, (c) dioctyl sebacate, (d) tricresyl phosphate.

TABLE 3.3 α-Peak Temperatures of Some Plasticizers

Plasticizers	α-Peak Temperature (°C)
Dibutyl phthalate	− 84.5
Dioctyl phthalate	− 71.5
Dinonyl phthalate	− 56
Tricresyl phosphate	− 45
Trioctyl phosphate	− 98
Dioctyl sebacate	− 98
Dioctyl tetrahydrophthalate	− 75.5

b) *Estimation of the Degree of Compatibility*

There is even an empirical relationship that can be used to estimate the degree of compatibility k:

$$k = \frac{T_r - T_m \text{ (measured)}}{T_r - T_m \text{ (estimated)}}.$$ 3.42

When k is less than 1.00, for example, 0.08, the compatibility is poor and the plasticization is usually minimal.

3.7.3   The Shape of the Dielectric Spectrum

The shape of the tan δ-vs-temperature curve, especially its half-width, may be modified by careful selection of a plasticizer. In cable insulation, the ideal situation is to have the dielectric spectrum as flat as possible. The key property for this consideration is the temperature coefficient of viscosity of plasticizers. From the chemical structural point of view, for plasticizers with molecular structures that are spherical or contain benzene ring, this coefficient is usually small, whereas for plasticizers with long aliphatic chains, this coefficient is usually large. Hence, based on the α-peak temperature and the temperature coefficient of viscosity, it is possible to adjust and control the shape of the dielectric spectrum with temperature.

3.7.4   The Three Choices for the α-Peak Temperature

For a PVC cable insulation, a definite operating temperature interval is usually given. Within this interval, one must fix an allowable upper limit of tan δ (for example, 0.1) to avoid any incidents caused by superheating of the insulation. To fulfill this requirement, there are three possible positions for the α-peak that can be used for selection and decision: (1) above the upper limit, (2) below the lower limit, and (3) within the specified interval.

Dioctyl phthalate is an example of the first possibility. In PVC the α-peak temperature is at a high level and its temperature coefficient of viscosity is relatively small. Hence, the spectrum is rather flat for temperatures in the vicinity of the peak. If the quantity of plasticizer can be reduced, the upper temperature limit may then extend still higher.

An example of the second possibility is a phenyl aliphatic sulfonate, $RSO_2OC_6H_5$, where R contains from 10 to 15 carbons. Its α-peak temperature is rather low, which will shift the α-peak of the PVC polymer below the operating temperature range. To avoid an early appearance of large tan δ values caused by conduction losses, the plasticizer must be carefully purified, especially regarding its ionic impurities. The lower limit of the temperature interval can be further lowered by simply increasing the plasticizer quantity (Fig. 3.22).[73]

Bipentaerythritol-(butyrate)$_6$ (pentanoate, hexanoate) is an example of the third case, known as ether-type pentaerythritol ester:

$$(RCOOCH_2)_3C-CH_2OCH_2-C(CH_2OOCR)_3,$$

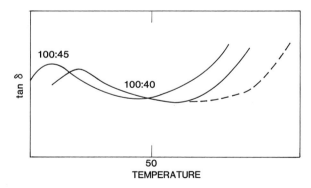

Fig. 3.22 The tan δ of PVC plasticized with phenyl aliphatic sulfonate.

where R is C_4H_9, C_5H_{11}, or C_6H_{13}. Its temperature coefficient of viscosity is very small because its molecular shape approximates a sphere. In spite of its unfavorable α-peak temperature, the resultant α peak temperature of the PVC polymer lies within the operating temperature interval, and the spectrum is rather flat. Its peak value is not high either. Its lower limit can be extend further down; however, its upper limit is determined by the conduction losses (Fig. 3.23).[73]

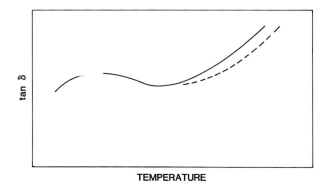

TEMPERATURE

Fig. 3.23 The tan δ of PVC plasticized with ether-type pentaerythritol ester.

3.7.5   The Use of Plasticizer Mixtures

The application of plasticizer mixtures in cable insulation is usually not recommended. Although the T_m of a PVC polymer with a plasticizer mixture can be estimated from

$$\frac{1}{T_m} = \frac{a}{a + b + c + \ldots}\left(\frac{1}{T_1}\right) + \frac{b}{a + b + c + \ldots}\left(\frac{1}{T_2}\right)$$

$$+ \frac{c}{a + b + c + \ldots}\left(\frac{1}{T_3}\right) + \ldots, \qquad\qquad 3.43$$

the temperature coefficient of viscosity may not be predictable, and the experience so far has been that the spectrum shape is not easily controllable. Thus, the practical wisdom has been that only one kind of a plasticizer is used in each formulation of PVC insulation for cables.

3.8   HOW TO KEEP THE TANGENT OF DIELECTRIC LOSS ANGLE LOW

Keeping the dielectric loss low has two aspects: (1) chemical and (2) physical. The chemical aspect involves the design and synthesis of molecules that lead to low tan δ values (short relaxation of polarization times), and the physical aspect involves such things as the effects of plasticization, molecular weight, and morphology.

Normally, one would expect that the important electrical properties of a polymer would be characteristic of that polymer's chemical structure and/or its other major components. In general, this is true for the dielectric constant and high-frequency dielectric loss phenomena.[130] However, for low-frequency dielectric loss (just like for dielectric strength), the dc and ac conductivities are highly sensitive to small amounts of moisture and other impurities. This also means that the dielectric properties are very sensitive to local inhomogeneities or structure defects, especially dipole introduction into the structure. For example, aggregation of polymer molecules of different sizes, depending upon the preparation and thermal history, leading to a specific so-called supermolecular structure can also introduce sufficient heterogeneity as far as the dielectric loss is concerned. In summary, to keep the tan δ low, elimination of impurities and structural heterogeneities is a must.

The two prime factors contributing to the loss factor ε'' are the dipole polarization and the ionic conduction. If the contribution from the ionic conduction is far greater than that from the relaxation loss (in nonpolar or weakly polar polymers in general or at high temperatures especially) the peak generated from the relaxation loss in the plot of tan δ vs frequency or temperature will be very broad.

The numerical value of tan δ is generally determined by both the polarity and the carrier mobility. The polarity determines the nature of the relaxation, and the relaxation time determines the numerical value of tan δ at a specific temperature and frequency for that relaxation. For the sake of keeping tan δ low, we must first evaluate the nature of the relaxation and relaxation time. What one attempts by the chemical control of tan δ is the control of the dielectric loss as a function of temperature and/or frequency.

3.8.1　Achievable Values of tan δ

There are many important practical uses for polymers with very low tan δ values. For example, the insulation of a 30-MHz ocean cable requires a dielectric loss of less than 60 μrad. (For insulations with small tan δ, the tangent loss is usually expressed in microradians of loss angle.) The insulation of microwave guides requires an even lower tangent loss.

Of course, for a low-loss polymer insulation, we must use non polar polymers in the first place. Polyethylene is preferable to polytetrafluoroethylene because the former is more workable. But even for well-purified general-grade polyethylene, tan δ is unacceptably high and special measures must be taken to reduce its tan δ value even further.

Matsuoka and Loan[131] found that to prepare polyethylene with very low dielectric loss angle, the value of tan δ at a constant frequency decreased with increasing density. This has been ascribed to the smaller number of short branches in the polymer.

Thus, here is a summary of the first four requirements for synthesizing a polyethylene with a *very low* tan δ:[132, 133]

(1) Use all means to prevent short-branch formation in the synthesis of polyethylene.
(2) Use all means to prevent short-branch formation in the subsequent processing of the polymer.
(3) Use all means to prevent unsaturation.
(4) Use all means to prevent oxidizing conditions in the synthesis and processing of the polymer. Carbonyl groups in polyethylene are main contributors to dielectric loss.

The effective dipole moment of a carbonyl group is very large: the value calculated is 2.8 D.[134] Fourier transform infrared spectroscopy has increased sensitivity in detecting low levels of infrared-absorbing groups in the polymers.[135, 136] Thus, progress in measuring low levels of carbonyl groups as well as other polar groups could lead to a situation in which the assignment of the total dielectric loss may be attributable to the various polar groups in a polyethylene material. The oxidation of polyethylene in air at elevated temperatures (100–140°C) produces a preponderance of carboxylic acid and ketone groups.[137] At lower temperatures less carboxylic acid and more ketone groups are generated.

3.8.2 Dipole Concentration and tan δ

The dielectric loss depends not only on dipole concentration but also on the polymer morphology. However, for ultrapure and carefully prepared polyethylenes, the morphologies are generally similar. Thus, it seems reasonable to attribute the dielectric loss at, for example, 30 MHz to the number of dipoles present.[138] If we consider that the carbonyl dipoles are moving according to the polymer dynamics, the intensity of the dielectric loss is then proportional to the square of the effective dipole moment.[139] Matsuoka et al.[138] found that the tan δ of purified polyethylene at 30 MHz was 97 μrad when the carbonyl concentration was 2.65×10^{-3} M and 51 μrad when the carbonyl concentration was 0.6×10^{-3} M. This means that to decrease the tan δ of polyethylene at 30 MHz to 1 μrad, the concentration of carbonyl groups cannot be higher than 0.045×10^{-3} M.

The values reported for ultrapure, low-loss-grade, mediumdensity polyethylenes is around 37 μrad at 30 MHz. Polyethylene with "zero" carbonyl content can be obtained by a technique called vacuum-melt extrusion and casting (VMEC). The lowest loss levels so far attained are less than 5 μrad at 12.5 GHz and 25–30 μrad at 28 GHz.

3.8.3 Physical Approaches to Low tan δ

Physical approaches to keeping the dielectric loss low include choosing either structural or molecular plasticizers with polarity lower than that of the polymer to be plasticized.

The tan δ of a polymer generally decreases as the molecular weight increases. In thermosetting polymers the tan δ decreases as the degree of cure increases. The decrease is largest at low molecular weights and at low degrees of cure. High molecular weight dispersity also helps decrease tan δ even as the molecular weight increases.

As the spherulite diameter of a given polymer decreases, the density increases and the tan δ values decrease. In general, an increase in density leads to a decrease in tan δ. Stretching of a semicrystalline polymer affects the unit cell of crystallization and often leads to a lower tan δ. Increasing crystallinity in a polymer almost always decreases tan δ.

3.9 POLYMERS WITH HIGH TAN δ IN DIELECTRIC HEATING APPLICATIONS

Practically all applications of polymers in electrical and electronics engineering require materials with a low tan δ. However, one application that takes advantage of a high value of tan δ is high-frequency dielectric heating. In this application, the efficiency of heating is usually compared by means of a comparison coefficient J, which is defined as

$$J = \frac{1}{\varepsilon \tan \delta},$$ 3.44

because the heat developed is proportional to both the frequency and the product of ε and tan δ. Some of the J-values for polymers are listed in Table 3.4. Data of this type may be used in practical situations. For example, if the time required for the high-frequency dielectric heating of a phenol formaldehyde resin in a certain duty cycle is 30s, then the time required for heating of polystyrene in the same duty cycle is 30 × (1330/1.9) = 421000s or 5.83h. Hence, polystyrene is a much poorer polymer for dielectric heating purposes.

Of course, the heat generated in the polymeric material comes from the tangent loss, but that loss may not come entirely from the relaxation loss. Rather, conductivity of the polymeric material may also contribute to the tan δ. This situation may be compared with ohmic heating of metals: the charge carriers are electrons, whereas those in dielectric polymeric materials may be ions.

TABLE 3.4 Comparison Coefficient of High-Frequency Dielectric Heating for Some Polymers[73]

Polymers	J
Polystyrene	1330
Polyethylene	1100
ABS resin	40
Polyethylene terephthalate	20–35
Poly(vinyl chloride)	20
Poly(methyl methacrylate)	4–15
Polyamides	1.5–15
Urea formaldehyde resin	3.8
Melamine resin	2.4
Phenol formaldehyde resin	1–1.9

3.10 POLYMERS WITH LOW TANGENT OF DIELECTRIC LOSS ANGLE BUT WITH HIGH DIELECTRIC CONSTANT

Although polymers with high dielectric constant are important engineering materials in their own right, such a polymer with a low dielectric loss is also important. For example, the inorganic ferroelectric material barium titanate is valuable because of high ε and low tan δ. Thus, certain inorganic compounds are materials with high spontaneous polarization but with very little relaxation loss. The effect of polarity and mobility must be well balanced in these novel materials. In polymeric materials this relationship has not been achieved as easily as in the inorganic materials. For example, in polar polymers the ε/temperatures and tan δ/temperature relationships are different (Fig. 3.24).

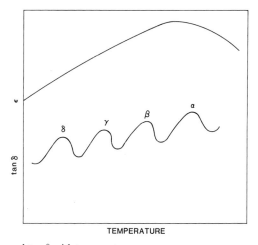

Fig. 3.24 Variation of ε and tan δ with temperature.

Thus, ε increases as the temperature increases, with only a maximum occurring because of the balance between the Kirkwood coefficient and the $1/T$ factor. For tan δ vs temperature, several maxima and minima occur. Thus, to develop the possibility of high ε and low tan δ, we must know how the relaxation time varies with the temperature, that is, we must treat the relaxation as a rate process.

3.10.1 Relaxation as a Rate Process

Kauzmann[12] has given an extensive analysis of dipole orientation as a rate phenomenon. He considered that molecular dipole orientation involves passage over a potential energy barrier with a certain probability of jumping from one orientation to another. By means of some simplifying assumptions, he obtained the polarization $P(t)$, the electric moment per cubic centimeter resulting from dipole orientation, as a function of time:

$$P(t) = P_0 e^{-k_0 t}, \qquad\qquad 3.45$$

where P_0 is the dipole polarizaton at the time $t = 0$ and k_0 is the rate constant for the activation of dipoles, that is, the jump rate or the average number of jumps made by a dipole in unit time. When t reaches a value such as

$$k_0 t = 1, \qquad\qquad 3.46$$

Eq. (3.45) becomes

$$P(t) = P_0/e. \qquad\qquad 3.47$$

This value of t is therefore the relaxation time τ, which may be found by

$$\tau = 1/k_0 \qquad\qquad 3.48$$

such that in this time the polarization will fall to $1/e$ of its initial value.

Since it is assumed that the process of molecular rotation requires an activation energy sufficient to overcome the energy barrier separating these two mean-equilibrium positions, the number of times per second such a rotation will occur is given by the Eyring rate expression:[140]

$$k_0 = \frac{1}{\tau} = \frac{kT}{h}\exp(-\Delta F/RT), \qquad\qquad 3.49$$

where k is the Boltzmann constant, h is Planck's constant, R is the gas constant, and ΔF is the free energy of dipole or ionic relaxation, defined by

$$\Delta F = \Delta H - T\Delta S, \qquad\qquad 3.50$$

where ΔH is the activation energy of dipole or ionic relaxation and ΔS is the entropy of activation. Then from Eq. (3.48),

$$k_0 = \frac{kT}{h}\exp(\Delta S/R)\exp(-\Delta H/RT), \qquad\qquad 3.51$$

or

$$\tau = \frac{h}{kT}\exp(-\Delta S/R)\exp(\Delta H/RT). \qquad\qquad 3.52$$

This is the relationship between relaxation time and temperature. Taking the logarithm of Eq. (3.52).

$$\ln\tau = \frac{h}{T}\cdot\frac{\Delta H}{R} + \ln\frac{h}{k} - \ln T - \frac{\Delta S}{R}, \qquad\qquad 3.53$$

and rearranging, we get

$$\ln \tau = \frac{\Delta H}{RT} - \ln T + \left(\ln \frac{h}{k} - \frac{\Delta S}{R} \right). \qquad 3.54$$

It can be seen from the nature of Eq. (3.54) that, because the last term on the right-hand side is independent of the absolute temperature T and because the contribution from the $\ln T$ term is small, a plot of $\ln \tau$ vs $1/T$ results in a linear relationship. The slope of the resulting straight line may thus be used to obtain the value of the activation energy ΔH in either kilocalories per mole or electron volts.

Activation Energy of Dielectric Relaxation.

In practice, a straight-line relationship is not always obtained because the actual dielectric loss process is not governed by a single-valued activation energy.
     Since from Eq. (3.34)

$$2\pi f_m = \frac{1}{\tau} \qquad 3.55$$

is a necessary condition for the tan δ peak, ΔH may be also estimated from the slope log f_m vs $1/T$. As T increases, f_m increases; the slope will be negative and the activation energy can be estimated from

$$\Delta H = F \text{ (slope)}. \qquad 3.56$$

TABLE 3.5 Activation Energies of Dielectric Relaxation of Some Polymers[73]

Polymers	Activation Energy ΔH kcal/mole			
	α	β	γ	δ
Polycarbonate	115	49	20	7
Polymethyl methacrylate	110	19	–	–
Polyethyl methacrylate	43	14	–	–
Polycyclohexyl methacrylate	53	–	–	–
Polymethyl ethacrylate	–	24	10	–
Polymethyl butacrylate	–	30	–	–
Polyethyl ethacrylate	45	7.2	–	–
Polymethyl chloracrylate	130	26	–	–
Poly(vinyl chloride)	120	15	–	–

The activation energies for some polymers estimated in this way are listed in Table 3.5. These values agree closely with those obtained from viscoelastic measurements.

3.10.2 Conclusion

To prepare polymers with low tangent loss but comparatively high dielectric constant, the estimation of relaxation time at different temperatures is important. Unfortunately, the relationships between the relaxation time and temperature are complex, and tracing them to a specific chemical structure is not always easy. Many more reproducible empirical data are needed before various predictive correlations will be of any value to the synthesis chemist.

3.11 SOLITON MODEL OF DIELECTRIC RELAXATION IN CRYSTALLINE POLYMERS

3.11.1 The Nature of the Soliton

A soliton is a nonlinear traveling wave that does not change shape or speed on collision with another soliton. Solitons have had many physical applications including order-disorder phase transitions, crystal dislocations, charge density waves, and Josephson junction transmission lines. This section presents evidence that the sine-Gordon soliton is the transition state for the α-relaxation in crystalline polyethylene. It is assumed that the soliton is generated in the amorphous chain-fold region, so an antisoliton need not enter the chain at the same time and place.[141] It moves up and down the chain by Brownian motion caused by collisions with neighboring polymer chains, twisting and untwisting the chain about its axis as it moves.

3.11.2 α-Relaxation

The first ideas about the origin of the α-relaxation involved point defect models. One was the so-called Reneker kink,[142] a 12-unit 180° twist with a contraction of half a lattice unit along the chain's c-axis direction. This involved a 12–13 kcal/mole creation energy and a 4 kcal/mole barrier to propagation. The other model was the Pechhold kink[143] (g^+tg^- configuration) with a 10 kcal/mole barrier to propagation.

These point-defect models have major problems, however, that make them unfeasible candidates for the source of the α-relaxation. First, they predict too low a dielectric intensity ($\varepsilon_0 - \varepsilon_\infty$) because of low equilibrium concentrations. They also predict the dielectric intensity to increase strongly with temperature, as the defect population does, when in fact no correlation between dielectric intensity and temperature is found. These models underestimate ω_{max}, the frequency at which $\varepsilon''(\omega)$ reaches a maximum, because the defects propagate very slowly because of barriers. Also, these models cannot explain the dependence on crystal thickness of the activation energy of shorter chain n-alkane homologues.

A different approach to explaining the α-relaxation was begun by Fröhlich in 1942,[144] who suggested a double quadratic well model with two equilibrium positions separated by a 180° rotation about the chain axis. That twisting, as opposed to rigid rotation about the chain axis, was established by the experimental work of Meakins.[145]

3.11.3 The RT-TT Model

In 1978, Mansfield and Boyd[146, 147] conducted the first serious quantitative study of this problem. They came up with the RT-TT (rotation twist-translation tension) model for the α-relaxation, which involves a 180° twist about the chain axis accompanied by a stretch of half a lattice unit along the chain axis. This corrects for the mismatch caused by the rotation and puts the chain back into crystal register (Fig. 3.25). They performed molecular mechanics calculations (in which the interactions between atoms are represented by mechanical analogues such as springs) on $C_{22}H_{46}$ as a model for polyethylene, arriving at a kink length of about 12 CH_2 units, about 15°/site twist, and an activation energy of 10.5 kcal/mole.

3.11.4 The RT-TT Model and the Soliton

In 1980 Mansfield[148] and Skinner and Wolynes[149, 150] independently recognized that the RT-TT model was essentially a soliton. This was proposed as early as 1949 by Frank and van der Merwe,[151] who were studying crystal dislocations at that time. Using impulsive stochastic dynamics and an Ising-type two-state approximation, they examined the dipole-dipole correlation function, which for nonpolar polymers is the same as the dielectric decay function, the Fourier transform of the frequency-dependent dielectric constant measured experimentally.

These systems are characterized by a coupling constant that is essentially the ratio of intramolecular to intermolecular interaction strengths. At sufficiently large values of the coupling constant, one can neglect the inherent lattice-spacing (discreteness) effects and treat the soliton as a freely diffusing particle (the continuum limit). It was found that this approximation was in excellent agreement with both the simulation results and dielectric experiments on polyethylene for a surprisingly large range of coupling constants. At lower values of the coupling constant, the lattice spacing results in coupling of excitation modes (phonons and solitons), leading to damping and eventual pinning of the soliton. In the pinned limit, it is expected that a discretized (hopping) diffusion model applies, but one finds that the pinned limit is outside the region of physical interest, where intramolecular forces dominate. Between these limits, it was observed that soliton velocities were "relativistic" and simulated Currie's model of the soliton moving in an "effectively" periodic potential. It is concluded that the continuum soliton two-state model fits very well the α-relaxation in polyethylene and is applicable to most nonpolar all-trans polymers.

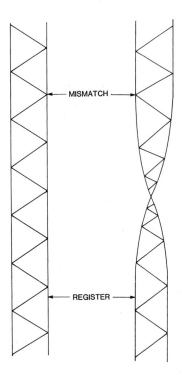

Fig. 3.25. The RT-TT model effect on crystal register. The c/2 stretch removes the mismatch induced by rotation about the chain axis. After Ref. 147.

3.11.5 The Soliton in Poly(vinylidene fluoride)

The only other real evidence to date for a probable soliton crystalline relaxation is in poly(vinylidene fluoride), where a very similar soliton mechanism is believed to be responsible for poling, a process in which randomly oriented crystallites are oriented in an electric field.[152, 153]

3.11.6 Summary

In summary, it has been demonstrated that the continuous limit of analytical studies is valid for discrete solitons well into relatively low coupling constants and that the α-relaxation of polyethylene is well approximated by Brownian motion of a sine-Gordon soliton going up and down the chain axis, rotating the polymer chain as it moves. Thus, for the first time, a computer simulation has allowed a definite mechanism to be assigned to a crystalline polymer relaxation rather than merely to a "distribution of relaxation times."[149]

3.12 REFERENCES

1. W. Siemens, Poggendorff Annalen der Physik und Chemie *125*, 137 (1864).
2. H. Pellat, Annales de Chimie et de Physique *18*, 150 (1899).
3. H. Pellat, Journal de Physique *9*, 313 (1900).
4. E. von Schweidler, Annalen der Physik *24*, 71 (1907).
5. K. W. Wagner, Annalen der Physik *40*, 817 (1913).
6. K. W. Wagner, in *Die Isolierstoffe der Elektrotechnik*, H. Schering, Ed., Julius Springer, Berlin (1924).
7. P. Debye, Physikalische Zeitschrift *13*, 97 (1912).
8. P. Debye, *Polar Molecules*, Chemical Catalog Co., New York (1929).
9. H. Fröhlich, *Theory of Dielectrics*, Oxford Univ., London (1949).
10. C. J. F. Böttcher, *Theory of Electric Polarization*, Vol. 1, Elsevier, Amsterdam (1973).
11. C. J. F. Böttcher, P. Bordewijk, *Theory of Electric Polarization*, Vol. 2, Elsevier, Amsterdam (1978).
12. W. Kauzmann, Revs. Mod. Phys. *14*, 12 (1942).
13. E. J. Murphy and S. O. Morgan, Bell System Techn. J. *16*, 493 (1937).
14. J. G. Kirkwood and R. M. Fuoss, J. Chem. Phys. *9*, 329 (1941).
15. E. J. Hennelly, W. N. Heston, Jr., and C. P. Smyth, J. Am. Chem. Soc. *70*, 4102 (1948).
16. G. Stokes, Trans. Cambridge Phil. Soc. *9*, 8 (1951).
17. C. P. Smyth, *Dielectric Behavior and Structure*, McGraw-Hill, New York (1955).
18. N. G. McCrum, B. E. Read, and G. Williams, *Anelastic and Dielectric Effects in Polymeric Solids*, John Wiley & Sons, New York (1967).
19. G. P. Mikhailov and T. I. Borisova, Vysokomol. Soed. *2*, 619 (1960).
20. G. P. Mikhailov, A. M. Lobanov, and V. A. Shvelev, Vysokomol. Soed. *3*, 794 (1961).
21. G. P. Mikhailov and A. M. Lobanov, Phys. of Solid State *5*, 1917 (1963) (in Russian).
22. G. P. Mikhailov and T. I. Borisova, A. S. Nygmankhodzhaev, Vysokomol. Soed. *8*, 969, (1966).
23. D. M. Mirkamilov and M. P. Platonov, Vysokomol. Soed. *11*, 1017 (1969).
24. V. P. Petrosyan, Vysokomol. Soed. *13*, 761 (1971).
25. J. Crossley and G. Williams, 1977 Annual Report Conference Electrical Insulation & Dielectric Phenomena, National Academy of Sciences, Washington, DC, 39 (1979).
26. A. Adam, Kolloid Zeitschrift und Zeitschrift für Polymere *180*, 11 (1962).
27. T. Tanaka and Y. Ishida, J. Phys. Soc. Japan *15*, 161 (1960).
28. N. I. Schichkin, J. Tech. Phys. *26*, 1461 (1956) (Russian).

29. W. Sommer, Kolloid Zeitschrift und Zeitschrift für Polymere *167*, 97 (1959).
30. S. Saito and T. Nakajima, J. Japan Soc. Test. Materials *9*, 283 (1960).
31. G. P. Mikhailov, S. P. Kabin, and T. A. Krylova, Soviet Physics–Technical Physics *27*, 1899 (1957) (English).
32. W. G. Oakes and D. W. Robinson, J. of Polymer Sci. *14*, 505 (1954).
33. P. J. Phillips, G. L. Wilkes, B. W. Delf, and R. S. Stein, J. Polym. Sci. A-2 *9*, 499 (1971).
34. R. A. J. Carson, Proc. Royal Soc. A *332*, 255 (1973).
35. E. Amrhein and H. Frischkorn, Kolloid Zeitschrift und Zeitschrift für Polymere *251*, 369 (1972).
36. R. G. C. Arridge and P. J. Borham, Polymer *19*, 603 (1978).
37. S. L. Aggarwal and O. J. Sweeting, Chemical Reviews *57*, 665 (1957).
38. F. M. Rugg, J. J. Smith, and R. C. Bacon, J. Polym. Sci. *13*, 535 (1954).
39. C.R. Ashcraft and R. H. Boyd, J. Polym. Sci., Polym. Phys. Ed. *14*, 2153 (1976).
40. P. J. Phillips, G. Kleinheins, and R. S. Stein, J. Poly. Sci. A-2 *10*, 1593 (1972).
41. J. Bares, Kolloid Zeitschrift und Zeitschrift für Polymere *239*, 552 (1970).
42. A. H. Scott, D. J. Scheiber, A. J. Curtis, J. I. Lauritzen, and J. D. Hoffman, J. Res. NBS *66A*, 269 (1962).
43. J. D. Hoffman, G. Williams, and E. Passaglia, J. Polym. Sci., Part C, No. 14, 173 (1966).
44. M. E. Baird and P. Blackburn, J. Mater. Sci. *7*, 836 (1972).
45. M. E. Baird and P. Blackburn, J. Mater. Sci. *9*, 1099 (1974).
46. Y. Ishida, K. Yamafuji, H. Ito, and M. Takayanagi, Kolloid Zeitschrift *184*, 97 (1962).
47. Y. Ishida, J. Poly. Sci. *A-2* (7), 1835 (1969).
48. P. J. Phillips, J. Poly. Sci., Polymer Physics Ed. *17*, 409 (1979).
49. G. P. Mikhailov, T. I. Borisova, and D. A. Dmitrochenko, Soviet Physics–Technical Physics *1*, 1857 (1956).
50. J. Heijboer, Die Makromoleculare Chemie *35A*, 86 (1960); Kolloid-Z. *171*, 7 (1970).
51. J. Schaefer, E. O. Stejskal, and R. Buchdahl, Macromolecules *10*, 384 (1977).
52. Y. Ishida, Kolloid Zeitschrift *168*, 29 (1960).
53. G. Williams, Trans. Faraday Soc. *60*, 1548 (1964).
54. G. Williams, Trans. Faraday Soc. *60*, 1556 (1964).
55. G. Williams, Trans. Faraday Soc. *62*, 2091 (1966).
56. G. Williams and D. C. Watts, Trans. Faraday Soc. *67*, 1971 (1971).
57. G. Williams and D. C. Watts, Trans. Faraday Soc. *67*, 2793 (1971).
58. G. Williams, D. C. Watts, and D. C. Nottin, Trans. Faraday Soc. *68*, 16 (1972).
59. F. Bueche, J. Appl. Phys. *24*, 423 (1953).
60. F. Bueche, J. Appl. Phys. *26*, 738 (1955).
61. F. Bueche, J. Chem. Phys. *21*, 1850 (1953).
62. I. N. Razinskaya, P. V. Kozlov, B. P. Shtarkman, and A. P. Ignateva, Vysokomol. Soed. *5*, 1850 (1963).
63. P. V. Kozlov, R. M. Asimova, and A. N. Perepelkin, Vysokomol. Soed. *4*, 134 (1962).
64. D. J. Mead and R. M. Fuoss, J. Am. Chem. Soc. *63*, 2832 (1941).
65. R. M. Fuoss and J. Y. Kirkwood, J. Am. Chem. Soc. *63*, 385 (1941).
66. D. J. Mead, R. L. Tichenor, and R. M. Fuoss, J. Am. Chem. Soc. *64*, 283 (1942).
67. R. M. Fuoss, J. Am. Chem. Soc. *63*, 369 (1941).
68. D. Broens and F. H. Müller, Kolloid Zeitschrift *140*, 121 (1955).
69. F. Wurstlin, Kolloid Zeitschrift *113*, 18 (1949).
70. F. Wurstlin, Kolloid Zeitschrift *134*, 135 (1953).
71. A. Dyson, J. Polymer Sci. *7*, 133 (1951).
72. S. N. Kolesov, Vysokomol. Soed. *8*, 650 (1966).
73. C. C. Ku and S. C. Wu, *Principles of Chemistry and Physics of Insulating Materials*, Xian Jiao Tong University, Xian (1974) (in Chinese).
74. G. P. Mikhailov, A. M. Lobanov, and D. M. Mirkamilov, Vysokomol. Soed. *8*, 1351 (1966).
75. R. M. Fuoss, J. Am. Chem. Soc. *63*, 378 (1941).
76. A. A. Tager, A. I. Suvorova, L. N. Goldyrev, V. I. Esafov, V. L. Berestova, and L. P. Topina, Vysokomol. Soed. *4*, 803, 809 (1962).
77. Y. V. Zelenev and G. M. Bartenev, Vysokomol. Soed. *6*, 915 (1964).
78. N. N. Morgunov, V. S. Skurikhina, V. P. Shuvaev, and B. I. Sazhin, Vysokomol. Soed. *15*, 1382 (1973).

79. S. N. Kolesov, N. P. Balaban, and I. A. Kildeev, Electricity, No. 4, 83 (1972) (in Russian).
80. Th. G. F. Schoon and O. Teichmann, Kolloid Zeitschrift *197*, 35 (1964).
81. V. A. Kargin, A. I. Kitaigorodskii, and G. L. Slonimskii, Kolloid J. *19*, 131 (1957) (in Russian).
82. B. Baker, R. P. Auty, and C. J. Ritenour, J. Chem. Phys. *21*, 159 (1953).
83. G. P. Mikhailov and B. I. Sazhin, Vysokomol. Soed. *1*, 29 (1959).
84. G. E. Golubkov, V. I. Elinek, and B. K. Artemev, Electrotechnics *37*, 33 (1966) (in Russian).
85. S. E. Bresler, E. N. Kazbekov, E. M. Saminskii, Vysokomol. Soed. *1*, 132 (1959).
86. S. N. Kolesov, Vysokomol. Soed. A *9*, 1960 (1967).
87. A. von Hippel and L. G. Wesson, Ind. Eng. Chem. *38*, 1121 (1946).
88. G. Schteser, *Electroinsulating Materials*, Moscow (1961) (in Russian).
89. H. Hogberg, S. E. Sovell, and J. D. Ferry, Acta Chem. Scand. *14*, 1424 (1960).
90. S. N. Kolesov, A. A. Buniyat-Zade, N. P. Balaban, V. A. Putintsev, and I. S. Kolesov, Electricity, No. 4, 89 (1975) (in Russian).
91. G. L. Slonimskii, A. A. Askadskii, and A. I. Kitaigorodskii, Vysokomol. Soed. *A12*, 494 (1970).
92. F. M. Smekhov, A. I. Nepomnyashchii, A. T. Sanzharovskii, and S. V. Yakubovich, Vysokomol. Soed. *A13*, 2102 (1971).
93. P. Girard, P. Abadie, and R. Charbonniere, J. Chem. Phys. *47*, 601 (1950).
94. B. E. Read, Polymer *3*, 529 (1962).
95. T. M. Connor, B. E. Read, and G. Williams, J. Appl. Chem. *14*, 74 (1964).
96. G. P. Mikhailov and M. P. Eidelnant, Vysokomol. Soed. *2*, 1552 (1960).
97. B. E. Read and D. Williams, Polymer *2*, 239 (1961).
98. T. G. Fox and P. J. Flory, J. Appl. Phys. *21*, 581 (1950).
99. K. Überreiter and G. Kanig, J. Colloid. Sci. *7*, 569 (1952).
100. H. Wilski, Kunststoffe *54*, 10 (1964).
101. J. R. Pourdon and M. Morton, J. Polym. Sci. *57*, 453 (1962).
102. G. P. Mikhailov and T. I. Borisova, Progress in Physics *83*, 63 (1964) (in Russian).
103. F. Wurstlin, Kolloid Zeitschrift *110*, 71 (1948).
104. F. Wurstlin, Kolloid Zeitschrift *120*, 84 (1951).
105. S. N. Kolesov, *Relaxation Phenomena in Solid State*, Voronegie, Moscow (1965) (in Russian).
106. G. S. Y. Yeh, J. Macromol. Sci. Phys. *B6*, 3 (1972).
107. G. S. Y. Yeh, J. Macromol. Sci. Phys. *B6*, 451 (1972).
108. G. S. Y. Yeh, J. Macromol. Sci. Phys. *B6*, 465 (1972).
109. T. E. Brady and G. S. Y. Yeh, J. Macromol. Sci. Phys. *B7* (2), 243 (1973).
110. G. S. Y. Yeh, CRC Critical Rev. Macromol. Sci. *1*, 173 (1972).
111. V. A. Kargin, G. L. Slonimskii and A. I. Kitaigorodskii, Kolloid Zeitschrift *19*, 13 (1957).
112. R. Hoseman, P. H. Lindenmeyer, and G. S. Y. Yeh, J. Macromol. Sci. Phys. *B15* (1), 19 (1978).
113. M. Gupta and G. S. Y. Yeh, J. Macromol. Sci. Phys. *B15* (1), 119 (1978).
114. M. Gupta and G. S. Y. Yeh, J. Macromol. Sci. Phys. *B16* (2), 225 (1979).
115. Y. A. Zubov, V. I. Selikova, and V. A. Kargin, Vysokomol. Soed. *A9*, 353 (1967).
116. V. A. Kargin, V. I. Selikova, and G. S. Markova, Vysokomol. Soed. *7*, 1495 (1965).
117. V. A. Kargin, Progress in Chemistry *25*, 1006 (1966) (in Russian).
118. B. I. Sazhin, M. P. Eiedelnant, M. A. Martynov, and T. N. Sarminskaya, Plast. Massy, No. 3, 47 (1969).
119. G. P. Mikhailov, J. Tech. Phys. *11*, 1395 (1951) (in Russian).
120. B. I. Sazhin, M. P. Eiedelnant, and O. N. Shulgin, Vysokomol. Soed. *B11*, 384 (1969).
121. A. M. Lobanov, B. I. Sazhin, V. P. Shuvaev, and M. P. Eiedelnant, Plast. Massy, No. 5, 58 (1970).
122. G. P. Mikhailov and M. P. Eiedelnant, Vysokomol. Soed. *2*, 287 (1960).
123. G. P. Mikhailov and M. P. Eiedelnant, Vysokomel. Soed. *2*, 1548 (1960).
124. Y. Ishida and K. Yamafuji, Kolloid Zeitschrift *203*, 26 (1965).
125. G. P. Mikhailov, A. M. Lobanov, and B. I. Sazhin, J. Tech. Phys. *24*, 1553 (1954) (in Russian).
126. B. I. Sazhin and T. P. Orlova, Plast. Massy, No. 10, 8 (1963).
127. W. Reddish and K. A. Buckingham, Proc. Inst. Elec. Eng. *114*, 1810 (1967).
128. G. M. Bartenev, Y.V. Zelenev, L. A. Osinsheva, Z. Y. Berestneva, B. G. Kalashnikova, and V. A. Kargin, Vysokomol. Soed. *B10*, 504 (1968).
129. S. A. Rice and J. Jortner in *Chemisty and Physics of the Organic Solid State*, D. Fox, M. Labes, and A. Weissberger, Eds., Vol 3, Interscience, New York (1967).

130. R. W. Sillars, *Electrical Insulating Materials and Their Applications*, Peter Peregrinus, Stevenage (1973).
131. S. Matsuoka and L. D. Loan, Plastics & Polymers *43*, 188 (1975).
132. H. Kishi, Y.Yamazaki, T. Nagasawa, H. Takashima, H. Fujita, and I. Tsuratami, Proceedings of 25th International Wire and Cable Symposium, 47 (1976).
133. W. L. Hawkins, W. Matreyek, and F. H. Winslow, J. Polym. Sci. *41*, 1 (1959).
134. W. Reddish and K. T. Barrie, IUPAC Symp. on Macromol., Wiesbaden, IA3 (1959).
135. P. Griffiths, *Chemical Infrared Fourier Transform Spectroscopy*, Wiley-Interscience, New York (1974).
136. D. J. Carlsson and D. M. Wiles, Macromolecules *2*, 589 (1959).
137. H. N. Cheng, F. C. Schilling, and F. A. Bovey, Macromolecules *9*, 363 (1976).
138. S. Matsuoka, J. H. Deane, D. L. Allara, J. Durana, and E. W. Anderson, 1977 Annual Report Conference Electrical Insulation & Dielectric Phenomena, National Academy of Sciences, Washington, DC, p. 264 (1979).
139. F. E. Karasz, *Dielectric Properties of Polymers*, Plenum, New York (1972).
140. H. Eyring, J. Chem. Phys. *4*, 283 (1936).
141. K. J. Wahlstrand, *Soliton Models of Dielectric Relaxation in Crystalline Polymers*, Ph. D. Dissertation, Harvard Univ., Cambridge, November, 1982.
142. H. Reneker, J. Polym. Sci. *59*, S39 (1962).
143. W. Pechhold, S. Blasenbrey, and S. Woener, Kolloid Zeitschrift *189*, 14 (1963).
144. H. Fröhlich, Proc. Phys. Soc. London *54*, 422 (1942).
145. R. J. Meakins, Trans. Farad. Soc. *55*, 1694 (1959).
146. R. H. Boyd, J. Polym. Sci., Poly. Phys. *13*, 2345 (1975).
147. M. C. Mansfield and R. H. Boyd, J. Polym. Sci., Polym. Phys. *16*, 1227 (1978).
148. M. C. Mansfield, Chem. Phys. Lett. *69*, 383 (1980).
149. J. L. Skinner and P. G. Wolynes, J. Chem. Phys. *73*, 4015 (1980).
150. J. L. Skinner and P. G. Wolynes, J. Chem. Phys. *73*, 4022 (1980).
151. F. C. Frank and J. H. van der Merwe, Proc. Roy. Soc. London *198A*, 205 (1949).
152. A. J. Hopfinger, A. J. Lewanski, T. J. Sluckin, and P.L. Taylor, in *Solitons and Condensed Matter Physics*, A. R. Bishop and T. Schneider, Eds., Springer-Verlag, New York, 1978.
153. H. Dvey-Aharon, T. J. Sluckin, P. L. Taylor, and A. J. Hopfinger, Phys. Rev. *B21*, 3700 (1980).

Chapter 4

DIELECTRIC BREAKDOWN OF POLYMERS

4.1   INTRODUCTION

Taking into account the wide range of materials encompassed by this topic, we have divided this chapter into two parts. Part I considers the prebreakdown phenomena in polymers, the treeing. We review the more significant proposed treeing mechanisms and their relationship to degradation and lifetime of plastics. Various additives for inhibiting treeing are also discussed.

Part II considers the practical aspects of breakdown of polymers in relation to their intrinsic breakdown strength. If steps are taken to prevent treeing, it is possible to measure a breakdown voltage known as the intrinsic strength of the material. This is usually one or more orders of magnitude higher than the typical dielectric breakdown of a polymer. At present, such pertinent treeing information on polymers in high electric fields is not readily available.[1] For example, careful laboratory studies of pure polyethylene in a uniform electric field showed the electric strength to be about 800 kV/mm or 20,000 V/mil.[2,3] However, any voids, rough surfaces, or contaminant particles will make this unachievable. Thus, studying the treeing phenomena in polymers is also a way of gaining knowledge about the long-term dielectric breakdown of polymers.

A complete theory of dielectric breakdown of polymers should involve material properties (constitutive equations), electrical constraints (Maxwell equations), and thermal behavior (heat conduction equations). None of this information is available.

Listed below for quick reference are more recent books, conference proceedings, and a symposium that amplify the subject matter of the chapter.

1. J. J. O'Dwyer, *Theory of Electrical Conduction and Breakdown in Solid Dielectrics*, Clarendon Press, Oxford (1973).
2. R. Bartnikas and R. M. Eichhorn, *Engineering Dielectrics, Vol. IIA, Electrical Properties of Solid Insulating Materials: Molecular Structure and Electrical Behavior*, ASTM Special Technical Publication No. 783, Philadelphia (1983).
3. I. Bunget and M. Popescu, *Physics of Solid Dielectrics*, Elsevier, Amsterdam (1984).
4. IEEE, Electrical Insulation Soc., *First International Conference on Conduction and Breakdown in Solid Dielectrics*, Universite Paul Sabatier, July 4–8, 1983.
5. Institute of Electrical and Electronics Engineers, Inc., *Fourth International Conference on Dielectric Materials, Measurements and Applications*, University of Lancaster, September 10–13, 1984.
6. Brown University, *Symposium Dielectric Phenomena*, IEEE, Electrical Insulation Society, New York (1985).

PART I. TREEING IN POLYMERS

4.2   HISTORICAL OVERVIEW

The earliest recognition of the fact that electrical discharges can damage and destroy dielectric materials goes back to the observations that lightning discharges can penetrate very thick sections of insulating material.[4] Electrical treeing as such was recognized and described as early as 1912,[5] and photographs of electrical tree growth in paper/oil cable insulation and in solid insulation were published in 1935 and 1936.[6,7] Summaries of the early work may be found in reports by Whitehead[4,8] and Mason.[9–11] Compilations of subsequent research results can be found in reports by Olyphant[12] and Parkman,[13] and a model for the complete mechanism of dielectric breakdown in solids is presented by Budenstein.[14,15] Since the 1970s, water trees have been gaining more attention in the review literature.[16–19] Methods for the detection, measurement, and interpretation of partial discharges have been reviewed by Kreuger[20] and Bartnikas and McMahon.[21] Records of partial discharge intensity as a function of time during initiation and growth of electrical trees have been also presented.[22,23]

Extensive studies on electrical treeing and methods of resisting it were carried out during the 1960s.[24–32] However, it was not until 1971 that cable users became generally interested. At that time Vahlstrom[33] showed the presence of electrical trees in some polyethylene-insulated power cables that had failed in service. Much more information is now available on the growth of trees in underground distribution-type power cables in commercial service.[33,34] Failure statistics on such cables insulated with extruded, high-molecular weight, thermoplastic polyethylene and chemically cross-linked polyethylene have been presented annually.[35-38] These data have been analyzed and compared with the experience of paper-insulated, lead-covered cables PILC.[39,40] The rate of increase in cumulative failures per 100 km for the first 10 yr of use of cross-linked polyethylene was shown to be less than one tenth that of PILC. Since treeing is generally accepted as the cause of long-term electrical failures in solid dielectrics, the failure statistics must then reflect the relative resistance of different materials and cable constructions to treeing.

4.3   BASIC OBSERVATIONS AND TERMS

The treeing in polymers is complicated by its diversity in nature, kind, and shape. Continuous dc as well as ac and pulsed dc excitation may lead to treeing. Direct current treeing breakdown is presumably associated with space-charge formation in polymers.[41] The role of space charge on breakdown thresholds has been explored for a variety of systems and under different conditions. Space charge is formed during the prebreakdown conduction phase, so the prebreakdown conduction mechanism influences the field distribution that will be present at the onset of breakdown conduction.[42] The electrostatic capacity of polymers increases when an electric field above a threshold field is applied because of the injection of electrons that oscillate near the cathode region.[43] Direct current treeing is extremely important in practical work because of the worldwide tendency to use ultrahigh-voltage dc transmission.

4.3.1   Two Kinds of Trees

In general, two kinds of trees exist in polymers: (1) electrical trees and (2) water trees. The former are generated by an electrical field alone, whereas the latter are generated by an electric field together with water or other chemicals. In addition, trees can form under a variety of initiation and growth circumstances. Thus, a large number of descriptive terms are used.[44-46] Electrical trees are called dendrites, branch-type or bush-type trees, spikes, strings, or bow ties; water trees are generally referred to as plumes, streamers, deltas, broccoli or bow ties (Fig. 4.1). Various staining techniques have been developed to render the trees permanently visible.[47,48]

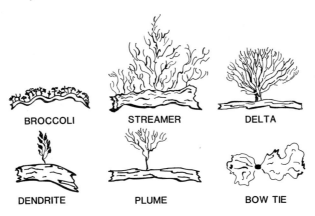

Fig. 4.1. Classification of trees.

Electrical trees that consist of hollow channels resulting from the decomposition of material are clearly visible in translucent or transparent solid dielectrics when examined with an optical microscope and transmitted light. On the other hand, fresh, unstained water trees appear diffuse and temporary. The channel-like nature of electrical trees has been demonstrated by cutting through trees in a dielectric section normal to the direction of growth and looking into the holes revealed with a scanning electron microscope (SEM).[17] The same technique is not fruitful when applied to water trees because they do not consist of permanent hollow channels that have resulted from similar decomposition of material. Rather, they seem to consist of very fine filamentary paths between small cavities through which moisture has penetrated under the action of a voltage gradient. It is not easy to resolve sufficient structural detail in water trees to permit careful study and to support conclusions about morphology. Optical microscopy with thin sections seems to offer the best hope, although even here good definition of the structure seems impossible. For example, one type is a string-of-beads structure, where the beads are water-filled cavities connected by microchannels through which moisture is transmitted.[49,50] However, if the tree growth occurs in the presence of reasonably pure water, when the electric stress and source of water are removed, the visibility of the trees decreases with time to zero. This phenomenon must indicate that the water drains out or diffuses away, after which the cavities and channels collapse.

The opposite effect has been observed in the case of mobile additives such as dodecanol,[51] chemical residues, or acetophenone,[52,53] which move to the region of maximum electric stress under the action of dielectrophoresis. These liquids are second phases, and as they fill the clear and obvious electrical tree channels, the channels become much less visible. The distinctions between electrical and water trees that have been emphasized so far are that water trees do not consist of permanent hollow channels as electrical trees do; water trees exhibit no branching, although overlapping growth sometimes makes this hard to recognize; and growing water trees consist of strings of water-filled cavities.

Electrochemical Trees

A small subclass of water trees is electrochemical trees. These trees are stained during growth because certain minerals or ions in the water that penetrate the dielectric under the action of electric stress. Practical examples are the sulfide bushes and trees in cables from Japan[54] and New Zealand.[55] X-ray diffraction and x-ray microanalytical studies showed both cuprous sulfide (Cu_2S) and cuprous oxide (Cu_2O) in the branches of the trees that grew in the Japanese cables, which were used for 6 yr in a chemical plant and immersed in water fairly rich in hydrogen sulfide. Trees of similar appearance were found in a cable retrieved after 7 yr of 12-kV underground service on the west coast of the United States in a region free from hydrogen sulfide. These very thick, opaque, and generally black trees have been called broccoli or bush-type trees. Neutron activation analysis of sections of a cable for copper ion concentration showed 0.45 ppm in regions with no trees, 35.0 ppm in regions with trees, and 1723.0 ppm in regions that included a conductor shield of carbon-impregnated tape.[56] Subsequent analysis by x-ray diffraction provided an unequivocal identification of Cu_2O in the trees. Hence, the copper ion can readily move through polyethylene under certain conditions.

The electrical and water trees described so far are called vented trees because their growth starts at the inner or outer surface of the insulation layer, that is, at the interface between the insulation and the semiconductive shield. Thus, the sources from which water is drawn into water trees and air into electrical trees are clear. Trees are also sometimes initiated by, and grow from, contaminant particles or cavities, which are sometimes waterfilled and remote from the surfaces of the insulation. The growth is usually symmetrical about the nucleus and extends in both directions parallel to the electric field.

Another example of electrochemical trees, based on the assumption that they are stained during growth, is the blue or green bow-tie tree. Such trees have been observed growing from opaque nuclei, and analysis of the nucleus by x-ray diffraction often proves it to be ferric oxide (Fe_2O_3). The nuclei are contaminants consisting of tiny iron particles agglomerated by the polymer, which has been gelled by localized overheating. A similar identification was made in the case of a vented, blue-colored tree nucleated by a particle of iron in the insulation shield.[55] Similar colored trees of brown, blue, and green have been observed starting from agglomerates of small grains containing iron, aluminum, and sulfur, respectively, both internally and at the semiconductor/shield insulation interface.[57]

4.3.2   Requirements for Tree Growth

An electric field and a stress concentration are required to initiate tree growth. The kind of tree that grows depends on the magnitude of the stress and the ambient conditions. In a dry environment, high stress is required and the trees are electrical. They grow by partial discharge, causing decomposition of material, and produce small hollow channels. In a wet environment, the voltage stress will determine whether electrical or water trees are produced. High stress can cause electrical trees in saturated dielectrics; lower stresses result in water trees but only after much longer times.[58] Access to free air or water is an important factor in tree growth. Such vented trees are capable of growing continuously for long enough times to bridge the electrodes and cause failure. A more likely result with water trees, however, is that they will grow long enough to reduce the effective insulation thickness to below that required to support the electric stress, after which failure will occur by electrical treeing. The electrical trees may grow slowly (although not as slowly as water trees) or rapidly as the result of an impulse such as could be produced by a surge or lightning strike.[34]

4.3.3   Nonvented Trees

Trees that start at an internal void or inclusion are called nonvented trees or bow ties. Because they do not have a free supply of air to support partial discharge or water to extend the microscopic filamentary paths, their growth seems to be limited. Bow-tie trees, which sometimes grow profusely, have not yet been observed to grow large enough to bridge the conductors in insulation of commercial thickness on wire or cable.

Observations have shown that nonvented electrical trees grow intermittently. Visible discharges alternate with longer periods of extinction. This phenomenon of extinction results from increased void pressure resulting from ionization.[29] Thus, when gas pressure in the tree has been reduced sufficiently by diffusion outward, ionization will occur again and the tree will grow a little longer or thicker. A relationship among electrical stress, growth rate, internal pressure in channels, and the appearance of trees has been documented.[59] A pressure variation was measured by Nawata and Kawamura,[22] and a similarity of appearance between electrical trees and branched lightning strokes has also been noted.[60] Analysis of the distances between branches and changes of direction of trees grown in poly(methyl methacrylate) showed that the mean length of branch segments is a significant parameter in treeing. This unit length is about 100 μm in poly (methyl methacrylate) and about 230 μm in polyvinylbutyral. A self-propagating streamer mechanism is proposed, which is limited in length by space charge accumulation at its tip.

SECTION A. ELECTRICAL TREEING

4.4   INITIATION OF ELECTRICAL TREES

The whole process of treeing can be divided into two distinct stages: (1) the inception stage and (2) the propagation stage. The relative duration of each stage is different for different cases, and the shape of the tree formed in each case is determined by the relative time difference.

Electrical treeing of ac excitation is due to the internal partial discharge within the polymer under a high electrical field. The internal discharge leads to chemical decomposition of the polymer. The energy sources of chemical decomposition come from the discharge energy of the gas (bombardment of accelerated charged particles, chemical reaction of activated particles, and thermal conduction) and the static energy of the field. A number of mechanisms have been proposed to explain the conversion of these energies into electrical treeing:[16]

(1) electron injection;
(2) emission and action of *hot* electrons;
(3) electromechanical compression from the field, which leads to mechanical damage;
(4) presence of microvoids or occluded air or impurities around any incidental asperity resulting from imperfect wetting;
(5) fatigue cracking from repeated polarity reversals; and
(6) local superheating and thermal decomposition.

The common requirement for all these mechanisms is a very high field. However, it is very hard to ascertain which mechanism will dominate in the inception of treeing because each mechanism has its own theoretical basis and practical evidence. A good case can be made for the electron injection mechanism.

4.4.1   Electron Injection Mechanism

In many cases the initiation of electrical trees seems to be the result of interfacial injection and extraction of electrons from a sharp, conductive point or edge that projects into a good insulator. High-field measurements in liquids show that injection occurs, and careful tests with needles in solids show that no initial void at the point is required to start tree growth.[61, 62] Electron injection into hexane was carried out at and above 1770 kV/mm, and striking photographs show breakdown paths in liquid dielectrics that look exactly like some electrical trees in solids.[63-66] It appears that as the pressure exerted on dielectric liquids increases, the failures look increasingly like those in solids.

Electron injection into solids has been observed[17, 29, 67-69] at electric stresses between 4 kV/mm (100 V/mil) and 300 kV/mm (7600 V/mil) for polyethylene and at 20 kV/mm (500 V/mil) for polyethylene terephthalate. This tremendous variation is observed because some workers report the gradient required to initiate visible tree growth in a short time and others measure the presence of charge electrically. The effect can be explained by field emission or Schottky emission depending on the intensity of the electric field.[67, 70]

a) *Work Function Effect*

Tanaka and Greenwood have also reported preliminary data suggesting that there is an effect of the work function when metal needles are used experimentally.[67] A silver-coated needle (silver work function = 4.3 eV) injects a given amount of electronic charge at lower voltage than does a steel needle (iron work function = 4.8 eV) in the same elapsed time. A similar finding in organic liquids has been reported,[71] and many conflicting results have been summarized.[72] Although such experiments are very difficult because of the rapid oxidation of pure metal surfaces, observations substantiate the assumption of charge emission. Equations of the form[68]

$$\log t_i = A \exp - [\{B(E_m - E_0)\} - 1] \qquad\qquad 4.1$$

where A and B are constants equal to 2.9 and 0.75, respectively, and E_0 = 470 kV/mm, a value below which the authors find that trees will not grow, have been presented to relate the applied electrical stress E_m and the time required for tree initiation, t_i.[67]

b) *Energetic Electrons*

After emission into a solid dielectric to a maximum distance of about 20 μm parallel to the field, some electrons may be trapped, some may drift out of range, and the rest will be attracted back to the electrode on the next half-cycle.[68,73] During their return, the electrons will be falling through a very high field and will accumulate energy. Any electron that can travel without collision for 1000 Å (0.1 μm) in a field of 100 kV/mm will accumulate 10 eV of energy, which is sufficient to ionize most hydrocarbons, including organic dielectrics.[74,75] It seems statistically reasonable that some ionization must occur by this mechanism because a voltage gradient of 100 kV/mm is possible at a stress concentration, an injection current of only 10^{-12} Å or a discharge of 0.02 pC per cycle at power frequency represents over 6×10^6 electrons per second, and the interspherulitic boundary structure of polyethylene as shown in electron photomicrographs is quite open.[76,77]

Experiments with energetic electron beams incident on hydrocarbons such as olefinic polymers and copolymers and rubbers show that dissociation and decomposition can occur, from which fragments appear as gases-hydrogen plus low-molecular-weight hydrocarbons.[74] This agrees with the results of gas analysis in treeing studies.[78] Hence, after the absorption of sufficient energy and the decomposition of material, the dielectric will contain a cavity within which partial discharge can occur, and the breakdown will propagate as a channel, which becomes a tree. If the initial void is vented so that a supply of oxygen is available, the tree growth can proceed by both electrical and chemical (oxidative) attack.

c) *Hot-Electron Theory*

A somewhat similar mechanism for the initiation of electrical treeing called the hot-electron theory, has been proposed and argued by several workers.[79-82] There are always some free electrons that move through a solid between traps. If these electrons, or some of them, move in a high electric field, they will accumulate energy and become "hot." Since electrons lose no appreciable energy in elastic collisions with much more massive atoms, they can gain the several electron volts of energy required to break organic molecular bonds in mean free paths of about 100 Å and fields of about 100 kV/mm.[82] This leads to molecular degradation and void formation.

4.4.2   Mechanical, Thermal, and Discharge Mechanisms

a) *Mechanical Stress*

A mechanical consideration of the situation in which a very high, divergent electric stress is exerted over a very small area suggests that, in time, the periodic Maxwell stress would produce fatigue failure. Since the force compresses the insulation along an extension of the axis of the conductive point that causes it, an induced force in the polymer tends to produce cracks or crazes parallel to the direction of the field.[69] The time delay is required between the application of voltage stress and the appearance of a crack or tree before sufficient damage accumulates to be visible. Although it is difficult to criticize this mechanism theoretically, two questions occur. First, how do the successful voltage stabilizers and tree-retardant chemical functionalities, which will be described later, operate to resist treeing in this mechanical system? Second, is it possible to electrically generate sufficiently high mechanical stresses to cause real fatigue in polyethylene? Calculation with the expression for mechanical stress,

$$S = 1/2 \; \varepsilon_0 \varepsilon_r E^2, \qquad\qquad 4.2$$

gives values that are fractions of the modulus of polyethylene when reasonable values for electric stress E are used.

b) *Thermal Decomposition*

Another mechanism that has been proposed to explain the initiation of electrical trees and dielectric failure in general is Joule or localized overheating combined with thermal decomposition.[9, 83] Mason points out that in electrical treeing, partial discharges liberate some heat, and conversion of even a small amount of the discharge energy into heat at the dielectric surface would raise the temperature of the volume eroded several hundred degrees Celsius. This mechanism requires the preexistence of a cavity within which partial discharge can occur. Of course, in the case of very lossy dielectrics, heat will be developed, and the temperature will rise in proportion to the loss index, $\varepsilon_0 \varepsilon_r$ tan δ, and the voltage squared, V^2, given by[84]

$$\Delta T = \pi V^2 f \varepsilon_0 \varepsilon_r \varrho \tan \delta, \qquad\qquad 4.3$$

where V is the root-mean-square voltage in volts, f is frequency in hertz, ε_0 is the permittivity of free space, ε_r is the relative permittivity of the dielectric material, ϱ is the thermal resistivity in degrees Celsius-meters per watt, and tan δ is the dissipation factor of the dielectric. The term ΔT will be in degrees Celsius and, at the site of a stress rise, would be increased by the stress enhancement factor.

c) *Impulse Trees*

Impulse trees have been observed and studied in terms of the effect of pulse shape and duration, material temperature, and dc prestressing.[85–88] The authors agree that positive pulses generate longer trees than do negative pulses and that the tree length increases with the temperature.

d) *dc Trees*

Until about 1974, no observations of trees in dc fields of constant polarity had been reported. It was considered unlikely that they could grow, even at stress concentrations, because polarity reversals were required. When polarity reversal did occur, or when surges or impulses were superimposed, treeing had been observed. Opposite polarity impulses were the most damaging. Electrical tree formation in PE can occur in high dc fields and is apparently associated with space-charge formation.[41] The effect is both polarity and rate dependent. It was observed that at a voltage increase rate of 1 kV/s, the inception stress was 27 MV/cm, or about 3.5 times the intrinsic electric strength of PE.

Using dc voltages, researchers at Bell Telephone Laboratories made measurements on telephone cables immersed in ocean water.[89] At stresses of 22 and 44 kV/mm, both vented and bow-tie trees were observed to grow continuously with time during a 200-h test. The bow ties are typical water trees, although polarity dependent, but some of the vented trees looked more electrical. The dc trees grow at a substantially lower rate than ac trees under the same conditions.

4.5   GROWTH OF ELECTRICAL TREES

4.5.1   Electrically Weakest Point

The only aspects of treeing that all workers agree on are that after the initiation of an ac electrical tree, which means that a cavity large enough to undergo partial discharge has been formed at the point of maximum stress, growth will continue because of the effects of discharges, and stress will propagate through the weakest part of the structure. In polyethylene the propagation is through the interspherulitic boundaries where the density of molecules is much reduced. This has been shown beautifully by the use of thin specimens and optical microscopy.[90-93] In one case it was shown that in a point-to-plane test geometry, tree growth started not at the point of maximum stress, which lay within a spherulite, but where the needle shaft passed between spherulites. The electrically weakest point in semicrystalline polymers such as polyethylene and polypropylene is at the junction of three or more spherulites. These results were verified by experiments on bulk samples relating the voltage required to initiate a tree to the size of spherulites in five samples of polyethylene and ethylene copolymers.[17, 94]

4.5.2   Ionization Results

When the gas in a cavity, which is initially air, is ionized to form a plasma, the ions transfer their energy to the surrounding walls in more than one way. Under appropriate conditions, an electron avalanche may form, which enhances the effect. As energetic electrons pass close to molecules of the dielectric, their coulombic fields polarize some molecular electrons in their orbitals. If the energy exchanged is greater than the energy binding an electron, the electron can be expelled, leaving a positive ion behind.[60]

The positive ion formed may carry an excess of energy and may be unstable, thus leading to a dissociation reaction and formation of a free radical fragment or stable molecule. It has been pointed out that dissociative ionizations occur with high probability in electric discharges.[74] The ionization results in the increase in molecular unsaturation, the formation of carbonyls and hydroperoxides, and the liberation of gases.[78, 95-97] The gases are hydrogen, carbon dioxide, water, methane, ethane, butane, and other hydrocarbons, mostly unsaturated. The effects of oxygen and moisture add carbon dioxide, nitrogen dioxide, nitrous oxide (N_2O), and nitric acid in small amounts. In earlier work, oxalic acid was identified on the surface of polyethylene after exposure to a corona discharge in damp air.[98] The appearance of these molecular fragments and reaction products as gas indicates that decomposition is under way and the development of cavities should be expected.

4.5.3   Discharge Extinction

There is some disagreement about the mechanism of discharge extinction and about whether the channel walls are conducting or not. Several workers have reported that the walls are nonconducting.[16, 78, 99] Most, however, feel that the channel walls become carbonized after absorbing charge for a finite time and therefore become conductive.[100, 101] One group has been working with electron spin resonance (ESR) to characterize the char that forms on the walls.[102] In either case, the electric stress and tree growth are probably not extended by the conductive path of channel walls to the sharp tip. Some workers argue, however, that discharges may shortcircuit the channels or may be extinguished and new paths initiated when the carbonized walls form an isopotential shield.[109] Periodic discharge extinction is more likely as a result of an increase in internal pressure or even the loss of electrons in the avalanche to the channel walls at the very fine tip of a growing tree.[103]

4.5.4 Tree Growth

The tree structure is extended by the movement of charge in discharge pulses through active tree branches to their microscopic points where the reactions continue. Work has been done with needle electrodes, some withdrawn partially to permit a cavity where the needle point had penetrated, and it follows that the cavity is conducting because of the presence of discharges.[104] The tree initiation time was shorter and the growth rate higher in the case where the needle had been withdrawn, probably because the cavity was vented to provide a continuous supply of air and prevent the possibility of a pressure increase.

It has been calculated that each discharge of 10 pC erodes about 10^{-15} cm^3 of polyethylene[105] and that 800 J/cm^3 vaporizes acrylic resins.[78] Another estimate suggests that a discharge of 1.5 pC can cause erosion of polyethylene by decomposition and carbonization of the channel walls.[101] That heat is liberated by discharges has been indicated by photomicrographs,[90] which clearly show a variation between spherulite sizes adjacent to (small) and remote from (larger) an electrical tree channel. The heat should be proportional to the magnitude of discharge and the size of the cavity or channel and should cause the growth rate to increase as the channel grows because of the temperature dependence of chemical reaction rates. The fact that discharges are discontinuous and runaway failure does not occur, even though dielectric strength decreases with temperature, suggests that thermal breakdown is not a major factor in tree growth.

Tree Shapes and Experimental Conditions

Tree shape and extension depend on the internal gas pressure inside the tree channel caused by the initial gas discharge. This pressure controls the subsequent gas discharge, which, in turn, influences the tree extension.

Tree extension is also strongly affected by the tree shape, which is of three basic kinds: 1) treelike, 2) bushlike, and 3) fanlike, all depending on the form and magnitude of the applied voltage, the kind of polymer, and the temperature. For example, in polyethylene at 30°C, the tree shapes at 10 and 12 kV are treelike, whereas at 14 and 16 kV they change with time to bushlike. Increased gas pressure in a tree channel sometimes combines with discharges in this channel to form a new tree channel in another direction. This is the origin of bushlike trees.

In brittle polymers with a rather high glass transition temperature, such as poly(methyl methacrylate), a fan-like pattern is generated. The different tree shapes found in poly(methyl methacrylate) as a function of voltage and temperature are summarized in Fig. 4.2.

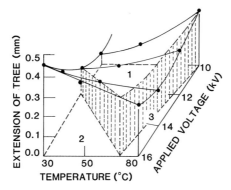

Fig. 4.2. Classification of tree shapes in PMMA as a function of voltage and temperature: (1) treelike, (2) fanlike, and (3) bushlike regions.

4.5.5 Conclusion

From the experimental observations reported, the following conclusions can be made about tree growth:[69]

(1) Tree extension is induced by internal gas discharge in the existing tree channel.

(2) The gas discharge is pulsative and lasts less than 0.1 μs.

(3) The velocity of extension of a tree channel during a pulse discharge is about 10^5 cm/s.

(4) The electric potential of a needle electrode is transferred to the tip of an existing tree channel through the conductive plasma of a gas discharge.

(5) The dielectric strength of the polymer films is nearly the same when two metal electrodes are used as when a plasma column of gas discharge is the electrode.

(6) The diameter of a tree channel is about 1 μm and is expanded gradually by repeated gas discharges.

From these results, we can conclude that the extension of tree channels is caused by a partial dielectric breakdown of a polymer resulting from the strongly divergent electric field induced by the conductive plasma in a gas discharge. The partial dielectric breakdown might be due to electron avalanche, mechanical breakdown, thermal decomposition, or impulse discharge depending on the physical and chemical nature of the polymer.

4.6 TESTING

Several testing procedures are available, and the one selected as the best should depend on how closely it models the mechanism that really produces trees or causes failure in practical insulation systems. Unfortunately, there is no agreement upon this point. The only common ground is that, except for the determination of the intrinsic breakdown strength of a given dielectric material, which is never realized in practice, the results are statistical and require testing of replicate specimens and use of statistical analysis.[1,2] The most popular modern treatment of these data is that developed by Weibull[105] and used with variations.[1,106] Recently this technique has been made more useful by the explanation of confidence limits[107] and the development of a computer program that has been made generally available by the authors.[108]

To test and compare the resistance of materials *per se* against electrical treeing, the concept of a standard defect is used in the needle test.[24–26, 29, 109] This test has been used both in its original form[31, 78, 110–112] and in modified form with a needle-shaped void,[104, 113] with a conductive conical cavity,[114, 115] and with mechanically stressed specimens.[116] The sharp needlelike electrodes have been made of, or plated with, different metals for comparison and investigation of the effect of the work function.[67] The test has been used to determine the voltage required to initiate a tree within a specified time, the time required at a specified voltage, and the time required to produce complete breakdown by tree growth through the test section. The basic test method has been written to separate and characterize the inception voltage and the voltage life of insulating materials under divergent field conditions. It is published in this form as the ASTM Standard Test Method for Evaluation of Resistance to Electrical Breakdown by Treeing in Solid-Dielectric Materials Using Diverging Fields (D 3756–79). Single-needle-plane and double-needle variations have been demonstrated to be reliable and reproducible. Alternatives to the needle test in its variations are the enclosed-cavity methods.[9, 117–121] Specimens also have been stressed in the field between crossed needles,[122] between molded-in steel balls,[1] in the form of insulated wire with square cross section[123] and sometimes real miniature cables, and in the form of extruded tubes filled with water and sometimes scratched on the inner surface to provide a stress concentration. The last two methods are more successful in the study of water treeing.

High frequency has been used in place of, or in addition to, overvoltage to obtain significant acceleration, although this is much more common in water-tree test methods.[23, 78, 121, 124–127] For electrical treeing, the cumulative damage per cycle appears to be linear up to several hundred hertz, and results are usually reduced to equivalent life at 50 or 60 Hz.

Study of Propagation Phase

The propagation of electrical treeing in polymers can be studied by the simultaneous measurement of light intensity and partial discharge. The emission of light has been studied using an image intensifier.[128] The detection of discharges shows that each category of tree is characterized by a particular discharge rate. Tree branch propagation is enhanced by the presence of electrical discharges in the microchannels, which are intermittent because of the release and the accumulation of gas pressure in the microchannels. These discharges can be detected either by observing the luminous phenomena that accompany them or by recording the associated current pulses. The discharge characteristics for different types of trees can be studied together with the evolution in time of luminous phenomena, and the discharge level and luminous activity both contribute to the aging of the polymeric insulation.[129] A knowledge of the propagation phase not only can give some ideas about how to suppress the growth of treeing, but also can aid the understanding of both the relationship between the initiation phase and the role of charge injection and the effect of space charge on the formation of microchannels. For a cavity, the delocalization of discharge is first observed by recording the corresponding pulse against time and then confirmed by optical observations. On the other hand, the study of the partial discharge characteristics of electrical trees has shown the existence of several distinct phases, which give a good idea of the nature and the localization of trees. Although there is still difficulty in correlating the maximum discharge magnitude and the life of the insulation, this magnitude variation is characteristic of the change in the types of tree.[23] The electrical properties of the material constituting the wall of a microchannel will vary with the following phenomena associated with the partial discharge activity:

(1) wall oxidation,[130]
(2) chemical degradation resulting from particle bombardment,[131]
(3) semiconducting deposit formation,[132]

(4) HNO$_3$ deposition in the presence of a nitrogen atmosphere,[133]

(5) temperature rise,[134]

(6) O$^+$ ion action,[135] and

(7) space-charge formation.[136]

The decrease in resistivity of the channel wall resulting from gas discharge is restricted to a localized zone of the insulation and does not encompass the entire sample.

Through the technique of polarized illumination, it is possible to take color microphotographs to study the growth of electrical trees.[91] In semicrystalline polymers, growing electrical trees usually pass through the interspherulite space; hence, by a rational heat treatment of the polymeric insulation, one may be able to modify its morphology and possibly modify or suppress the propagation of electrical trees.

4.7   INHIBITION OF ELECTRICAL TREEING

There are many approaches to the problems of reducing or even eliminating electrical treeing in insulation systems. The original treeing problems, which were very serious in paper/oil cables, were overcome by careful drying and degassing of both paper and oil and the development of self-contained and pressurized oil-filled constructions.

4.7.1   Effect of Cable Construction

A number of methods for tree reduction have been developed since the advent of extruded solid insulation for cables and molded rubber connectors and terminations. Probably the greatest improvement in tree resistance of cables resulted from the replacement of impregnated conductive tapes by extruded layers of semiconductive polymers.[137,138] The change limited the number of loose fiber ends that often protruded into the insulation layer and acted as needle points and stress risers that make treeing easy. A subsequent improvement was a method to extrude more than one layer per pass through the extrusion line. This method eliminates the condensation of moisture and settling of dirt on the individual layers, which can occur if the cable must be wound onto reels and unwound again between each pass.

At present, three layers can be applied almost simultaneously in one triple-crosshead extrusion die or by two crosshead dies, one a double, in tandem. The advantage achieved is an improvement in the smoothness and uniformity of bonding at interfaces by maintaining absolutely clean surfaces between the application of successive layers. It is now reported that a cable manufactured with very smooth interfaces between semiconductor shields and insulation and free of large contaminants and voids is not subject to electrical treeing under normal operating condition.[139] This is very likely true if tight interfacial bonds and full walls are used as most cable makers agree.[140] An improved cable construction designed to resist the injection of electrons by use of coaxial emission shields has been patented,[141] and a sulfide capture sheath to inhibit the growth of sulfide trees has been described.[54]

The introduction of cross-linked polyethylene as a replacement for thermoplastic polyethylene offered higher temperature service and improved chemical resistance. Cross-linked polyethylene also gives longer voltage life and high dielectric strength except in short-time tests. Although the electrical improvements were at first attributed to cross linking, it was later recognized that the property actually improved was the resistance to treeing. This improvement resulted from the presence of acetophenone, one of three chemical residues from the peroxide-initiated cross-linking reaction.[142] The treeing resistance was only temporary and decreased to the level of conventional polyethylene as the acetophenone escaped from the cross-linked polymer as a result of its high vapor pressure. The finding has been verified by others who have used acetophenone as a tree-retardant additive.

4.7.2   Process Changes to Resist Treeing

The approach to the problems of treeing from voids is to eliminate the voids. This has been essentially accomplished in the case of microvoids that result from chemical cross-linking. Several processes to accomplish this have been developed, and a few typical samples will be outlined here.

a) *Steam Heating*

The use of steam has been minimized.[143] The process involves a conventional steam continuous-vulcanizing (CV) line to which a 400-kHz hollow cylindrical ultrasonic transducer has been added at the entrance end of the cooling water bath. The ultrasonic generator is reported to produce several kilowatts of power and to be capable of heating the inner layers of insulation so that the heat required for complete cross-linking is provided both externally by steam and internally by vibration and molecular friction. The increase in line speed of 50% or more reduces the residence time in the steam leg and therefore the extent of moisture penetration, which is the source of microvoids. A somewhat similar process, which adds conductor preheating and induction heating to a steam CV line, has been reported.[144, 145] The process minimizes the time in the CV tube by providing heat internally from the hot conductor as well as externally from steam.

b) *Radiation Curing*

A method that eliminates steam but still uses water for cooling is called the radiation-curing process (RCP).[146] Here the cable passes through an infrared heat source, a hot tube, in a pressurized inert gas atmosphere. It is then precooled in gas before it enters a water-cooling zone. Such an arrangement postpones the opportunity for moisture penetration until the outside layers of insulation have cooled somewhat and the permeability of the insulation has, therefore, decreased. A similar method that uses heated gas, usually nitrogen but occasionally SF_6, has been also described.[147]

c) *Oil Bath Heating*

The complete elimination of both steam and water in the CV process has been accomplished by use of oil for both heating and cooling of the cables.[148, 149]

d) *Long Extrusion Die*

An interesting approach to the elimination of both oil and gas, since either can penetrate molten polymers under pressure, is the Mitsubishi and Dainichi continuous vulcanization (MDCN) process[150] in which a very long extrusion die is used. Dies up to 15.24 m (50 ft) long have been reported, and very high pressures are developed. The object is to achieve extrusion, heating, and cross-linking in separate steps but all within the same die. All of these various dry processes have been developed primarily to produce cross-linked insulation free of voids and the danger of partial discharge within them. They have been introduced with evidence of reduced void content and therefore claim substantially improved properties. These claims await the test of time; so far the most obvious advantage has been an increase in the manufacturing line speed.

e) *Electron Beam Curing*

In the United States, electron beam machines are used for radiation cross-linking of wire insulations. In this process voids can be generated, but they can also be avoided by controlling the dose rate. However, the range-energy relationship of electrons in matter imposes a limitation on the thickness of insulations that can be treated in this way. The highest energy electron beam machines, which offer high power levels to make reasonable line speed possible and are easily available at present, are about 2.5 MeV. This energy gives electron penetration through hydrocarbons about 9 mm (350 mils) thick. The range-energy relationship sets a real limitation on any given machine because, if electrons are not energetic enough to traverse the insulation section completely and individually, they will form a space charge until they subsequently escape collectively to ground. This occurs by the formation of treelike figures in which channels are often carbonized. Recent estimates show that processing costs are no longer prohibitive, and several commercial polymers are recommended for this purpose. In 1978, 6.6-kV cables in Japan[151] and 15-kV cables in the United States[152] were radiation cross-linked.

4.7.3   Power Cable Construction

With all the process changes that have been introduced to minimize void formation, problems may still arise from the presence of minute voids and imperfections generated by differential thermal expansion effects. These voids may form at the interfaces between the insulation and both the inner metal (usually copper and aluminum) core and any outer metal sheath (Fig. 4.3). An incidental void next to the inner core would cause a gas discharge in the high-field region next to the core, and the cable would have a lower discharge inception voltage. It is very difficult to prevent voids altogether, but the associated electrical breakdown problems may be solved by interposing a layer of conductive shielding between the metal and the insulation. The conductive layer, usually a carbon black composite of a copolymer of ethylene and vinyl acetate, bonds firmly to the insulation. The carbon black is added at sufficiently high levels that the copolymer turns out to be a highly loaded composite. The vinyl acetate is important for modifying the mechanical and adhesive properties of the conductive copolymer. Because of the conductivity of the copolymer, the conductive layer takes up substantially the same voltage as the adjacent metal, and so no electrical stress is imposed on the voids, which are therefore rendered innocuous. The cable industry takes advantage of this design in all medium- or high-voltage cables using polyethylene and ethylene-propylene rubber as the insulating materials. Today, a polyethylene-insulated high-voltage power cable rated at 275 kV and containing no additives is commercially available.[153]

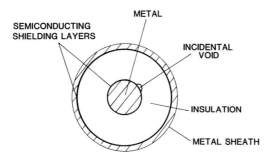

Fig. 4.3. Cross section of a power cable.

For medium or lower voltage cables, the use of less expensive technology along with the use of additives may still be the most widely practiced approach. Hence, the study of the nature of additives and their mechanisms for inhibiting electrical treeing is not only of theoretical importance but also of practical importance.

4.7.4   Tree-Retardant Additives

After improvements in construction and process parameters had been made, research on tree inhibition by means of additives followed several different routes. There are additives used to

- capture energetic electrons chemically (voltage stabilizers),
- slow down discharge path growth electrically,
- make the surface of internal cavities conductive,
- increase the bulk conductance to grade the field, and
- interfere physically with tree propagation (finely divided solids).

The simplest solution so far appears to be the control of partial discharging within cavities. Cavities discharge because they are usually filled mainly with air. Since air has a relative permittivity of unity, the voltage stress within the cavities is higher than that in the surrounding medium. In addition, air has a lower breakdown strength than the surrounding medium. Two widely used solutions are to (1) fill the cavity with another material that has a higher dielectric constant and breakdown strength or (2) use a slightly incompatible additive that can confer some conductivity on the walls of the cavities.

a) Filling of Cavities

When cavities are filled with oil under pressure,[154, 155] an electronegative gas such as sulfur hexafluoride (SF_6),[156, 157] some other gases,[158-160] or even water,[49, 80, 161] partial discharges are prevented, propagation of trees is retarded, and the lifetime under some conditions is extended.

b) Semiconductive Additives

The addition of slightly incompatible and semiconductive liquids in low concentration also minimizes tree growth, apparently because their incompatibility with the surroundings makes them collect or bloom at free surfaces such as those of cavities and interfaces. When the cavity is surrounded by an isopotential surface, no voltage gradient can exist within, and therefore there will be no discharge. Fujiki et al.[162] discuss this effect quantitatively and present a list of appropriate additives:

- diphenyl-p-phenylenediamine
- phenyl-α-naphthylamine
- 4-bromodiphenyl
- pentachlorophenol

Many of these additives could also provide voltage stabilization by functioning as electron acceptors.

c) Voltage Stabilizers

The next approach was to add various organic materials to the polymers to absorb energetic electrons before they could react with the insulation. This idea may have been suggested by a treatment used in the 1930s when moth balls, naphthalene, or p-dichlorobenzene were dropped into transformer oil to extend the lifetimes of oilfilled transformers.[163] In 1936, the use of purified resin (abietic anhydride, a condensed ring organic structure that accepts electrons) in cable oils was reported to stabilize and prolong the life of cables.

During the 1960s, the Simplex Wire and Cable Co. was a leader in this field and made considerable progress in the use of organic additives, which they called voltage stabilizers.[164] The more effective compounds used are listed in Table 4.1. It was also found that the following two combinations of additives were especially outstanding:

o-Nitrotoluene, 1.5%; and 2.0%
2,4-Dinitrotoluene, 0.25%
Diphenylamine, 0.25%

TABLE 4.1 Voltage Stabilization Additives*

Compound	Chemical Formula	Melting Point (°C)
2-Nitrodiphenylamine	NO_2, ring–N(H)–ring	75
2,6-Dinitrotoluene	ring with NO_2, $-CH_3$, NO_2	60
2,4-Dinitrodiphenylamine	O_2N-ring (NO_2)–N(H)–ring	157
Anthranilonitrile	ring with NH_2, CN	51
o-Nitroanisole	ring with NO_2, $O-CH_3$	10
o-Nitrodiphenyl	ring–ring with NO_2	37
1-Fluoro-2-nitrobenzene	ring with F, NO_2	<30
2-Bromonaphthalene	naphthalene with Br	59

* Source is Ref. 164.

The explanation of voltage stabilization offered was that these additives are thought to function through their capability to absorb energetic electrons and thereby prevent or delay the occurrence of the electron avalanches that lead to failure of polyolefin insulation. The additives are believed to slowly return to their original state by releasing the absorbed energy to the matrix as heat. According to the Simplex patents, their effective additives have the following in common:

(1) at least one electron acceptor group, an unsaturated radical containing a π bond such as NO_2, CN, C = O, $\bigcirc$, or a polycyclic aromatic;

(2) an electron donor group such as amino and lower alkyl radicals, for example, $N(CH_3)_2$, NH_2, and CH_3;

(3) potential hydrogen bonding between the acceptor and donor group by a transferable proton, as when they are ortho on a benzene ring;

(4) reversibility of the proton transfer between groups;

(5) an aromatic ring structure to facilitate transfer of charge between substituent groups;

(6) adequate size and complexity of the conjugated system (aromatic rings) to provide for electron capture and subsequent energy dissipation without producing bond rupture; and

(7) adequate solubility of the additive in the insulating material.

This early work on voltage stabilizers provided an impetus for much subsequent additives work. For example, such other compounds as o-nitrotoluene,[156] ferrocene, siloxane oligomers, and hydroxyquinoline,[165] dodecanol[51] and organic silanes[166] among others have been used. Ferrocene used in 5% concentration was observed to approximately double the dielectric strength of polyethylene, and the breakdown showed no signs of treeing.[112]

TABLE 4.2 Condensed-Ring Aromatics Evaluated as Voltage Stabilizers.[110]

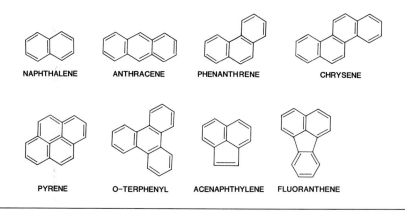

NAPHTHALENE   ANTHRACENE   PHENANTHRENE   CHRYSENE

PYRENE   O-TERPHENYL   ACENAPHTHYLENE   FLUORANTHENE

After comparing the characteristic voltages for about 30 additives, 8 well-characterized condensed-ring hydrocarbons were selected for further study.[110] These hydrocarbons, given in Table 4.2, were chosen because their molecular orbital energy levels, physical and chemical properties and their ionization potentials were known.[167, 168] These eight compounds were blended with high-molecular-weight, low-density polyethylene above the melting points of each at 5 wt% concentration. Double-needle geometry is used to determine characteristic voltage (DNCV) for each (Table 4.3). To allow for the effects of different molecular weights of the additives, a quantity defined as the molal voltage stabilization coefficient (MVS) was calculated from each DNCV by subtracting from it the DNCV of the polyethylene alone and dividing by the molal concentration of the additive, M:

$$MVS = \frac{\Delta DNCV}{M}. \qquad\qquad 4.4$$

Since $\Delta DNCV$, the increase in DNCV caused by the presence of additives, is expressed in kilovolts, and M, the molal concentration of additive, is expressed in moles per kilogram, the MVS has units of kilovolts-kilograms per mole. Values of the MVS are also listed in Table 4.3.

TABLE 4.3 Molal Voltage Stabilization Coefficients

Additive	DNCV (kV)	MVS kV.kg/mole	Ionization Potential[a] (eV)
o-Terphenyl	9.0	33±23	8.43
Naphthalene	10.0	38±18	8.10
Phenanthrene	10.0	53±18	8.09
Chrysene	11.2	169±23	7.80
Fluoranthene	14.0	222±20	7.72
Acenaphthylene	16.3	267±15	–
Pyrene	16.3	315±20	7.55
Anthracene	22.4	495±18	7.32

[a] References 160, 161.

Attempts were made to correlate the MVS with a few theoretical molecular orbital parameters such as the total electron energy, the energy of the highest occupied orbital, the energy of the lowest vacant orbital, and the electron affinity. However, these correlations were not fruitful. Good correlation was observed between the MVS and the ionization potential in electron volts. The relationship is shown in Fig. 4.4 Examination of the figure suggests the

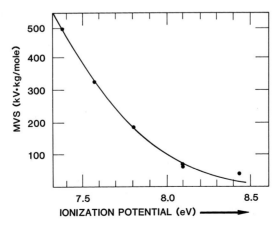

Fig. 4.4. Correlation of MVS with the ionization potential.

simple explanation that, since all of the eight additives confer resistance to the initiation of electrical treeing in polyethylene, all of them have lower ionization potentials than the approximately 10 eV for polyethylene, and the additives with increasingly lower ionization potentials give increasingly greater protection. The probability of ionization of the stabilizer is greater than that of the polyethylene by an amount proportional to the difference between their ionization potentials. A plot of the logarithm of the ionization potential vs the MVS, as in Fig. 4.5, suggests that either the ionization potential of polyethylene under the conditions of this experiment is about 8 eV or, if it is really 10 eV, a difference of more than 2 eV between the ionization potentials is required for effective stabilization.

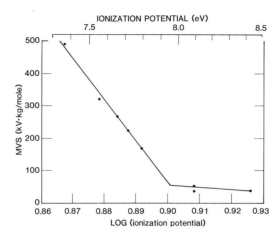

Fig. 4.5. Relationship between MVS and the ionization potential.

A possible mechanism for the electrical aging and voltage stabilizer action may be postulated. When high-energy electrons (above 10eV) collide nonelastically with the polymer molecule, the molecule is ionized:

$$e^{-*} + (CH_2)_n \longrightarrow (CH_2)_n^{\bullet+} + 2e^-$$

The energies of secondary electrons and high-energy electrons after nonelastic collisions are all less than 10 eV. The polymeric radical cation formed possesses excess vibrational energy. This energy can either be lost as heat or the cation can decompose when it reacts with another hot electron:

$$\underset{\overset{|}{H}}{\overset{\overset{|}{H}}{(C)_n^{\bullet+}}} + e^{-*} \longrightarrow \underset{\overset{|}{H}}{\overset{\overset{|}{H}}{(\overset{\bullet}{C})_n}} + H^\bullet$$

The degradation of polymeric free radicals may lead to chain breaking and formation of volatile low-molecular-weight products. New microvoids may be formed, which mark the inception of electrical treeing. This process can be inhibited in three ways:

(1) The voltage stabilizer can be more easily ionized than the polymer:

$$e^{-*} + \underset{R_2}{\overset{R_1}{\diagdown}}\!\!\!\bigcirc \longrightarrow \underset{R_2}{\overset{R_1}{\diagdown}}\!\!\!\bigcirc(+\bullet) + 2\,e^-$$

(2) The formed radical cation can react with another hot electron and regenerate the original voltage stabilizer:

$$\underset{R_2}{\overset{R_1}{\diagdown}}\!\!\!\bigcirc(+\bullet) + e^{-*} \longrightarrow \underset{R_2}{\overset{R_1}{\diagdown}}\!\!\!\bigcirc$$

(3) The voltage stabilizer molecule can quench the ionized polymer molecule by direct electron transfer to the ionized polymer molecule:

$$\left(\!\!\begin{array}{c}H\\ -\overset{|}{\underset{|}{C}}{}^{+\bullet}-\\ H\end{array}\!\!\right)_n + \underset{R_2}{\overset{R_1}{\diagdown}}\!\!\!\bigcirc \longrightarrow \left(\!\!\begin{array}{c}H\\ -\overset{|}{\underset{|}{C}}-\\ H\end{array}\!\!\right)_n + \underset{R_2}{\overset{R_1}{\diagdown}}\!\!\!\bigcirc(+\bullet)$$

d) *Bulk Conductance Additives*

Various chemical additives have also been used to increase the effective conductance of the dielectric and thus resist electrical treeing by field grading.[112]

e) *Inorganic Fillers*

Extensive efforts to overcome or minimize treeing have concentrated on the production of superclean resins and the elimination of contamination in insulations, but it has also been observed that treeing can be inhibited by the presence of certain finely divided inorganic fillers.[31, 169–173] The selection of materials, usually minerals, particle size and shape, and surface treatment are apparently critical because most workers have reported that foreign materials lead to early dielectric failure both in laboratory experiments and in service. The minerals most often used are calcined clay, mica, and titanium dioxide as well as carbon black. It would be interesting to rationalize this apparent anomaly by discovering at what concentration level certain contaminant particles become filler and thereby resist treeing rather than initiate it.

Although no mechanisms of tree resistance are stated for the case of particulate, inorganic additives, some speculation concerning polyethylene exists. In this partially crystalline material, in which spherulites with high molecular density alternate with amorphous boundaries having low molecular density, the particles will locate in the boundaries where there is sufficient free volume for accommodation. As the concentration of particles increases, the volume fraction of crystallinity will decrease because particles must be segregated in non-crystalline regions by the process of crystallization. As the boundaries between spherulites – which are the pathways for normal growth of electrical trees – accept particles, the resistance to propagation increases. The pathways simply become blocked with materials that are very resistant to degradation by partial discharge.

4.8   POLYMER STRUCTURAL CONSIDERATIONS

From the study of additives, we can learn about the relationship between structure and the efficiency of treeing inhibition. Our knowledge can then be profitably applied to structural considerations of the polymers themselves. After the DNCV has been determined, the stability against electrical treeing has to be represented further by the double-needle voltage life (DNVL) at a certain voltage, which then represents the endurance life under certain voltage. The DNCV is used to estimate the ability to resist treeing inception, whereas the DNVL is used to estimate the ability to resist treeing propagation; hence, they are mutually supplemental parameters. Table 4.4 lists the stabilities against electrical treeing of some polymers.[110] Polysulfone, polyethylene terephthalate, and polycarbonate lead the list. All of these polymers contain aromatic rings in their backbones.

For various kinds of polyethylene, the stabilities of its copolymers are the lowest, LDPE has a higher stability, and HDPE has the highest stability. These stabilities are in the same order as the crystallinities of these polymers. Although antioxidant stabilization of voltage and cross-linking *per se* may not always improve the stability, the by-products of the cross-linking agents often are active voltage stabilizers.

Polymer Blends

After improvements had been made in cable construction, process parameters, and tree-retardant additives, there was still the problem of the additives losing their effectiveness over longer periods as a result of either volatilization, decomposition, or long-term incompatibility with the substrate.

TABLE 4.4 Double-Needle Test Data on Commercial Insulations[110]

Polymers	DNCV (kV)	DNVL (h)	
		15 kV	20 kV
Polysulfone	29.0	>120	>120
Polyethylene terephthalate	25.0	–	–
Polycarbonate	19.0	–	–
Fresh XLPE (Contains acetophenone)	18.0	–	–
Thermoplastic PE with voltage stabilizer	15.5	25.0	–
Polystyrene	12.5	>120	–
LDPE (M.I. = 0.2) with antioxidant	11.0	–	–
HDPE	10.5	41.5	–
LDPE (M.I. = 0.2)	8.0	23.8	–
LDPE (M.I. = 2.0)	7.3	13.9	–
XLPE (vacuum treatment after cross linking)	6.5	11.1	–
Polypropylene	7.0	–	–
Ethylene −18% vinyl acetate copolymer	5.5	6.5	–
Ethylene −18% vinyl acrylate copolymer	5.0	7.5	–
Ethylene-propylene rubber	–	6.5	–

Another approach to electric treeing inhibition then involved the use of polymer blends for coating compositions. Polymer blending for improving mechanical properties of electric wire insulation was practiced as early as 1968. High-density polyethylene was blended with low-density polyethylene as the base material. In a 1973 Japanese patent, a styrene/butadiene copolymer was used to improve the impact strength of low-density polyethylene.[174] A 1978 report claimed that the use of a high-density/low-density polyethylene blend increased the electrical treeing inception voltage.[175] However, the report was brief with only minimal experimental detail.

Wu and Chen[176] have reported a detailed examination of this approach to electrical treeing inhibition and experimental details on the use of styrene/butadiene low-density polyethylene and high-density/low-density polyethylene blends.

The blends examined were (1) 0, 10, 20, and 30% styrene/butadiene copolymer (SBR) in low-density polyethylene and (2) 5, 10, 15, and 20% high-density (0.96 g/cm^3) polyethylene in low-density (0.91 g/cm^3) polyethylene. The samples were subjected to an ac current at a fixed 8-kV source. Some of the findings are given in Table 4.5 and the other results are given as conclusions.

TABLE 4.5 Effect of Polymer Blending on Tree Growth and Length

Parameter	LDPE		SBR			HDPE	
	100	10	20	30	10	15	20 wt%
T_1[a]	~0	198	127	54	25	70	90
T_2[b]	300	100	200	230	150	170	160
T_3[c]	–	2180	2200	–	75	30	2100
$T_1 + T_2 + T_3$	2300	2478	2527	2284	250	270	2350
Length, μm[d]	1300	300	600	1400	450	500	400

[a] T_1 – induction period for tree initiation in minutes.
[b] T_2 – growth period of the tree in minutes.
[c] T_3 – the saturation period of tree development in minutes.
[d] The length of the tree after saturation period of tree development is in micrometers.

Conclusions

(1) The 20% SBR/LDPE blend increased the inception voltage for tree formation by 80%.
(2) The 30% HDPE/LDPE blend increased the inception voltage for tree formation by 30%.
(3) The general polymer toughening approach is also effective in increasing the treeing inception voltage, increasing the induction period to treeing, prolonging the tree growth and development, and decreasing in general the size of the tree.
(4) Detailed study of the morphological changes introduced by blending of polymers and process parameters used in their blending should allow one to develop an optimum morphological structure for such compositions that would raise their insulating capability in cable-coating applications.

4.9 EFFECTS OF TEMPERATURE, VOLTAGE, AND MECHANICAL STRAIN

A difference has been noted in the breakdown strength E_B of partially crystalline polymeric dielectrics when their structural ordering and crystallinity are changed. The effect of annealing on the E_B of polyethylene is an increase with increasing crystallinity or density, and the maximum effect is detected after annealing at 95°C.[177] The effects of electric stress on treeing have been reported in almost every paper on the subject. In general, increasing the electric stress, either by increasing the voltage or by changing the electrode or imperfection geometry, decreases the time required to initiate trees and causes them to grow faster and thicker.

Tests that apply electric and mechanical stress simultaneously show that the mechanical stress, or more likely the strain, has a significant effect on the growth of electrical trees. Voltage applied normal to uniaxially stressed sheets of polyethylene exhibited time to failure as an inverse function of mechanical strain.[28, 29] Similar observations have been reported for cable and molded specimens. It was found that mechanical stress decreased the lifetime and damaged the tree shape. The branches tended to grow in a plane perpendicular to the direction of mechanical stress.

SECTION B. WATER TREEING

4.10 INTRODUCTION

The presence of moisture in electrical insulation was recognized as deleterious long before water trees were discovered.[178, 179] Water treeing as such was being discussed in the early 1970s. The chief differences between water treeing and electrical treeing are tabulated in Table 4.6.[180] In the early years, it was thought that water trees could not form in a dc field; however, water trees have been found in polymeric insulating materials even under the influence of dc stress.[89, 181] Since water treeing originates at a relatively low voltage and can change into electrical treeing that leads to a breakdown,[34] the study of the effects of water treeing on a cable life in service is very important.

TABLE 4.6. Chief Differences between Water and Electrical Treeing*

Item	Electrical Treeing[a]	Water Treeing[a]
Treeing inception voltage	Very high	0
Presence of water	Not necessary	Necessary
Time of inception	Long	Short
	$t = \dfrac{A_o}{f^x E^n}$	
Time of propagation	Short	Long
	$t = \dfrac{A_1}{f^x E}$	$t = \dfrac{A_2}{f^x E}$
Breakdown	Direct	After conversion to electrical treeing

* Source is Ref. 180.
[a] t-time; f-frequency; E-field strength; A_0, A_1, A_2-constants ($A_1 \ll A_2$); x–~1; n–9 to 20.

There are two different types of water trees: (1) water trees that begin growing at the surface of the inner or outer conductor, and (2) water trees that begin growing at impurities and voids within the insulation – the so-called bow-tie trees. For the former, the application of extruded semiconductive layers on the inner and outer conductor surfaces can prevent or suppress the initiation and growth of water trees. As for the latter, their effect on the service life of a cable is still not clear.[182] Bow-tie trees can be classified into two types: symmetrical and unsymmetrical.

Water trees can be seen under magnification to consist of many small voids. They disappear after drying but reappear when submerged in hot water. Microvoids of 0.1 to 1 μm are usually present at the roots of water trees. The other basic characteristics of water trees are as follows:

(1) The inception and growth of water trees are little affected by the temperature.
(2) No partial discharge is required for water treeing.
(3) Water trees are formed by water-filling microvoids.
(4) Mechanical stress is usually observed in the region with water trees.

In addition to polyethylene, water trees have been found also in epoxy resins,[182] silicone rubber,[183] poly(vinyl chloride),[184] and polypropylene,[185] among others. It appears that water trees in epoxy resins under dc stress may be initiated by a chemical reaction between water and resin. Hence, water trees in epoxy resins might be different from those, for example, in polyethylene and cross-linked polyethylene.

4.11 INITIATION OF WATER TREES

Water trees grow from points of electric stress concentration that are also moisture or moisture-vapor sources. They grow parallel to the electric field into the surrounding insulation. Apparently the moisture source need not necessarily consist of condensed water but may be vapor of at least 65–70% relative humidity.[186, 187] If we assume dielectric heating of water at power frequency, then the source of water, perhaps a small cavity, would be the hottest place with the highest vapor pressure and the highest electric stress. All these conditions tend to force water vapor to move from the source into the surroundings.

4.11.1 Moisture Vapor Permeability

It is well known that organic polymers and plastics are permeable to gases and moisture vapors. A list of selected polymers and their water vapor permeability data are given in Appendix 6. Among all the polymers used in large volume, particularly for flexible electrical insulation, polyethylene has the lowest moisture vapor permeability. Polyisoprene hydrochloride has the same moisture vapor permeability characteristics as polyethylene; however, it is used less for insulation. The only common polymers with *lower* permeability are poly(vinylidene chloride) (Saran), polytrifluorochloroethylene (Kel-F), poly(p-xylylene), poly(2-chloro-p-xylylene), and poly(dichloro-p-xylylene).[188–190]

Currently, there is no agreement as to whether an ac or dc field promotes moisture vapor diffusion in polyethylene or not.[191–196] Some of this conflicting evidence consists of the following: When tritiated water was used, water absorption was promoted by the electric field only after water trees were formed. Then the water absorption was proportional to the third power of the tree length, that is, the tree volume.[194] However, work carried out on miniature cables to simulate actual use conditions indicated that there was no effect of voltage stress at actual service conditions of 4–8 kV/mm and that water penetration was diffusion controlled.[195] Chemical potential calculations presumably also suggested that electrical stress will not accelerate moisture vapor penetration at operating stress.[196] Other work concludes that the rate of absorption of water depends on both the nature and the concentration of ions dissolved in the water.[197] The point that there is a connection between the growth of water trees and the conductivity of water[198–200] and between ion concentration and pH[201] has been verified.

However, even without the applications of ac and dc fields, water can penetrate into the interior of polymers by (1) diffusional force,[202] (2) mechanical force resulting from Maxwell stress,[183, 203] and (3) dielectrophoresis.[204]

4.11.2 Mechanisms of Water Treeing

If we consider water penetration into a polymer as the first step toward inception of water treeing, then the mechanism of water treeing is mainly the mechanism of propagation of water, which is a rather complex problem to evaluate. Many different mechanism have been proposed by different investigators, and certainly it is possible, even likely, that several parallel mechanisms are at work during the propagation of trees, the importance of each depending on conditions and materials involved.[205] Once treeing is initiated, it is believed that another mechanism takes over and governs the growth of water trees.[206, 207] The various mechanisms of water treeing may be discussed in terms of chemical, electrical, electrostatic, thermal, and mechanical effects.

a) *Chemical Effect*

The propagation of water trees from a chemical effect is full of diversity. Because of internal discharge, the water itself may be decomposed:

$$2H_2O \rightarrow 2H_2 + O_2 .$$

The presence of internal discharge is verified by the appearance of a white spot in polyethylene when a water needle is used.[208] The liberation of gas during water treeing has been verified.[209] Oxidation of the walls of channels and cavities occurs either as a prerequisite to or during water-tree growth. This became apparent with the observation that the water trees, which vanished from sight as the material in which they grew dried, could be made to reappear simply by soaking the material in hot water with no electric stress applied. For water to wick into virgin hydrophobic polyethylene in this way would be impossible. Only after surface oxidation will water even spread on polyethylene, and here we see it penetrating into and reopening the cavities and voids that had collapsed. Thus, the polymer surfaces have become hydrophilic. The oxidation reaction has been confirmed in a number of ways, for example, by dye staining.[210] The basic dye cannot bind to polyethylene unless the latter is oxidized, for instance, to carboxylic acid groups that cause methylene blue to be absorbed. The iodostarch color reaction during water treeing also suggests the formation of nascent oxygen from the decomposition of water.[199] Furthermore, an apparent correlation between the extent of hydroperoxy and carbonyl groups in the polymer molecules and the water-tree growth rates has been demonstrated.[211, 212] The presence of oxygen-containing groups can also be detected by infrared spectroscopy.[213] Hence, it may be concluded that the growth of water trees is related to the oxidation reactions in the polymer.

b) *Electrical Effect*

It has been suggested that at the surface of a particle or at the end of a water tree, there may exist an air-filled cavity, which may be small yet large enough to satisfy Paschen's minimum and, hence, increase the possibility of microdischarges at this point.[199, 214]

For calculating such discharges, an equation for the magnitude of discharge in picocoulombs has been given as[16]

$$Q = \varepsilon_r \varepsilon_0 A \left(\frac{E_{max}}{E_{av}} \right) \frac{\Delta V}{d} , \qquad\qquad 4.5$$

where ε_r is the relative permittivity, ε_0 is the permittivity of free space, A is the discharge area, E_{max}/E_{av} is the stress enhancement caused by a nonuniform electric field, ΔV is the local collapse in voltage associated with the discharge, and d is the spacing between electrodes or between the discharging cavity and the counterelectrode. The partial discharge level has been calculated to be between 0.00002 and 0.02 pC using Eq. (4.5) and assuming (1) a point radius of 1–10 μm; (2) a stress enhancement of 10–100; (3) a gap breakdown of 345 V, which is the Paschen minimum in air; and (4) that the discharge area is a circle of a size equal to the point (d = 1 cm and ε_r = 2.1).

Some of the energy of such a discharge decomposes water into hydrogen and oxygen gases at high pressures. The iodostarch color reaction mentioned earlier indicated that oxygen was formed and that experiments produced it only when high stress enhancements were provided to induce discharging. It was also shown that internal gas at 300 atm (and possibly considerably less) can cause cracking of polyethylene. In considering this argument, it is important to remember that the breakdown strength of wet air is lower, perhaps as low as 25% of that for dry air.[215] After surface oxidation and cracking, water penetrates into the damaged region, and the process continues.

c) Electrostatic Effect

The other mechanisms involve some form of direct electrostatic action on condensed or vapor-phase water. Two such mechanisms involve dielectrophoresis,[208, 216] and chemical potential effects.[50, 199] The present-day tendency is to use them to explain the saturation of electrical insulations exposed to wet surroundings rather than treeing. Still other proposals involve electroosmosis, electrostriction, and bulk phenomena as possible mechanisms.

Dielectrophoresis. Dielectrophoresis is an electrokinetic effect used in pumping and stirring liquids, separation of components in a suspension, and precipitation of suspensions.[217–219] Dielectrophoresis considers the movement of uncharged but polarizable particles or molecules in a divergent field. The force on such a particle can be described with the diagram in Fig. 4.6. If the field diverges from a positive electrode to a negative electrode, an uncharged spherical particle will be polarized by induction as shown. Since the negative side of the induced dipole exists in a stronger field than the positive side, the particle will be attracted toward the region of greatest field intensity if its dielectric constant exceeds that of its surroundings. Changing the polarity of the electrodes will reverse the polarization of the particle so that attraction will continue. Hence, the effect will be the same in ac or dc fields. The direction of motion into or out of the field depends on the dielectric constants only.

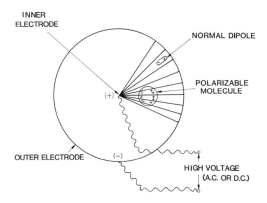

Fig. 4.6. Diagram of forces acting on dipoles and induced dipoles suspended in an inhomogeneous electric field.

By considering clusters of water molecules as particles of 500–Å radius it has been calculated that moisture will be drawn into regions of high dielectric field.[216] The effect would not work with molecular water because the distance of the charge separation would be too small, and it cannot explain water treeing directly because the directions of water movement in water treeing and dielectrophoresis are opposite. In water treeing the moisture moves away from the highest stress. However, this effect may well explain moisture aggregation and the movement of voltage stabilizers to regions of maximum stress.

Chemical Potential. The chemical potential of water condensed in a cavity is lower than that dissolved in its molecular state.[196] Therefore, condensation is natural, and microvoids will be filled in a homogeneous distribution, which is frequently observed as an opaque ring roughly at the center of the cable insulation. In a growth mechanism, which creates voids, the voids must be filled with condensing or clustering water from the surroundings. In fact, it has been reported that water content decreases in the vicinity of bow-tie water trees.[220]

Electroosmosis. The force of electroosmosis or electroendosmosis has been also proposed as a mechanism.[221] Here water moves through pores under the action of an electric field because of the existence of an electrical double layer in which ions of one sign are attached to the pore walls while ions of the other sign are carried by the liquid. The thickness of the double layer has been reported to be only about 50 pm. In about 1879, Helmholtz published equations for the transport of liquids in pores open on both ends and those closed on one end. In the case of a pore closed at one end and oriented parallel to the electric field, the electroosmotic pressure p in newtons per square metre is given by

$$p = \frac{\zeta \varepsilon_r V}{4.5 \pi a^2 \cdot 10^9},$$ 4.6

where ζ is the electrokinetic or zeta potential, ε_r is the relative dielectric constant of the liquid, V is the applied voltage, and a is the radius of the pore. With the assumptions that ζ = 10 mV, ε_r = 78, and V = 10 kV, it can be calculated that the pressure exerted at the closed end of the pore for a = 1 nm, 10 nm, 100 nm, and 1 μm will be 20×10^6, 220×10^3, 2200, and 22 atm, respectively. Thus, we see that for very fine channels the pressures can be enormous, and 0.05-μm channels have been reported by others.[222] When the polarity of the applied ac voltage reverses, the water pulls back away from the end of the channel. Hence the effect is a hammering at the end or point of the channel. Under these conditions, creep or ductile failures of a polymer might be expected to result in fissures. This effect should vanish under dc stress, so it cannot explain dc water treeing. Water treeing should increase with stress and frequency and also with temperature if the yield strength of the dielectric decreases with temperature.

Electrostriction. Water treeing has been explained also as a result of electrostriction.[50, 223, 224] Electrostriction describes the variation in the dimensions of a dielectric under the influence of an electric field; the effect is independent of the polarity of the field. The case of interest to us is a small water-filled cavity or a longer but very thin channel immersed in another dielectric and in a strong electric field. The effect of the field is to stretch the cavity parallel to the field twice for each cycle of applied ac voltage. Tree growth resulting from this mechanism is postulated as an example of environmental fatigue fracture. It is further proposed that under high-voltage conditions, the water itself provides a surface-active environment, decreasing the surface tension at the extremities of the cavity and changing the effect to one of environmental stress cracking or, more properly, environmental stress corrosion cracking. The situation is analogous to the effect of surface-active agents and aqueous detergents, which decrease the surface tension when used to test the properties of plastics. A reduction in surface tension, of course, permits the cavity a greater change in shape in compliance with the same stress and could help explain the jetting reported.

Bulk Phenomena. Although most workers believe that failure follows some finite time after complete electrode bridging by the longest tree, when the channel becomes capable of carrying the fault current, it has been suggested that failure occurs when a certain overall level of deterioration has been reached.[47] That is, the number of microtrees observed is proportional to the time of voltage application, and the number of microtrees initiated per unit time is proportional to the average electric stress. These observations are illustrated in Figs. 4.7 and 4.8. Hence, treeing and failure seem to be bulk phonomena rather than weak-link effects. Another difference reported is the existence of an apparent critical stress for generation of microbow-tie water trees. Values of 3.3 and 20.0 kV/mm are given for two different specimens.[201] Most other workers have not observed any critical stress but assume that longer times are required at lower stresses.

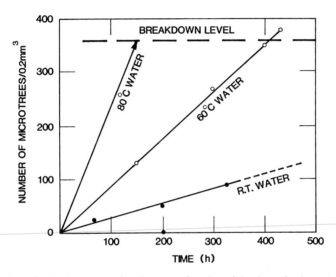

Figure 4.7. Number of microtrees per unit volume as a function of the time of voltage application.

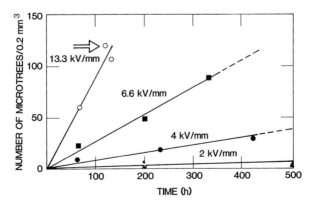

Fig. 4.8. Rate of increase of microtrees per unit volume with electrical stress as a parameter.

d) *Thermal Effect*

Thermal failure resulting directly from dielectric heating of insulation is not a likely explanation for the mechanical damage associated with water treeing, because the power factor and the electric stress are usually both too low. However, it has been proposed that water-filled cavities and microcavities will enlarge when the water within them expands because of Joule or dielectric heating.[49, 223] Furthermore, in expanding, the cavities will become more spherical. As evidence, it has been shown by changes in optical birefringence that mechanical strain accompanies the increase of electric stress in insulation. These observations suggest that increasing electric stress causes the water in cavities to heat and expand, which in turn generates mechanical forces that strain the insulation material and break molecular chains, thus increasing the size of cavities or forming new ones. This is an example of ductile failure. If one can start by assuming an elongated cavity with its major axis parallel to the field and filled with water (Fig. 4.9), which expands and becomes more spherical, then an elegant explanation is offered for the formation of a string of voids that may be the structure of a water tree. As the cavity becomes spherical, tensile and compressive forces are developed in the insulation parallel to the original major and minor axes, respectively. Microcavities or submicrocavities then may be formed in the locations of tension. If they fill with water and many of them can aggregate to form a large cavity, an interesting argument can be made for the formation of a row of beads or pearls. This proposed structure has been shown in the well-known sketch of Tanaka et al. (Fig. 4.10).[49, 223]

There are problems with the mechanism just offered because (1) the electric stress required may not be possible in a water-filled void and (2) it is difficult to explain how vented water trees dry out and disappear so rapidly if the cavities are not connected. In conclusion, it is suggested that although this mechanism is possible, growth by electrostriction effects is more likely.

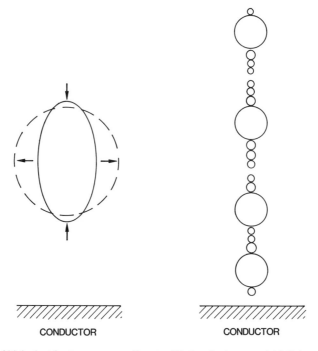

Fig. 4.9. Effect of high electric stress on a small water-filled cavity in a nonrigid dielectric section.

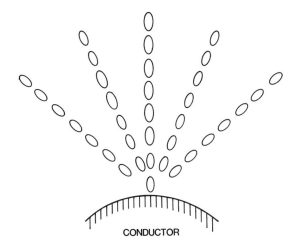

Fig. 4.10. Schematic drawing of water-tree growth.

e) *Summary of Water Treeing Mechanisms*

The microporosity of polymers plays a very important role in the mechanisms of water treeing.[225] The water absorption of molded polyethylene decreases when the specimen is molded at a higher pressure, which leads to increased density, and density is directly related to micropore content in a specimen.[226] Heat treatments to adjust crystallinity by melting and recrystallization also increase the density and thus decrease water absorption.[177] Small voids can also "heal" themselves during a heat treatment; hence, the density increases.[227]

Morphology of the polymer is also an important factor to be considered. For example, cavities are usually associated with the impingement site of three or more spherulites.[77] Hence, taking measures to control spherulite growth during crystallization is important for the prevention of both electrical and water treeing. As small spherulites produce a large number of small cavities and large spherulites produce a fewer number of larger cavities, it is necessary to control this parameter in establishing the optimum morphology. For example, the use of aliphatic cross-linking agents usually leads to a very fine morphology, in which the spherulites obtained are very small and give no appearance of the presence of microscopic voids.

Mechanical stresses in cable insulation are internal stresses generated during the processing step or subsequently under use conditions. In mechanically stressed polymers, the generation of submicrocracks caused by stress may lead to mechanochemical reactions generating free radicals,[228] which in turn may generate paths for water treeing.[229]

Environmental stress cracking of polymers is a type of environmental fatigue fracture that occurs when a high-voltage field decreases the surface tension at the polymer/water interface.[224] When the ratio of the yield stress to the surface tension is small, environmental stress cracking occurs. Because the yield stress decreases as the temperature increases and the surface tension is relatively temperature independent, water-tree growth should increase with temperature. However, another investigation holds just the opposite view.[230]

In view of the multitude of observed phenomena about water treeing and the contradictory results, it is difficult at this time to judge possible water treeing mechanisms with certainty and determine what, in fact, is essential and what is accidental in what has been observed.

4.12 GROWTH OF WATER TREES

Once the inception of a water tree has taken place, large variations in the rate of growth have been observed. Thus, for example, the growth rate has been fitted by a power curve,[39, 201, 221] to a logarithmic function of time,[198] and as a linear function for short times proportional to the frequency and the conductivity of the water used.[199]

In most cases the growth rates are not linear and typically decrease with time. Thus, comparisons between materials must be done after equal test periods. An interesting approach to this problem has been to compare the rate constants for growth under the assumptions that (1) the water trees are conductive in comparison to an insulation like polyethylene, and (2) the electric field at the boundary of a growing water tree can be calculated by the expression

$$E = \frac{V \sqrt{1 + r/d}}{r \tanh^{-1}\left(\sqrt{1/(1 + r/d)}\right)}. \qquad 4.7$$

In Eq. (4.7), V is the applied voltage; r, the point electrode radius, is identified with L, the length of the growing tree; and d is $3.18 - L$, the distance to the ground electrode. A plot of dL/dt versus E^2 for experimental data gives a straight line with slope K, which is the rate constant for water treeing.[39, 201, 220] Thus,

$$\frac{dL}{dt} = KE^2 \qquad 4.8$$

and

$$\frac{dL}{E^2} = Kdt. \qquad 4.9$$

Knowing E as a function of L from Eq. (4.7), we can numerically integrate Eq. (4.9) to provide a value for K from a single measurement of tree length.

It is significant that the same value for K is obtained for observations after 1 and after 10 days.[39] It substantiates the assumption that in bush-type water trees, which tend to grow in water-tree tests, the many channels help to shield each other, and the effective sharpness of the point becomes the radius of the end of the tree.

Another set of observations that needs further elucidation is the fact that propagation rate presumably decreases with increasing polymer chain rigidity.[231] However, it has also been observed that the growth rate of water treeing actually accelerated at low temperatures, presumably because of increased chain stiffness at the low temperature and inability to dissipate fracture energy.[230]

Other factors that have been shown to affect tree growth rate are (1) cross-linking in general retards growth rate; (2) chemical cross linking compared with the equivalent radiation cross-linking level retards growth rate more (this effect, however, is due mainly to the cross-linking agent decomposition products, which act as treeing inhibitors); and (3) the nature of the water. Water, which contains dissolved salts or minerals, shows not only an accelerated absorption of water by the insulation but also an accelerated propagation of water trees.[57, 194, 200, 232] Thus, the rate of growth has been shown to depend on the ionic concentration in water.[197] Antioxidants also generally accelerate water treeing.

4.13   TESTING

Testing methods of water treeing have developed along three lines: (1) standard defect methods that introduce a controlled stress concentration into the specimens, (2) miniature or full-size finished cable or cable core that is exposed to simulated use conditions, and (3) uniform field tests that use Rogowski or similar electrodes.

4.13.1 Standard Defect Methods

Standard defect methods use compression-molded specimens with multiple sharp conical depressions (Fig. 4.11).[199,201] A voltage of 1–10 kV at a frequency of 600 Hz–8 kHz is applied to the specimen for a fixed time, usually one to a few days. When the specimen is removed from the water, 1.27-cm-diameter cylinders, each containing one conical depression, are punched out and stained to render the trees permanently visible. The dyed cylinders are then thinned with a microtome to enhance their clarity and contrast for microscopic examination.

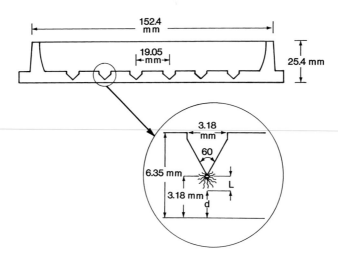

Figure 4.11. Compression-molded specimen with conical depressions. Source is Ref. 201

4.13.2 Cable Test Specimens

In another approach, cable test specimens were used because they contained all the effects of extrusion, cross-linking, and cooling.[200] In addition, a controlled, water-filled standard defect was also introduced into the specimen (Fig. 4.12). The 3-mm-diameter reservoir drilled into the insulation is filled with water or a solution during testing. After the specimen is mounted in a holding fixture, a needle is pushed through the seal and the solution and radially into the insulation to within 2 mm of the inner semiconducting shield. Withdrawing the point of the needle into the reservoir leaves a needle-shaped defect, which fills with water. A needle electrode is then used. With this arrangement the effects of temperature and conductivity of the liquid have been investigated.

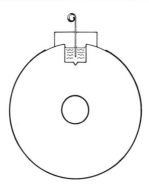

Figure 4.12 Cable test specimen with a water-filled standard defect.

4.13.3 Practical Field Conditions Test

The Association of Edison Illuminating Companies (AEIC) has written a water-tree test designed to come as close as possible to field conditions while providing reasonable acceleration. It is included as Section B.5 in AEIC CSS-79, Specification for Thermoplastic and Cross-linked Polyethylene, and Section B.7 in AEIC CS6–79, Specification for Ethylene Propylene Rubber Insulated Shielded Power Cables. The test uses 4.6-m (15-ft)-long (active shielded length) 15-kV cables with a 4.39-mm (175-mil) wall and a No. 1/0 AWG compressed Class B stranded aluminum conductor. Unfortunately, the test results reported to date have not been very consistent. Better results have been obtained in a modified version of the above test using large water tanks at fairly constant temperature containing 16 specimens.[233]

4.14   INHIBITION OF WATER TREEING

Since water trees, just as electrical trees, are presumably initiated by stress concentration, contaminant particles, and voids as well as by the presence of water, many of the methods mentioned for electrical tree inhibition also apply for water trees. Extruded semiconductive shields provide smooth interfaces with insulation, and cleaner materials provide fewer particulate contaminants. Both of these conditions are intended to reduce the stress concentrations. The various new dry-curing methods for cross-linking are also intended to minimize the number of voids and microvoids as well as the amount of moisture introduced into an insulation during cable manufacture.

Thus, two approaches are generally used in the inhibition of water treeing: cable construction and chemical additives.

4.14.1   Cable Construction

a) *Continuous Metal Sheath*

The experience of Consolidated Edison Company of New York as well as reports from other countries indicate that power cables that are completely enclosed in a continuous metal sheath are not subject to water treeing until the sheath is somehow damaged. It has even been claimed that cables operating above 5 kV/mm (125 V/mil) should be required to have a watertight sheath.[198] Unfortunately, the use of a metal sheath adds considerable expense and inconvenience to the cable production.

b) *Modern Cable Design*

A cable design that incorporates most of the knowledge about resistance to electrical and water treeing has been patented.[234] The cable consists of the following elements from inside to outside: (1) a standard conductor filled with a strand-blocking compound to prevent longitudinal flow and water filling; (2) an extruded semiconductive shield; and (3) an extruded emission shield, which has a dielectric constant several times higher than that of the primary insulation. The emission shield provides a graded dielectric to minimize localized electrical stresses and electron injection. The fourth element is the primary dielectric (preferably PE or XLPE) covered by the fifth element, an emission shield, and sixth element, an extruded semiconductive insulation shield. A surrounding metallic shield is itself surrounded by an extruded plastic jacket. The metallic shield is of copper lapped longitudinally to permit thermal expansion and contraction. Such modern cable designs offer promise of longer life by overcoming thermal expansion problems. However, they are extremely expensive to produce.

4.14.2 Chemical Additives

An extremely wide variety of additives are used and in most cases they are used without any mechanism or explanation being offered for the observed effects. Initial classification of some of these additives into the following classes has been made:

(1) water-tree-inhibiting or growth-rate-retarding additives,

(2) electrolytic additives, and

(3) voltage-stabilizing additives.

a) *Water-Tree-Inhibiting or Growth-Rate-Retarding Additives*

Two of the more successful commercial insulating systems that have been used for years are thermoplastic, non-cross-linked polyethylenes: (1) UCAR TR6202, introduced by Union Carbide Corporation,[166, 235] and (2) TREBAN 100 by E. I. DuPont.[51] The Union Carbide product contains silane and the DuPont product contains dodecanol as the additives. Both additives claim no increase in breakdown voltage E_B or inhibition of trees. Rather, they act to retard the rate of growth. The dodecanol molecules are mobile enough to move to the region of highest stress, fill the tree tips, and become a field-grading sphere.

 Another patented system consists of the use of acylalkanone complexes of copper, iron, cobalt, chromium, magnesium, or cerium as additives to resist water treeing.[236] Also discussed are diketones, substituted salicylic acid, and a Schiff's base formed from an amine and salicylaldehyde. The advantages claimed are that the formation and growth of water trees are strongly suppressed or permanently prevented.

 An interesting idea for the use of nonionic surfactants and metallic salts of fatty acids in the suppression of water-tree formation has recently been offered.[237] The use of the above-mentioned additives makes the insulation (XLPE for example) more wettable, and thus it will no longer be possible to increase pressure by constraining water within the hydrophobic surfaces of a cavity or channel. Data were presented to demonstrate that the number and size of bow-tie trees were decreased significantly by this approach.

b) *Electrolytic Additives*

The chief function of electrolytic additives is to prevent more water from entering the voids, reducing the electric stress in voids containing water, and increasing the chemical potential of the voids. Incorporation of strong electrolytes can control the water pressure generated in voids.[196] A minimum pressure, which is a function of concentration, defines the operating range of resistance to tree generation. Hence, in the use of electrolytic additives, great care must be taken in adjusting the concentration to adjust the chemical potential in the voids to the proper level. Some experimental results in the use of electrolytic additives and their concentrations are summarized in Table 4.7.[238]

TABLE 4.7 Some Experimental Results of Electrolytic Additives

Electrolytes	Quantity per 100 g PE	Time to Water Trees
No additive	0	After 272 h water trees initiated
NaCl, Na_2SO_4, $MgSO_4$, $NaNO_3$, $Ca(NO_3)_2$, $CaCl_2$, $MgCl_2$, $CdSO_4$.	8×10^{-5} mol	After 455 h no water trees
Na_2SO_4	8×10^{-6} mol.	After 455 h no water trees

c) *Voltage Stabilizing Additives*

These additives act to stabilize the voltage and thus suppress water-treeing initiation by discharges. They also serve to increase the stability of polyethylene toward oxidation and may enhance the rigidity of the chains.[231] Chemically, they are of the same type as those used to suppress electrical treeing. Especially, if other types of additives are used, voltage stabilizers must be used to enhance or bring out the intended effects of the other additives.

4.15 CRITERIA FOR TREE-RESISTANT INSULATION

Clearly, tree-resistant insulations will have high dielectric breakdown strengths. What should the criteria for a tree-resistant insulation then be? Since one of the most widely used and best insulating materials is polyethylene, the criteria may be specified in reference to this material. Thus, the material should satisfy the following requirements:

(1) It should effectively resist the initiation of treeing of at least 100% increase in threshold voltage.
(2) It should resist propagation of treeing so that the growth rate is only 5–10% that of conventional polyethylene.
(3) The chemical composition should change only accordingly with thermal and electrical aging and the presence of moisture.
(4) Any tree-retardant additive should be free to migrate to growing cavities or regions of very high electric stress.
(5) The material should be capable of being cross-linked.
(6) The material should possess a low loss factor.
(7) The material should present no toxicological hazards.

PART II. DIELECTRIC BREAKDOWN IN POLYMERS

4.16 INTRODUCTION

As no known polymer is completely free of conduction processes, charges are expected to diffuse away eventually under the influence of their own field, even though this may take many years in extreme cases. Low-level conduction in insulating materials can originate in a variety of ways. Often it is attributed to impurities that provide small concentrations of charge carriers in the form of ions and/or electrons. At high fields, the electrodes may also inject new carriers into the polymer, causing the current to increase more rapidly with voltage than one would expect from Ohm's law. At very high fields, these and other processes, often involving conduction over a surface, inevitably lead to complete failure of the polymer as a dielectric. This phenomenon is known as the dielectric breakdown. Although the breakdown may seem to be a part of conduction, it is nevertheless a separate phenomenon as we will discuss it in detail.

If the voltage across a piece of any dielectric material is steadily increased, at some point any imperfection in the material or its surroundings will become apparent, and total breakdown will eventually ensue. Phenomenologically, the final event is localized, sudden, and catastrophic. Thus, the existence of a maximum voltage that a dielectric material will support for a long time without failing leads to the concept of dielectric strength, which can be defined as the breakdown voltage divided by the thickness of the material. In other words, dielectric strength is the maximum electric field that the material can sustain indefinitely.

The intrinsic dielectric strength of a homogeneous solid is evidently very high, usually in excess of 100 kV/mm, and proves to be a very elusive fundamental property. The reason for this is that a particular material may often more easily fail in many different ways, which have more to do with its environment, physical state, purity, and the types of electrodes used than with its basic chemical constitution. However, chemical constitution may affect the physical state, purity, and sensitivity of the material to the environment.

Thus, to control the dielectric strength of a polymer chemically, we have to know the mechanisms of dielectric breakdown of polymers. If we want a polymer that has high breakdown voltage or dielectric strength, then we need to understand the physics of the breakdown processes to a much higher degree than we currently do. Many years of hard work have gone into the study of the physics of dielectric breakdown, and as a result, many mechanisms of breakdown have been elucidated. It is the multitude of breakdown mechanisms that generally limits the effective strength of a polymer in practical situations.

4.17 HISTORICAL OVERVIEW

The first breakdown theory of solid dielectrics was the thermal breakdown theory of Wagner in 1922.[239] In this theory, the dielectric breakdown was discussed in terms of the conditions necessary to break down the thermal balance between Joule heating resulting from the conduction current and its dissipation. This theory succeeded in explaining qualitatively the experimental observations of dielectric breakdown phenomena in the high-temperature region.

However, the temperature dependence of electric strengths of solid dielectrics contains components in both the low- and high-temperature regions. It was difficult to explain the dielectric breakdown phenomena in the low-temperature region by the thermal breakdown theory. This eventually led to the recognition of the existence of the electronic conduction current in solid dielectrics. The investigations of time lag,[240] the direction of the breakdown path,[241] and other studies[4, 83] suggested that the dielectric breakdown of solids may also result from an electronic process such as current multiplication by collision ionization of high-speed electrons. With time it was realized that the electronic process played an important role in some breakdown processes. For example, the interactions between hot electrons, accelerated by the applied electric field, and phonons attracted much interest as a subject of theoretical physics from 1940 to 1950. These studies dealt quantitatively with the quantum mechanical solid-state physics, and the breakdown mechanisms began to be understood, mainly for the alkali halide single crystals because their structures were relatively simple. Within this framework a number of different breakdown theories evolved according to differences in the approximations and the energy exchange processes made; however, the agreement between the theories and the experimental results was poor. This was partly because the theories included unknown basic quantities and partly because many secondary effects could not always be eliminated in the experiments.

4.17.1 Electromechanical Breakdown Theory

Later, studies of time lag for the breakdown suggested that the thermal breakdown was not the only breakdown process in the high-temperature region. Proposals were made to modify the collision ionization of electrons with the space-charge effect[242, 243] and to consider what role the interaction between the conduction electrons and the electrons trapped in the impurity level plays in the energy exchange process, the so-called Fröhlich's amorphous theory.[244] Furthermore, the electromechanical breakdown theory was proposed because the breakdown characteristics of polymers in the temperature region near the melting (or softening) point are similar to their mechanical characteristics.[245] This theory states that the breakdown is caused by the mechanical deformation resulting from Maxwell stress under the applied electric field. It was specific to polymers and succeeded in explaining the breakdown characteristics of many polymers in the high-temperature region. Another breakdown theory specific to polymers was the free-volume breakdown theory.[79] This theory was especially applicable to the breakdown phenomena of polymers around the glass transition temperature region.

4.17.2 Summary

In summary, the fundamental breakdown processes can be roughly classified into electronic processes and the purely thermal process. Furthermore, regardless of the current multiplication process, there exists the mechanical breakdown process, in which the mechanical deformation under the applied electric field dominates the breakdown phenomena. Finally, although many breakdown theories have been proposed, it is still difficult to decide which mechanism, if any, plays a dominant role in the general breakdown process.

4.18 BASIC OBSERVATIONS

4.18.1 Dielectric Breakdown Strength

The measured values of the breakdown voltage E_B of solid dielectrics are greatly influenced by the experimental conditions. For instance, when voltage is applied to a solid specimen kept in a surrounding medium of liquid or gas, a partial discharge in the surrounding medium occurs mainly at the edge of the electrode before a complete breakdown of the solid dielectric takes place. This phenomenon, the edge effect, influences E_B of solids and always decreases it. To eliminate this effect, special forms of specimens and electrodes have been developed.[2, 246-248] If breakdown voltage/sample thickness of some typical polymers is measured carefully with a dc voltage to eliminate the edge effect, the following characteristic results are obtained:[2, 246-253]

(1) The breakdown voltages of polymers are generally in the range of 1 to 9 MV/cm at 20°C.
(2) In general, the maximum values of the breakdown voltage of polymers are obtained in the low-temperature region. These values for polar polymers are more than 10 MV/cm and are higher than those for nonpolar polymers.
(3) The highest breakdown voltage ever obtained for a polymer is 15 MV/cm at −190°C for polyvinyl alcohol.

4.18.2 Temperature Dependence

Both the physical and electrical properties of polymers change with temperature. The temperature dependence of the dielectric breakdown is of prime importance in analyzing the breakdown mechanism. In general, the temperature dependence of the breakdown voltage of polymers is roughly divided into the following two regions:

(1) Low-temperature region. In this region, breakdown voltage increases slightly with increasing temperature.
(2) High-temperature region. In this region, breakdown voltage decreases with increasing temperature.

4.18.3 Time Dependence

In general, dielectric breakdown occurs some time after the voltage application. This time delay for the breakdown varies from a very short time of about 10^{-9} s to more than several hours, depending on the breakdown mechanism.

For the short time delays, for which the dielectric breakdown is mainly caused by the electronic processes, this time delay is called the *time lag* and shows statistical features of gas breakdowns. In general, the time lag consists of both the statistical time lag t_s and the formative time lag t_f. For the distribution of the observed time lag t, the following relationship has been derived:[254]

$$N(t)/N_O = \exp[-(t-t_f)/t_s] ,\qquad\qquad 4.10$$

where $N(t)$ is the number of the experiments in which breakdown does not take place before the time t in a series of N_O experiments under the same conditions, t_s is the mean statistical time lag (this is also called the statistical time lag), and t_f is assumed to be constant for a given electric field. Figure 4.13 shows the Laue plot of the time lag $[\ln(N(t)/N_O)$ vs t] in the

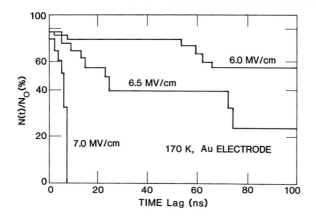

Fig. 4.13. Laue plot of time lag in dielectric breakdown of polyethylene. Source is Ref. 255.

dielectric breakdown of polyethylene in the low-temperature region.[255] The statistical time lag estimated from the slope of a linear graph of the Laue plot varies depending on the applied electric field and the electrode materials. These results suggest the occurrence of the electron avalanche breakdown mechanism.

4.19 THEORIES OF DIELECTRIC BREAKDOWN

Some of the material summarized here and in sections 4.21 and 4.29 is presented in greater detail in the chapter by Nelson of the book by Bartnikas and Eichhorn.[357]

4.19.1 Single-Electron Models

Von Hippel established the framework from which a number of theories of intrinsic breakdown have developed.[241] An insulating solid will always have a small number of electrons that are thermally excited into the conduction band from the valence band or from donor levels in the forbidden energy gap. Such an electron may be accelerated in an applied field and energy would be lost to the lattice of a crystalline material by phonon interactions. Breakdown for this model is presumed to take place when the average rate of energy gain from the field is greater than that lost in collisions to the host material.

According to this model Fig. 4.14 shows rates of gain and loss of energy as a function of electron energy W. A family of curves A depicts the average rate of gain for various applied fields. Von Hippel's criterion corresponds to $A(E_c)$, where the rate of gain always exceeds the rate of loss B for all electrons, and no equilibrium can arise.

The low-energy breakdown criteria inherently makes the assumption that all electrons in the conduction band have the same energy at a given field strength. Fröhlich has shown that breakdown is possible for fields substantially less than E_c.[256] From the distribution of energies some electrons may exhibit energies up to the ionizing energy W_{ion}, at which ionizing collisions will take place. By considering an electron of energy W in a field E_1, we can see from Fig. 4.14 that if $W' < W < W_1$, then energy will be lost to the lattice until stability is gained at energy W'. For a chance fluctuation creating an electron having an energy in the

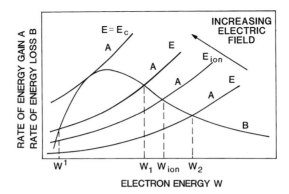

Fig. 4.14. Schematic representation of intrinsic breakdown criteria based on electron energies gained from the field and lost to the lattice.

range $W_1 < W < W_{ion}$, however, the rate of energy gained from the field will be greater than that dissipated, and thus the resulting instability will lead to breakdown. At lower fields such as E_2, even electrons with energies as high as W_{ion} will lose energy faster than they can gain it. From these arguments the highest field for which an equilibrium can be obtained is that given by E_{ion}, which is the (high-energy) criterion adopted by Fröhlich.

From the study of ionic crystals, it has become apparent that anisotropy in electrical breakdown is possible. Differences in electronic strength along different crystallographic directions have been documented in several cases.[257, 258] Such behavior is not accounted for by the basic single-electron theories of intrinsic breakdown. The preferred paths for breakdown suggest that oriented electron avalanches are implicated. In polymers, not only is there a crystallinity effect, as depicted in Fig. 4.15, but there is also evidence of the probability that discharge patterns tend to follow the spherulite boundaries in a semicrystalline material.[259] This has been demonstrated for polyethylene and polypropylene.[260]

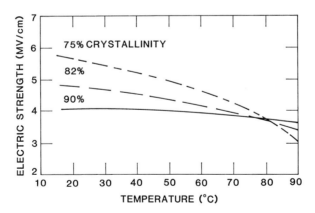

Fig. 4.15. The effect of crystallinity on the electric strength of high-density polyethylene (after Ref. 261).

4.19.2 Collective Electron Models

A further study of Fig. 4.14 shows that no applied field greater than E_{ion} is capable of providing a stationary state for the electron system if interactions with the lattice are the only losses considered. This was corrected by postulating that the high-energy electrons exchange energy by collision with other electrons.[262] Such interelectron interactions can then prevent the instability of electrons with energies greater than W_1 since, after collision, energies of both interacting particles can be below W_1. Thus, in this case, the loss and gain of energies must be averaged over the Maxwellian energy distribution:

$$A(E,T,T_0) = B(T,T_0) .$$

4.11

The maximum value of the field, E_c, corresponding to the temperature T_c for which Eq. (4.11) can be satisfied, provides the critical field value for breakdown. Thus, as the field is increased, the electron temperature rises to maintain stability until $E > E_c$ when the energy balance is lost and the whole free-electron system undergoes a runaway.

The theories so far introduced are applicable only to pure crystalline materials at low temperatures. Experimental determination of breakdown strength often shows a temperature region for which there is a reduction in electric strength. This is illustrated in Fig. 4.16 for a range of polymer materials.[263] It has been postulated that above a critical temperature the density of electrons becomes sufficiently high to render electron-electron interactions of greater importance than electron-lattice interactions.[244] Following a criterion for breakdown similar to that used previously for the low-temperature case, calculations show that the critical breakdown field predicted by the hot-electron concept changes with temperature according to

$$E_c = \left(\frac{c}{\Delta W^{1/2}}\right) \exp\left(\frac{\Delta W}{2kT}\right), \text{ for } T > T_c$$

4.12

where c is a constant defined by Fröhlich in terms of the frequency of lattice vibration, T_c is the critical temperature above which electron-electron interactions assume importance, and k is the Boltzmann constant.

Thus, not only does the intrinsic electric strength decrease at high temperatures, but the admixing of foreign atoms should give rise to a decrease in the transition temperature T_c.[264] The work in polymeric materials also indicated that the effect of chlorinating polyethylene, having an average molecular weight of 17 000, was to decrease the transition temperature, as shown in Fig. 4.17, but the negative slopes at low temperatures are not in accordance with the basic theory.[250, 251] The differences indicated for the hot and cold chlorinations also pointed to the fact that the distribution of chlorine atoms in the polymer chain may be important in determining the electric strength in addition to crystallinity effects.

The predictions of collective electron theories are not by any means in agreement with all the experimental evidence. The introduction of styrene into a butadiene matrix has been shown to increase the transition temperature for the characteristic fall in electric strength from −93°C for a pure polybutadiene specimen to −79°C for a 75/25 copolymer,[263] which is not explained by the Fröhlich amorphous theory. The merit of the collective electron approach, however, lies in the fact that it should predict a truly intrinsic breakdown value that is independent of electrodes, voltage applications, or specimen thickness. This is not a feature of theories relying on avalanching or other phenomenological mechanisms.

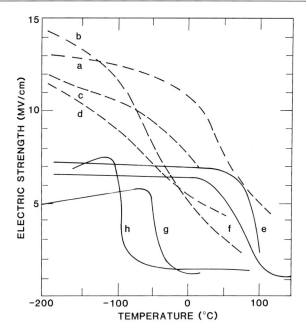

Fig. 4.16. Examples of the temperature dependence of the dc electric strength of a range of polar (broken lines) and nonpolar (solid lines) polymers: (a) poly(methly methacrylate), (b) polyvinyl alcohol, (c) poly(vinyl chloride/vinyl acetate), (d) 55% chlorinated polyethylene, (e) atactic polystyrene, (f) low-density polyethylene, (g) polyisobutylene, and (h) polybutadiene.

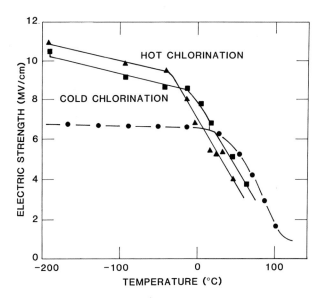

Fig. 4.17. Comparisons of the temperature dependence of breakdown of polyethylene (broken line) with 8% chlorinated polyethylene (solid lines). Source is Ref. 251.

4.20 PRINCIPAL MECHANISMS OF DIELECTRIC BREAK-DOWN

Dielectric breakdown mechanisms are strongly affected by the complicated physical and chemical structures of polymers, impurities, and carrier traps whose nature and origin are not well known yet. The breakdown process is complex also because it involves not only charge transfer in the bulk dielectric but also across the dielectric-metal interfaces. The principal mechanisms of dielectric breakdown in polymers may be listed as

(1) electronic,
(2) thermal,
(3) electromechanical, and
(4) gas discharge.

4.20.1 Electronic Breakdown

Conventionally, electronic breakdown is known as the electrical breakdown initiated by the small number of electrons that are available for acceleration by the applied field. In an ideal dielectric with insulation-type band structure, no free electronic carrier (electrons or holes) exists. In actual cases, however, few free carriers exist in the extended state (conduction or valence band) because of intrinsic or extrinsic mechanisms such as injection from electrodes or thermal dissociation of impurities (donor or acceptor type). The current density j for this carrier density n under field E is given by[265]

$$j = nev_d = ne\chi E = \gamma E ,\qquad\qquad 4.13$$

where v_d and χ are drift velocity and mobility of the carriers, respectively, and γ is the conductivity of the polymer. Both n and χ are complicated functions of the electric field E and temperature T of polymers, showing strong non-Ohmic characteristics.

By analogy with the mechanism of sparking in gases, we can imagine that a Townsend-like avalanche may occur whenever the field is high enough for a conduction electron to gain sufficient energy to excite more electrons by collisions. This is known as the electron multi-plication mechanism. For polymers and other molecular and amorphous solids at higher temperatures, the combined number of electrons in localized excited states and in a conduc-tion band will be relatively high, so electron scattering will have to predominate. When an electric field feeds energy directly to the conduction electrons, because the transfer of energy from these electrons to the lattice is rather slow, the electron temperature may rise above the

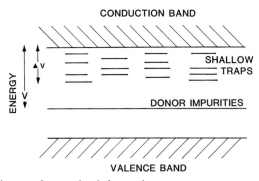

Fig. 4.18. Schematic diagram of energy levels for a polymer.

lattice temperature. The theory of electronic breakdown, applicable to polymers, was then proposed by Fröhlich.[244]

Figure 4.18 shows a schematic diagram of energy levels for a polymer where conduction electrons are derived from impurity levels lying deep in the forbidden zone and a set of shallow traps spread below the conduction band edge ($V \gg \Delta V \gg kT$). In an applied electric field E, the energy is directly transferred to the conduction electrons at a rate $W = jE$. If we suppose that each electron is accelerated for an average time τ between collisions, at which its energy is completely randomized, then the mean drift velocity of the conduction electrons v_d in the field direction is

$$v_d = -\frac{eE\tau}{m},$$ 4.14

where m is the mass of electrons. The current density j resulting from drift of all the conduction electrons (concentration) is

$$j = nev_d = \frac{ne^2E\tau}{m}.$$ 4.15

Then the energy transfer rate is

$$W = Ej = \frac{ne^2E^2\tau}{m}.$$ 4.16

The concentration of conduction electrons in the semiconductor is

$$n = C(T)e^{-V/2kT},$$ 4.17

where $C(T)$ is a factor that varies only slightly with temperature but depends on the effective density of states in the conduction band. Then

$$W = \frac{e^2E^2\tau}{m} C(T)e^{-V/2kT}.$$ 4.18

The energy gained from the field then will be rapidly shared among the conduction and trapped electrons by electron-electron collisions. The concentration of trapped electrons can be expressed approximately as

$$n_T = C_T(T)e^{-(V-\Delta V)/2kT},$$ 4.19

where the factor $C_T(T)$ depends on the density of trapping states and varies also only slightly with temperature.

If we assume a high density of traps, which is usually the case, the concentration of trapped electrons will greatly exceed the concentration of conduction electrons, and it will be mainly trapped electrons that are responsible for transferring energy to the lattice.[266] For example, in polyethylene, electrons are concentrated in regions of low electron density, produced by microbrownian motion of amorphous parts and liberating electrons from traps, for example, in the interfacial regions between amorphous and crystalline parts. Liberated electrons may flow easily along the c-axis of crystalline lamellae and contribute to the energy transfer from the electric field to the bulk of polyethylene.

At low field, an equilibrium electron temperature will be attained, where energy lost to the lattice is just balanced by the energy gained from the field. But at fields above a critical value E_c, the balance is no longer possible, and this critical value is now defined as the breakdown strength. The critical value can be estimated from

$$E_c \sim e^{\Delta V/4kT_0},$$ 4.20

which leads to a decrease in dielectric strength as the temperature rises. The physical interpretation for this behavior is that the relative numbers of conduction electrons vs trapped electrons increases with temperature as a result of gaining more kinetic energy from the field.

4.20.2 Thermal Breakdown

Whenever there is sufficient dielectric loss, especially conductivity loss, present in a polymer to produce appreciable Joule heating in an applied field, the possibility of breakdown caused by the thermal effect exists because the accompanying rise in temperature will increase the conductivity. Of course, in an alternating field, the additional heat generated through one or more of the relaxation processes will exhibit thermal effects too, which will hasten the onset of any thermal runaway condition. Whether thermal breakdown develops or not will depend on the rate at which heat is conducted away to the surroundings.

Although the failure of solids by partial discharges is not being covered here, internal discharges may significantly contribute to the losses exhibited by an imperfect solid. The rise in tan δ occurring at voltages in excess of discharge inception increases the risk of thermal breakdown. Relying on discharge measurements made at the electrodes, we can estimate by this method the dissipation factor attributable to internal discharges.[21]

The thermal and current continuity equations may be used to describe conditions for thermal instability. For dc conditions, thermal continuity for a unit volume of dielectric is given by

$$\sigma E^2 = C_v \frac{dT}{dt} + \text{div}(\kappa \text{ grad } T), \qquad 4.21$$

where electrical and thermal conductivities are given by σ and κ, respectively, and C_v is the specific heat at constant volume. The heat input is here balanced by the heat required to raise the temperature and that lost by conduction. For ac, the input term is given by $E^2 \omega \varepsilon_0 \varepsilon''$, where ω is the angular frequency and ε'' is the imaginary part of the dielectric constant. For current density continuity

$$\text{div } J = 0. \qquad 4.22$$

A solution of Eqs. (4.21) and (4.22) is not usually possible in the general case since σ and κ are functions of temperature, σ is field dependent, and the boundary conditions are generally complicated. Examination of these two equations under ac and dc conditions gives the following. For dc, Eq. (4.22) implies that σE must be constant. If the material under investigation suffers a small rise in temperature, E must necessarily fall, thus leading to a smaller power input (σE^2) in Eq. (4.21). In this case, the process is self-compensating. Under ac conditions it is $E \omega \varepsilon_0 (\varepsilon' - j\varepsilon'')$ that must remain constant. Since $\varepsilon' \gg \varepsilon''$, E remains unchanged, and thus the ac power input must increase in response to a change in ε'' as the temperature rises.

Thus, the high-temperature operation of lossy materials under high-frequency sustained alternating stresses represents dangerous condition from the standpoint of thermal breakdown. However, not all of these conditions have to be met for a thermal runaway situation to occur.

a) *Impulse Thermal Breakdown*

For the adiabatic case (applied electric field of short duration), Eq. (4.21) may be simplified and the dielectric temperature may be estimated from the spatially independent equation

$$C_v \frac{dT}{dt} = \sigma E^2, \qquad 4.23$$

which defines the thermal conditions for impulse thermal breakdown. This condition is favored at high temperatures because of the large ratio of electrical to thermal conductivities.

Eq. (4.23) is a good assumption only if the time to breakdown, t_c, is given by the inequality

$$t_c < \frac{C_v d^2}{\kappa} \qquad\qquad 4.24$$

where d is the interelectrode distance.

An approximate expression for the time to breakdown under impulse thermal conditions has been derived:[267, 268]

$$t_c \cong \frac{C_v k T_0^2}{B_1 \sigma E_c^2}, \qquad\qquad 4.25$$

where σ is the conductivity appropriate to the ambient temperature T_O and the particular breakdown field strength.

The conductivity of polyethylene is increased by doping with additives, and under these circumstances, impulse thermal breakdown results from a conductivity based on the Poole-Frenkel effect in the temperature range of 0–75°C.[269] Comparison with experimental results indicates that a thermal mechanism can explain breakdown if 100 W/cm^3 is assumed for the Joule heating.

b) Steady-State Conditions

Impulse thermal failure is not as important as thermal failure under sustained voltage application. If near-steady-state conditions prevail, $(dT/dt) \to 0$ in Eq. (4.21). For a plane parallel thick slab of stressed dielectric a solution of the equation is readily accomplished. Should failure occur at the melting temperature T_m, the breakdown voltage is given by

$$V_c^2 = 8 \int_{T_a}^{T_m} (\kappa/\sigma) dT, \qquad\qquad 4.26$$

where T_a is the ambient temperature at the electrode surface. Under ac conditions, σ may be replaced by $\omega \varepsilon_0 \varepsilon''$ with little error. Equation (4.26) defines thermal steady-state breakdown in terms of only the thermal conductivity κ and the electrical conductivity σ. There is no dependence on thickness because a reduction in electric stress with increased dielectric thickness is compensated by poorer thermal conduction.

From the industrial viewpoint, a number of important applications require polymer films to be operated at high temperatures. For these applications, polyimide film, which has a loss tangent of 0.003 or higher at 25°C and 1 kHz, is often employed. However, above 200°C the losses rise rapidly, presumably because of ionic conduction. It has been suggested that at high temperatures the charge carrier is protonic and is supplied from the residual nonreacted polyamic acid.[270] Some support for this has been provided by hydrolytic and heat treatments carried out in conjunction with conductivity and breakdown measurements on polyimide and polyamide-imide films.[271]

Estimates of the temperature rise based on the conductivity data together with the behavior of the electric strength provide a basis for believing that thermal failure is an important mechanism in polyimides. It is predicted that there exists a critical current density at which a steep temperature rise is initiated (Fig. 4.19), leading to dielectric breakdown.[271] This computation is made on the basis of the application of a ramp stress of 0.2 MV/cm/s applied to films at an initial ambient temperature of 300°C. The ultimate strength depends on the ionic jump distance assumed in the conduction model for the conductivity. A comparison with experimental breakdown and conduction characteristics leads to an estimate of 75 Å for the ionic jump distance in polyimide film and 3 eV for the zero-field activation energy for the process.

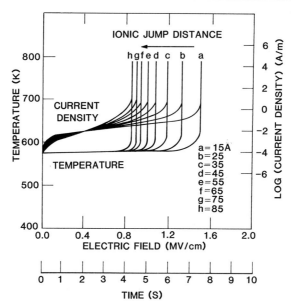

Fig. 4.19. Critical current vs temperature rise in polyimide film.

4.20.3 Electromechanical Breakdown

This mechanism is based on the fact that the breakdown characteristics of polymers in the temperature region near the melting (softening) temperature are similar to their mechanical characteristics changes. The breakdown is caused by the mechanical deformation resulting from Maxwell stress under the applied electric field.[245]

For instance, electrodes attached to the surface of a polymer specimen during a dielectric breakdown test will exert a compressive force on the polymer by mutual Coulombic attraction as the voltage is imposed. If this is sufficient to cause appreciable deformation at fields below the intrinsic breakdown value, the dielectric strength of the polymer will be reduced. The attractive force F is given by the differential of the energy U stored in the system with respect to the thickness d of the material at constant applied voltage:

$$F = \left|\left(\frac{\partial U}{\partial d}\right)_v\right| = \frac{\partial}{\partial d}\left(\frac{1}{2}\,CV^2\right)_v.$$

4.27

For a parallel-plate capacitor with a capacitance C and a polymer with cross-sectional area A and dielectric constant ε, the compressive force per unit area is

$$\frac{F}{A} = -\frac{1}{2}\,\varepsilon_0\varepsilon\left(\frac{V}{d}\right)^2.$$

4.28

Since the compression caused by the electrical force is balanced by the mechanical elastic restoring force, at equilibrium

$$\frac{1}{2}\,\varepsilon_0\varepsilon\left(\frac{V}{d}\right)^2 = Y\ln\left(\frac{d_0}{d}\right),$$

4.29

where Y is Young's modulus for the polymer and d_0 is the initial thickness of the specimen. Solution of Eq. (4.29) for d gives the equilibrium thickness of the polymer slab under the applied voltage. For a given value of V, $d^2\ln(d_0/d)$ reaches a maximum value when $d/d_0 =$

$\exp(-1/2) \approx 0.6$, then no real value of V can produce a stable equilibrium for values of d/d_0 less than 0.6. For the stable thickness ratio, further increase in V then produces mechanical collapse. The critical field is

$$E_c = \left(\frac{Y}{\varepsilon_0 \varepsilon}\right)^{1/2}.$$

4.30

In other words, the highest apparent dielectric strength E_a that can be observed is

$$E_a = \frac{V_c}{d_0} = \frac{d}{d_0} E_c \approx 0.6 \left(\frac{Y}{\varepsilon_0 \varepsilon}\right)^{1/2}.$$

4.31

Thus, the electromechanical breakdown may also be considered the mechanical intervention of dielectric breakdown of polymers when the mechanical effect plays a secondary role. This breakdown is inherent to polymers and is successful in explaining the breakdown characteristics of polymers in the higher temperature regions. It has to be noted that the above simple treatment totally ignores any deviations from linear elastic behavior at large strains.

Apparently, the low values of breakdown strength of many rubberlike polymers are described quantitatively by Eq. (4.31), and many plastics fail by the electromechanical mechanism at higher temperatures. In the case of PE and XLPE,[272] the Young's modulus of XLPE does not decrease as much with temperature as that of PE, whereas their dielectric strengths behaviors with temperature are similar.

4.20.4 Gas Discharge Breakdown

This mechanism may be considered the chemical intervention of dielectric breakdown of polymers, in which the chemical effect plays the secondary role. According to recent experimental evidence, this mechanism involves the creation of gaseous channels through the dielectric.[15] The high conductance of breakdown appears to be associated with these channels, not with conduction through the solid itself. The dielectric strength of a gas is very much less than that of a solid dielectric (about 3 kV/mm) so during the application of a high voltage to a polymer, discharges are likely to occur at an early stage in any gas that is at the edges of the electrodes or may be occluded as bubbles in the polymer. Such external and internal discharges tend to damage the polymer, and repeated discharges then lead to a dielectric failure. The high temperature in the discharges readily causes the polymer degradation to carbon and gaseous products. This process is often accelerated by reaction of ozone and other active products, such as nitrogen oxides formed in the gaseous discharge. Under a direct voltage, discharges will recur only after surface charges deposited by the previous discharge have had time to leak away, but under an alternating voltage, discharge will be repeated with every half-cycle and the problem becomes much more severe.

The central problem in the theory of this mechanism of breakdown of polymers is to explain the development, in a strong electric field, of a macroscopic gaseous channel through the polymer before the large change of conductance characteristic of dielectric breakdown. As new experimental evidence accumulates, a case can be made for associating the high conductance of breakdown with a gaseous conducting path rather than a high electron current in the solid.[14, 272-274]

4.21 POLYMER STRUCTURE AND DIELECTRIC BREAKDOWN

Many unknowns still remain regarding the dielectric breakdown processes of polymers. The complex nature of polymer macromolecules, often compounded by partial crystallinity and polar groups, makes interpretation of any measurements difficult. However, since the chain length, order, orientation, an linkage all have known effects on mechanical properties, it is at least logical to seek links between structural parameters and electrical properties. The room-temperature properties of chlorinated polyethylenes depicted in Fig. 4.20 indicate that there are at least superficial correlations between the mechanical and electrical properties of some dielectrics.[251, 252] For polymers, at least, an understanding of these relationships is important in many practical insulation applications.

The essential feature of the temperature dependence of electric strength for most linear polymers is illustrated in Fig. 4.21.[246, 259] The temperature range can be classified into three

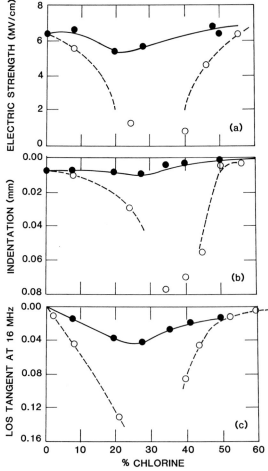

Fig. 4.20. Correlation between the mechanical and electrical properties for a range of chlorinated polyethylenes. The solid line indicates cold chlorination; the broken line indicates hot chlorination: (a) electric strength, (b) mechanical hardness, (c) dielectric loss. (after Oakes [251])

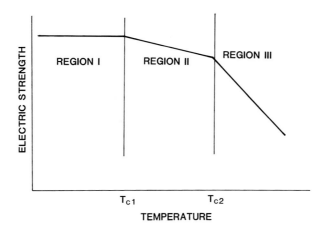

Fig. 4.21. Outline of the temperature dependence of electric strength of linear polymers.

TABLE 4.8 Corresponding Breakdown Processes for Regions I, II, and III in Fig. 4.21[a]

Region	Molecular State	Corresponding Breakdown Process
I	Glasslike	Electron avalanche breakdown
II	Rubberlike	(a) Collective breakdown for amorphous dielectrics (b) Thermal breakdown (c) Free-volume breakdown
III	Plastic-flow	(a) Thermal breakdown (b) Electromechanical breakdown

[a] Secondary effects: space charge, local heating, Maxwell stress.

TABLE 4.9 Various Factors Affecting Electric Strength of Linear Polymers[246, 259]

Factor	Electric Strength[a] Region		
	I	II	III
Introducing polar molecules	+	?	+
Increasing molecular weight	*	+	+
Cross-linking	*	*	+
Increasing crystallinity	−	+	+
Higher degree of molecular stereoregularity	−	+	?
Impurity ⟋ with rich π electrons	+	*	*
Impurity ⟍ which decreases specimen resistivity	*	−	−

[a] Symbols in the table mean: + increase, − decrease, * not sensitive, ? unknown.

divisions: Regions I, II, and III. Corresponding to each region, the technology of the linear polymers and the possible breakdown processes are summarized in Table 4.8. These descriptions are based on the consideration of various factors listed in Table 4.9. In this section, the recent results on the correlations between the dielectric breakdown and the inherent nature of polymers is presented in detail.

4.21.1 Chemical Structure

a) *Polar Groups*

Polymers at low temperature possess high values of E_B. In the high-temperature region, E_B decreases with rising temperature and falls steeply at higher temperatures where the polymers begin to soften (plastic flow). The relationships between the dielectric breakdown and the introduction of polar groups may be summarized as follows:

(1) In the temperature dependence of E_B of nonpolar polymers, the critical temperature (T_c) between low- and high-temperature regions clearly exists. For polar polymers, however, a low-temperature region and T_c are not clearly defined.

(2) The introduction of a polar group in a polymer structure brings about an increase of E_B in the low-temperature region.

The breakdown mechanism in the low-temperature region is considered to be an electron avalanche breakdown process based on the results of time lag for the breakdown,[256] the thickness dependence of E_B, and the effect of impurities.[275] The scattering of the accelerated electrons by dipoles causes E_B at low temperature to increase.[250]

Whether Fröhlich's amorphous breakdown, thermal breakdown in the high-temperature region, or electromechanical breakdown at higher temperatures near the melting point takes place depends on the type of polymer and the method of applying the voltage. The effect of polar groups in the high-temperature region is not completely clear yet.

b) *Molecular Weight*

The dependence of E_B for polyethylene on the molecular weight at room temperature is illustrated in Fig. 4.22.[1] Clearly, E_B increases with increasing molecular weight. However,

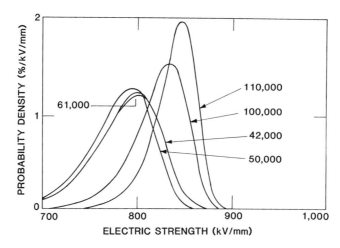

Fig. 4.22 Influence of molecular weight on the electric strength of low-density polyethylene with ac voltage. Parameter is the weight average of the molecular weight.

the T_c of polyethylene exists near room temperature, so it is difficult to discuss the exact relationship between the breakdown mechanism and the molecular weight without knowledge of the effect of molecular weight on the temperature dependence of E_B.

c) *Molecular Conformation*

Isotactic and atactic polypropylenes have different molecular conformations in the arrangements of methyl side groups. The E_B of the former is lower than that of the latter in the low-temperature region, but in the high-temperature region their relation is reversed.[252] These results in the low-temperature region are thought to be related to the difficulty of the electron acceleration caused by irregular conformation in atactic polypropylene.

d) *Cross-Linking*

In general, the E_B of linear polymers increases with the cross-linking,[253] and especially in the high-temperature region cross-linking leads to the rise of the melting point and makes E_B increase markedly. These results show that the electromechanical breakdown resulting from Maxwell stress takes place near the melting point. As an example, the effect of high-energy radiation on the dielectric breakdown of polyethylene is shown in Fig. 4.23.[245]

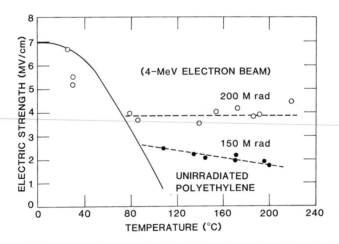

Fig. 4.23. Effect of high-energy radiation on the dielectric breakdown of polyethylene at high temperature. The dotted lines represent the theoretical values of electromechanical breakdown. Source is Ref. 245.

4.21.2 Solid-State Structure

a) *Crystallinity*

Semicrystalline polymers have both crystalline and amorphous regions. The E_B in these polymers is influenced by the structure of the crystalline region and the degree of crystallinity. Figure 4.24 shows the dependence of E_B of polyethylene with dc voltage on the degree of crystallinity that was changed by varying the annealing process on the high-density polyethylene film.[261] Below 80°C, E_B increases with decreasing crystallinity, but above 80°C, the effect of crystallinity is reversed. The results above 80°C are considered to be related to the electromechanical breakdown. For the results below 80°C, the qualitative explanation

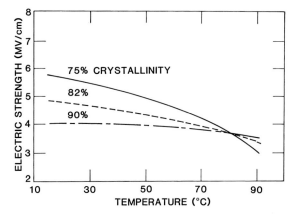

Fig. 4.24. Effects of crystallinity on the electric strength of high-density polyethylene with different annealing processes. Source is Ref. 261.

employed the modified Fröhlich's amorphous breakdown theory in which an increase in the depth of shallow trap levels for electrons was postulated to have been brought about by an increase in crystal boundaries as a result of a decrease in crystallinity.

The breakdown characteristics of ethylene-vinyl acetate copolymer (EVA) and their blends in the low-temperature region are shown in Fig 4.25.[276,277] The E_B of EVA and blends rises with an increase in vinyl acetate (VA) content, possibly because of the increased electron scattering associated with the decrease in crystallinity and the increase in polar groups. Furthermore, the E_B of EVA is nearly equal to that of blends at the same VA content. This result shows that the dielectric breakdown in the low-temperature region is not influenced solely by the degree of crystallinity but also by the individual size of microcrystallites, suggesting that electron avalanche occurs over a region much larger than the size of microcrystallites.

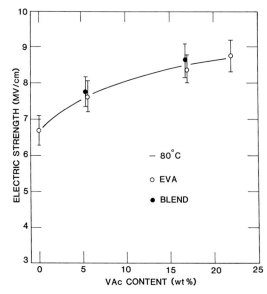

Fig. 4.25. Dielectric breakdown of ethylene-vinyl acetate copolymer, and their blends at low temperature. Sources are Refs. 276, 277.

b) *Internal Strain*

The elongation process in forming polymer films generates internal strain. The dependence of E_B of polyethylene with dc and ac voltage on the elongation rate is shown in Fig. 4.26.[278] The E_B varies in a complicated manner with the elongation, possibly because of the orientation of lamella structures and the rearrangement of free volumes. However, there are many unknown aspects of the relationship between the solid structures of the polymers and their dielectric breakdown phenomena.

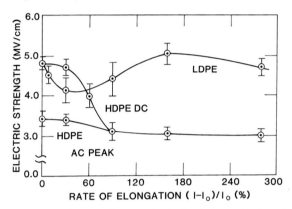

Fig. 4.26. Effect of elognation on the electric strength of polyethylene with dc and ac (peak) voltage; 1 and 1_0 are the effective length of film with and without elongation, respectively. Source is Ref. 278

c) *Molecular Motion*

The molecular motion of polymers changes with temperature. As the temperature rises, polymers show glasslike, rubberlike, and plastic-flow behavior. A characteristic molecular motion exists for each state. As summarized in Table 4.8, the electron avalanche and the

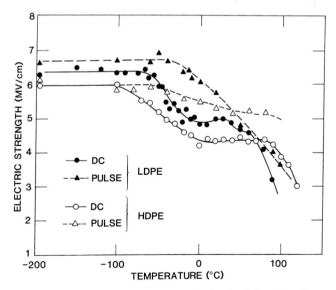

Fig. 4.27. Temperature dependence of the electric strength of polyethylene film. Sources are Refs. 276, 277.

electromechanical breakdown processes are considered to be dominant in glasslike and plasticlike states, respectively. The temperature dependence of E_B of polyethylene measured at small temperature intervals, especially in the glass transition temperature region, is shown in Fig. 4.27.[276,277] As the temperature rises, E_B decreases for dc voltage around the glass transition temperature. The E_B of high-density polyethylene begins to decrease at a lower temperature than that of low-density polyethylene. At pulsed voltage, E_B begins to decrease at a higher temperature than that with dc voltage.

These results suggest that the released segmental molecular motion and/or the increased rearrangement of free volumes enhance the electron transport in the amorphous region and facilitate the occurrence of the electron avalanche breakdown.

d) *Free Volume*

Electric strength data for atactic polystyrene, which is a nonpolar amorphous material, is shown in Fig. 4.28 superimposed on x-ray measurements of the average interchain distance as a function of temperature.[279] The addition of the plasticizer dibutyl phthalate (~2.7%)

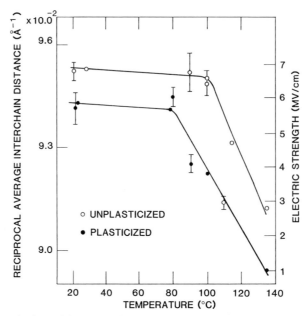

Fig. 4.28. Reciprocal values of the average interchain distance in polystyrene as a function of temperature. The data with error bars show the corresponding dc electric strength for both plasticized and unplasticized materials.

lowers the transition temperature as well as the breakdown characteristics. This has been interpreted in terms of the increase and redistribution of free volume occurring above T_g.[279] On the same basis, the electric strength E equals

$$E = \frac{\Delta W}{e\ell_x},$$ 4.32

where ΔW is the energy increment of the conduction electrons after passing through a free volume whose average field-directed length is ℓ_x of a nonpolar polymer. The length ℓ_x is related to the specific free volume v by Eqs. (4.33) and (4.34). For $T < T_g$, where the

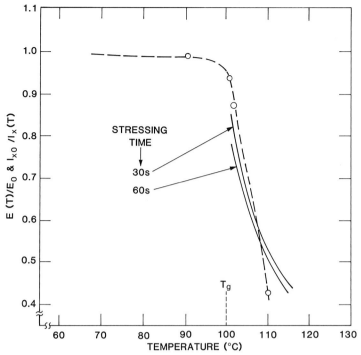

Fig. 4.29. Comparison between the theoretical value of $\ell_{x0}/\ell_x(T)$ from Eqs. (4.33) and (4.34) and the experimental electric strength ratio $E(T)/E_0$ for unplasticized polystyrene. The solid lines are theoretical values; the broken line is experimental value.

specific free volume is denoted by v_0, we have

$$\ell_{xo} = 0.5d \left[1 - \frac{\log(\zeta v_0)}{\log[1 - (1 - v_0)^6]} \right]; \qquad\qquad 4.33$$

and for $T \geq T_g$, we have

$$\ell_x(T) = 0.5d \left(1 - \frac{\log \left\{ \zeta v^2(T) \left[\dfrac{t}{\tau(T)} \right] \right\}}{\log \left\{ 1 - [1 - v(T)]^6 \right\}} \right), \qquad\qquad 4.34$$

where d is the diameter of an individual hypothetical spherical void, t the stressing time, τ the molecular relaxation time, and ζ a constant. The variation of v and τ with the temperature above T_g may be predicted by the Williams-Landel-Ferry (WLF) equation.[280] In this way, Eqs. (4.33) and (4.34) may be used with Eq. (4.32) to predict the temperature-dependent change in electric strength $E(T)$ relative to a value E_0 below T_g. With appropriate constants for unplasticized polystyrene, such a prediction has been made in Fig. 4.29, showing that a free-volume approach may be used to explain the reduction in strength with temperature.[279]

e) *Rigid Skeleton Structure*

A high-temperature polymer shows an excellent thermal endurance because of its rigid skeleton structure. The electric strength of polyimides, however, decreases markedly with the rising temperature above room temperature in spite of their stable chemical and mechanical properties in the high-temperature region (Fig. 4.30).[269, 281] This result, as well as

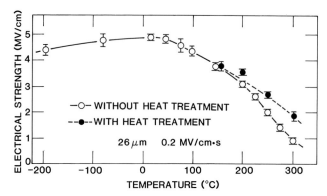

Fig. 4.30. Temperature dependence of the electric strength of polyimide film; heat treatment: 7 days at 300°C. Source is Refs. 264, 269.

the results of the dependence of the electric strength on the rising rate of electric stress and the specimen thickness, shows that the breakdown at high temperatures is a thermal breakdown process. Ionic species supplied from the residual nonreacted groups in the polymer play an important role for increased conductivity and lowered electric strength. From the numerical calculations of the electric strength caused by impulse thermal breakdown, it becomes clear that there exists a critical current density at which a steep temperature rise is initiated, resulting in the dielectric breakdown (Fig. 4.19).

f) Crystalline Interface

A polyethylene thin film consisting of spherulites is prepared by a xylene-solution casting method in an attempt to make the spherulites and their boundaries parallel to the electrode.[92] Films with clear spherulite structures about 200 μm in diameter were generated.

The breakdown patterns can be classified as either single-hole or propagating breakdowns. The latter have no relation to the intrinsic nature of the film. For the single-hole breakdown, the breakdown occurs much more often at the spherulite boundaries, particularly at the triple point of boundary lines, than at the inside of the spherulite. The effective thickness of the boundary is almost the same as that of the spherulite part. From these

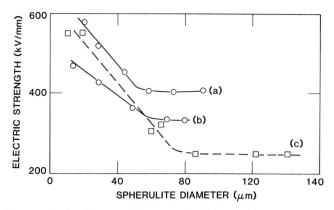

Fig. 4.31. Impulse strength of polymer specimens as a function of spherulite mean diameter: (a) high-density polyethylene, 50 μm thick; (b) high-density polyethylene, 77 μm thick; (c) polypropylene, 80 μm thick. Source is Ref. 282.

results, it will be concluded that the breakdown strength is weak along the spherulite boundaries, which is consistent with the direction of the preferred propagating path of tree breakdown in semicrystalline polymers.

In Fig. 4.31 is shown the effect of morphology on breakdown in high-density polyethylene and polyprophylene. The tests were conducted with 1.5- to 40-µs impulses on specimens in which the spherulite size was modified by heat treatment in the range of 5–145 µm. The strength is reduced with the spherulite dimension until the latter becomes about equal to the specimen thickness. It is concluded from these results that breakdown channels occur mainly in the interspherulite space of the material. The effect of the size of the spherulites is accounted for by the interspherulite regions having a lower density and irregular structure. As the spherulite size increases, the density of the polymer within the interspherulite space decreases and a reduction in electric strength and other properties is observed. Thus, the implication is that by a change in morphology, a significant modification in electrical properties may be engineered. It would be expected that for cables, the insulation has a nonuniform distribution of spherulite sizes. This occurs because crystallization from the melt depends critically on the cooling conditions so that for an insulation, the outer portions will suffer a higher rate of cooling and thus tend to have smaller spherulite sizes. Overheating of polymer cables can also have an impact on the subsequent electric strength, as a result of changes in morphology.[177]

g) Cohesive Energy Density

The cohesive energy density (CED) is a parameter that characterizes the energy required to separate the bulk molecular material into infinitely separate molecules:

$$CED = \zeta^2 = \frac{W_{vap}}{V_m},$$
4.35

where ζ is the solubility parameter, W_{vap} the evaporation energy, and V_m the molar volume. The solubility parameter may also be used to measure the degree of secondary bonding such as dispersion, dipole, and hydrogen bonding. Table 4.10 compares the electric strength of a range of polymers with their corresponding CEDs. Thus, polar materials having a high CED yield the highest electric strength. Furthermore, such materials may also be identified by their change in strength, which is a continuously decreasing function of temperature because of the breakup of dipole-dipole interactions. Nonpolar materials have a more constant strength in the glassy state.

TABLE 4.10 Comparison of the Electric Strength of Some Polymeric Materials with Their Cohesive Energy Densities (CED)[a]

Polymer	Polar (P) or Nonpolar (N)	CED (J/Cm³)	Electric Strength at −195°C (MV/cm)
Polydimethylsiloxane	N	233	2.1
Polyisobutylene	N	254	5.1
Polyethylene	N	261	6.8
Polybutadiene	N	274	6.5
Polystyrene	N	364	7.2
Polyvinylacetate	P	370	12.2
Poly(methyl methacrylate)	P	377	13.4

[a] After Sabuni and Nelson.[283]

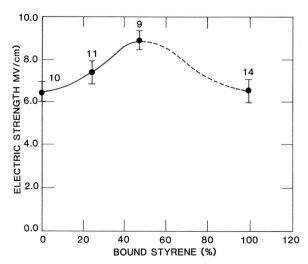

Fig. 4.32. The variation of the electric strength of butadiene/styrene copolymers. The figures above the error bars represent the number of specimens used in generating the mean. Source is Ref. 263.

There appears to be a correlation also between the CED and the free-volume calculations. In Fig. 4.32 is illustrated the electric strength of butadiene-styrene copolymers measured at −195°C. The copolymers gave low-temperature electric strengths greater than either of the homopolymers and this followed the changes in the percentage of free volume tabulated by Ferry:[284] for polystyrene, polybutadiene, and a 76.5/23.5 random copolymer, the respective values are 0.032–0.033, 0.039, and 0.021. This effect is similar to that observed by von Hippel[285] in a mixed-crystal system in which the replacement of KCl by RbCl increased the electric strength to a point after which it fell toward the strength of RbCl.

In the context of this discussion it may be proposed that the plasticizer molecules tend to neutralize some of the intermolecular cohesive energy. This would automatically create an increase in interchain distance d_a since the intermolecular energy $W(d_a)$ is approximately d_a^{-6}. The consequent loosening of the structure would allow more freedom for segmental mobility at a lower temperature and thus explain reduction in transition temperature. Since at low temperature the electric strength is determined by the energy exchange between the charge carriers and the structure, the increase in free volume of the plasticized material would provide more suitable conditions for breakdown. Neither the amount nor the distribution of free volume is temperature dependent below T_g, and thus explains the constancy of strength.

h) Band-Gap Energy

A correlation between electric strength and band-gap energy that has been observed with alkali halide crystals (Table 4.11)[286,287] may also be applicable to polymers. As a result of impact ionization, electrons in the conduction band may transfer energy to valence electrons to create an avalanche of electrons at breakdown fields. Thus the energy gap could be an important physical parameter in determining the breakdown field strength.

TABLE 4.11 The Electric Strength of the Alkali Halide Crystals in Comparison with Band-Gap Energy[286, 287]

Compound	Band-Gap Energy (eV)	Electric Strength (MV/cm)
LiF	12.0	3.1
NaF	$\geq$ 10.5	2.4
KF	10.9	1.9
NaCl	8.6	1.5
NaBr	7.7	0.81
RbBr	7.7	0.63
KI	$\geq$ 6.2	0.57
RbI	$\geq$ 6.1	0.49

i) *Impurities*

Some of the impurities are the various residual catalysts or their fragments and various additives typically used in polymers. Their properties and the state of dispersion have a great influence on E_B. In general, impurities, which cause high electrical conductivity and are distributed in a form of microparticles, cause a marked decrease in E_B.[288] The additive pyrene, which has a number of π-electrons in its molecule and makes a molecular dispersion, raises E_B at low temperature because of energy absorption through the interaction with the accelerated electrons (Fig. 4.33.).[275] The additive AS-1, which supplies a charge carrier and increases the electrical conductivity, lowers E_B at high temperature because of the thermal breakdown process.[281]

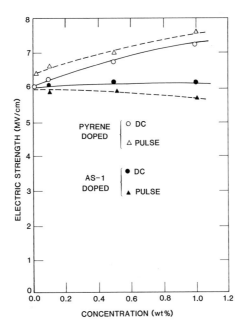

Fig. 4.33 Influence of impurities on the dielectric breakdown of polyethylene at $-196°C$.

4.22 EFFECT OF PLASTICIZATION ON DIELECTRIC BREAKDOWN

Plasticization is commonly used to modify the physicomechanical properties of polymers. However, there is also a possibility for this modification to alter the electrical properties in an unfavorable direction. We have already discussed the effect of plasticization on tan δ. The discussion of plasticization on dielectric breakdown E_B will provide additional means for clarifying the breakdown mechanism of polymers in general.

Addition of a plasticizer to a polymer weakens its intermolecular forces and generally disturbs its supermolecular structure. For practical purposes the glass transition temperature is always lowered.[289] Lowering of T_g means the extension of Region II into Region I (Figure 4.21), which leads not only to a decrease in dielectric strength, but also the change in breakdown mechanism. The general trend of plasticization is to lower the value of E_B.[290]

When poly(methyl methacrylate) is plasticized with dibutyl phthalate, the dielectric strength decreases as the quantity of plasticizer increases.[252] Furthermore, the shapes of the temperature dependence curves of E_B are nearly the same, the only difference being a lowering of the T_g. Thus, the decrease in E_B may be correlated with the lowering of T_g of polymers.

The absorption of moisture of polymers may be also considered a kind of plasticization, and hence the values of E_B will be affected. For example, when rubber is immersed in water for 24 h, its E_B may decrease from 12 to 29%.[291] When ethyl cellulose, cellulose triacetate, or cellulose acetobutyrate is exposed to air at a relative humidity of 65%, its E_B is decreased as much as 40% of the original value within a few minutes.[292] The decrease has been attributed to macroscopic nonuniformity introduced by plasticization.[293]

4.22.1 Molecular and Structural Plasticization

a) *Polystyrene*

The difference in effect between molecular and structural plasticizers can be illustrated with polystyrene.[294] When styrene or toluene as a molecular plasticizer is added to polystyrene, the decrease in E_B at first is nearly linear with the quantity of plasticizer added and eventually decreases and approaches a constant value. When a structural plasticizer such as transformer oil is used, the dielectric strength drops at first very rapidly when the percentage concentration of transformer oil is less than 1%, then passes through a minimum value and rises again up to a stabilized value as the concentration of transformer oil increases gradually. These relationships are illustrated in Fig. 4.34.[295]

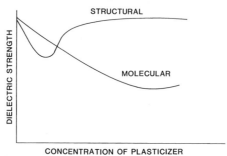

Fig. 4.34. Schematic diagram of the difference in effect between molecular and structural plasticizers for polystyrene.

These differences in effect between molecular and structural plasticizers are due to the differences in the mechanism of plasticization. Noncompatibility differences between the two types of plasticizer do not seem to be the predominant factors as the density differences in the two cases are only minor (Table 4.12).

TABLE 4.12 Densities of Polystyrenes in Relation to Their Plasticizer Contents[295]

Toluene		Transformer Oil	
Content (wt%)	Density (g/cm^3)	Content (wt%)	Density (g/cm^3)
0	1.056	0	1.056
1	1.050	1	1.052
5	1.039	5	1.046
10	1.032	9	1.041
15	1.024	15	1.031

The molecular plasticizer molecules act to weaken the intermolecular interactions of polymers and to fill in the interspace of super molecular structure and modify it to a certain extent.[296] This leads to a "loosened" polymeric structure and an increased mean free path of carriers, which facilitates the storage of energy and thus leads to an electronic breakdown. When toluene is added to polystyrene, the dielectric strength decreases with increasing toluene content. When the toluene content passes 20 wt%, the dielectric strength stays essentially constant with further increases of toluene. This is because the supermolecular structure of polystyrene has already been modified.

For the transformer oil-polystyrene system, because the structural plasticizer cannot penetrate far into the polymer and because only a limited quantity of this plasticizer can fit into the interspace of the supermolecular structure, the decrease in the dielectric strength is most drastic at low levels of plasticizer. Then, in the vicinity of 1%, the supermolecular structure of polystyrene has already been modified to the extent possible, and further addition of transformer oil acts only to fill any possible microvoids; hence, E_B rises again to a constant value.

b) *Polyethylene and Poly(Vinyl Chloride)*

When a similar study is extended to polyethylene and poly(vinyl chloride), the results are less clear.[297] When dibutyl phthalate as a molecular plasticizer is added to poly(vinyl chloride) and transformer oil is added to polyethylene as a structural plasticizer, their effect on the value of E_B is similar and is of the same nature as that of the structural plasticizer illustrated in Fig. 4.34. The final constant values are higher than those of the nonplasticized polymers themselves. In the case of poly(vinyl chloride) the "constant" value decreases again at extremely high plasticizer contents (Fig. 4.35).

A possible interpretation of these confusing results may be as follows: Since the transformer oil is a structural plasticizer for both polystyrene and polyethylene, the initial decrease in dielectric strength is due to the modification of their supermolecular structures. The increase in dielectric strength after the minimum is due to the filling of microvoids originally present in these polymers. This can be confirmed by observations under a polarized-light microscope. The reason for the higher elevation of dielectric strength of polyethylene over that of polystyrene may be due to its higher content of the original microvoids compared with polystyrene.

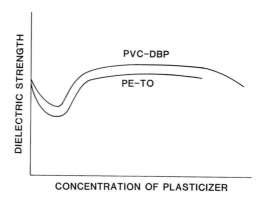

Fig. 4.35. Schematic illustration showing the effect of plasticization on poly(vinyl chloride) and poly-ethylene. Source is Ref. 297.

The effect of molecular plasticization of poly(vinyl chloride) follows its mechanical properties behavior. When its mechanical properties, for example, tensile strength and Young's modulus, are plotted against the molecular plasticizer's content, a maximum is exhibited in these properties when elongation exhibits a minimum.[298] These results correlate well with the results obtained from both the infrared and x-ray structural analyses showing that the regularity of the supermolecular structure also exhibits a maximum at a certain level of molecular plasticizer content.[299] These results are also corroborated by polarized-light and electron microscopic observations.[300] Thus, the maximum range of dielectric strength in poly (vinyl chloride) may also be correlated with an increase in regularity of its supermolecular structure.[301,302] When the content of plasticizer is over 40%, this regularity then begins to collapse, and the value of E_B decreases.

4.23 EFFECT OF FILLERS ON DIELECTRIC BREAKDOWN

Fillers are used in polymers to reduce their cost and to improve their physicochemical properties. Furthermore, in the processing of polymers into insulating products, the incorporation of small quantities of small particles of mechanically derived impurities is unavoidable. These impurities may then also have to be considered fillers. Hence, solid fillers seem to be one of the integral parts of polymers in general.

In some cases the presence of solid fillers tends to increase E_B, whereas in others they tend to decrease the E_B. There are also cases in which the addition of solid filler makes no difference in E_B. Interpretation of these facts is always in controversy.

For example, in the early years in the study of the dielectric strength of rosin, it was found that the addition of 1% carbon black led to a 90% drop in E_B; however, further addition caused no additional drop.[303] The introduction of 0.1% of boroaluminosilicate glass dropped E_B by two-thirds of its original value with no additional drop upon further additions. When quartz is used as a filler, there is no effect on E_B. According to the interpretation of the authors of that time, the effect of carbon black and boroaluminosilicate was due to their conductivities and dielectric constants, which are greatly different from those of rosin, and this then leads to the distortion of the electric field. The minimal effect of quartz was presumed to be due to the ε and σ being close to those for the rosin.

4.23.1 Fillers in Synthetic Polymers

For synthetic polymers, early results on polyethylene also showed that the introduction of lead carbonate in quantities up to 1% decreased E_B in direct proportion to the quantity of lead carbonate added.[286] At a 1% content of lead carbonate, E_B has already dropped to 80% of it original value. However, addition of small quantities of SiO_2 or TiO_2 to polyethylene terephthalate had minimal effect on E_B.[304] Addition of SiO_2 or MgO to polyethylene, within the range 1–50 wt%, decreased the impulse breakdown strength by 50–60% while increasing the ε.[305] Addition of kaolin (up to 30 wt%) to a plasticized poly(vinyl chloride) increased its E_B with increasing quantity of kaolin.[306] With 30 wt% of kaolin, E_B of some plasticized PVC compositions may be increased up to 23–26%.

To illustrate the effect of a filler on the physical state of a polymer, we examine the effects of quartz powder on E_B of polyethylene and polystyrene. At room temperature polystyrene is amorphous and in the glassy state, whereas polyethylene is semicrystalline and in the rubbery state. When a fine powder of quartz is added to these polymers, the effects are very similar (Fig. 4.36). When the weight percentage of quartz is around 1%, E_B drops sharply to 82% for polyethylene and to 73% for polystyrene. But the values of ε and σ of quartz are very close to those of polyethylene and polystyrene and hence cannot explain the decrease in E_B by a distortion of the electric field.

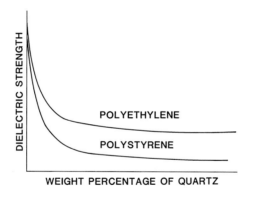

Fig. 4.36. Schematic diagram of the effect of quartz on E_B of polyethylene and polystyrene.

a) *The Effect of Fillers on Mechanical Properties*

It is well known that some fillers can exert tremendous influence on the mechanical properties of rubbers.[307] According to their effectiveness, fillers may be classified into three groups: (1) active, (2) semiactive, and (3) inactive. The active fillers, such as carbon black, can increase mechanical strength of rubbers to a high degree because the small particles of the active fillers are able to change the morphology of rubber and establish chemical bonding with it. When the volume percentage of the active fillers reaches 10–15%, a supermolecular structure is formed, which insures regular orientation of the rubber phase.[308,309]

The semiactive fillers, such as graphite, exhibit minimal influence on the mechanical strength of rubbers. Only when the volume percentage of graphite reaches about 10% does the mechanical strength of rubber increase slightly.

The addition of inactive fillers, such as silica glass powder, will actually decrease the mechanical strength of rubber. The decrease is drastic at first; then the rate gradually decreases with further addition.

b) *The Effect of Fillers on Electrical Properties*

By analogy with the filler effect on mechanical properties, there are also three kinds of fillers as far as their effect on electrical properties is concerned.[310, 311] The fact that lead carbonate, quartz, TiO_2, and MgO had no effect or actually decreased E_B can be attributed to their inert nature and their particle size, which was not sufficiently fine to influence the supermolecular structure. On the other hand, when kaolin is added to poly(vinyl chloride), it raises E_B because kaolin acts as a nucleating agent and an active morphology modifier.[305, 312] For example, x-ray structural analysis on unfilled and filled polycaprolactam fibers confirmed that nucleating fillers resulted in the formation of a new fine structure.[312]

When methyl red is used as a nucleating agent in high-density polyethylene and is processed into a film with a thickness of 0.06 mm, the value of the dielectric strength varies with the quantity of methyl red used (Table 4.13).[297] The addition of methyl red leads to the formation of uniform fine spherulites and improves the uniformity of the electric field within the specimen. Consequently, the mean free path of electrons and the diffusion coefficient of charge carriers both decrease.

TABLE 4.13 Relationship of Dielectric Strength of HDPE Film with Methyl Red Content[297]

Methyl Red (wt%)	Dielectric Strength (kV/mm)
0	370
0.5	410
1.0	415

4.23.2 Summary

The effect of conducting fillers on the dielectric breakdown can be summarized as follows: experiments on the direct current conductivity indicated that the presence of a low (<3%) concentration of fine, dispersed carbon black particles in the insulating matrix did not alter the basic insulating properties of polyethylene.[313] Analysis of the transient conductivity data revealed broad relaxation-type peaks in the loss factor at very low frequencies, which were interpreted as interfacial polarization occurring at the amorphous/crystalline interfaces. However, detailed step-response measurements under a high field as a function of temperature and applied field have revealed a near-quadratic dependence of the steady-state conduction current on the applied field.[314] The steady-state and transient absorption and desorption currents can be interpreted as manifestations of space-charge-limited conduction and charge carrier trapping. Hence, the general effect of conductive fillers is to decrease E_B, but the effect is small under low-field conditions.

4.24   EFFECT OF MOLECULAR WEIGHT ON DIELECTRIC BREAKDOWN

It is already well known that the dielectric strength of gaseous and liquid dielectrics depends on the molecular weight. The dielectric strength of gases and aliphatic hydrocarbons increases linearly with molecular weight. For polyethylene, the direct current dielectric strength also increased with increasing molecular weight when the melt index was in the 0.3 bis 200 range and the measurements were made in the temperature range from −95 to 80°C (Table 4.14).[315,316]

TABLE 4.14 Relationship between Dielectric Strength and Melt Index of Polyethylene

Temperature (°C)	Dielectric Strength (kV/mm)								
	M. 1. = 200			M. I. = 70			M. I. = 0.3		
	Min.	Mean	Max.	Min.	Mean	Max.	Min.	Mean	Max.
−195	680	730	770	620	670	720	720	750	790
5	59	64	69	–	–	–	–	–	–
20	47	57	63	57	63	67	64	72	76
30	35	53	61	52	56	59	–	–	–
40	46	48	50	48	48	50	62	65	69
50	37	49	41	39	41	43	47	56	62
60	34	35	38	34	37	39	51	53	55
70	20.5	27.5	30.5	27.5	30,5	33.5	44.5	46.5	51.5
80	22.7	23.8	24.7	26	28.2	30	39.4	42.4	48.3

In any molecular weight-dielectric strength correlation work, it is important that any low-molecular-weight fractions are taken into account or are removed from the sample for proper evaluation of the correlation. Otherwise, the plasticizing effect of the low-molecular weight fraction will affect the dielectric strength values. The dielectric strengths of a polyester and a phenol-formaldehyde resin also increase with increasing molecular weight if residual monomers and low-molecular-weight fractions are removed.[317,318]

4.24.1   Dielectric Strength vs Molecular Weight

The general trend of dielectric strength with molecular weight for polystyrene and polyvinyl acetate is illustrated in Fig. 4.37. For polystyrene the molecular weights ranged from 100 to 10^5 and the measurements were taken on 0.07- to 0.4-mm-thick films at −20 to +20°C.[319] For polyvinyl acetate the molecular weights ranged from 86 to 8.4×10^4, and the measurements were made on 0.25-mm-thick films at 20°C.[320] The absolute functional relationship between dielectric strength and molecular weight for different polymers (especially those involving different experimental conditions) may be different, yet the general trend is the same in all cases. The rate of increase of dielectric strength with molecular weight at first is very slow, then very rapid, and finally very slow again. This also holds true when impulse voltage is used instead of alternating voltage of 50 Hz.[321]

The functional relationship of dielectric strength and molecular weight can be represented by an empirical equation of the type

$$E_B = A + B \exp(-K/m), \quad (kV/mm) \qquad 4.36$$

where A, B, and K are constants. Examples of some of these constants are given in Table 4.15. The empirical Eq. (4.36) can be extended also to other polymers including HDPE and LDPE.[322–325]

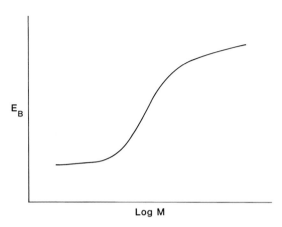

Fig. 4.37. Schematic diagram of the variation in dielectric strength with molecular weight for polystyrene and polyvinyl acetate. Source is Refs. 319, 320.

4.24.2 Molecular Weight and Supermolecular Structure

The inflection point in Fig. 4.37 corresponds to a change in supermolecular structure and regularity of molecular conformation with molecular weight. The influence of molecular weight on the supermolecular structure and molecular conformation can be checked by electron microscopy[325] and x-ray structural analysis.[326] For example, when the molecular weight of polyvinyl alcohol,[301, 302] atactic polystyrene,[327] and poly(methyl methacrylate)[328] increased, the stereoregularity of their molecular conformations also increased along with an increase in dielectric strength.[326]

TABLE 4.15 Examples of Values of A, B, and K[319, 320]

Polymer	Voltage	Sample Thickness (mm)	Temperature (°C)	Constant		
				A	B	K
Polystyrene	Alternating, 50 Hz	0.4	−20	42.5	39	9000
Polystyrene	Alternating, 50 Hz	0.4	20	34	37	9000
Polystyrene	Alternating, 50 Hz	0.1	20	130	43	9000
Polystyrene	Impulse	0.07	20	190	130	15000
Polyvinylacetate	Alternating, 50 Hz	0.25	20	59	26	6000

a) *Polyethylenes*

In the case of polyethylenes, the increase in molecular weight is accompanied by a decrease in spherulite diameter and hexane vapor penetration coefficient. However, in polyethylenes an increase in molecular weight is also accompanied by an increase in branching, which leads to an increased molecular complexity. As a consequence of increasing complexity, the melt viscosity increases, which retards the rate of crystallization, and both the crystallinity and the size of spherulites decrease. As the size of spherulites decreases, the number of spherulites increases, and the density of the interspherulitic space then increases, which leads to a decreased hexane vapor penetration coefficient and an increased dielectric strength.

b) *Cellulose Acetate*

In the case of cellulose acetate, a rigid chain polymer, the situation is just the reverse. Some of the physicochemical properties of cellulose acetate are listed in Table 4.16.[322] The dielectric strength was measured under impulse voltage conditions. The samples were divided into two parts: one was dried in the presence of calcium chloride before the breakdown test, and the other was kept in air at 67% relative humidity at 20°C for 1 h. As the molecular weight increased, both the density and the dielectric strength decreased, whereas moisture permeability increased. As the chain length of macromolecules increased, their rigidity also increased, which hindered the orientation and relaxation processes, resulting in a decreased polymer density and increased mean free path of electrons, leading to decreased dielectric strength.

TABLE 4.16 Some Properties of Cellulose Acetate[322]

Molecular Weight ($\times 10^4$)	Dielectric Strength (KV/mm)		Density (g/cm^3)	Moisture Permeability (g/cm^2 mm Hg)	$\tan \delta \times 10^2$, 20°C, 10^4 Hz
	Dry	Moist			
4.1	400	350	1.385	550	1.32
5.8	380	320	–	–	1.00
6.1	380	315	–	–	1.00
7.0	360	305	–	605	1.26
9.8	345	290	1.325	650	1.24
11.4	333	270	1.295	–	–
14.2	320	260	–	–	1.12
16.0	310	250	1.180	700	1.24

The increase of chain rigidity with increasing molecular weight is due to an increase in the length of the molecular motion segmental unit. When these samples were observed under an electron microscope, the nonuniformity of their surfaces in the form of microcavities and globular formation was very apparent. The size of these nonuniformities increases with increasing molecular weight.

4.25 EFFECT OF MORPHOLOGY ON DIELECTRIC BREAKDOWN

Polymeric insulating materials with good engineering characteristics may be obtained not only through the synthesis of new chemical compositions but also by the modification of the morphology of existing polymers.[329] Some of this was brought out in the previous section in connection with the effects of molecular weight on the supermolecular structure.

In the early years, it was already known that there was a connection between the breakdown and the morphology and crystallinity content.[330] The smaller the crystallite size, the denser the amorphous part, and the higher the dielectric strength, which was identical to the relationship between impulse mechanical strength and the size of spherulites in polyethylene, in which case impulse mechanical strength decreased with increasing size of spherulites.[331]

On the other hand, dielectric properties in semicrystalline polymers, especially electrical conductivity, thermally stimulated current, and electrical breakdown, have often been explained by either a model based on inorganic crystals that have vacancies and interstitial points as electron traps or an electronic band model of an amorphous semiconductor that has a diffuse edge of states of density into a forbidden gap. However, none of this is very pertinent, and the dielectric properties of semicrystalline polymers should be correlated with what is known about their morphology.[332]

4.25.1 Dielectric Strength and Spherulite Size

Dielectric strength increases with decreasing spherulite size in HDPE, LDPE, isotactic polystyrene, and polypropylene and in amorphous atactic polystyrene whose supermolecular structure contains globular units.[333] By decreasing the spherulite size, we can also lower tan δ and the air and water permeabilities.

The type and the size of spherulites depends on a number of factors, primarily the polymer molecular structure, mechanical drawing, annealing, and the presence of nucleating agents. Of course, molecular weight, plasticization, and fillers are also important factors. Thus, by an appropriate heat treatment the spherulite size in HDPE can be controlled within 5–80 μm and that in PP to 145 μm.[334] In general, E_B decreases as the spherulite size increases until the mean spherulite diameter equals the specimen thickness, at which point breakdown channels are formed in the interspherulitic space.

When steel double-needle electrodes are used, it is then possible to measure E_B of a microregion or E_B in a spherulite and in the interspherulite space separately. For PP, E_B of a spherulite has a maximum value of 690 and a minimum of 540 with a 90% breakdown of 660 kV/mm. In intraspherulitic space, E_B has a maximum value of 330 and a minimum of 120 with a 90% breakdown of 300 kV/mm.[335] The reason why E_B in intraspherulitic space is lower is that its lower density and therefore conducting paths and discharge channels are preferentially generated in this region. Furthermore, because in the process of crystallization impurities and noncrystalline material are expelled from the ordered regions, such material also settles in the boundaries of the spherulites.

The use of scanning electron microscopy in the study of the morphology of XLPE and PP insulation confirmed the mechanism of breakdown.[77,91] For instance, by careful control of heat treatment, the spherulite size of PP film can be adjusted to anywhere from 5 to 650 μm. As the spherulite size increases from 5 μm, the lowering of E_B in the intraspherulitic space at first is very fast, then gradually slows down until the mean spherulite diameter is about the same as the film thickness, and E_B approaches a constant value of 150 kV/mm. For the E_B of the spherulite itself, when there are no observable defects under the electron microscope within the spherulite, its E_B is independent of the spherulite's size and is a constant value of 750 kV/mm. However, as the size of spherulites increases, the number of defective spherulites generally tends to increase. Since E_B of defective spherulites is lower and may even approach that of intraspherulitic space, the general trend then is that E_B of spherulites will decrease as their size increases. However, the technique for measuring E_B of a spherulite is somewhat limited by the available electrode diameters, the smallest being around 20 μm. Thus, only spherulites with diameters larger than 20 μm can be evaluated.

4.25.2 The Effect of Mechanical Drawing

Mechanical drawing also has a profound effect on the morphological structure of polymers. For example, it has been observed that larger spherulites appear to flow with no shape changes into the neck region of the drawn sample, whereas smaller spherulites undergo a complete morphological change. Such change could be accompanied, for example, by recrystallization of the existing structure.[336] Hence, in the mechanical drawing of polymers, such as polyethylene film, not only orientation but also complete change of the super-molecular structure may take place. In the direction perpendicular to the axis of drawing, the size of structural units decreases, leading to a decrease in the mean free path of electrons and thus an increase in dielectric strength.[310]

Using the IR dichroism technique, we can observed that with drawing the orientation function of the c-axis in the crystalline lamella increases and that of the a-axis decreases.[337] However, E_B generally varies in a complicated manner with elongation, possibly because of the orientation of lamellae structure and the rearrangement of the free volume.[278] Decrease of regions of low electron density with increasing draw ratio can also be demonstrated by a small-angle x-ray scattering technique.[338, 339] The kind of variation in E_B for HDPE possible by this technique of controlling dielectric strength is illustrated in Table 4.17.[340]

TABLE 4.17 Mechanical Drawing of HDPE vs E_B

Sample	E_B (kV/mm)
Nonoriented	460
Oriented:	
Parallel to drawing axis	351
Perpendicular to drawing axis	510

4.25.3 The Effect of Polystyrene Morphology

The supermolecular structure of polystyrene consists of globular units.[124] The size of the globular units can be controlled by the selection of proper solvents. The effects of two solvents on polystyrene morphology and E_B are illustrated in Table 4.18.[333] The molecular weight was 2.3×10^5 and the globular units from m-xylene were uniform and comparatively small, whereas those from carbon tetrachloride were relatively large and less uniform. The densities in both cases were equal, yet their dielectric strengths differed greatly. Hence, the globule size, like the spherulite size, can influence E_B to a certain extent. Uniform, small globules help to build a uniform field within the film, leading to a decreased mean free path of electrons and thus an increased dielectric strength.

TABLE 4.18 Solvent Effect on Polystyrene Morphology and E_B

Solvent	E_B kV/mm (at 90%)	Globular Diameter (Å)	Density (g/cm³)
m-Xylene	460	400–900	1.03
Carbon tetrachloride	260	800–3000	1.03

4.26 ADDITIVES TO IMPROVE DIELECTRIC STRENGTH

The effect of fillers on dielectric strength may be negative or positive. For example, if they function as nucleating agents, the effect will be positive. The efficiency of a nucleating agent depends on its chemical nature and its dispersed particle size. Both methyl red and ceresine are among the best nucleating agents known for polyethylene. Ceresine is an ozokerite or mineral wax that has been purified with sulfuric acid. Its chemical structure consists of a highly branched aliphatic hydrocarbon, and the material typically exists in a microcrystalline form.

4.26.1 Dielectric Properties of Polyethylene-Ceresine System

The dielectric properties of ceresine itself are E_B = 15 kV/mm, tan δ = 0.0018, and ϱ_v = 1×10^{12} ohm · cm. The effect of ceresine on polyethylene dielectric properties is illustrated in Table 4.19.[297] The solution-cast films were dried in a vacuum oven (10^{-2} torr) at 90 to 100°C. Addition of small amounts of ceresine increased both E_B and ϱ_v and decreased tan δ. The dielectric properties reached optimum for ceresine contents of 0.75–1%. Increase of ceresine above 1% led to a decrease in E_B and ϱ_v and an increase in tan δ. Examination of these samples under a microscope showed that the spherulite size of the original samples was much larger than that of the samples with 1% ceresine. The 1% ceresine samples possessed the smallest and most uniform spherulite structure, which again increased with ceresine content above 1%.

TABLE 4.19 Relationship Between Dielectric Properties of Polyethylene-Ceresine System and Ceresine Content[297]

% Ceresine Content	Hot Roll-Pressed Samples		m-Xylene Solution Cast Samples				
	LDPE	HDPE			tan δ	ϱ_v (ohm · cm)	Density (g/cm³)
	Impulse Voltage (kV/mm)			Alternating Voltage (50 Hz, kV/mm)			
0	290	240	230	210	0.00065	0.9×10^{14}	0.915
0.25	460	250	360	520	0.00043	4.5×10^{14}	0.919
0.5	490	280	500	280	0.00035	7.3×10^{14}	0.920
0.75	570	280	550	280	0.0020	1.2×10^{15}	0.915
1	590	320	370	320	0.00045	9×10^{14}	0.915
2	–	240	280	240	0.0006	–	0.915
3	430	250	250	250	0.00061	–	0.915
5	350	–	250	–	0.00065	0.9×10^{14}	0.915
12	270	–	218	200	0.00085	0.7×10^{14}	–

The chemical and physical structure of ceresine enables it to act as a nucleating center, which leads the entire polyethylene-ceresine system to become even more uniform than that of the original polyethylene with the generation of an increased number of smaller size spherulites. When the concentration of ceresine is more than 1%, ceresine begins to agglomerate in the interspherulite regions, causing a decrease in density of that region and an increased nonuniformity of the electric field.

The morphological structure of polyethylene formed after the incorporation of the optimum amount (0.75–1.0%) of ceresine is rather stable. No exuding of ceresine has been observed after 1 yr of sample preparation.[297]

4.26.2 Properties of a Nucleating Agent

The general structural requirements for a nucleating agent appear to consist of a fine crystal bulk structure and a highly branched molecular structure. Its dielectric properties should be as close as possible to those of the polymers in which it is to be incorporated. Ceresine can be used in polyethylene and polypropylene. For other polymers, other appropriate compounds should exist.

4.26.3 Importance of the Macromolecular Structure

The success of ceresine in improving the dielectric properties of polyethylene is just the beginning of a new approach in the control of the dielectric properties of polymers in general. As far as the nucleation phenomena are concerned, in addition to the importance of the chemical and physical characteristics of the nucleating agents, equally important is the macromolecular structure of the polymer to be nucleated. The morphology of polymers is profoundly influenced by molecular weight, molecular weight distribution, and the degree of branching of the polymer chains.[342] In the processes of crystallization and supermolecular structure formation, the linear chains crystallize first and with the fastest rates, leaving the highly branched chains behind in the interspherulitic space. This leads to a decreased density of the interspherulitic space. However, an increase in branching of macromolecules limits their mobility, and as a result they may act as nucleation centers leading to a fine spherulitic structure.[343] The molecular weight also has a direct effect on the density of the interspheruli-tic space. The higher the molecular weight, the more spherulites a chain is likely to trans-verse and the higher the density of the interspherulitic space as a result. Hence, molecular weight and branching are two variables, control over which combined with an appropriate nucleating agent can lead to better dielectric properties of the insulation.

4.27 HOW TO KEEP DIELECTRIC STRENGTH HIGH

The worldwide tendency to use ultrahigh-voltage and dc transmission lines makes the demand for better polymer insulation increasingly greater and urgent.

In general, there are two types of dielectric strength to be considered. The one that is measured in a laboratory in a very short time interval is conventionally known as the short-time dielectric strength. However, for the design and successful operation of a high-voltage insulation, another kind of dielectric strength is used, known as the long-time dielectric strength. This topic is intimately associated with the electrical aging of polymers and will be treated in a separate section.

Since the unit of dielectric strength is voltage per unit length, one may assume that any polymer, regardless of its dielectric strength, could be used in insulation and that the high voltage can be assured by simply increasing the thickness of the insulation. In practice, however, this does not work out that way, and most polymers break down long before a certain level of voltage can be achieved. This is because of thermal, electromechanical, and electrochemical breakdown processes occurring in polymers. The reason that polyethylene is so widely used as a high-voltage cable insulation is that the various secondary electrochemical breakdown processes can be suppressed.

4.27.1 Structure and Dielectric Strength

If one inspects a list of polymers and their corresponding dielectric strengths (Appendix 3), one sees only a general relationship between their chemical structures and dielectric strengths. The reason for this is that we still do not understand all the factors involved that determine a material's dielectric strength. Nevertheless, some structural guidelines may be derived from the temperature dependence of dielectric strength for most linear polymers. The general trend for all polymers is that the dielectric strength decreases with increasing temperature. This is so because the secondary breakdown processes become more important with increasing temperature.

Since amorphous and semicrystalline polymers possess glass transition and flow transition temperatures at which a major decrease in dielectric strength occurs, the dielectric strength may then be directly linked to the fundamental physical constants of polymers, and thus provide one means in polymer structure selection for high dielectric strength.

4.27.2 Polarity and Dielectric Strength

Generally speaking, the highest values of dielectric strength for polymers lie in the range of 100–900 kV/mm at 20°C. These values are higher than those for ionic crystals 50–100 kV/mm at 20°C. These high values are obtained in the low-temperature region. The values for polar polymers may even exceed 1000 kv/mm. The highest dielectric strength ever obtained for a polymer was 1500 kV/mm at −190°C for polyvinyl alcohol.[253] This result agrees with the general observation that the polar groups tend to increase the value of the dielectric strength.

The nature of the polarity effect on the value of dielectric strength in the region below T_g is a phenomenon of theoretical interest too. Polarity in polymers usually exerts a negative effect on the values of ε and tan δ, yet it exhibits a positive effect on E_B. The presence of polar groups in the polymer tends to increase the glass transition temperature of the amorphous phase. Even in the case of polyethylene, which is a nonpolar polymer, its E_B in the region below T_g also increases at lower temperature.[275] Since the breakdown process of polyethylene at low temperatures is presumably electron avalanche, a possible mechanism for the increase in E_B at a low temperature is the scattering of accelerated electrons under the high field by the few dipoles along the polyethylene chain.[249] As for the region between T_g and T_m, the effect of polar groups on the value of E_B is not very clear yet because of a debate as to whether the break down mechanism is Fröhlich's amorphous breakdown or thermal breakdown, which involve the nature of polymers and the modes of application of the electric field.

In summary, the detailed interpretations of the structural factors are still being debated, and definitive statements must be left for the future. Nevertheless, the need for high-dielectric strength polymeric materials, especially in cryogenic insulation, increases almost by the day.

4.27.3 Solutions for Keeping Dielectric Strength High

Because of the extremely complicated nature of the phenomena involved in dielectric break-down, the solutions for keeping the dielectric strength high are necessarily many. Since treeing is the prebreakdown phenomenon observed, measures used to inhibit it will have a direct effect on keeping the dielectric strength high. Thus, to reduce treeing certain purely physical factors such as smooth insulation surface and freedom from protrusions, skips, and contaminants have to be controlled. The concentration of microvoids must be kept to a minimum. If the residual void concentration in the cable is unaccetpably high, its impregnation with a monomer catalyst combination and *in situ* polymerization may have to be attempted.[344] Lauryl methacrylate and vinyl toluene have been used; the number of voids was decreased by this treatment and long-term breakdown strength was observed to increase. Another purely mechanical solution to inhibition of water treeing is to use a metal sheath or lining over the insulation. Finally, the use of various treeing inhibitors as a last resort is also an approach to keeping the dielectric strength high.

Nucleating Agents

The use of fillers to increase the dielectric strength is not very widespread because no extensive correlations have been developed for this approach to high dielectric strength. However, a small subgroup of such materials, the so-called nucleating agents, has been found to increase the dielectric strength. Unfortunately, the available data are still limited to only a few such additives and essentially to only polyethylene as the insulating material. Thus, how general this approach may turn out to be is still not known.

In summary of the various structural, molecular weight, morphological, and physical factors, the following can be said about keeping the dielectric strength high: introduction of polar groups in a polymer will increase its dielectric strength. Increasing the molecular weight, crystallinity, and cross-link density will increase the dielectric strength. Polymers with high cohesive energy density have high dielectric strength. A high band-gap energy has been associated with high dielectric strength in alkali halide crystals, and such a correlation may be also applicable to organic polymeric materials.

4.28 ELECTRICAL AGING

Up to now, what has been discussed has been short-term dielectric breakdown phenomena. However, most of the materials are being used for high-voltage insulation requiring long service life. Extrapolation of short-term dielectric strength data to long-term behavior is a very risky proposition. Thus, the magnitude of long-term dielectric strength must be determined by a thorough study of all known secondary effects induced by the high field. Unfortunately, the high-voltage-induced secondary effects are rather complex. Even under a uniform electric field, because of the formation and the disappearance of space charges, the effective internal field within a polymer is distorted into a nonuniform field.[345]

4.28.1 Gas Discharge Effects

During the application of a high voltage to a polymer insulation, discharges are likely to occur at an early stage in any gas at the edges of the insulation or occluded as bubbles in the solid polymer, especially when the uniform field is distorted. The occurrence of a local high field will hasten the process of discharge. Hence, we must first review the effects of gas discharges in more detail to see how they will effect the long-term dielectric breakdown.

Under a uniform field, the breakdown of gases is a cumulative process, and spark voltages follow Paschen's law, which says that the minimum voltage V_s necessary to produce a spark across a gas gap is a function of the product of gas pressure P and length of the gap ℓ:

$$V_s = f(P\ell) . \qquad 4.37$$

Paschen's law curve of V_s vs $P\ell$ exhibits a minimum. For air, when the units of P are millimeters of mercury and those of ℓ are centimeters, the value of $P\ell$ corresponding to the minimum is 0.567, and that of V_S is 275 V. In general cases, $P\ell$ is always greater than 1, which means V_s increases with increasing $P\ell$. Then we can deduce that at constant gas pressure, the breakdown field strength increases toward shorter gaps (very steeply for gaps smaller than 1 mm at atmospheric pressure).

Internal Discharges

Internal discharges are a common feature of polymeric insulation because voids are very easily left in the material at the processing stage unless special measures are taken. Since the dielectric constant of a gas filling the void, ε_g, is usually less than that of the polymer, ε, the local field E_g in the void is certainly greater than the field E in the bulk of the polymer:

$$E_g = \frac{\varepsilon E}{\varepsilon_g}. \qquad 4.38$$

Of course, E_g depends to some extent on the shape of the void: the effect is greatest for a disk-like void lying perpendicular to the field. If $\varepsilon_g = 1$, the maximum voltage V_i that can be applied to the polymer without a discharge in the void is then

$$V_i = E_B d' \left[1 + \frac{\frac{d}{d'} - 1}{\varepsilon} \right], \qquad 4.39$$

where E_B is the dielectric strength of the enclosed gas and d and d'are the thicknesses of the polymer and the void, respectively. In combination with Paschen's curves for gaseous breakdown, Eq. (4.39) suggests that the voltage at which discharge begins, decreases with increase in void size. This has been verified for air in artificially made cavities.[346]

For an insulator to have a long service life, gas discharges must be completely absent at the working voltage. For this reason, the voltage at which discharge starts, conventionally referred to as the discharge inception voltage V_i, is an important characteristic of a polymeric insulator for high-voltage applications. It is also an important parameter for the determination of working voltage and long-term breakdown strength.

The discharge inception voltage is also important to the design of high-voltage insulation systems that do not fail by the premature onset of air discharge at conductor boundaries when air is present. In this way, the possibility of breakdown by edge discharges at a given applied voltage must be considered and may be checked theoretically.

4.28.2 Surface Discharge

In many practical situations, an insulator is most likely to fail through deterioration of its surface.[347] However, very few basic studies are being conducted in this area. What work is being done in this area deals with the development of degradation tests by accelerated methods.

a) *Corona Resistivity*

Empirically, the corona resistivity of a polymer has been expressed as a weight change ΔW as follows:[348]

$$\Delta W = Pt + Q\,(1 - e^{-t/\tau}),\tag{4.40}$$

where P is a characteristic constant of weight loss, Q is a characteristic constant of weight gain by oxidation, t is time, and τ is an another constant. Table 4.20 lists the values of P and Q for various polymers.

TABLE 4.20 Corona Resistivity Constants of Some Polymers[348]

Polymers	P	Q
Polyimide	0.00	1.1
Siloxane polymers	0.05	6.0
Polyaromatic amides	0.15	13.8
Polyethylene	0.24	2.4
Poly(vinyl fluoride)	0.32	0.0
Polytetrafluoroethylene	0.35	0.0
Polystyrene	0.35	0.7
Copolymer of tetrafluoroethylene and hexafluoropropylene	0.45	0.0
Polyethylene terephthalate	0.46	6.0
Polycarbonate	0.57	9.5
Poly(vinyl chloride)	0.60	3.2
Polypropylene	0.88	6.0
Cellulose acetate	1.35	38.0

b) *Tracking*

Deposition of dirt and moisture must inevitably allow some conduction over the surface, although good insulators will recover quickly as the heating effect of the leakage currents tends to clean up the surface. Under these conditions some polymers tend to suffer permanent damage, called tracking, leading to a complete electrical breakdown. Tracking initiates as the surface dries out and a narrow, dry band forms. Most of the voltage is then dropped across the higher resistance of the dry band, and this can cause sparks to pass through the surface layer. If these sparks char the polymer, a conductive track may develop across the surface of the insulator, and this will finally result in flash-over, the polymer sometimes bursting into flames at this stage.

Standard tracking tests, designed to meet various sets of operating conditions, such as those set by the International Electrochemical Commission in 1959, are used to rank polymers in an order of susceptibility to tracking.[349]

Dust-Fog Test. The dust-fog test (ASTM D2132–6T) can be taken as an example to illustrate the standard tracking test. The polymer is coated with a solid contaminant containing 3% sodium chloride and is exposed to an artificial fog.[350] A potential difference of 1500 V is applied across the surface by means of copper electrodes 1 in. apart. The criterion for failure by tracking is the time taken for the electrodes to be bridged by a track across the surface. The time to track in hours is then used as the parameter of susceptibility to tracking. Table 4.21 lists some typical values of polymers in this test.[351] Although the mechanism of tracking is rather complex, the results of some standard tracking tests show that one can make some generalizations for linking the tracking resistivity of polymers to their chemical structure. For example, polymers based on aromatic compounds or with weakly bonded or easily oxidized pendent groups are very liable to pyrolysis in a way that deposits carbon and are especially prone to tracking.[352, 353]

TABLE 4.21 Tracking Resistance Property Measured by Dust-Fog Test[351]

Polymer	Time to Track (h)
Polytetrafluoroethylene	600
Polypropylene	191
Poly(methy methacrylate)	162
Polyethylene	33
Polystyrene	0.9
Poly(vinyl chloride)	0.3

Antitracking Additives. For polymers with poor tracking resistance property, it is common to expect that the incorporation of an additive may improve the antitracking property. However, since the mechanism of tracking is very complex and the details of the tracking mechanism are not clear, the choice of additives is strictly empirical. For example, it is well known that the addition of aluminum oxide hydrate improves the tracking resistance properties of butyl rubber but not that of epoxy resins.[354] Epoxy casting resins especially suffer surface discharge in highly humid environments (60% or higher relative humidity) and undergo chemical degradation of the surface.[355] Formation of nitric acid was observed, and if the density of the gaseous decomposition products was high, the degradation was even more accelerated. Aluminum oxide hydrates in epoxy resins actually degrade their dielectric properties. Quartz on the other hand, is a very good antitracking additive for epoxy resins, although the reasons for this are obscure.

Surface-Active Agents. Another polymer with poor antitracking characteristics is polycarbonate. Experiments have been conducted to study the influence of surface-active agents on the tracking resistance of wet polycarbonate.[356] Results indicated that the higher the surface activity of the wetting agent, the better it wetted the polycarbonate and the lower was the antitracking ability of the polycarbonate. In contrast to this, if the surface activity of the wetting agent was low and the "wetting" agent was separated into minute droplets upon application of a high potential, the droplets effectively worked to inhibit the tracking!

4.28.3 Relationship Between Effective Working Stress and Service Life

Just as in other forms of aging studies, the ultimate objective of the electrical aging study is to determine a relationship between effective working stress and service life. It is well known that the distribution function of breakdown probability ψ is of the form of the Weibull distribution:

$$\psi(t,G) = 1 - \exp(-Ct^aG^b) , \qquad\qquad 4.41$$

where G is the effective value of field strength from applied voltage, t is time, and a, b, and C are constants of polymers depending on temperature and other environmental conditions.

Another expression commonly used by the electrical engineering profession is the so-called power inverse law of electrical aging:

$$L = \frac{\gamma}{G^n},\qquad\qquad 4.42$$

in which L is the service life of the insulation. Both γ and n are parameters of electrical aging of polymers and depend on the processing technology of the insulation as well as temperature and other environmental parameters.

For a specific polymer, if different values of n are obtained at different ranges of field strength, then the mechanism of breakdown is changing because of the change in the field.

When the aging test is made under constant field, Eq. (4.41) turns out to be

$$\psi(t) = 1 - \exp(-C't^a),\qquad\qquad 4.43$$

where

$$C' = CG^b.\qquad\qquad 4.44$$

Rearranging Eq. (4.43), we get

$$\frac{\ln\dfrac{1}{1-\psi}}{t} = C't^{a-1}.\qquad\qquad 4.45$$

The left side of Eq. (4.45) can be calculated from experimental data, and its physical significance seems to be breakdown rate. If we use R to represent this rate, Eq. (4.45) becomes

$$R = C't^{a-1}.\qquad\qquad 4.46$$

The Three Stages of Breakdown

When R vs t is plotted, its general relationship is similar to that shown in Fig. 4.38, which can be divided into three stages. The first stage is called "defects breakdown." Because of the presence of defects in the test specimen, breakdown occurs within a relatively short time interval after the application of the field. In this state, R decreases with t: hence, a < 1. The second stage is called "random breakdown." In this stage, the effect of defects in the specimen has already disappeared, and the breakdown takes a random form. During this stage, R remains constant, and from Eq. (4.46) when a = 1,

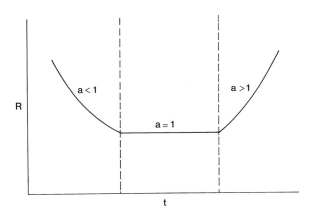

Fig. 4.38 Relationship Between R and t.

$$R = C't^0 = C' = \text{constant} .$$ 4.47

The third stage is called the "aging breakdown" stage. The breakdown is caused by a gradual aging of the material. In this stage, R increases with t; hence, a > 1. Only when a is a constant value greater than 1 can a straight line be obtained on Weibull coordinate paper. If a is not a constant, then the aging mechanism is changing. Therefore, a can be called an aging coefficient. In an ideal design of an insulation, the difference between short-term and long-term dielectric strength is as small as possible, and that means one desires an a as small as possible.

4.29 EXPERIMENTAL TEST METHODS

Reliable electric strength data for solids are important from both the scientific and the industrial standpoints. The strength exhibited is critically dependent on the method of testing. In specifying a reliable experimental procedure the following must be considered: the uniformity of the field, the homogeneity of the dielectric, the ambient medium, the temperature, the voltage type and control, the electrode nature and contact, the mechanical support of the dielectric, and the accuracy of thickness and voltage measurements.

4.29.1 Experimental Electric Strength Tests

The two most widely accepted types of test specimens are the recessed and the McKeown types. These tests use quasi-uniform field geometries to avoid the treeing associated with highly divergent fields and constraining failure to a localized region.

a) *Recessed Specimens*

The most reliable measurements, judged by the large values that have been obtained compared wiht those of other measurements, have been recessed specimens (Fig. 4.39).[357]

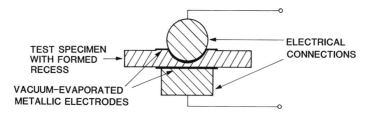

Fig. 4.39. Example of a recessed test specimen.

The recess is machined or molded in the material to form a highly stressed region. Electrodes are formed by vacuum-evaporating a metallic layer onto the surfaces of the recessed material to eliminate any gas gap between the electrode and the specimen. Electrical connections to the specimen is via the metallic sphere as shown in Figure 4.39.

b) *McKeown Specimens*

Another widely used test specimen configuration is that of McKeown (Fig. 4.40), in which a disk of the test material is placed in a hole provided in a supporting insulator such as

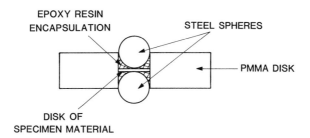

Fig. 4.40. A McKeown specimen.

poly(methyl methacrylate).[2] The sample is contacted by the two spherical electrodes and the assembly is vacuum impregnated with epoxy resin. These specimens usually yield electric strength values higher than those obtained with a recessed procedure. The reasons for this reproducible difference are not fully understood.

A development of the McKeown specimen is to completely embed the electrodes in the dielectric to be investigated. Measurements in low-density polyethylene with embedded 20-mm stainless steel spheres gave an electric strength of 750–850 kV/mm.[358] This is far above that obtained with a recessed specimen.[359]

The recessed and encapsulated types of specimen may be adapted for particular requirements. For example, the contacting electrodes in the recessed specimen case may be made movable to allow assessment of any dimensional changes of the specimen during stressing.[315,360]

c) Self-Healing Breakdown

Because of differences between specimens large numbers of tests must be conducted to obtain a statistically meaningful average. For thin film specimens, however, the differences in specimen thickness may be minimized and large numbers of measurements made using self-healing breakdowns. This is arranged by applying evaporated-metal electrodes of 500 to 1000 Å in thickness to a thin film of the material. The thin dielectric allows the use of only small voltages to obtain breakdown.[361] When the voltage is raised, the weakest point on the film will break down, generating a puncture in the film. Energy from the capacitor-type specimen will flow into the discharge site, and give power densities as large as 10^9 W/cm^2. This will cause an arc with temperatures up to 4500 K and rapid evaporation of the electrodes at the discharge site. This self-healing process removes sufficient amounts of the electrode material to relieve the local stress, and produce a nonshorting discharge site, Fig. 4.41. The breakdown holes are typically 1–100 μm diameter. This technique has been

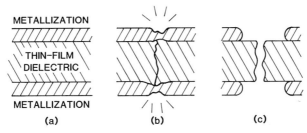

Fig. 4.41. The self-healing process in a metallized thin film specimen: (a) the specimen structure; (b) breakdown of the dielectric and local evaporation of the electrodes; (c) the resulting cleared site. Source is Ref. 357.

used for studying the breakdown of inorganic and polymer films.[362, 363] Many capacitor designs capitalize on this self-healing effect to provide clearing of imperfections.[364]

d) *Other Electrodes and Ambient Media*

In specialized applications, mercury[365] or electrolytic solutions may be used as conforming electrodes.[366, 367] The ambient medium can also be employed in some applications to provide the necessary stress grading. In these circumstances, a high permittivity or a weakly conducting liquid can be used to maintain the field in any series liquid gap at an acceptably low level. The use of a high dielectric constant or conduction liquids can also be helpful for grading voltages at the edges of electrodes without the need for contouring. In this context, water has sometimes been used in the pulse-power field.[368]

4.29.2 Standard Electric Strength Tests

There is a need for a simple industrial breakdown test for evaluating materials under standardized conditions. The major standards used for these purposes are listed in Table 4.22. Most of the standards call for ac breakdown tests to be carried out on specimen configurations that correspond to the geometrical form of the solid being tested. The tests that may be conducted fall into three categories:

(1) time breakdown tests, in which the voltage is raised from zero at a uniform rate to achieve average breakdown over a specified duration of time (usually 10–20 s);
(2) the 20-s step-by-step test, in which starting at a voltage of 40–50% below the probable breakdown voltage, the test stress is increased in steps specified in a prescribed table with a 20-s waiting time between each increase. Here, the electric strength is based on the highest value withstood for 20 s;
(3) the withstand test, which is essentially a pass-fail proof test in which a specified electric stress has to be withstood by the specimen for a prescribed length of time (often 1 min).

Most of the standards listet in Table 4.21 involve static testing. However, one test, the ASTM Dielectric Proof-Voltage Testing of Thin Solid Electrical Insulating Materials [D 1389-63 (1977)] involves dynamic testing of dielectric films and other flat materials.

TABLE 4.22 Standards for the Evaluation of the Electric Strength of Solid Insulating Materials[357]

Standard	Country	Scope
IEC 243	International	Recommended methods of testing for electric strength of solid insulating materials at power frequencies
ASTM D 149–75	United States and Canada	Dielectric breakdown voltage and dielectric strength of electrical insulating materials at commercial power frequencies
ASTM D 1389–62 (1977)	United States and Canada	Dielectric proof-voltage testing of thin solid electrical insulating materials
BS 2918	Britain	Determination of electric strength of solid insulating materials at power frequencies
NC C26–225	France	Methods of testing insulating materials; determination of electric strength
VDE 0303	West Germany	VDE specifications for electrical tests of insulating materials
J1S C2110	Japan	Testing methods for electric strength of solid insulating materials

4.29.3 Other Methods

Many other techniques have been used to characterize the mechanism of breakdown and some of them are listed in Table 4.23 along with the original references.

Particularly useful measurements are: conduction current as it relates to prebreakdown and breakdown, thermally stimulated conductivity as it relates to the activation energies for electron and hole traps, optical methods providing additional data on breakdown, and chemical methods providing chemical structural data.

TABLE 4.23 Diagnostic Techniques for the Investigation of Solid Dielectrics[358]

Method	Measurment Type	Information Gained	Typical References
Electrical	Conductivity measurement	Determination of nature and behavior of charge carriers	369–371
	Dielectric dispersion	Identification of relaxation	241, 372, 373
Optical	Microscopy	Examination of microstructure of materials, damage morphology, and breakdown products	374–376
	Luminescene	Spatial, temporal, and spectral resolution of emission from excited species before breakdown	377–379
	Photoelastic studies	Determination of the mechanical effects of electric stress and glass transition phenomena in polymers	367, 380, 381
	Kerr effect measurement	Electric field measurement in transparent dielectrics	382
Mechanical	Mechanical relaxation	Determination of structural parameters	383–385
	Dimensional changes	Evaluation of electromechanical effects	315, 360
	Acoustic pulse method	Charge distribution measurements	386, 387
Thermal	Thermally stimulated currents	Investigation of charge storage and transport, molecular relaxation, trapping	372, 385, 388
	Differtial thermal analysis and scanning calorimetry	Determination of transition regions, percentage crystallinity and amounts of cross-linking in polymers	332, 367, 389
Chemical	Infrared spectrocopy, gel permeation chromatography, electron paramagnetic resonance, etc.	Examination of chemical and structural changes	388, 390, 391
Radiation	X-ray analysis	Determination of structural parameters	367, 392, 393
	Electron beam probing	Charge recall and space charge determination	394, 395

4.30   REFERENCES

1. P. H. H. Fischer and K. W. Nissen, I.E.E.E. Transactions on Electrical Insulation *EI-11,* 37 (1976).
2. J. J. McKeown, Proceedings of the Inst. of Electrical Engineers *112,* 824 (1965).
3. J. A. Knaur and P. P. Budenstein in "1978 Ann. Report, Conference on Electrical Insulation and Dielectric Phenomena," National Academy of Sciences – National Research Council, Washington, DC, 1979.
4. S. Whitehead, *Dielectric Breakdown of Solids,* Clarendon Press, London, 1951.
5. E. H. Rayner, Journal of the Institution of Electrical Engineers *49,* 3 (1912).
6. D. M. Robinson, Journal of the Institution of Electrical Engineers *77,* 90, (1935).
7. D. M. Robinson, *Dielectric Phenomena in High Voltage Cables,* Chapman & Hall, London, 1936.
8. S. Whitehead, *Breakdown of Solid Dielectrics,* Ernest Benn, London, 1932.
9. J. H. Mason, in *Progress in Dielectrics,* Vol. 1, J. S. Birks and J. H. Schulman, Eds., Heywood and Co., London, 1959.
10. J. H. Mason, Electrical Research Association Report L/T 192, Leatherhead, England, 1948.
11. J. H. Mason, Proceedings of the Institution of Electrical Engineers *98,* 44, (1951).
12. M. Olyphant, Jr., "A Compiled Study of Treeing in Insulation," Internal Report, Minnesota Mining and Manufacturing Co., Minneapolis, 1962.
13. N. Parkman in *Physics of Plastics,* P. D. Richie, Ed., Iliffe, London, 1965.
14. P. P. Budenstein, "Dielectric Breakdown in Solids," National Technical Information Service, U.S. Department of Commerce, Technical Report RG-75–25, Order No. AD-A012 177, Washington, DC, 1974.
15. P. P. Budenstein, I.E.E.E. Transactions on Electrical Insulation *EI-15,* 225 (1980).
16. G. Bahder, T. W. Dakin, and J. H. Lawson, Proceedings, Conference Internationale des Grands Reseaux Electriques, Paper No. 15–05, Paris, 1974.
17. R. M. Eichhorn, I.E.E.E. Transactions on Electrical Insulation *EI-12,* 2 (1977).
18. J. A. Wiersman, Electra, No. 55, p 25 (December 1977).
19. H. C. Doepken, Jr., and Y. Klinger, 1980 I.E.E.E. International Symposium on Electrical Insulation, Conference Record 80CH149G-9E1, p. 208, Boston, June 1980.
20. F. H. Kreuger, *Discharge Detection in High Voltage Equipment,* Elsevier, New York, 1965.
21. R. Bartnikas and E. J. McMahon, Eds., *Engineering Dielectrics, Volume I. Corona Measurement and Interpretations,* ASTM STP 669, American Society for Testing and Materials, Philadelphia, 1979.
22. M. Nawata and H. Kawamura, Electrical Engineering in Japan *88,* 45 (1968).
23. R. J. Densley, I.E.E.E. Transactions on Electrical Insulation *EI–14,* 148 (1979).
24. D. W. Kitchin and O. S. Pratt, American Institute of Electrical Engineers, Transactions, Power Apparatus and Systems *77,* 180 (1958).
25. D. W. Kitchin and O. S. Pratt, American Institute of Electrical Engineers, Transactions, Power Apparatus and Systems *81,* 112 (1962).
26. O. S. Pratt, I.E.E.E. Transactions on Power Apparatus and Systems *PAS-87,* 1609 (July 1968).
27. G. H. Hunt, U.S. Patent 3,445,394, May 20, 1969.
28. E. J. McMahon and J. R. Perkins, I.E.E.E. Transactions on Power Apparatus and Systems *PAS-82,* 1128 (1963).
29. E. J. McMahon and J. R. Perkins, I.E.E.E. Transactions on Power Apparatus and Systems *PAS-83,* 1253 (1964).
30. M. Olyphant, Jr., I.E.E.E. Transactions on Power Apparatus and Systems *PAS-69,* 1106 (1963).
31. M. Olyphant, Jr., Insulation, (February-April 1963).
32. W. Vahlstrom, I.E.E.E. 1971 Conference on Underground Distribution, Conference Record 71C42-PWR, p. 222, Detroit, 27 September–1 October 1971.
33. J. H.Lawson and W. Vahlstrom, I.E.E.E. Transactions on Power Apparatus and Systems *PAS-92,* 824 (1973).
34. T. P. Lanctoe, J. H. Lawson, and W. L. McVey, I.E.E.E. Transactions on Power Apparatus and Systems *PAS-98,* 912 (1979).
35. W. A. Thue, in minutes of 60th Meeting, Insulated Conductors Committee, I.E.E.E. Power Engineering Society, April 1977, Appendix F1.

36. W. A. Thue in minutes of 62nd Meeting, Insulated Conductors Committee, I.E.E.E. Power Engineering Society, April 1978, Appendix V-D1.

37. W. A Thue in minutes of 64th Meeting, Insulated Conductors Committee, I.E.E.E. Power Engineering Society, May 1979, Appendix V-A.

38. W. A. Thue, data presented at 1980 Spring Meeting of Task Force 5–25, Insulated Conductors Committee, I.E.E.E. Power Engineering Society, April 14–16, Philadelphia, Pennsylvania (1980).

39. R. M.Eichhorn, Kabelitem, No. 155, Publ. No. PP-71-18, Union Carbide Corp. New York, 1980.

40. W. A. Thue, J. W. Bankoske, and R. R. Burghardt, Proceedings, Conference Internationale des Grands Reseaux Electriques, Paper No. 21–10, Paris, 1980.

41. M. Ieda and M. Nawata, I.E.E.E. Trans. EI-12, 19 (1977).

42. D. B. Watson, J. Phys. D 5, 410 (1972).

43. H. Sakamoto and K. Yahagi, J. Appl. Phys. Japan 17, 1959 (1978).

44. G..Bahder and C. Katz, "1972 Annual Report, Conference on Electrical Insulation and Dielectric Phenomena," National Academy of Sciences-National Research Council, Washington, DC, p. 190, 1973.

45. G. Bahder, C. Katz, J.H. Lawson, and W. Vahlstrom, I.E.E.E. Transactions on Power Apparatus and Systems PAS-93, 977 (1974).

46. S. Inoue, M. Okada, N. Terao, T. Taguchi, M. Matsui, K. Sasaki, and K. Hirose, Dainichi-Nippon Cables Review, No. 57, p. 40, April 1974.

47. M. Matsubara and S.Yamanouchi, "1974 Annual Report, Conference on Electrical Insulation and Dielectric Phenomena," National Academy of Sciences-National Research Council, Washington, DC, p. 270, 1975.

48. A. C. Ashcraft and R. M. Eichhorn, I.E.E.E. Transactions on Electrical Insulation EI-13, 198 (1978).

49. T. Tanaka and T. Fukuda, "1974 Annual Report, Conference on Electrical Insulation and Dielectric Phenomena," National Academy of Sciences-National Research Council, Washington, DC, pp. 239 (1975).

50. H. Matsuba and E. Kawai, I.E.E.E. Transactions on Power Apparatus and Systems PAS-95, 660 (1976).

51. E. J. McMahon, I.E.E.E. Transactions on Electrical Insulation EI-16, 304 (1981); U.S. Patent 4,206,260, March 6, l980.

52. H. Wagner, Elektrotechnische Zeitschrift A96, 158 (1975).

53. H. Wagner and J. Wartusch, I.E.E.E. Transactions on Electrical Insulators EI-12,395 (1977).

54. T. Tabata, H. Nagai, T. Fukuda, and Z. Iwata, I.E.E.E. Transactions on Power Apparatus and Systems PAS-91, 1354 (1972).

55. E. H. Reynolds, R. M. Hinde, and R. M. Black, "1972 Annual Report, Conference on Electrical Insulation and Dielectric Phenomena," National Academy of Sciences-National Research Council, Washington, DC, p. 125, 1973.

56. O. K. Spurr and R. M. Eichhorn, Kabelitem, No. 145, Pulb. No. F-44155 A, Union Carbide Corp., New York, 1972.

57. J. Sletbak and A. Botne, I.E.E.E. Transactions on Electrical Insulation EI-12, 383 (1977).

58. R. M. Eichhorn, "1973 Annual Report, Conference on Electrical Insulation and Dielectric Phenomena," National Academy of Sciences-National Research Council, Washington, DC, p. 289, 1974.

59. G. Löffelmacher, Elektrotechnische Zeitschrift A96, 152 (1975).

60. D. B Watson and S. C. Chin, New Zealand Journal of Science 20, 357 (1977).

61. K. C. Kao in "1969 Annual Report, Conference on Electrical Insulation and Dielectric Phenomena," National Academy of Sciences-National Research Council, Washington, DC, p. 122, 1970.

62. G. Coe, J. F. Hughes, and P. E. Secker, British Journal of Applied Physics 17, 885 (1966).

63. W. R. L. Thomas and E. O. Forster in Conjunction and Breakdown in Dielectric Liquids, J. M. Goldschvarta, Ed., Delft University Press, Delft, The Netherlands, 1975.

64. P. Wong and E. O. Forster, Canadian Journal of Chemistry 55, 1890 (1977).

65. J. Fleszynski, B. Lutynski, and J. I. Skowronski, Journal of Electrostatics 7, 47 (Aug. 1979).

66. W. G. Chadband and J. H.Calderwood, Journal of Electrostatics 7, 75 (Aug. 1979).

67. T. Tanaka and A. Greenwood, I.E.E.E. Transactions on Power Apparatus and Systems PAS-97, 1749 (1978).

68. M. Stoica, F. T. Tanasesco, G. Giurgiu, and A. Ifrim, Proceedings, Conference Internationale des Grands Reseaux Electriques, Paper No. 15–11, Paris, 1978.
69. M. Ieda and M. Nawata, "1972 Annual Report, Conference on Electrical Insulation and Dielectric Phenomena," National Academy of Sciences-National Research Council, Washington, DC, p. 143, 9173.
70. H. J. Wintle, I.E.E.E. Transactions on Electrical Insulation EI-12, 242 (1977).
71. J. L. Maksiejewski and H. Tropper, Proceedings of the Insulation of Electrical Engineers 101, Part II, p. 183, (1954).
72. T. J. Gallagher, Simple Dielectric Liquids-Mobility, Conduction, and Breakdown, Clarendon Press, Oxford, 1975.
73. P. Mark and M. Allen in Annual Review on Materials Science, Vol. 3, R. Huggins, Ed., Annual Reviews Inc., Palo Alto, CA, 1973.
74. A. Chapiro, Radiation Chemistry of Polymeric Systems, Interscience, New York, 1962.
75. National Bureau of Standards Circular No. 20, June 1969.
76. A. Keller, Philosophical Magazine 2, No. 8, 1171 (1957).
77. J. Muccigrosso and P. J. Phillips, I.E.E.E. Transactions on Electrical Insulation EI-13, 172 (1978).
78. H. Matsuba and S. Hoh, Electrical Engineering in Japan 89, 96 (1969).
79. J. Artbauer, Kolloid Zeitschrift 202, 15 (1965).
80. B. Yoda and M. Sakaba, Hitachi Review 18, 406 (1969).
81. O. Böttger and R. Patsch, Bulletin des Schweizerischen Elektrotechnischen Vereins; Verbandes Schweizerischer Elektrizitätswerke 65, 221 (1974).
82. R. Patsch in "1975 Annual Report, Conference on Electrical Insulation and Dielectric Phenomena," National Academy of Sciences-National Research Council, Washington, DC, p. 323, 1976.
83. J. J. O'Dwyer, The Theory of Electrical Conduction and Breakdown in Solid Dielectrics, Clarendon Press, Oxford, 1973.
84. R. Bartnikas, H. C. Doepken, R. M. Eichhorn, G. W. Rittmann, and W. D. Wilkens, I.E.E.E. Transactions on Power Apparatus and Systems PAS-99, 1575 (1980).
85. F. Noto, N. Yoshimura, M. Nishida, and T. Fukuzono, 1978 I.E.E.E. International Symposium on Electrical Insulation, Conference Record 78H1287–2-EI, Philadelphia, p. 126, 12–14 June 1978.
86. F. Noto, N. Yoshimura, and T. Oota, 1976 I.E.E.E. International Symposium on Electrical Insulation, Conference Record 76CH1088–4-EI, Montreal, Canada, p. 205, 14–16 June 1976.
87. Y. Sakamoto, H. Fukagawa, T. Shikama, K. Kimura, and H. Takehans, "The Effect of dc Prestress on Opposite Polarity Impulse Breakdown in XLPE Cables," Paper A76 461–4, I.E.E.E. Summer Power Meeting, Portland, Oregon, July 1976.
88. H. Nakayama, K. Nakanishi, S. Hirabayashi, and Y. Inuishi, 1978 I.E.E.E. International Symposium on Electrical Insulation, Conference Record 78CH128–2-EI, Philadelphia, 12–14 June 1978.
89. E. A. Franke, J. R. Stauffer, and E. Czekaj, I.E.E.E. Transactions on Electrical Insulation EI-12, 218 (1977).
90. H. Wagner, "1974 Annual Report, Conference on Electrical Insulation and Dielectric Phenomena," National Academy of Sciences – National Research Council, Washington, DC, p. 62, 1975.
91. H. Wagner, I.E.E.E. Transactions on Electrical Insulation EI-13, 81 (1978).
92. K. Kitagawa, G. Sawa, and M. Ieda, Japan Journal of Applied Physics 19, 389 (1980).
93. K. Kitagawa, G. Sawa, and M. Ieda, Japan Journal of Applied Physics 20, 87 (1981).
94. Y. Nitta, Proceedings of the 17th Japan Conference on Materials Research, p. 232, 1974.
95. M. Dole, Report of Symposium IX on Chemistry and Physics of Radiation Dosimetry, Army Chemical Center, MD. p. 120, 1950.
96. A. Charlesby, Proceedings of the Royal Soc. of London A215, 187 (1952).
97. T. Ito, M. S. A. A. Hamman, M. Schiomi, and T. Sakai, in "1980 Annual Report, Conference on Electrical Insulation Dielectric Phenomena," National Academy of Sciences-National Research Council, Washington, D.C. p. 227, 1980.
98. E. J. McMahon in "Engineering Dielectrics, Vol. 1, Corona Measurement and Interpretation," ASTM STP 669, R. Bartnikas and E. I. McMahon, Eds., American Society for Testing and Materials, Philadelphia, P. 221, 1979.
99. M. Olyphant, Insulation, p. 42, April 1963.

100. W. Bell, M. Mulcahy, P. Bolin, and F. Tse, Insulation/Circuits, p. 33, Dec. 1970.
101. G. P. Delektorskii, Elektrochestvo *81*, No. 11, 73 (1961).
102. J. Dib, O. Dorlanne, M. R. Wertheimer, A.Yelon, G. Bacquet, and J. R. Densley, 1978 I.E.E.E. International Symposium on Electrical Insulation, Conference Record 78CH1287-2-EI, Philadelphia, 134, 12–14 June 1978.
103. D. W. Aukland, A. B. Borishade, and R. Cooper, Proceedings of the Inst. of Electrical Engineers *124*, 1263 (1977).
104. S. Grzybowski and R. Dobroszewski, 1978 I.E.E.E. International Symposium on Electrical Insulation, Conference Record 78CH1287-2-EI, Philadelphia, p. 122, 12–14 June 1978.
105. W. Weibull, Journal of Applied Mechanics *18*, 293 (1951).
106. G. C. Stone and R. B. van Heeswiik, I.E.E.E. Transactions on Electrical Insulation *EI-12*, 253 (1977).
107. G. C. Stone and J. F. Lawless, 1978 I.E.E.E. International Symposium on Electrical Insulation, Conference Record 78CH1287-2-EI, Philadelphia, p. 13, 12–14 June 1978.
108. G. C. Stone and J. F. Lawless, Paper R79–34 (FORTRAN Program Listing), available from I.E.E.E. Computer Society Publications Office, Long Beach, California.
109. E. J. McMahon and J. R. Perkins, "Techniques for Studying Volume Discharges and Treeing in Organic Insulating Compounds," I.E.E.E. Conference Paper No. C73–257–3, 1973.
110. A. C. Ashcraft, R. M. Eichhorn, and R. G. Shaw, 1978 I.E.E.E. International Symposium on Electrical Insulation, Conference Record 76CH1088–4-EI, Montreal, Canada, p. 213, June 14–16 1976.
111. L. Ligethy, P. David, and E. Zelenyanszky, Research and Development in Hungarian Cable Works, English edition, p. 29, 1978.
112. J. C. Devins, S. J. Rzad, C. W. Reed, D. K. Bartosh, and T. W. Stines, "New Class of Additives to Inhibit Tree-Growth in Solid Extruded Cable Insulation," Final Report CONS/1827–1, Energy Research and Development Administration, Division of Electric Energy Systems, Washington, D.C, 1976.
113. T. Yasui, Sumitomo Electric Technical Review *10*, 49 (1967).
114. F. Feichtmyr and F. Wurstlen, Kunststoffe *58*, 10 and 713, (1968).
115. R. Jocteur, E. Favrie, and H. Auclair, "Influence of Surface and Internal Defects on Polyethylene, Electrical Routine Tests on Polyethylene," Paper F76–454–9, I.E.E.E. Power Engineering Society Summer Meeting, Portland, OR., July 1976.
116. E. Kindij, in 1972 Internationales Symposium für Hochspannungstechnik, Technische Universität Munich, Munich, pp. 408 and 413, 1972.
117. F. H. Kreuger, "Determination of the Internal Discharge Resistance of Dielectric Materials," I.E.E.E. Conference Paper No. 68 TP 603-PWR, I.E.E.E., New York, 1968.
118. F. H. Kreuger, I.E.E.E. Transactions on Electrical Insulation *EI-3*, 106 (1968).
119. D. Kind, Proceedings of the 6th Symposium on Electrical Insulation Materials, Institute of Electrical Engineers of Japan, p. 185, 1973.
120. T. Tanaka and Y. Ikeda, I.E.E.E. Transactions on Power Apparatus and Systems *PAS-90*, 2692 (Nov-Dec. 1971).
121. H. Ilamoto, M. Kanazashi, and T. Tanaka, "Deterioration of Insulating Materials by Internal Discharge," Paper No. F76 315–2, I.E.E.E. Power Engineering Society Summer Meeting, Portland, Oregon, 1976.
122. H. Wagner, AEG-Kabel Technische Mitteilungen, H. 1, Allgemeine Elektrizitäts Gesellschaft (AEG), Rheydt, West Germany, 1973.
123. N. Srinivas, S. M. Allam, and H. C. Doepken, Jr. in "1976 Annual Report, Conference on Electrical Insulation and Dielectric Phenomena," National Academy of Sciences-National Research Council, Washington, DC, p. 380, 1978.
124. E. J. McMahon and J. R. Perkins, "Surface and Volume Phenomena in Dielectric Breakdown of Polyethylene," Paper DP 62–858 presented at Delaware Bay Section, American Institute of Electrical Engineers, Middle Eastern District Meeting, Wilmington, Deleware, May 8, 1962.
125. P. R. Howard, Proceedings of the Institution of Electrical Engineers *98*, No. II, 365 (1951).
126. F. Noto and N. Yoshimura in "1974 Annual Report, Conference on Electrical Insulation and Dielectric Phenomena," National Academy of Sciences-National Research Council, Washington, DC, p. 207, 1975.
127. L. J. Frisco, Electro-Technology, p. 10, Aug. 1961.

128. C. Laurent and C. Mayoux, I.E.E.E. Trans. *EI-15*, 33 (1980).
129. C. Laurent, C. Mayoux, and A. Sergent, I.E.E.E. Trans. *EI-16*, 52 (1981).
130. Y. Tsukui and Y. Koho, Elec. Eng. Japan *92*, No. 4, 9 (1972).
131. T. W. Dakin, H. M. Philofsky, and W. C. Dievens, AIEE Trans. *73*, 155 (1954).
132. O. E. Gendy, Ph.D, Thesis, University of Edinburgh (1977).
133. M. Olyphant, I.E.E.E. Trans. *EI-2*, 92 (1967).
134. S. Sakata, S. Hirabayashi, and Y. Inuishi, Elec. Eng. Japan *92*, No. 4, 1 (1972).
135. C. Mayoux and Bui Ai, J. App. Phys. *44* 3423 (1972).
136. C. Mayoux, in 2nd Intl. Conf. on Gas Discharge, I.E.E., London (1972).
137. A. L. McKean, F. S. Oliver, and S. W. Trill, I.E.E.E. Transactions on Power Apparatus and Systems *PAS-86*, 1 (1967).
138. Y. Fujisawa, T. Yasui, Y. Kawasaki, and H. Matsumura, I.E.E.E. Transactions on Power Apparatus and Systems *PAS-87*, 1899 (1968).
139. G. Bahder, G. S. Eager, D. A. Silver, and R. G. Lukac, I.E.E.E. Transactions on Power Apparatus and Systems *PAS-95*, 1552 (1976).
140. E. J. McMahon, Proceedings Conference Internationale des Grands Reseaux Electriques, Discussion, Paper No. 15–50, Paris, 1974.
141. G. Bahder, G. S. Eager, and D. A. Silver, U.S. Patent 3,885,085, May 20, 1975.
142. R. M. Eichhorn, 1972 I.E.E.E. Underground Transmission Conference, Conference Record 72-CHO-608-0-PWR (Supp.), Pittsburgh, pp. 282–286, May 22–24, 1972.
143. E. Mori, S. Isshiki, T. Shiromizu, S. Yamamoto, S. More, K. Iwanabe, H. Oshima, M. Ieda, and T. Ieda, Fujikura Technical Review, p. 40, 1974.
144. J. E. Baker and C. C. Shackford, U.S. Patent, 4,043,722, August 12, 1977.
145. D. R. Augood, "A New Cross-Linking Process for Extruded Dielectric Cable," Paper No. 81 SM311–0, I.E.E.E. Power Engineering Society Summer Meeting, Portland, Oregon, July 1981.
146. Japanese Patent No. 46–19849, June 3, 1971.
147. T. Mitzukami, K. Takahashi, C. Ideda, N. Kato, and B. Yoda, I.E.E.E. Transactions on Power Apparatus and Systems *PAS-94*, 467 (1975).
148. M. Takaoka, M. Seki, H. Oshima, and M. Hasegawa, Wire Journal, p. 64, June 1980.
149. U.S. Patent 3,997,288 to Furukawa Electric Co., Japan, December 14, 1976.
150. K. Otani, Japan Plastics, p. 15, November-December 1974.
151. T. Sasaki, F. Hosoi, M. Hagiwara, K. Araki, E. Saito, H. Ishitani, and K. Vesugi, "Development of Radiation Cross-Linking Process for High Voltage Power Cable," Second International Meeting on Radiation Proceedings, Miami, Florida, October 22–26, 1978.
152. R. M. Eichhorn and G. I. Addis, "Irradiated Polyethylene Insulation for Sodium Conductor Cable," Conference Paper No. 68 CP 61-PWR, I.E.E.E. Winter Power Meeting, New York, January 18 February 2, 1968.
153. K. Kojima, T. Fukui, Y. Uamada, S. Katoi, and K. Yatsuka, I.E.E.E. Trans. *PAS-100*, 203 (1981).
154. T. Hayami, I.E.E.E. Transactions on Power Apparatus and Systems *PAS-88*, 897 (1969).
155. T. Hayami and Y. Yamada, "1972 Annual Report, Conference on Electrical Insulation and Dielectric Phenomena," National Academy of Sciences-National Research Council, Washington, DC, p. 239, 1973.
156. M. Morita, M. Hanai, and H. Shimanuki, "1972 Annual Report, Conference on Electrical Insulation and Dielectric Phenomena," National Academy of Sciences-National Research Council, Washington, DC, p. 299, 1973.
157. W. H. Mears, minutes of the I.E.E.E. Insulated Conductors Committee, Open Forum, Denver, Colorado, 1973.
158. A. L. Williams and S. Verne, U.S. Patent 3,800,017, 1974.
159. F. H. Kreuger, Proceedings, Conference Internationale des Grands Reseasux Electriques, Paper No. 21–02, Paris, 1970.
160. T. Kojima, M. Hanai, K. Yagi, K. Okusa, M. Alihara, and K. Haga, I.E.E.E. Transactions on Power Apparatus and Systems *PAS-93*, 579 (1974).
161. G. H. Hunt, M. J. Koulopoulos, and P. H. Ware, American Institute of Electrical Engineers, Transactions, Power Apparatus and Systems *77*, 25 (1958).
162. S. Fujiki, H. Furusawa, T. Kuhara, and H. Matsuba, I.E.E.E. Transactions on Power Apparatus and Systems *PAS-90*, 2703 (November-December 1971).
163. H. Halperin and C. E. Betzer, Electrical Engineering, p. 1074, October 1936.

164. Some of the U.S. and British patents on voltage stabilizers issued to Simplex are British patents 1,083,113, August 2l, 1964; 1,116,398, October 1965; 1,021,681, March 9, 1966; U.S. Patents 3,482,033, August 4, 1966; 3,445,394, June 1967; 3,346,500, October 10, 1967; 3,350,312, October 31, 1976; 3,542,684, October 1968; 3,629,110, October 2, 1968; 3,533,183, July 28, 1970.

165. H. Kato, N. Maekawa, S. Inoue, and H. Fujita in "1974 Annual Report, Conference on Electrical Insulation and Dielectric Phenomena," National Academy of Sciences-National Research Council, Washington, DC, p. 229, 1975.

166. R. J. Turbett and A. C. Ashcraft, U.S. Patent 4,263,158, April 21, 1981.

167. M. A. Slifkin, Nature p. 877, November 1963.

168. J. B. Birks, *Photophysics of Aromatic Molecules,* Wiley, New York, 1970.

169. B. Yoda and Y. Sekii, I.E.E.E. Transactions on Power Apparatus and Systems *PAS-90,* 2682 (November-December 1971).

170. B. T. MacKenzie, M. Prober, and R. C. Lever, in "1972 Annual Report, Conference Electrical Insulation and Dielectric Phenomena," National Academy of Sciences-National Research Council, Washington, DC, p. 232, 1973.

171. E. H. Reynolds, in "1972 Annual Report, Conference on Electrical Insulation and Dielectric Phenomena, National Academy of Sciences-National Research Council, Washington, DC, p. 463, 1973.

172. D. Kind and L. Schiweck, in "1969 Annual Report, Conference on Electrical Insulation and Dielectric Phenomena," National Academy of Sciences-National Research Council, Washington, DC, p. 128, 1970.

173. N. Singh, A. C. Bruhin, and R. C. Lever, in "1972 Annual Report, Conference on Electrical Insulation and Dielectric Phenomena," National Academy of Sciences-National Research Council, Washington, DC, p. 247, 1973.

174. Japanese Patent 74–31,929 (1973).

175. Y. Nitta, M. Funayama, I.E.E.E. Trans. on Electr. Insul. *EI-13,* 130 (1978).

176. Wu Jiong and Chen Shantong, Journal of the Xian Jiao Tong Univ. *17,* 79 (1983) (in Chinese).

177. Y. Nitta, H. Fukugawa, and H. Takashima, I.E.E.E. Transactions on Electrical Insulation *EI-13,* 62 (1978).

178. T. Hazen, Wire Journal, p. 1527, Nov. 1960.

179. W. M. Hladik, 13th Annual Wire and Cable Symposium, U.S. Army Signal Corps, Atlantic City, 1964.

180. G. Bahder and C. Katz in "1972 Annual Report, Conference on Electrical Insulation and Dielectric Phenomena," National Academy of Sciences-National Research Council, Washington, DC, p. 190, 1973.

181. R. Noto, I.E.E.E. Trans. *EI-15,* 251 (1980).

182. T. Yoshimitsu and H. Mitsui, Proc. 11th Symposium Electr. Insul. Materials *P-8,* 101 (1978) (Japanese).

183. N. Yoshimore, F. Noto, and K. Kikuchi, I.E.E.E. Trans. *EI-12,* 411 (1977).

184. Y. Nitta, Trans. I.E.E. Japan *94A,* No. 4, 17 (1974).

185. T. Hayami, AIEE Japan *45* 235 (1974).

186. T. Yoshimitsu and T. Nakakita in "1978 IEEE International Symposium on Electrical Insulation, Conference Record 78CH1287–2-EI, Philadelphia, p. 116, 12–14 June 1978.

187. J. Sletbak and A. Botne, I.E.E.E. Transactions on Electrical Insulation *EI-12,* 383 (1977).

188. J. A. Barrie, *Diffusion in Polymers,* J. Crank and G. S. Park, Eds., Academic Press, New York, 1968.

189. J. Pinsky, Modern Plastics *34,* 145 and 237 (April 1957).

190. Charles E. White, Union Carbide, personal communication (1972).

191. T. Mizukami, S. Kuma, and K. Soma, "1977 Annual Report, Conference on Electrical Insulation and Dielectric Phenomena", National Academy of Sciences-National Research Council, Washington, D.C. l978, p. 316.

192. R. L. Hamilton, Bell Systems Technical Journal, p. 391, February 1967.

193. R. M. Eichhorn, Polymer Engineering and Sciences *10,* 32 (1970).

194. C. T. Meyer and A. Chamel, I.E.E.E. Transactions on Electrical Insulation *EI-15,* 389 (1980).

195. J. C. Chan and S. M. Jaczek, I.E.E.E. Transactions on Electrical Insulation *EI-13,* 194 (1978).

196. H. Matsuba, E. Kawai, and K. Sato, 1976 I.E.E.E. International Symposium on Electrical Insulation, Conference Record 76CH1088–4-EI, Montreal, Canada, p. 224 June 12–24, 1976.

197. D. W. Aukland and R. Cooper, Proceedings of the Institution of Electrical Engineers *122,* 860 (1975).
198. E. Favrie and H. Auclair, "Effect of Water on Electrical Properties of Extruded Synthetical Insulations Application on Cables," Paper No. A79 411–0, I.E.E.E. Power Engineering Society Summer Meeting, Vancouver, BC, Canada, July 15–20, 1979.
199. Y. Nitta, I.E.E.E. Transactions on Electrical Insulation, *EI-9,* 109, 1974.
200. R. Fournie, J. Perret, P. Recoupe, and Y. LeGall, 1978 I.E.E.E. International Symposium on Electrical Insulation, Conference Record 78CH 1287–2-EI, Philadelphia, p. 110, June 12–14, 1978.
201. A. C. Ashcraft, "Water Treeing in Polyethylene Dielectrics," Paper No. 3A-13 World Electrotechnical Congress, Moscow, U.S.S.R., June 1977.
202. H. Matsuba and E. Kawai, Trans. IEE Japan *95-A,* No. 10, 1 (1975).
203. T. Miyashita and T. Inoue, Trans. IEE Japan *90,* 937 (1970).
204. T. Tanaka, Tech. Rep. of CRIEPI (Japanese), No. 72059 (1972).
205. S. L. Nunes and M. T. Shaw, IEEE Trans. *EI-15,* 439 (1980).
206. E. J. McMahon, IEEE Trans. *EI-13,* 277 (1978).
207. J. Sletbak, IEEE Trans. *PAS-98,* 1358 (1979).
208. T. Tanaka, T. Fukuda, S. Suzuki, Y. Nitta, H. Goto, and K. Kubota, IEEE Trans. On Power Apparatus and Systems, *PAS-93,* 693 (1974).
209. L. Minnema, H. A. Barneveld, and P. D. Rinkel, "1979 Annual Report, Conference on Electrical Insulation and Dielectric Phenomena," National Academy of Sciences-National Research Council, Washington, DC, p. 480, 1980.
210. A. C. Ashcraft and R. M. Eichhorn, IEEE Trans. *EI-13,* 198 (1978).
211. J. Rye, P. M. Brown, G. J. LePoidevin, and W. T. Eeles, 1975 I.E.E. Conference on Dielectric Materials, Measurements, and Applications, Churchill College, Cambridge, England.
212. J. Rye, P. M. Brown, and W. T. Eeles, Journal of Physics D *8,* L16 (1975).
213. A. Garton, R. J. Densley, and A. Bulinski, IEEE Trans. *EI-15,* 500 (1980).
214. T. W. Dakin, "1974 Annual Report, Conference on Electrical Insulation and Dielectric Phenomena," National Academy of Sciences-National Research Council, Washington, DC, p. 197, 1975.
215. L. B. Loeb, *Electrical Coronas,* University of California Press, Berkeley, 1965.
216. T. Tanaka, Y. Nitta, and T. Fukuda, "1972 Annual Report, Conference on Electrical Insulation and Dielectric Phenomena," National Academy of Sciences-National Research Council, Washington, DC, p. 216, 1973.
217. H. A. Pohl, J. Appl. Phys. *29,* 1182 (1958).
218. H. A. Pohl in *Electrostatics and Its Applications,* A. D. Moore, Ed., Wiley Interscience, New York, 1973.
219. W. F. Pickard, *Progress in Dielectrics,* J. B. Birks and J. Hart, Eds., Academic Press, New York, 1965.
220. H. Heumann, R. Patsch, M. Saure, and H. Wagner, Proceedings Conference Internationale des Grands Reseaux Electriques, Paper No. 15–06, Paris, 1980.
221. G. Mole, "A Mechanism of Water Treeing in Polyethylene Cable Insulation," Paper No. 64, Section 3A, World Electrotechnical Congress, Moscow, U.S.S.R., June 12–15, 1977.
222. "On Water Trees in Organic Insulating Materials, Parts I and II," Technical Reports 94 and 111, Institute of Electrical Engineering of Japan, Study Committee of Electric Stress Resistance in Insulating Materials, F. Noto, Chairman, 1974 and 1979.
223. T. Tanaka, T. Fukuda, and S. Suzuki, I.E.E.E. Transactions on Power Apparatus and Systems *PAS-95,* 1892 (1976).
224. L. Minnema, H. A. Barneveld, and P. D. Rinkel, I.E.E.E. Transactions on Electrical Insulation *EI-15,* 461 (1980).
225. A. L. McKean, K. Tsuji, H. C. Doepken, Jr., and A. Zidon, IEEE Trans. *PAS-97,* 1167 (1978).
226. D. W. Auckland, R. Cooper, and C. Walker, Proc. IEE *125,* 776 (1978).
227. D. Mangary, K. D. Kiss, and H. C. Doepken, Jr., Organic Coatings Plastics Chemistry Preprints *38,* 418 (1978).
228. S. N. Zhurkov, V. A. Zakrevsky, V. E. Korsukov, and V. S. Kuksenko, J. Polym. Sci., Part A-2 *10,* 1509 (1970).
229. S. Yamanouchi, T. Shiga, and H. Matsubara in "1975 Annual Report, Conference on Electrical

Insulation and Dielectric Phenomena," National Academy of Sciences-National Research Council, Washington, DC, p. 386, 1975.

230. B. S. Bernstein, N. Srinivas, and P. N. Lee, in "1975 Annual Report, Conference on Electrical Insulation and Dielectric Phenomena," National Academy of Sciences-National Research Council, Washington, DC, p. 296, 1978.

231. M. Morita, M. Havai, H. Shimanuki, and F. Aida, in "1975 Annual Report, Conference on Electrical Insulation and Dielectric Phenomena," National Academy of Sciences-National Research Council, Washington, DC, p. 335, 1978.

232. D. W. Auckland and R. Cooper, in "1973 Annual Report, Conference on Electrical Insulation and Dielectric Phenomena," National Academy of Sciences-National Research Council, Washington, DC, p. 71, 1974.

233. R. Lyle and J. W. Kirkland, "An Accelerated Life Test for Evaluating Power Cable Insulation," Paper No. 81 WM 115-5, IEEE Power Engineering Society Winter Meeting, Atlanta, Georgia, February 1–6, 1981.

234. G. Bahder, G. S. Eager, D. A. Silver, U.S. Pat. 3,885,085, May 20, 1975.

235. R. M. Eichhorn and R. J. Turbett, IEEE Transactions on Power Apparatus and Systems *PAS-98*, 2215 (1979).

236. European Patent, No. 27,300 to Philips Gloeilampen NV, April 22, 1981.

237. K. Soma and S. Kuma, 1980 IEEE International Symposium on Electrical Insulation, Conference Record 80 CH1496-9-EI, Boston, p. 212, June 12–14, 1980.

238. H. Matsuba, E. Kawai, and K. Sato, Proceedings 8th Symposium on Electrically Insulating Materials (Japanese), III-3, 133 (1975).

239. K. W. Wagner, AIEE Trans. *41*, 288 (1922).

240. W. Rogowski, Arch. Elektrotech *19*, 569 (1930).

241. A. von Hippel, J. Appl. Phys. *8*, 815 (1937).

242. Y. Inuishi, K. Onishi, Y. Tada, and N. Suita, J. Inst. Elect. Engrs. of Japan *76*, 913 (1956).

243. J. Artbauer and J. Griac, Proc. Inst. Elect. Engrs. *112*, 818 (1965).

244. H. Fröhlich, Proc. Roy. Soc. *A-188*, 521 (1947).

245. K. H. Stark and C. G. Garton, Nature *176*, 1225 (1955).

246. M. Ieda, G. Sawa, and M. Nagao, "On the Temperature Dependence of Electric Strength of Polyethylene," Internationales Symposium Hochspannungstechnik, Zürich, 5.1–04, 587 (1975).

247. A. E. W. Austen and H. Pelzer, J. Inst. Elect. Engrs. *93*(I), 525 (1946).

248. D. W. Watson, IEEE Trans. *EI-8*, 6 (1973).

249. I. D. E. Ball, Proc. Inst. Elect. Engrs. *98*, 84 (1951).

250. W. G. Oakes, J. Inst. Elect. Engrs. *95*(I), 36 (1948).

251. W. G. Oakes, J. Inst. Elect. Engrs. *96*(I), 37 (1949).

252. J. Artbauer and J. Griac, "The Instrinsic Electric Strength of Polymers and Its Relation to the Structure Part I: Experimental," Acta Technica CSAV, No. 3, p. 416, 1966.

253. K. Amakawa, T. Moriuchi, T. Yoshida, and Y. Inuishi, J. Inst. Elect. Engrs. of Japan *84*, 129 (1964).

254. J. M. Meek and J. D. Craggs, *Electrical Breakdown of Gases*, John Wiley & Sons, New York, 1978.

255. I. Kitani and K. Arii, Trans. Inst. Elect. Engrs. of Japan *94-A*, 251 (1974).

256. H. Fröhlich, Proc. Roy. Soc. *A160*, 230, (1937).

257. R. Cooper, D. T. Grossart, and A. A. Wallace, Proceedings of the Physical Society (London) *B70*, 169 (1957).

258. J. W. Davisson, in *Progress in Dielectrics,* Vol. *1,* J. B. Birks, Ed., Wiley, New York, p. 235, 1961.

259. M. Ieda, I.E.E.E. Transactions on Electrical Insulation *EI-15*, 206 (1980).

260. H. Wagner, in "1974 Annual Report, Conference on Electrical Insulation and Dielectric Phenomena," National Academy of Sciences-National Research Council, Washington, DC, p. 62, 1975.

261. H. Miyauchi and K. Yahagi, Transactions of the Institute of Electronics and Communication Engineers of Japan *92-A*, 36 (1972).

262. H. Fröhlich and B. V. Paranjape, Proceedings of the Physical Society (London) *B69*, 21 (1956).

263. H. Sabuni and J. K. Nelson, Journal of Materials Science *12*, 2435 (1977).

264. A. von Hippel and G. M. Lee, Phys. Rev. *59*, 824 (1941).

265. Y. Inuishi, I.E.E.E. Trans. *EI-15*, 139 (1980).

266. K. Yahagi and Y. Maeda, Memoirs of the School of Science and Engineering, Waseda University, No. 41, 31 (1977).
267. R. Cooper, R. M. Higgin, and W. A. Smith, Proceedings of the Physical Society *B76*, 817 (1960).
268. S. Chou and H. Brooks, J. Appl. Phys. *41*, 4451 (1970).
269. K. Miyairi, G. Sawa, and M. Ieda, Electrical Engineering in Japan *92*, 531 (1972).
270. E. Sacher in "1976 Annual Report, Conference on Electrical Insulation and Dielectric Phenomena," National Academy of Sciences-National Research Council, Washington, DC, p. 33, 1978.
271. M. Ieda, M. Nagao, and M. Hikita, Proceedings International Symposium on High Voltage Engineering, Paper 21.05, Milan, 1979.
272. J. M. Lloyd and P. P. Budenstein, Final Rep., Grant DAHCO4–74 GOO47, U.S. Army Research Office (1977).
273. P. P. Budenstein and J. M. Lloyd in "1975 Ann. Rep. Conf. Elect. Insul. Dielec. Phenom.," National Academy of Sciences-National Research Council, Washington, DC, p. 303, 1978.
274. J. M. Lloyd and P. P. Budenstein in "1977 Ann. Rep. Conf. Elec. Insul. Dielec. Phenom.," National Academy of Sciences-National Research Council, Washington, DC, p. 339 (1979).
275. K. Miyairi, T. Yamandi, G. Sawa, and M. Ieda, J. Inst. Elect. Engineers of Japan *91*, 1962 (1971).
276. M Nagao, S. Toyoshima, G. Sawa, and M. Ieda, Trans. Inst. Elect. Engrs. of Japan *97-A*, 617 (1977).
277. M. Nagao, G. Sawa, and M. Ieda, Trans. Inst. Elect. Engrs. of Japan *96-A*, 605 (1976).
278. S. Mita and K. Yahagi, Japan J. Appl. Phys. *14*, 197 (1975).
279. H. Sabuni and J. K. Nelson, Journal of Materials Science *14*, 2791 (1979).
280. M. L. Williams, R. F. Landel, and J. D. Ferry, Journal of the American Chemical Society *77*, 3701 (1955).
281. M. Ieda, M. Nagao, M. Hikita, and G. Sawa, the 3rd International Symposium on High Voltage Engineering, 2.1–05, 1979.
282. S. N. Kolesov, I.E.E.E. Transactions on Electrical Insulation *EI-15*, 382 (1980).
283. H. Sabuni and J. K. Nelson, Journal of Materials Science *11*, 1574 (1976).
284. J. D. Ferry, *Viscoelastic Properties of Polymers,* Wiley, New York, 1970.
285. A. von Hippel, Zeitschrift für Physik *88*, 358 (1934).
286. A. K. Vijh, Journal of Materials Science *9*, 2052 (1974).
287. P. R. Couchman, G. R. Proto, and C. L. Reynolds, Journal of Materials Science *11*, 576 (1976).
288. U. Shinohara and M. Kimura, J. Inst. Elect. Engrs. of Japan *77*, 1300 (1957).
289. R. F. Boyer, J. Appl. Phys. *25*, 825 (1955).
290. N. I. Vorobeev, Elektrichestvo, No. 3, 75 (1960).
291. I. D. Troyszky and I. M. Chernobelskaya, Trans. Elec. Ind. (Russian), No. 5, 18 (1963).
292. P. N. Schervak, Plasti, Massy, No. 9, 40, 1963.
293. S. Chaithed, *Breakdown of Solid Dielectrics,* (Russian), Gosenergoizdat, Moskow, 1957.
294. S. N. Kolesov, *Ionization, Corona, and Dielectric Strength,* (Russian), Znanie, Kiev, 1969.
295. H. Wilski, Kunststoff *54*, 1 (1964).
296. S. N. Kolesov, Doctoral Thesis, Moscow Energetics Institute, 1968.
297. S. N. Kolesov, Elektrichestvo, No. 9, 80 (1968).
298. I. N. Razinskaya, B. P. Schmarkman, and P. V. Kozlov, Vysokomol. Soedin. *6*, 427 (1964).
299. R. N. Kessenik, V. G. Sotnikov, V. G. Trippele, Y. N. Schumilov, Y. G. Gruzdeva, and A. P. Pobelichenko, J. Gomsky Polytech. Inst. (Russian) *126*, 36 (1964).
300. B. P. Schmarkman, T. L. Yatzenina, L. I. Vidyaikina. V. L. Balakirskaya, and D. H. Bort, Vysokomol. Soed. *7*, 333 (1965).
301. J. Artbauer and J. Griac, Acta Technica *11*, 416 (1966).
302. B. P. Schmarkman, T. L. Yatzenina, and V. L. Balskirskaya, Vysokomol. Soed. *A12*, 149 (1970).
303. S. S. Gumin and L. N. Zakgein, J. Tech. Phys. (Russian) *5*, 1380 (1935).
304. S. H. Antonov, E. B. Fainstein, and N. V. Andrianova, Plasti. Massy, No. 12, 51 (1963).
305. V. S. Dmitrievsky, V. S. Korolev, G. M. Grudnina, and F. P. Cheschkov, Symposium on Breakdown (Russian), Part I, Novosibirski (1969).
306. W. Reicherdt and B. Hosselbrath, Plast. und Kaut. *12*, 528 (1965).
307. P. V. Kozlov and B. N. Korastelev, J. Phys. Chem. (Russian) *31*, 653 (1957).
308. B. A. Dogadkin, Proc. 3rd Symposium on Colloidal Chemistry (Russian), Academy of Science, U.S.S.R. (1955).

309. B. A. Dogadkin, L.L. Fedyoukin, and V. E. Gube, Colloid Chem. (Russian) *19*, 287 (1957).
310. V. A. Kargin, Progress in Chemistry (Russian) *25*, 1006 (1966).
311. G. L. Slonimskii and V. I. Pavlev, Vysokomol. Soed. *7*, 1279 (1965).
312. V. A. Marichin, A. I. Shuzeker, and A. A. Yastrebinsky, Phys. Solid (Russian) *7*, 441 (1965).
313. H. St.-Onge, IEEE Trans. *EI-11* 20 (1976).
314. H. St.-Onge, IEEE Trans. *EI-15*, 350 (1980).
315. R. A. Fava, Proc. IEE *112*, 819 (1965).
316. P. Fisher, "1974 Ann. Rep. Conf. Elect. Insul. and Dielectric Phenomena", National Academy of Sciences-National Research Council, Washington, D.C., p. 661, 1975.
317. A. K. Vardenberg, N. V. Vinogradova and N. A. Petuhova, Trans. Elect. Industry (Russian), No. 8, 4 (1960).
318. I. F. Kanovez and L. F. Grigoreeva, Plasti, Massy, No. 3, 15 (1961).
319. S. N. Kolesov, Y. P. Vaulina, and L. N. Heraskov, Rep. Acad. Sci. U.S.S.R. (Russian) No. 5, 19 (1967).
320. S. N. Kolesov, L. A. Voedenskaya, and L. N. Heraskov, Plasti. Massy, No. 9, 22 (1967).
321. S. N. Kolesov and G. I. Geifman, J. Univ. Phys. (Russian), No. 5, 156 (1968).
322. S. N. Kolesov, N. P. Balaban, I. A. Kiledeev, and I. S. Kolesov, Vysokomol. Soed. *B15*, 888 (1973).
323. L. A. Laius and E. V. Kuvshinsky, Vysokomol. Soed. *3*, 215 (1961).
324. S. N. Kolesov, A. A. Buniyat-Zade, N. P. Balaban, I. S. Kolesov, and V. A. Putintsev, Electrichestve, No. 4, 89 (1975).
325. M. J. Richardson, J. Polym. Sci., Part C, No. 3, 32 (1963).
326. I. P. Losev, O. V. Smirnova, and E. V. Smurova, Plasti. Massy, No. 9, 10 (1962).
327. Th. G. F. Schoon and O. Teichmann, Kolloid Z. und Z. Polymere *197*, 35 (1964).
328. Th. G. F. Schoon and R. Kretschmer, Kolloid Z. und Z. Polymere *197*, 45 (1964).
329. S. N. Kolesov, *Structural Electrophysics of the Polymer Dielectrics* (Russian), Izd. Uzbekistan, Tashkent, 1975.
330. S. M. Ohlberh, J. Roth, and R. A. V. Raff, Appl. Polym. Sci. *1*, 114 (1959).
331. S. N. Kolesov, Vysokomol. Soed. *10*, 582 (1968).
332. K. Yahagi, IEEE Trans. *EI-15*, 241 (1980).
333. S. N. Kolesov, N. P. Balaban, and L. N. Kheraskov, Vysokomol. Soed. *12*, 366 (1970).
334. S. N. Kolesov, Elektrichestbo, No. 9, 84 (1970).
335. S. N. Kolesov and L. N. Kheraskov, Vysokomol. Soed. *B12*, 266 (1970).
336. V. A. Kargin, G. P. Andrianova, and G. G. Karadash, Vysokomol. Soed. *9*, 289 (1967).
337. S. Onogi, T. Asada, A. Hirai, and K. Kameyama, Zairyo (Japanese) *14*, 322 (1965).
338. K. Yahagi and S. Mita, 1975 Conf. on Dielec. Mater., Meas., and Appl., IEEE Conf. Pub. No. 129, 187 (1975).
339. W. Glenz, N. Morosoff, and A. Peterlin, Polym. Lett. *9*, 211 (1971).
340. A. M. Lobanov, G. B. Schnakovskaya, O. S. Romanovskaya, and B. I. Sasuin, Vysokomol. Soedin. *B11*, 755 (1969).
341. P. I. Zubov, V. A. Voronkov, and L. A. Suhareva, Vysokomol. Soedin. *B10*, 92 (1968).
342. S. N. Kolesov, N. P. Balaban, V. A. Putintsev, and I. S. Kolesov, Vysokomol. Soedin. *B18*, 5 (1976).
343. E. H. Andrews, P. J. Owen, and A. Singh, Proc. Roy. Soc. *A324*, 79 (1971).
344. D. Mangary, K. D. Kiss, E. Malawei, and H. C. Doepken, Jr., "1978 Ann. Rep. Conf. Elect. Insul. Dielec. Phenom.", National Academy of Sciences-National Research Council, Washington, D.C., p. 195 (1979).
345. A. Bradwell, R. Cooper, and B. Varlow, Proc. IEE *118*, 247 (1971).
346. T. Ito, T. Sakai, and Y. Toriyama, "1973 Ann. Rep. Conf. Elect. Insul. Dielec. Phenom.", National Academy of Sciences-National Research Council, Washington, D.C., P. 267 (1974).
347. T. Kouno, IEEE Transactions on Electrical Insulation *EI-15*, 153 (1980).
348. Japanese Electrical Soc. Techn. Report (in Japanese), II, No. 43 (1976).
349. International Electrochemical Commission Publication, No. 112 (1959).
350. M. Nishida, N. Yoshimura, and F. Noto, Trans. IEE Japan *99-A*, 121 (1979).
351. M. J. Billings, A. Smith, and R. Williams, IEEE Transactions on Electrical Insulation *EI-2*, 131 1967).
352. F. Noto and K. Kawamura, IEEE Transactions on Electrical Insulation *EI-13*, 418 (1978).

353. K. Kawamura and F. Noto, Trans. IEE Japan *98A*, 579 (1978).
354. R. S. Norman and A. A. Kessel, Trans. AIEE *77*, III, 632 (1958).
355. M. Tsuchihashi, Y. Murakami, S. Sasakura, and T. Tachibana, 1978 Natl. Conl. Rec. IEE of Japan, No. 266, 263 (1978) (in Japanese).
356. E. Hirasawa, S. Matsuda, and K. Hirabayashi, 1978 Natl. Conl. Rec. IEE of Japan, No. 226, 263 (1978).
357. R. Bartnikas and R. M. Eichhorn, Eds., *Engineering Dielectrics, Volume 2A. Electrical Properties of Solid Insulating Materials: Molecular Structure and Electrical Behavior,* ASTM STP783, American Society for Testing and Materials, Philadelphia, 1983, pp. 505, 506.
358. P. Fischer, "1974 Annual Report, Conference on Electrical Insulation and Dielectric Phenomena," National Academy of Sciences – National Research Council, Washington, DC, p. 661, 1975.
359. A. E. W. Austen and H. Pelzer, Journal of the Institution of Electrical Engineers *93(1)*, 525 (1946).
360. E. C. Hsu, I.E.E.E. Transactions on Electrical Insulation *EI-13*, 110 (1978).
361. S. Sapieha, M. R. Wertheimer, and A. Yelon, I.E.E.E. Transactions on Electrical Insulation *EI-14*, 229 (1979).
362. N. Klein in *Advances in Electronics and Electron Physics,* Vol. 26, L. Marton and C. Marton, Eds., Academic Press, New York, 309 (1969).
363. N. Klein, I.E.E.E. Transactions on Electron Devices *ED-13*, 788 (1966).
364. J. Brettle, Proceedings 1979 I.E.E.E. Conference on Dielectric Materials, Measurements, and Applications, Birmingham, United Kingdom, p. 86, 1979.
365. V. K. Agarwal and V. K. Srivastava, Thin Solid Films *8*, 377 (1971).
366. J. Vermeer, Physica *20*, 313 (1954).
367. J. Blok and D. G. LeGrand, J. of Appl. Physics *40*, 288, (1969).
368. I. D. Smith in "1979 Annual Report, Conference on Electrical Insulation and Dielectric Phenomena," National Academy of Sciences-National Research Council, Washington, DC, p. 171, 1980.
369. T. J. Lewis in "1976 Annual Report, Conference on Electrical Insulation and Dielectric Phenomena," National Academy of Sciences-National Research Council, Washington, DC, p. 533, 1978.
370. K. Amakawa, T.Yoshida, T. Moriuchi, and Y. Inuioshi, Electrical Engineering in Japan *84(I)*, 50 (1964).
371. S. M. Sze, J. Appl. Phys. *38*, 2951 (1967).
372. M. Ieda, Y. Takai, M. Nagao, and G. Sawa, Proceedings, 1975 IEE Conference on Dielectric Materials, Measurements, and Applications, Cambridge, United Kingdom, p. 249, 1975.
373. W. T. Lynch, J. Appl. Phys. *43*, 3274, (1972).
374. A. Grinberg and D. M. K. de Grinberg, J. Appl. Physics *45*, 2007 (1974).
375. P. Wang and V. van Buren, J. Electrochem. Soc. *117*, 127 (1970).
376. Y. Namiki, H. Shimanuki, F. Aida, and M. Morita, I.E.E.E. Transactions on Electrical Insulation *EI-15*, 473 (1980).
377. R. Cooper, C. T. Elliott, British J.Appl. Phys. *17*, 214a, 481 (1966).
378. R. Coisson, C. Paracchini, G. Schianchi, J. of the Electrochem. Soc. *125*, 581 (1978).
379. D. W. Auckland, A. B. Borishade, and N. Gravill, Journal of Physics E (Scientific Instruments) *8*, 847 (1975).
380. H. Sabuni, "The Effect on Some Structural Parameters on the Electric Stress of Polymeric Dielectrics," Ph.D. Thesis, Univ. of London, 1978.
381. R. Cooper and A. A. Wallace, Proceedings of the Physical Soc. *B66*, 1113 (1953).
382. R. E. Cooper, T. Cheng, K. Kantak, and A. Rein in "1977 Annual Report Conference on Electrical Insulation and Dielectric Phenomena," National Academy of Sciences – National Research Council, Washington, DC, p. 255, 1979.
383. A. V. Tobolsky, *Properties and Structure of Polymers,* Wiley, New York, 1960.
384. K. Deutsch, E. A. Hoff, and W. Reddish, J. Polym. Sci. *13*, 565 (1954).
385. T. Nishitani, K. Yoshimo, and Y. Inuishi, Japanese Journal of Applied Physics *14*, 521 (1975).
386. P. Laurenceau, G. Dreyfus, and J. Lewiner, Phys. Rel. Lett. *38*, 46 (1977).
387. A. Migliori in "1979 Annual Report, Conference on Electrical Insulation and Dielectric Phenomena," National Academy of Sciences-National Research Council, Washington, DC, p. 315, 1980.

388. S. Nakamura, G. Aswa, and M. Ieda, Japanese Journal of Applied Physics *16,* 2165 (1977).
389. J. L. Haborgield, J. Tanaka, J. F. Johnson in "1976 Annual Report, Conference on Electrical Insulation and Dielectric Phenomena," National Academy of Sciences-National Research Council, Washington, DC, p. 453, 1978.
390. P. Durand, Proceedings, 1975 I.E.E. Conference on Dielectric Materials, Measurements and Applications, Cambridge, United Kingdom, p. 11, 1975.
391. M. Ieda, Y. Takai, and T. Mizutani, Proceedings 1979 I.E.E. Conference on Dielectric Materials, Measurements and Applications, Birmingham, United Kingdom, p. 294, 1979.
392. P. P. Budenstein and P. J. Hayes, J. Appl. Phys. *38,* 2837 (1967).
393. D. K. DasGupta and K. Doughty, Appl. Phys. Lett. *31,* 585 (1977).
394. G. M. Sessler, J. E. West, D. A. Berkley, and G. Morgenstern, Phys. Rev. Lett. *38,* 368 (1977).
395. D. W. Tong, 1980 I.E.E.E. International Symposium on Electrical Insulation, Boston, p. 179, 1980.

Chapter 5

ELECTRICAL CONDUCTION IN POLYMERS

5.1 INTRODUCTION

Conductivity is one of the most widely varying physical properties known. It covers some 32 orders of magnitude from the best conductors with σ of 10^{10} $(\Omega\,cm)^{-1}$ at 1 K to the best insulators with σ of 10^{-22} $(\Omega\,cm)^{-1}$. Understanding the electrical conduction of polymers is important in two areas: (1) the generation of high-performance electrical insulators and (2) the synthesis of metallically conducting polymers. For purely practical reasons, there is always a need to produce materials with lower conductivity $[<10^{-10}$ $(\Omega\,cm)^{-1}]$ than are currently available for high-quality communications cables, optical fibers, and low-loss power cables. There is also a need for better materials of intermediate conductivity $[10^{-9}$ to 10^{-2} $(\Omega\,cm)^{-1}]$ to eliminate static charge in conveyor belts, carpeting, clothing, satellite antennas, and bushings; for electromagnetic shielding materials in the form of coatings and various housings, generally requiring conductivities in excess of 10^{-2} $(\Omega\,cm)^{-1}$; and for materials to use in the manufacture of video disks, which consist of a conductive surface greater than 10^{-1} $(\Omega\,cm)^{-1}$ overcoated with a thin dielectric layer. Finally, there are both the hope of generating organic polymers with conductivities equal to the best of metals and the dream of creating organic superconductors with high transition temperatures.

From the purely scientific point of view, despite the enormous amount of work already done on conduction processes, two questions remain to be answered:

(1) What is the true conduction process in the best insulating polymers?
(2) Why do very heavily doped conjugated polymers not show a higher conductivity than they do?

In Part 1 of this chapter we examine some basic concepts of conduction processes with the goal of thus better understanding such dielectric problems as loss tangent, treeing, dielectric breakdown, metal/insulator/metal structures, and surface and contact effects.

In Part 2 we examine current bulk conduction mechanisms in the metallically conducting polymers, the synthetic approaches to such polymers, and the subject of superconductivity in polymers.

Listed below for quick reference are more recent books and review articles that amplify the subject matter of the chapter.

 1. R. Bartnikas and R. M. Eichhorn, eds., *Engineering Dielectrics, Vol. IIA, Electrical Properties of Solid Insulating Materials: Molecular Structure and Electrical Behavior,* ASTM Special Technical Publ. No. 783, Philadelphia (1983).
 2. V. Shah, *Handbook of Plastics Testing Technology,* John Wiley & Sons, New York (1984).
 3. C. B. Duke and H. W. Gibson, "Conductive Polymers", M. Grayson, ed., *Kirk-Othmer: Encylopedia of Chemical Technology,* Vol. 18, Third Edition, John Wiley and Sons, New York (1982).
 4. H. W. Gibson and J. M. Pochan, "Acetylene Polymers", in Mark, Bikales, Overberger, Menges, eds., *Encyclopedia of Polymer Science and Engineering,* Vol. I, Second Edition, John Wiley and Sons, New York (1985).
 5. I. Bunget and M. Popescu, *Physics of Solid Dielectrics,* Elsevier, Amsterdam (1984).
 6. A. R. Bishop, D. K. Campbell, and B. Nicolaenko, eds., *Nonlinear Problems: Present and Future,* North Holland Publ. Co., Amsterdam (1982).
 7. J. C. W. Chien, *Polyaceytlene: Chemistry, Physics, and Material Science,* Academic Press, Orlando, Florida (1984).
 8. G. Wegner, M. Monkenbusch, G. Wieners, R. Weizenhoefer, G. Lieser and W. Werner, Mol. Cryst. Liq. Cryst. *118,* 85 (1985).
 9. R. H. Baughman, Contemp. Top. Polym. Sci. *5,* 321 (1984).
10. IEEE Electrical Insulation Soc., *First International Conference on Conduction and Breakdown in Solid Dielectrics,* Universite Paul Sabatier, Toulouse, France, July 4–8, 1983.
11. J. Lowell and A. C. Rose-Innes, Advances in Physics *29,* 947 (1980).

PART 1. CONDUCTION PROCESSES IN INSULATING POLYMERS

5.2   BASIC CONCEPTS

5.2.1   Free-Electron Fermi Gas Model

The free-electron Fermi gas model is quite useful for explaining the conductivity in metals. Sodium provides an illustration. According to this model, sodium metal consists of Na^+ ions and N valence-active 3s orbitals with one electron in each. The electrons are treated as N "particles in a three-dimensional box," while the Na^+ ions are ignored.

The allowed wave functions (molecular orbitals) for the electrons are calculated in the same manner as those for N noninteracting particles in a box. The Pauli exclusion principle states that only two electrons of opposite spin are allowed per orbital or, equivalently, each orbital is considered to be two separate orbitals each containing at most one electron. The latter approach is used by Kittel in counting the number of filled orbitals in the ground state of a metal.[1] The number of filled orbitals in the ground state is therefore N. The energy of the highest filled orbital in the ground state of a metal is called the Fermi energy, E_F. The Fermi energy can be calculated from the electron density and fundamental constants as

$$E_F = h^2/2m[3\pi^2N/V]^{2/3}, \qquad\qquad 5.1$$

where N equals the number of electrons (in this case also the number of orbitals), V is the volume of the three-dimensional box, h is Planck's constant, and m equals the mass of an electron. From Eq. (5.1) the Fermi energy of sodium is calculated to be 3.23 eV.[1]

Another interesting property that can be calculated from Eq. (5.1) is the "density of states" at the Fermi level. Density of states refers to the number of filled or unfilled molecular orbitals with a specific energy. Therefore, the density of states at the Fermi level is the number of orbitals with an energy at or near the Fermi energy. According to the free-electron Fermi gas model, the density of states at the Fermi level, $N(E_F)$, is

$$N(E_F) = 3N/2E_F . \qquad\qquad 5.2$$

For sodium, the density of states at the Fermi level calculated from Eq. (5.2) is $\sim3 \times 10^{23}$ states/eV.[1] This result means that the energy of the next highest orbital is about 10^{-23} eV above the Fermi energy. Since this value is infinitesimally small compared to the thermal energy kT, where k is Boltzmann's constant, a "continuum" of filled and empty orbitals will exist.

The density of states as a function of energy for a free electron in three dimensions, at absolute zero, is shown in Fig. 5.1. The shaded area represents filled orbitals, and E_F is the energy of the highest occupied orbital. At any temperature above absolute zero, empty orbitals just above the Fermi level may be populated with electrons promoted by the thermal energy, as shown by the dashed curve in Fig. 5.2.

The band-structure model is an extension of the free-electron model. Electrons are now treated as being only nearly free, and they interact weakly with the ions from which they came. The ions are arranged in rigid positions in a regular crystalline lattice. When an electron travels through the crystalline lattice, it encounters a regular periodic potential caused by its interactions with the ions. As a consequence of these interactions, bands of wave functions form, extending over the entire crystalline lattice and separated by energy gaps. In Fig. 5.3, energy is plotted versus wave number (momentum quantum number) k for

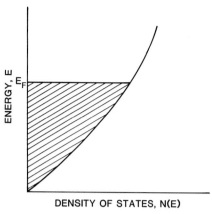

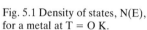

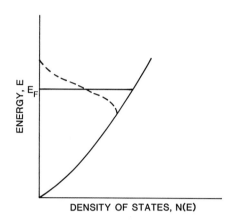

Fig. 5.1 Density of states, N(E), for a metal at T = O K.

Fig. 5.2 Density of filled states, N(E), for a metal at T > O K.

the motion of an electron in a one-dimensional periodic potential with length a. Note the formation of energy gaps–that is, the regions of energy containing no wave functions. In the figure, wave number k designates allowed energy states for electrons associated with an array of ions in a crystalline lattice, just as quantum numbers designate allowed energy states for electrons associated with the positive nucleus of an atom. At values of k = ±π/a, each wave function is separated in energy from the next by a jump in energy called a band gap. Therefore, each band of allowed energy levels is followed by a gap containing no allowed energy levels. Within each band there is a continuum of states; adjacent orbitals within a band have an infinitesimally small energy difference, analogous to the free-electron Fermi gas model. Between the bands the band gap energy may be large, on the order of 1 eV.

In Fig. 5.4, the two bands in an insulator (a) are contrasted with those in a metal (b). The bands consist of a large number of molecular orbitals differing only minutely in energy. The vertical direction corresponds to increasing energy. In an insulator, the lower energy band, called the valence band, is completely filled with electrons. A separation, known as the energy gap E_G lies between the highest filled level in the valence band and the lowest level in the empty upper band, called the conduction band. No states or orbitals are available for electrons in the energy gap. The highest energy electrons in the ground state must gain additional energy, equal to E_g, before they can reach empty orbitals and become mobile, so that electrical conduction can occur.

In a metal, the lower (valence) band is only half filled with electrons. The Fermi energy lies at the top of the filled portion of this band. At any temperature above absolute zero, the electrons at the Fermi level will have enough thermal energy to populate some of the empty levels in this band. The electrons will then be in only partly occupied molecular orbital bands, which extend throughout the entire crystalline lattice. Thus, under an applied electric field, the electrons in a metal will become mobile.

In the ground state of an insulator, all bands are either completely filled or completely empty, whereas in the ground state of a metal at least one band is only partly filled.

An insulator is characterized by its band gap E_g. At absolute zero, any solid with an energy gap is nonconducting. However, at any finite temperature, there is a probability that some electrons will be thermally excited across the energy gap into the lowest unoccupied molecular orbital band (the conduction band), leaving behind unoccupied positive holes in the valence band. Since the electrons in the bottom of the conduction band and the positive

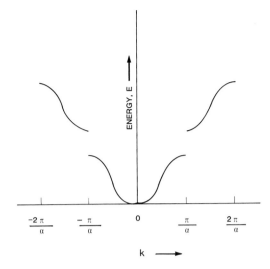

Fig. 5.3 Energy vs wave number k for motion of an electron in a one-dimensional periodic potential.

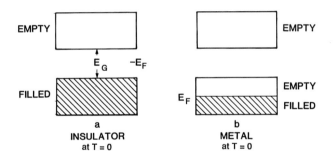

Fig. 5.4. Bands in an insulator and a metal. Shaded areas represent filled energy levels.

holes in the top of the valence band are in molecular orbitals that extend throughout the entire material, both can contribute to the conduction process.

The size of the energy gap determines whether thermal excitations will lead to appreciable conductivity. An illustrative calculation can be made for materials with different band gaps by using the fraction of electrons excited across the band gap at any temperature T, which is roughly equal to $e^{-E_g/2kT}$.[2] At room temperature, $kT = 0.025$ eV so, in a material having a band gap of 4 eV, thermal energy can promote a fraction of electrons of e^{-80} or $\sim10^{-35}$ across the band gap. Therefore, the number of carriers is minute, and the electrical conductivity, as given in Eq. (5.3), is small, and the material with a band gap of 4 eV at room temperature is considered an insulator. However, in a material having a band gap of 0.25 eV at room temperature, a fraction of electrons of e^{-5} or $\sim10^{-2}$ can be thermally promoted across the band gap. This material shows appreciable conductivity by electrons in its conduction band and holes in its valence band at room temperature and is considered a semiconductor.

Semiconductors are insulators at absolute zero, but their energy gaps are small enough to permit appreciable conductivity because of thermal excitations at room temperature. A material having an energy gap less than 2 eV at room temperature is generally classified as a semiconductor. The free-electron Fermi gas model uses this concept to explain electrical conductivity in a metal. At temperatures above absolute zero, the accessibility of unoccupied orbitals near the Fermi level allows unpaired "free electrons" to move under the influence of an external applied electric field. This produces an electric current.

5.2.2   Energy Band Structure

The energy band structure outlined here is presented in greater detail in books by Kittel,[1] and Ashcroft and Mermin.[2] Conductivity is directly proportional to the number density n of mobile carriers, electrons, and/or positive holes and their mobility μ as

$$\sigma = ne\mu , \qquad\qquad 5.3$$

where e indicates the absolute value of the electronic charge. As is clear from the discussion of the free-electron Fermi gas model, a high density of states (proportional to n at any temperature) at the Fermi level allows electron mobility and therefore conductivity. However, the free-electron model describes conductivity only in metals. A more sophisticated model, the energy band structure, is used to present a unified description of conductivity in metals, semiconductors, and insulators.

a) *Ionization Energy vs Band-Gap Energy*

The matters of interest for polymeric insulators are the ionization energy of the solid, the method of propagation of free electrons and free holes, and the possibility that energy will be transported in the material, perhaps giving rise to ionization away from the original excitation site.

The minimum energy required to ionize a material in the solid state is the band-gap energy E_g. The earliest estimates for polymers were based on the model used with considerable success for molecular solids.[3,4] In this approximation method, the ionization energy W_g of the isolated molecule is known from gas-phase studies. In the solid matrix, ionization is accompanied by polarization of the surrounding molecules, with a consequent reduction in the total energy requirement. If the polarizability of a molecule is α, then the polarization energy associated with a single-point charge is

$$W = \frac{1}{2} \sum \alpha \left(\frac{e}{4\pi\varepsilon_o r^2} \right)^2 , \qquad\qquad 5.4$$

where e is the elementary charge, ε_o is the dielectric constant of free space, r is the distance from the charge to a molecule, and the sum is over all molecules. This expression can be evaluated explicitly for a simple cubic lattice.[5] With a lattice spacing x, we have

$$W_{cubic} = \frac{16.5e^2\alpha}{32\pi^2\varepsilon_o^2 x^4} . \qquad\qquad 5.5$$

If we use the Clausius-Mosotti relation for replacing α with the real dielectric constant ε',

$$\frac{N\alpha}{3\varepsilon_o} = \frac{\varepsilon' - 1}{\varepsilon' + 2} \qquad\qquad 5.6$$

and the number of molecules per unit volume is given by $N = x^{-3}$. We then obtain

$$W_{cubic} = \frac{e^2 \left(1 - \dfrac{1}{\varepsilon'}\right)}{8\pi\varepsilon_0 x} \left(\frac{3\varepsilon'}{\varepsilon' + 2}\right) \left(\frac{16.5}{4\pi}\right).$$ 5.7

The values of the numerical factors are $[3\varepsilon'/(\varepsilon' + 2)] = 1.8$ for $\varepsilon' = 3$, and $16.5/4\pi = 1.31$. Since the act of ionization in vacuo either requires an energy W_g and yields an electron at infinity plus an ionized molecule (gas phase) or requires an energy E_s and yields an ionized molecule plus a polarized matrix (solid phase), we obtain as a first approximation[6]

$$W_g = E_s + W .$$ 5.8

The argument now runs that the internal ionization within the solid generates two widely separated charges at rest, so the band-gap energy E_g must be given by

$$E_g = W_g - 2W .$$ 5.9

Numerous corrections can be applied in the computation of the polarization energy W. As one moves out from a point charge, dielectric screening occurs because the field resulting from the point charge is offset by the contributions from the induced dipoles. In the continuum limit, the point charge is assumed to occupy a spherical, molecular-sized region of radius a, and the material outside is characterized by a dielectric constant ε'. Then, simple electrostatics gives the energy W as the difference between the energy stored in the medium and the vacuum energy,

$$W_{cont} = \frac{e^2 \left(1 - \dfrac{1}{\varepsilon'}\right)}{8\pi\varepsilon_0 a} .$$ 5.10

This result should be contrasted with that obtained from the cubic lattice bare-field formula (Eq. 5.7), which is twice as big if $æ = a$. Using $\varepsilon' = 3$ and $a = 5$ Å, we find $W_{cont} = 0.97$ eV. However, the choice of a value for *a* is not part of the continuum procedure, so this result is not well-defined. W_{cont} includes all the dipole-dipole interaction energy but none of the discreteness on an atomic scale, so it overestimates the shielding and underestimates the energy, even if one can justify a particular choice of *a* on other grounds. W_{cubic}, or the appropriate variants for other lattices, overestimates the energy because of the lack of shielding. In addition, W_{cubic} does not include dipole-dipole interaction energies, although these can be taken care of.[4] If the energy bands are relatively narrow, this type of calculation can provide a reasonably good correlation between the gaseous ionization energy W_g, the solid-state value E_s, and the solid-state band gap, according to Eqs. (5.8) and (5.9).

For the type of polymers considered here, the bands are wide, so the approximation of well-defined narrow levels fails, and the calculation is no longer valid except in broad outline. Nevertheless, it makes the point that the band-gap energy should be a couple of electron volts smaller than the gaseous ionization energy.

b) *Exciton Bands*

The elementary excitations of isolated repeat units are coupled by bond overlap, normally treated as a dipole-dipole interaction. The overlap gives rise to a band of states, the exciton band, capable of propagating the excitation along the polymer chain. Since the states are unchanged, they do not enter directly into conduction phenomena, but they appear to accent the energy transport.[7,8] In alkanes, the carbon-carbon sigma bond excitons are primarily responsible for the transfer process, although there are carbon-hydrogen bond excitons as well. The thresholds for these two exciton bands lie at 8.5 and 10 eV above the valence band, respectively, and the bands carry considerable oscillator strength. Consequently, they may be responsible also for the threshold of the optical absorption spectrum.

Except for not knowing the exact position of the features on the energy level diagram for a polymer, we think the exciton system may play a role in radiation-induced electrical conductivity. The exciton band provides an efficient method of removing energy and hence contributes to the geminate recombination of ion pairs,[7] which depresses conductivity in comparison with purely local thermal degradation. The mean free path for excitons has been estimated experimentally at about 3000 Å.[9]

Work begun on conjugated systems shows that in these systems the optical absorption may be largely due to the exciton band, which is now well separated from the ionized states.[10]

5.2.3   Trapping and Detrapping

The material summarized here and in the next two sections is presented in greater detail in the chapter by Wintle of the book by Bartnikas and Eichhorn.[11]

a) *Physical Characteristics*

Charge carriers in insulators and semiconductors can be trapped at impurity atoms or physical defects and in other ways. Immobilization of the carrier reduces conductivity and so contributes to the insulating nature of the material. The capture rate for free electrons by a single trapping level can be written in terms of a time constant τ as

$$\left(\frac{dn}{dt}\right)_{capture} = -\left(\frac{n}{\tau}\right), \qquad\qquad 5.11$$

and here we can regard this lifetime toward trapping as a constant for a given material. By analogy, with a simple kinetic theory gas, we can write this mean free time in the form

$$\tau = \frac{1}{N_t \Lambda v}, \qquad\qquad 5.12$$

where v is the mean velocity of the free electrons, N_t is the trap concentration, and Λ is the capture cross section. Typically, $v = 10^7$ cm s^{-1} in a wide-band material, while N_t can conceivably be as high as 10^{19} cm^{-3}, corresponding to one center per 1000 repeat units. The range of possible values for Λ is wide. Simple capture by a site of atomic dimensions leads to $\Lambda \cong 10^{-15}$ cm^2, but this simple capture requires that the combined trap and carrier system must be able to get rid of at least some of the binding energy during the few femtoseconds when the carrier is traversing the site. This is unlikely to happen, since typical phonon relaxation times are 100 fs, whereas photon loss requires 10 ns. Consequently, the effective cross section may well be much smaller than the geometric size of the site. Centers that have a potential barrier to capture (repulsive centers) will also have small cross sections. Capture centers that are charged with a polarity opposite to the carrier sign (coulombic centers) naturally attract carriers, and their cross sections are nearer 10^{-12} cm^2.

Strictly speaking, Eq. (5.11) should be written in a reaction kinetics formulation, with a rate constant of A_1, as

$$\left(\frac{dn_t}{dt}\right)_{capture} = A_1 n(N_t - n_t), \qquad\qquad 5.13$$

where n_t is the concentration of filled traps. This is illustrated in Fig. 5.5. Clearly, Eqs. (5.11)

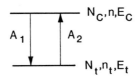

Fig. 5.5. Capture (A_1 process) and excitation (A_2 process) of an electron at a trap site.

and (5.12) apply to the limiting case of $n_t \ll N_t$, but more generally $A_1 = \Lambda v$. The detrapping reaction takes place with a rate constant of A_2, at a rate given by

$$\left.\left(\frac{dn_t}{dt}\right)\right|_{\text{excitation}} = A_2 n_t (N_c - n).$$ 5.14

If we insert the thermal equilibrium conditions of Fermi statistics and detailed balancing, it follows that

$$A_2 = A_1 \exp\left[\frac{-(E_c - E_t)}{kT}\right].$$ 5.15

This model for trapping was originally developed by Shockley and Read.[12]

The trap depth ($E_c - E_t$) is simply the binding energy of the charge in the center. In principle, this energy can be calculated if the Schrödinger equation can be solved for the particular combination of impurity and matrix being considered. In practice, the energy is normally found by experimental methods.

The dipole trap is one type of center that may be important in polymers, but it is not discussed in the usual literature referring primarily to inorganic materials. It has a long history in another field[13] and has more recently been discussed in the context of solids.[14] The cross section is comparable to the Coulomb trap value.

The polaron is a trap well known in radiation chemistry, but it has not been discussed with reference to electrical insulation.[15] In its simplest form, it is the charge surrounded by the polarized region discussed before. In fact, a strain field also surrounds the charge, and at the same time kinetic energy is enhanced by confinement of the carrier to a small region. Since the polaron arises from the relaxation of the matrix around the charge, there is no capture cross section as such. The problem has been studied theoretically at several levels of sophistication. Chemists usually calculate the binding energy by adding up the various quasi-independent contributions to the total energy, and they obtain values in the region of 1 eV.[15-17] Physicists, however, write an electron-lattice Hamiltonian and recognize the possibility of two deep polaron bands, although the mobility may be so small that the bands become *de facto* localized states.[18] These states have been labeled the optical or large polaron and the acoustic or small polaron. (However, the term "small polaron" is also used in conjunction with the optical polaron.) The former is associated with the transverse or optical phonons and the latter with the longitudinal or acoustic phonons. Low moduli of elasticity favor the acoustic polaron, while a large polarizability at frequencies exceeding about 10^{13} Hz favors the optical polaron. It is not at all clear which would be the ground-state structure in a polymer and even less certain whether the binding energy would bear out the chemical calculation. The energy depth is itself a function of temperature, increasing for the acoustic polaron as the temperature rises. The ambiguities arise because calculating the two coupling constants accurately is difficult.

Despite these problems, a number of authors have recognized that there will be a spread in the values of the trap depth in any real material, because of the thermal agitation of atoms about their mean position[19] and the random orientation of dipoles in a glassy structure.[20] The dispersion in energy they suggest amounts to several tenths of an electron volt.

b) *Trap Depths and Identities*

The most studied trap system is the low-temperature physically trapped electron in alkane and alcohol glasses, formed by high-energy irradiation of the material. The electron is located in a cavity typically 0.8 eV ± 0.3 eV deep.[22] Electron paramagnetic resonance (EPR) shows a sharp singlet in these systems at 77 K and below, which disappears on warming. The trapped electrons vanish with an activation energy near 0.2 eV for the thermally activated process.[21] It is assumed that the optical transition is a Franck-Condon transition to an excited state whereas the thermal transition is much lower because the matrix relaxes.[17,23] Presumably the trapping level deepens as the temperature rises[24] which is consistent with the acoustic polaron model, since the material soften with rising temperature. These observations were made on an ethanol glass, for which there are still other observations not understood.

Thermally stimulated conductivity (TSC) and thermally stimulated luminescence (TSL) are more sensitive techniques to study traps. Typical curves are illustrated in Fig. 5.6. Because much of the work has been done in the range of 77 to 300 K, the traps that are important in insulating polymers at field operating conditions have been studied less. Furthermore, much uncertainty still exists in the assignments of the peaks. One approach used to

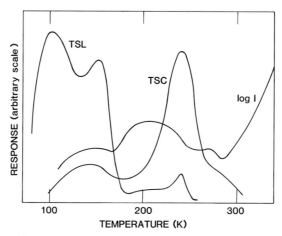

Fig. 5.6. Comparison of TSC, TSL, and isochronal currents for polyethylene. Source is Ref. 11

minimize this difficulty is to attempt simultaneous TSC and TSL observations.[25–27] It is difficult to obtain such parameters as energies, frequency factors and number densities because of the complications of retrapping, trap distributions, changes in frequency factor with temperature and many disposable parameters in general.[28–30] Thus, the published values of trap depths must be taken with caution.

c) *Conclusion*

Distinguishing between polar and charge trapping effects is difficult. The assumption is always made that the behavior of materials charged by corona or electron beam must be due to charge motion, but this is not necessarily true. We should be able to overcome this problem by using the recently developed thermal,[31] electron beam,[32] Raman,[33] and compression wave[34] methods of charge location in conjunction with studies of time or temperature dynamics.

Trapping may take place at chemical groups, impurities, or physical irregularities, or there may be self-trapping. Molecular chains have also been considered,[35] and a global classification scheme has been proposed,[36] but these suggestions have not proved very fruitful in practice. Undoubtedly, molecular motion is important in releasing charge, as evidenced by TSC peaks at the glass transition and by enhanced release when the material is plasticized.[37] The chemical species has been unambiguously defined only in polystyrene deliberately doped with various aromatic compounds.[38] The capture cross sections were of molecular size. The discussion shows that a polymer's morphology and thermal history may be as important as its chemical structure in determining the trapping effects.

5.2.4   Carrier Mobility

How fast do carriers move in typical polymers? Upon initiating current flow, especially by increasing the carrier density by means of ionizing irradiation, the carriers may be largely free. After an adequate lapse of time, typically a few milliseconds, thermal equilibrium is established with the traps, and from then on the average mobility is very low. This later mobility dominates the steady-state conductivity of the material. Its value varies considerably with material and temperature, but the value of 10^{-11} cm^{2}V^{-1}s^{-1} at 20°C (to within a couple of orders of magnitude) has been found for various polyethylenes. This very low mobility accounts in part for the weak conductivity of such plastics.

a) *Voltage Decay Method*

The most common method of measuring mobility is to monitor the surface voltage decay of a corona-charged specimen. The deposited charge leaks from the unmetalized top face to the grounded bottom electrode. The charge initially moves downward with a well-defined front, which reaches the electrode with a transit time of

$$\tau_{tr} = \frac{d^2}{\mu V_{so}},$$
                                                                                          5.16

where d is the specimen thickness and V_{so} is the initial surface voltage. In this open-circuit mode, there is no abrupt change in the measured (or apparent) surface voltage or in its time derivative. Thus, there is no clear marker of the transit time, and the mobility must be deduced by curve fitting. One of the earliest papers[38] in this field, and still the most comprehensive, shows that the mobility follows an Arrhenius temperature dependence with activation energies in the range of 0.5 to 1.2 eV. Corrections to the basic theory are required if the material shows deep trapping (permanent immobilization of the charge compared with the experimental time scale of about 1000 s),[38, 39] if it shows significant dark conductivity in addition to the space-charge-driven voltage decay,[40] or if the mobility is itself field dependent.[39] Many of the experimental results show an artifact, called the crossover phenomenon, in which strongly charged specimens apparently lose their charge at a rate that is unexpectedly fast compared with weakly charged specimens. Its origin has been traced in part to the effect of light in the corona discharge,[41] which injects charges from surface states, and in part to the effect of excited molecules adjacent to the surface. Consequently, the measured decay curves will reflect the fact that charge was injected into the bulk long before the start of measurement and that some charge has been held up in surface states.[42] The detailed charging history now governs the observed effect. In some cases, however, the measurements of surface voltage decay given in the literature may have been improperly interpreted, and the quoted mobility values must be regarded with some suspicion until more detailed investigations are carried out. In other cases, such as that of nylon, the method seems reliable.[43] The specific chemical state of the polymer may have considerable effect on the mobility, as work on oxidized polyethylenes has shown.[44] In principle, the surface voltage decay method can be employed to estimate dark conductivity, and hence carrier density, by a method that avoids interference from the nature of the contact.[45]

b) *Radiation-Induced Conductivity (RIC) Method*

In the RIC method, half of the specimen is under continuous irradiation and takes up a steady-state radiation-induced conductivity. This part acts as an injecting contact to the other (lower) half, which carries a space-charge-limited current (SCLC) to the lower electrode.[46] The parameters appearing in this model are an electron-hole pair yield η and a (μ'τ') product for the upper layer. Here, μ' is a mobility and τ' is a carrier lifetime, but the product may involve appropriate contributions from carriers of both signs. In the lower half, the mobility μ of the carrier being drawn across this region appears in the analysis. The depth of the irradiated region can be inferred from the current measurements, it can be assessed directly by use of electrometers on both front and back faces in the split Faraday cup arrangement,[47] or it can be estimated by the thermal pulse technique applied to the stored charge.[31] By careful consideration of the measured current as a function of the electron beam current, beam energy, and applied voltage, we can estimate the influence that these various parameters exert on the batch of specimens being tested and at least estimate the value of μ. One group quotes a value of 10^{-12} cm^{2}V^{-1}s^{-1} for electrons in PET at room temperature.[46] A second group gives a value of 10^{-9}cm^{2}V^{-1}s^{-1} for holes in FTFE but notes that this value is three orders of magnitude larger than that given by the surface voltage decay method.[48]

c) *Space-Charge-Limited Conduction (SCLC) Measurement Method*

Steady-state space-charge-limited conduction measurements are, in principle, simple to interpret. They rely on the well-known Mott and Gurney relation for the current density

$$J = \frac{9\mu\varepsilon'\varepsilon_o V^2}{8d^3}.$$

5.17

When it can be established that the conduction mechanism is indeed SCLS, which is not easy, the analysis is straightforward. An example has recently been given for polyvinyl acetate[49], and a number of analyses of PE give consistent results[50,51] with an activation energy of about 1.2 eV. The main difficulty is that measurements are few because the carriers are rarely freely injected.

d) *Transit-Time Measurement Method*

Many values of mobility are deduced from transit-time measurements. The measurements fall into three broad groups, comprising transient dark injection studies, steady oscillations, and excited injection. Measurements of transit-time under transient space-charge-limited conditions are few because electrodes are not normally good carrier sources. Nevertheless, some measurements have been made at a fairly high field ($\sim 4 \times 10^5$ V/cm). The standard transit time relationship[52]

$$t_1 = \frac{0.79d^2}{\mu V}$$

5.18

is used to obtain mobilities.[53,54] Unfortunately, in some cases, either the mechanism has not been confirmed by the corresponding steady-state measurements or the transient and steady-state values disagree.[55,56] Consequently, it is hard to rely on the values quoted for these measurements. The use of electrolytic contacts has provided some useful data,[53] but in some cases the current was not freely injected and its buildup was controlled by diffusion.[57]

In a number of systems, regular oscillations have been observed. They have periods of about 1 s, occur at fields of approximately 1 MV/cm, and seem to be similar to Gunn oscillations. Consequently, the period is just the transit time. Mobilities deduced on this basis are two to three orders of magnitude higher than other low mobilities.[58] One school of thought attributes these oscillations to avalanching phenomena.[59, 60] Since some of the work deals with iodine-saturated or ion-saturated specimens and some deals with conventional films,[61, 62] while yet other work has confirmed that halogen absorption leads to a marked increase in steady-state mobility,[63] the precise mechanism remains in doubt.

The third approach involves direct excitation of excess carrier density in a thin layer adjacent to one electrode. The excitation can be done by a light pulse or by an electron beam pulse. In contrast to the measurements discussed earlier, the excitation lasts for a short time compared with the transit time, and an applied voltage is used to select the sign of the required carrier. Several overlapping processes occur.[64] They may include geminate recombination; drift of carriers of either or both signs in the irradiated layer; recombination and trapping in the irradiated layer; exit of carriers from the front-irradiated electrode; drift of carriers of one sign across the unirradiated region, with trapping; and exit from the rear electrode. At the very least, two trapping times, one recombination time, and two transit times are required to account for the observed current-time curves. An extensive analysis of such measurements has yielded the sign of the mobile carrier and estimates of the mobility in a number of polymers,[64] although again there are conflicting interpretations.[65] Since much of the work has been carried out at temperatures in the neighborhood of 80°C, direct comparison with the results outlined earlier is not possible in general. Allowing for reasonable thermal activation (not necessarily of Arrhenius form) the observed values, typically $10^{-6} \mathrm{cm^2 V^{-1} s^{-1}}$, are not inconsistent with those found by other methods.[66] However, since the source materials differ widely, what constitutes agreement and what amounts to contradiction is not clear, since nominally the same polymer may exhibit a wide range of mobilities from one research group to another. Likewise, the mobility of positive and negative carriers may differ by many orders of magnitude in some materials,[67] but not in others.[65]

e) Experimental Difficulties

Three main difficulties lie in the way of obtaining a definitive understanding of mobility behavior through experiments. They are the reproducibility of the polymer substance and its impurities, the apparent field dependence of the mobility, and the problem of dispersion time. A number of authors have analyzed their data in terms of a field-dependent mobility.[58, 68, 69] Although one analytic solution describes the discharge of a specimen having such a mobility,[39] there is no real reason to expect that the effective mobility, or trap-modulated mobility, should have a field dependence. One possibility is that the detrapping rate is enhanced by the Poole-Frenkel effect.[70] Since the trapping sites are not likely to be charged when empty, field-induced reduction of the barrier height will be only weakly field dependent.[71] Since the surface voltage decay experiments also are largely controlled by the motion of carriers in the low-field region, the experiment should yield some appropriately weighted mobility that rises weakly with field. The data are conflicting on this point.

Many reports of transit-time measurements suggest that the current-time curves obey a so-called universal scaling law that lacks the time dependence expected from simple theory. This is true for doped PVK[72] and other polymers.[65] In general, this effect is attributed to polaron hopping between localized sites. However, recent papers have established theoretically that one cannot distinguish between the random walk models used in the hopping approach and the conventional multiple-trapping, multiple-release model.[73–75] A consequence of this calculation is that the knees or breaks in the current-time curves do not reflect the true transit time. If they are used, the apparent mobility deduced will be field dependent. A detailed critique of the usual methods of analysis has recently been given.[76] In retrospect, it appears possible that many of the transit-time experiments based on pulsed excitation suffer from this defect, and the range of parameters used in any one set of experiments is insufficient for checking the validity of results.

The nature of the carriers involved is also not clear. When electrolytic contacts are employed, the natural assumption is that ions are injected, but this may not necessarily be the case. When electron-hole pairs are formed, the final carrier may still be an ionic particle, which of course can undergo physical trapping in the host matrix.[77]

In conclusion, the sign of the charge carrier can be selected for the pulsed transit methods. It is probably known in the case of surface voltage decay, but it remains indeterminate when voltage step methods are used. The long-time slow mobilities are probably trap controlled; however, the literature values should be viewed with skepticism.

f) Fast Mobilities

Transit-time measurements on time scales faster than the work described in the last section have been reported. Mobilities in the range of 10^{-3} to $10^{-4} cm^2 V^{-1} s^{-1}$ have been observed and studied by step-voltage application,[78] optical photoinjection,[59,79] and excitation by pulsed electron beam.[65,80,81] In most cases mobility has an activation energy of about 0.3 eV with at least one report of a very small activation energy below T_g.[82]

The question of high mobilities in plastics still exists,[83] whether some polaronic entity is the carrier in polymers,[84] and what is the real cause of the widely ranging observed mobilities?

5.2.5   Conduction Mechanisms

a) Bulk-Limited Mechanisms

A variety of processes may restrict the conduction of charge across a dielectric. To set the stage for discussion we first consider current density for a one-dimensional case in which a slab of polymer is held between two metal electrodes.[85,86] Some of the material summarized in this section is discussed in greater detail in the books by O'Dwyer,[85] Lampert and Mark,[86] and Bartnikas and Eichhorn (Chapter 3).[11] Because the lateral dimensions of the electrodes and specimen are much bigger than the thickness d, edge effects and fringing fields can be ignored. Thus, the current density J has been shown to be

$$J = \sigma E + eD_0 \frac{\partial p}{\partial x} + \frac{\partial D}{\partial t} =$$

$$= J_{cond} + J_{diff} + \frac{\partial D}{\partial t}, \qquad 5.19$$

where σ is the conductivity, E is the electric field, e is the elementary charge, D_0 is the diffusion coefficient, and D is the electric displacement. The displacement-current density is $\partial D/\partial t$. The particle-current density is composed of the conduction-current density, $J_{cond} = \sigma E$, and the diffusion current, $J_{diff} = eD_0 \partial p/\partial x$. When J_{cond} and J_{diff} are added up they give the current density caused by charge transport, J_c, called the convection-current density or the particle-current density,

$$J_c = \sigma E + eD_0 \frac{\partial p}{\partial x}. \qquad 5.20$$

For a one-dimensional model, $J = J_c(t)$ is independent of x, so in time-varying situations the displacement-current density and the particle-current density are complementary.

Ohmic Conduction. The elementary behavior occurs in the steady state ($\partial D/\partial t = 0$) with a neutral material [the charge density p (x, y, z, t) = p (x) and in this case is zero throughout the material] and a constant carrier density (∂p/∂x = 0). Then,

$$J = \sigma E = pe\mu E .$$ 5.21

This equation implies that the free-carrier concentration p and any trapped-carrier concentration p_t are exactly balanced by an equal negative charge concentration n_{total}. Since $(n_{total} - p_t) \equiv p$ is a constant, a homogeneous material is involved in which n_{total} and p_t are fixed. This situation is common in metals, and neutrality holds in the bulk of most homogeneous semiconductors, but it is not expected in good insulators.

Deviations from the simple ohmic relation will be due to barrier layers adjacent to the electrodes and inhomogeneities in the bulk of the material. For most polymers the relationship holds at fields up to 10^4 V/cm.

What mechanism gives rise to a conductivity that is independent of the field? From Eq. (5.21) such conductivity would require a constant carrier concentration and a constant mobility. For electronic conductivity the microscopic mobility is controlled by scattering of the carriers by lattice vibrations. With the scattering cross section S and the thermal carrier velocity v_{th}, one obtains the mean free path λ and the mean free time τ.

$$\lambda \cong \frac{1}{SN} , \tau \cong \frac{1}{v_{th}SN} ,$$ 5.22

where N is some atomic concentration of scatterers. If the assumption is made that the impulse received from the external field is destroyed on impact, then

$$eE\tau = mv_{drift} ,$$ 5.23

where m is the effective mass and v_{drift} is the mean velocity of drift in the field direction. Then the electronic mobility is deduced as

$$\mu_0 = \frac{v_{drift}}{E} = \frac{e\tau}{m} = \frac{e}{mv_{th}SN} ,$$ 5.24

and the microscopic mobility is governed entirely by the electron-lattice interaction through the quantities m and S. For the case $v_{drift} \ll v_{th}$, S is effectively constant.

Polaron motion and hopping between localized states may also lead to ohmic response in amorphous materials.[87–89] Typically, the polaron size is assumed to be comparable to atomic or molecular dimensions and the polaron is considered to hop from a site to a site with an activation energy of about 1/2 W_p where W_p is the polaron binding energy. Whether this is so for nonpolar and quasi-continuous solids is not very clear.

In amorphous semiconductors hopping between localized states is well known.[87,89] A group of states (levels) due to impurities, physical disorder, or band tails in the band gap may exist close to the Fermi level resulting in an adequate concentration of electrons in these states and an adequate concentration of empty states. Thermal excitation and de-excitation of an electron from a full state to an empty one now can occur. This process exhibits a Boltzmann-like probability and assumes the following form

$$\Gamma = \upsilon \exp \left[-\frac{W}{kT} - 2\Xi\alpha \right]$$ 5.25

where a is the site separation, Ξ is an overlap parameter, and W is the separation in energy. It is possible that a carrier located on a particular site has a number of adjacent sites each with its own W and a values leading to the process known as variable range hopping. In three dimensions, using the optimum jump probability the conductivity σ is given by

$$\sigma = \sigma_3 \exp \left\{ -C_3 \left[\frac{N(E)kT}{\Xi^3} \right]^{-1/4} \right\} ,$$ 5.26

where σ_3 and C_3 are constants and $N(E)$ is the density of localized states. If in the place of the optimum jump probability some other critical probability value Γ_c is used then the calculation may be reduced to that of the percolation mechanism in which the conductivity is controlled by the most resistive link.[90]

Classic hopping within a forbidden gap is also possible. At large trap densities the potentional wells will overlap, and the barrier height between successive traps will be less than the trap ionization energy. Hopping may take place. Because the overlap will always occur for long-range potentials, it is discussed in the context of coulombic wells[91] with the barrier height being

$$\Delta H = W_1 - \frac{e^2}{\pi \varepsilon' \varepsilon_0 a},$$ 5.27

where W_1 is the trap ionization energy and a is the separation of centers. At high concentrations, this system can go over into a tunneling arrangement or into an impurity band if $\Delta H \rightarrow 0$.

How are the inhomogeneities reflected in the observed electrical parameters? Several treatments of random suspensions have been used and no one has been all inclusive as to particle size, shape and conductivity variations.[92-95] For the case when the inclusions are more conductive than the lost ($\zeta > 20$) and their volume fraction is large enough for them to be in contact the following semiquantitative fit has some succes

$$\sigma_{eff} = \sigma_m[4 \ln \xi - 11] ,$$ 5.28

where

$$\sigma_i = \xi \sigma_m ,$$ 5.29

σ_{eff} is the apparent conductivity, and σ_m and σ_i the conductivities of the matrix and the inclusions, respectively. If the above conditions are not met one is forced to using the Maxwell-Garnett relation as a guide, which is valid only at low concentrations of the inclusions

$$\frac{\sigma_{eff}}{\sigma_m} \leq 1 + 3\beta c + 3\beta^2 c^2 + \ldots (\xi > 1)$$ 5.30

and

$$\beta = \frac{\xi - 1}{\xi + 2},$$ 5.31

where c is the volume fraction of the inclusions.

What is the effect of a barrier layer on low-field conductivity? Two treatments have been used, one treating the material as a layered structure and using Wagner equations by adding the resistances in series[96] and the other calculates the linearized small-signal response in the zero frequency limit.[97,98] This technique requires prior knowledge of the shape and constitution of the barrier which is not always known.

What is the carrier concentration itself? Many uncertainties exist. The free-carrier concentrations n and p may be estimated by using the Fermi level concept. The effective densities of states N_v and N_c may be estimated from the band structure calculations. In impure materials the number densities and energy depths of trapping levels are uncertain. Little is known about the deeper traps, important at temperatures above room temperature, and the very shallow traps which control the effective mobility μ_{eff}. Thus, it is not possible to estimate carrier concentrations with any certainty and there is little basis upon which to make predictions of carrier densities.

In summary, the Arrhenius dependence of conductivity can be due to a temperature variation of the carrier concentration, change of the mobility, or both. A concentration-dependent activation energy suggests hopping between localized states, and non-Arrhenius behavior may be associated with variable-range hopping.

Nonlinear Conduction. The nonlinear response of current to applied voltage can be due to Joule heating, charge injection or the Poole-Frenkel enhancement.[84, 86, 99–103] While the heat balance at thermal breakdown conditions has been investigated in some detail, less is known about the current-voltage characteristics at lower applied voltages. If a standing temperature gradient should exist in a polymer the nonlinearity effect may be quite significant.

If a charge is injected at the electrode-polymer interface, a large excess carrier density at the injecting electrode will exist and a space-charge-limited current will flow. A material, that may be ohmic at low applied voltages may now follow the quadratic law at a voltage V_x given by

$$V_x \cong \frac{eP_0 d^2}{\varepsilon' \varepsilon_0},$$

5.32

where P_0 is the thermal carrier concentration. At this point, the mobility will usually be trap controlled. At some large voltage all the traps will be fully occupied and any further increase in voltage will lead to carrier generation which can not be trapped and thus will possess certain microscopic mobility μ_0. The voltage V_{TFL} at which the traps are filled, is

$$V_{TFL} \cong \frac{eP_1 d^2}{2\varepsilon' \varepsilon_0}.$$

5.33

The various regimes for a one-carrier space-charge-limited current are illustrated in Fig. 5.7. The above account is an oversimplification of the actual situations because of the effects of

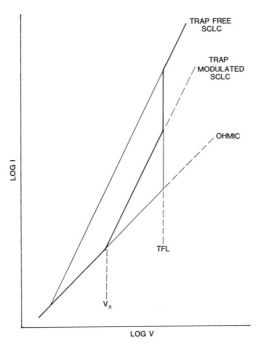

Fig. 5.7. The possible regimes for a one-carrier space-charge-limited current. Source is Ref. 11.

distribution in trap energies, carrier diffusion, field-dependent mobilities, velocity-dependent capture cross sections of traps and the field enhancement release from traps – the Frenkel effect. These effects yield a higher power law for V, higher inverse power law for d in Eq. (5.17) and make indistinct the transition at V_{TFL}.[104–108] Additional complications may occur as a result of double injection and recombination of the carriers of opposite sign.[86, 109]

At low fields the barrier height is depressed linearly with the applied field and the carrier escape probability is exponential. The resulting current is proportional to the difference between the foreward and the backward jump rates. When this is extended to very high fields the foreward rate will increase and the backward rate becomes negligible. The effective mobility then becomes exponential and the temperature-dependent from of the Pool equation is[110]

$$\sigma \propto \exp\left(\frac{eEa}{2kT}\right). \qquad 5.34$$

Tunneling is another mechanism by which emission of carriers from traps can be enhanced at high fields with a probability of escape per unit time Γ

$$\Gamma \propto \exp\left[-\frac{4\sqrt{2m}}{3he}\frac{(E_c - E_t)^{3/2}}{E}\right], \qquad 5.35$$

where $\hbar = h/2\pi$, with the Planck's constant $h = 4.1357 \times 10^{-15}$ eVs. In actual situations both, the partial thermal excitation, followed by tunneling through the thinner barrier, take place.[112, 113]

Hot-electron concept has also been advanced.[114, 115] The carriers pick up energy from the applied field and are not in thermal equilibrium with the matrix. They can be speeded up to ionization energies at breakdown and even prebreakdown fields. "Ballistic" electrons have been observed that can travel substantial distances in a semiconductor without being thermalized. The ballistic electrons are hot electrons injected into the semiconductor by tunneling.

b) Electrode-Limited Mechanisms

Schottky Emission. Charge injected from a metal to an insulator or semiconductor at medium fields may take place by field-assisted thermionic emission, a process known as Richardson-Schottky effect or simply Schottky emission.[116] It is analogous to the Poole-Frenkel effect. The force exerted on a particle at a distance x from the interface is given by

$$F = eE - \frac{e^2}{4\pi\varepsilon'\varepsilon_0(2x)^2}; \qquad 5.36$$

it is zero at the top of the effective potential curve. The work done on the particle is

$$W = -\int Fdx = -eEx + \frac{e^2}{4\pi\varepsilon'\varepsilon_0}4x + \phi. \qquad 5.37$$

The constant of integration has been chosen so that $W \equiv \phi$ at a large distance from the electrode under zero applied field. For nonzero fields, W has a maximum value ϕ_{app} at the point where $F = 0$. This distance, x_m, is on the order of a few nanometres. This gives the result

$$\phi_{app} = \phi - \beta_s E^{1/2}, \qquad 5.38$$

where

$$\beta_s = \left(\frac{e^3}{4\pi\varepsilon'\varepsilon_0}\right)^{1/2}. \qquad 5.39$$

Consequently, the current density drawn over this barrier will be

$$J = AT^2 \exp\left(-\frac{\phi}{kT}\right)\exp\left(\frac{\beta_s E^{1/2}}{kT}\right),$$
     5.40

where A is the Richardson-Dushman constant. Currents that obey Eq. (5.40) will thus show up as straight lines on a Schottky plot of log J versus $E^{1/2}$. This calculation omits any backflow from the insulator. At low fields, this reverse flow is significant[117] and leads to an essentially ohmic contact at fields below about 10^4 V cm^{-1}. At fields greater than 10^6 V cm^{-1} tunneling through the barrier becomes the more probable process. The current through the barrier will be the product of the flux of electrons of given energy approaching the barrier from the metal, and the transmission probability, integrated over the available energies. Hole injection can also occur by tunneling of electrons from the valence band.

c) Steady-State Behavior

A number of mechanisms yield ohmic dependence at low fields. At higher fields, the response is nonlinear. Again, several mechanisms are operating. For a given polymer, selecting the particular conduction mechanisms responsible for the observed effects is difficult, largely because conductivity and mobility measurements as functions of field and temperature are not sufficient to make the identification. Furthermore, more than one mechanism may be operating at the same time. To illustrate, a particular specimen may inject by the Schottky mechanism, conduct by the Poole-Frenkel mechanism, and at the same time store significant charge. The result is that the field is everywhere different and (except at one coordinate) not equal to (V_{appl}/d). Consequently, the slopes in Schottky plots of the data will in general correspond to neither β_{PF} nor β_s, and the plots will show some curvature.[118]

Each case thus must be considered on its own merits; there is no well-defined set of criteria by which particular conduction models can be identified in any given case. Although additional information may be available in the form of transient currents and photoconduction, the conclusions drawn in many experimental papers are based on inadequate foundations.

d) Current Transients

Application of voltage to a dielectric, causes an immediate charge transfer in the external circuit, corresponding to the charging up of the specimen capacitance. Following this, a decreasing transient current will flow until the steady dc value is reached. This transient dielectric absorption current corresponds to a further charging up of the electrodes. For dipolar materials, the transient current is related to the dielectric constant $\varepsilon'(\omega)$ in the frequency domain by a transformation based on the Kramers-Kronig relation, so absorption current measurements complement dielectric loss measurements.[119]

Under charge injection conditions the result ist that the field is reduced at the source electrode and enhanced at the drain. If the source electrode can provide an unlimited supply of carriers at zero field, one obtains the full space-charge-limited decay. The more usual case is that the rate of supply of carriers depends on the field and that some significant trapping takes place in the bulk. Then, the particle-current density at the source electrode will decrease with time as the field there falls. The general result is that the measured current, the sum of particle and displacement currents, falls as t^{-n} ($n \leq 1$) under these conditions.[120, 121, 122]

The process of electrode polarization or blocking also leads to current decrease with time. As the carriers of one or both signs are prevented from leaving the specimen and pile up in front of the drain electrode space charge sets up a reverse field, which tends to inhibit further charge flow. This effect can be very complicated, and the current may exhibit a wide variety of time dependence depending on the precise conditions at the electrodes.[123–125]

Current transient may also be due to hopping conduction. The phonon-assisted tunneling between impurity states is known to give an ac conductivity that is frequency dependent, $\sigma_{ac} \propto \omega^v$. The exponent v is normally close to 0.8. At low frequencies, the carrier motion can follow the field without phase delay and therefore with low loss, while this is not possible at high frequencies.[91, 126, 127]

e) *Photoexcitation of Carriers*

Bulk Excitation. Irradiation of insulating material by hard gamma rays or fast electrons causes it to become conductive because of the excess carriers generated. In the steady state

$$\sigma = e g_f \mu_0 \tau_r = \frac{e g \mu_0 \tau_r}{1 + \Theta^{-1}}, \qquad 5.41$$

where g_f is the free-carrier generation rate, τ_r is the recombination lifetime, and g is the total carrier excitation rate. The existence of shallow trapping levels is through the Θ term. Consequently, the radiation-induced conductivity (RIC) depends on the quantities μ_0 and Θ, the recombination time, and the generation rate. If the concentration of recombination centers is large, the centers will not become saturated during irradiation and τ_r will be essentially constant. The generation rate g is the product of two quantities, the intrinsic generation rate and the escape probability Γ. The intrinsic generation rate is proportional to the dose rate $\dot{\gamma}$. The escape probability is the Onsager probability,[128] although now because the excited carrier has considerable excess energy it will travel some distance from its countercharge before it is thermalized and the diffusion mechanism becomes valid. Since there will be a distribution of these thermalization ranges, it is common to choose a single thermalization length r_0, typically in the range of 1 to 6 nm. Thus,

$$g = K \varrho \dot{\gamma} \Gamma(E, r_0), \qquad 5.42$$

where K is a constant of proportionality.

Expressions for $\Gamma(E, r_0)$ are available in the recent literature.[128–132] It follows from Eqs. (5.41) and (5.42) that the induced conductivity will be proportional to the dose rate and the maximum excitation rate will be

$$g_{max} = \frac{\dot{\gamma} \varrho}{W_{pr}}, \qquad 5.43$$

where W_{pr} is the energy for ionized-pair production and is typically 30 eV per ion pair. The conductivity will be temperature dependent through both Γ and Θ, and weakly through μ_0. It will be field dependent at fields exceeding 10^4 V cm^{-1} and will become saturated at fields equal to the breakdown field.

The above phenomena are known as the prompt conductivity in the radiation effects literature.[133] There are also delayed effects, exhibited by a finite risetime and a very long tailed decay after irradiation ends. These effects may be due to trapping and recombination kinetics,[134] dose enhancement,[135, 136] Compton current,[136, 137] carrier drift[138] and track effects.[139, 140] They are prominent at low dose rates[141] and give rise to the sublinear dependence of apparent conductivity on dose rate $\dot{\gamma}$,[142]

$$\sigma \sim \dot{\gamma}^z \quad \frac{1}{2} \leq z \leq 1. \qquad 5.44$$

Interband recombination and an exponential distribution of traps may account for this power law. The understanding of this low dose rate response is not very clear.

Transient photocurrents may be induced by optical excitation below the band-gap energy if impurities or localized chemical moieties can be ionized. Such photocurrents can remain above the dark level only of the irradiation serves to empty shallow traps. The value of Θ, the trapping parameter, is reduced under illumination, and at the same time the current is bulk limited.[144] Transitions from emission-limited to bulk-limited photocurrents have been observed.[145, 146]

Photoemission. Depending on the sign of the applied drift field, either electrons or holes can be injected from the electrode into the insulating polymer. The probability of injection is proportional to the density of states in the electrode material and the density of states in the transport band of the insulator; calculations for particular forms of these densities give the result[147]

$$Y \simeq (h\nu - \theta_0)^b ,$$ 5.45

where Y is the quantum yield in charges per absorbed photon and θ_0 is the appropriate threshold energy. The index b can have a range of values but is typically 2 or 3.

This is based on the assumption that all carriers formed with an energy exceeding the barrier height escape. At large excess energies, the yield curves should extrapolate properly. At photon energies just below the threshold, some escape of carriers into the bulk is possible, so there is no sharp cutoff at the threshold. This may account for the tailing at the foot of yield curves. The mechanism of direct annihilation with the image charge may also contribute.[148]

The thresholds for hole injection and electron injection in insulating polymers, are of the order of 4 eV. If the material does not contain chromophores that absorb at this energy, both front and rear electrodes will be illuminated and carriers of both signs will be injected simultaneously. Often this complication has been overlooked. A second complication is that the static space-charge fields that lead to band bending at the electrodes may overlap in thinner specimens, thus leading to an apparent change of threshold energy with thickness.

By using band-gap light, which is strongly absorbed, carrier production occurs close to the front illuminated electrode and the sign of the carrier drawn across the specimen is now selected according to the direction of the applied field. The yield curves will again follow a power law of the form of Eq. (5.45),[149] but the energy threshold will be in the vacuum ultra-violet range. There is also a possibility that carrier injection below the threshold energy might occur by means of the biexcitonic mechanism observed in anthracene.[150]

5.2.6   Contact Charging

a) *Introduction*

Much of the work presented here is discussed in great detail in a review article by Lowell and Rose-Innes.[151] Other reviews and discussions may be found in Refs. 152–154. When two materials are touched or rubbed together electric charge is usually transferred from one to the other. If one of the materials is a good insulator, so that the charge persists on its surface for a long time, the effects of the charge transfer are readily apparent: sparks may be produced, and light objects may be so strongly polarized by the field that they fly towards the charged insulator. Although such phenomena have been known for a long time the phenomenon of contact charging is still little understood.

In the last 10 years progress has been made towards an understanding of the contact charging of solids, mainly because of an improvement in the reliability of experimental results. The experiments are being done in vacuum rather than in air, and much work has been done on organic polymers and other materials which are fairly well-defined. More recently, the increased scientific activity in this field appears to be due to the general increase of interest in surface phenomena. But a greater stimulus may have been the import-ance of static charging in industry, where it may be either a nuisance or useful. For example, sparks generated by static charging may cause explosions in mines, flour mills and supertankers; a person charged to a high potential may easily destroy an MOS transistor by merely touching the gate electrode; nylon clothing soils easily because charge transferred to it attracts dirt; and shocks from nylon carpets are not uncommon. On the other hand, electrostatic precipitators are important in controlling pollution; electrostatics has greatly improved the technology of spray-painting; and electrostatic copying (xerography) is now a major industry.

b) *Metal-Insulator Contacts*

The charge acquired by an insulator from a metal that touches it may depend not only on the nature of the insulator, but also in some circumstances, on the particular metal and on the type and duration of the contact. So it is not really possible to define a "typical" charge density, even for a given insulator. It is nevertheless, useful to have some idea of the range of charge density commonly encountered and some of the data is assembled in Table 1.

How Much Charge is Transferred? It can be seen from Table 1 that for organic polymers (the materials most studied) the charge density is usually in the range 10^{-5} to 10^{-3} C/m^2. Less information is available for other materials, but what there is suggests that the charge density falls in roughly the same range.

A charge density of 10^{-4} C/m^2 corresponds to one elementary charge for about every 10^4 surface atoms. Clearly, contact electrification is a small effect in an absolute sense, and it is possible that it might be caused by quite small concentrations of impurities or physical defects. On the other hand, it is in another sense a large effect; even at the lower end of the range, the charge densities are close to the limit, $\sim 5 \times 10^{-5}$ C/m^2, which would produce enough field to break down air (at atmospheric pressure the breakdown is typically about 3×10^6 V/m). At the upper end of the range, the field due to the charge density is approach-

TABLE 5.1 Order of Magnitude of Charge Density Observed on Various Materials After Contact With Metals*

Material	Charge density C/m^2 (~~cm^{-2}~~)	Remarks	Reference
Polyethylene	5×10^{-6}–10^{-4}	In air, mercury contacts	155
	5×10^{-5}	In air, sliding contact	156
	2×10^{-5}	In vacuum	157
	10^{-4}	In vacuum, sliding contacts	158
Polytetrafluoroethylene	3×10^{-5}	In vacuum	159
	7×10^{-5}	In air, sliding contact	160
	2×10^{-4}	In vacuum, sliding contact	161
	2×10^{-3}	In vacuum, prolonged rolling contact	162
Nylon	10^{-3}	In vacuum, mercury contact	164
	10^{-3}	In vacuum, prolonged rolling contact	164
Polycarbonate	10^{-3}	In vacuum, prolonged rolling contact	165
Polyimide	3×10^{-3}	In vacuum, prolonged rolling contact	165
Silicone rubber	10^{-4}	In vacuum, intimate contact	166
Solid paraffins	10^{-5} or less	In air, mercury contact	155
Anthracene	10^{-3}	In vacuum, (elastic contact assumed)	167

* Source is Ref. 151.

ing the dielectric strength of common insulators, so that the charge could conceivably be limited by breakdown in the insulator itself, as Weaver et al.[168] have pointed out.

How Quickly is Charge Transferred? The question of the rate of charge transfer is of great interest. It has an important bearing on whether the charge is transferred to bulk or to surface states.

Direct measurements by Davies[157] of the time dependence of contact electrification showed that total charge transferred to polyethylene by contact to a metal increases with the time of contact, reaching an apparently constant value after about 15 min. A time dependence was also found for metal-glass contacts, but in this case the saturation occurred more rapidly. Davies pointed out that in the case of polymers the charge may increase with the time of contact for two entirely different reasons: (1) because the transfer of charge is a slow process; or (2) because of a gradual incrase in the contact area. (Polymers are viscoelastic and also much softer than metals, and so will slowly deform at the region of contact.) Medley[163] has found that the charge transferred to polymers by contacts to liquid mercury is independent of time, which suggests that the second explanation is the correct one. Furthermore, with soft rubbers, where there is little uncertainty about the area of contact, the charge transfer has been shown to be complete in times less than about 3 s. Homewood and Rose-Innes[169] have carried out a direct investigation of the importance of viscoelastic deformation in determining the total charge; they pressed metal spheres against flat surfaces of Teflon and measured how both the charge and area of contact changed with time. They found that the increase in charge with time of contact can be wholly accounted for by the increase in the area of contact. Thus, in this case at least, the increase of charge with time is due to viscoelastic increase in the area of contact.

Direct methods of measuring the time dependence of the contact charge cannot easily be used for times of contact less than about a second, for it is difficult to make and break contact in shorter times without introducing uncertainty in the force of contact (which of course affects the contact area.) Wahlin and Backstrom[161] have pointed out that the dependence of the charge on time of contact can be deduced from experiments on sliding contacts, if the charge is measured as a function of the speed of sliding. Suppose that a metal sphere is pressed against the surface of an insulator, so that it touches the insulator over a circular region of radius r; if now the sphere is slid (or rolled) along the surface, charge will be deposited along a track of width 2r. If the speed of sliding is v, a given point on the track will have been in contact with the metal for a time of about 2r/v. Therefore, if the charge transfer depends on the time of contact, the relationship may be discovered by measuring the velocity dependence of charge transfer. It is assumed that the charge transfer process is the same during sliding as it is for static contacts, and that no back-flow of charge occurs. Wahlin and Backstrom found that the charge deposited along a track on Teflon was independent of the speed of sliding, and they deduced that charge transfer must be completed in less than a few hundredths of a second. Similarly, Elsdon and Mitchell[170] measured the charge transfer in sliding contacts to nylon and polyethylene; they analyzed the dependence on speed and deduced that the charge transfer took about 10^{-2} s. Although the direct experimental evidence is sparse, it seems probable that the transfer of charge is usually complete in less than 1 s.

Repeated Contacts. It is a rather surprising experimental fact that the charge on an insulator can be steadily increased by touching it repeatedly at the same place with the same metal. [159,171-181] Usually the rate of increase of charge decreases as contacts are repeated and, after many contacts, the charges may appear to saturate. But in some cases, at least this saturation is illusory; a plot of the charge as a function of the logarithm of the number of contacts reveals that the charge continues to increase evan after a large number of contacts, although the rate of increase may become very slow.[159]

An explanation of the increase of charge with number of contacts might be that the charge transferred depends on the total time of contact. However, this simple explanation is probably not generally correct. First, charge transfer seems to occur very quickly, in a time less than the duration of individual contacts in most experiments; furthermore, specific experiments on anthracene[167] and some polymers[159] have shown that the increase in charge transfer brought about by repeating the contact cannot be explained in this way; in each case, N contacts each of duration t seconds transferred much more charge than a single contact of duration Nt seconds.

An obvious and trivial explanation of charge build-up is that the contacting metal touches a different part of the insulator every time a contact is made. It is difficult to rule out this possibility altogether, but in some materials at least it seems implausible. For example, if a metal sphere about 1 cm in diameter contacts Teflon with a force of 0.1 N the plastically deformed indentation is about 0.5 mm in diameter and the accuracy of replacing the metal sphere is much better than that. Of course, it is possible that the contact does not occur over the whole area of the indentation, but there is reason to believe that the true area of contact is about half the apparent area. If this is true, inaccuracy in relocating the contact could account for an increase of a factor of ~2 in the charge but not for the order of magnitude increase commonly observed after a sufficiently large numbers of contacts. Repeated contacts to polymers may cause the contact area to increase gradually because of the viscoelastic flow of the insulator. Such an increase certainly occurs in Teflon[169] but is much too small to account for the increasing charge in repeated contacts.

Repeated contacts may be expected to increase if the insulator is slightly conducting, because when the metal is withdrawn the charge will tend to spread (under its own Coulomb repulsion) over the surface or into the body of the insulator making room, so to speak, for more charge to be deposited in the next contact.[171] However, on the next contact, part of the previously deposited charge may be expected to flow back to the metal, and a complicated non-equilibrium situation may exist which is difficult to analyze. Nevertheless, it is intuitively clear that the charge may increase with increasing number of contacts, though less and less rapidly because the back-flow of charge to the metal will increase as charge builds up on the insulator.

In polymers such as Teflon the charge is very immobile; a spot of charge deposited on the surface remains virtually undiminished for many hours. It is therefore unlikely that the increase in charge with repeated contacts can be due to charge flowing away from the point of contact. Moreover, the rate of accumulation of charge does not change when the time between contacts is increased;[159] this evidence is not conclusive, however, for it may be that the effective conductivity is very field-dependent so that the charge spreads rapidly for a very short time, and very slowly thereafter.

An additional possible mechanism for build-up of charge on polymers may be that in these materials, charge penetration is assisted by a kind of mechanical stirring.[159] Contact to a polymer such as polyethylene, if at all forceful, causes plastic deformation which is accompanied by quite extensive molecular motion. After breaking contact "recovery" of the polymer causes further molecular motion. It may be that on each contact this "stirring" carries filled traps down into the polymer and brings unfilled ones to the surface, where they can be filled on the subsequent contact. A number of contacts would therefore distribute electrons in a disturbed layer below the surface. A mechanism of this kind is of course applicable only to polymeric materials, and probably even then only above their glass transition temperature. The fact that the charge builds up in a similar way in a variety of polymers with glass transitions both below and above room temperature is difficult to explain in terms of the model.[159]

To summarize, if an insulator is repeatedly contacted at the same spot by a metal, the charge is transferred to an insulator increases at each contact. Why this happens is not, however, understood. Several explanations have been put forward but each of these is applicable to only a certain kind of insulator. Whether there is a general explanation, or whether a different mechanism operates for each kind of insulator (e.g. polymers or inorganic crystals) is not yet clear.

Electron Energies. There is sufficient evidence to suggest that the contact charge is determined by the difference in energy between the metal Fermi level E_F and some energy level E_0 characteristic of the insulator.

For many insulators the charge density after contact with a metal (often sliding, rolling or repeated contact) has been found to be correlated with the work function of the metal (or, perhaps, the electronegativity, which is closely related). This correlation had been recognized in a qualitative sense for a long time[182, 183] and has been quantitatively established in modern work.[157, 161, 164, 184–186] Within the experimental scatter, which is often large, the charge density has been found to vary linearly with the work function for glass,[185] alkali halides,[186] and a variety of organic polymers.[157, 158, 161, 164, 184] Other workers[152, 167, 187, 188] have found the charge to be dependent on the work function, though nor linearly. In the chemically simplest polymers, polyethylene and Teflon, there is disagreement about the relationship of the contact charge to the work function of the contacting metal; some workers[156, 159, 170] have found the charge to be independent of the contacting metal while others[161, 164] have reported an approximately linear relationship. It may be that this disagreement reflects the importance of the type of contact. The charge acquired after many contacts may be much greater than that acquired in single contact and it is conceivable that the charge may depend on the work function of the metal when the charge is large but not when it is small; an example of how this might happen is given by Lowell.[159] If the contact charge on the insulator depends on the metal work function it is very probable that charge transfer is by electrons[157, 164] rather than by, for example, surface ions.

Many insulators may charge negative or positive depending on whether the work function of the contacting metal is small or large. Therefore, the insulator must contain empty states that can accept electrons from the metal, as well as full ones that can donate electrons. The energy of both kinds of electron state must be close to the Fermi energy of metals; that is, about 4 to 5 eV below the vacuum level. One possibility is that there are many electron states at the same energy E_0, but some of them are empty and some occupied. Alternatively, electron states may be distributed over a wide range of energy, states below a certain energy E'_0, being full and those above empty. It is a curious fact that the values of E_0 or E'_0 show very little variation over a wide range of polymers.[165]

Polyvinylchloride	4.85 eV
Polyimide	4.36 eV
Polytetrafluoroethylene	4.26 eV
Polycarbonate	4.26 eV
Polyethyleneterephthalate	4.25 eV
Polystyrene	4.22 eV
Nylon 66	4.08 eV

This remarkable constancy is unexplained. It is very tempting to suppose that these energies are constant because charge transfers into states associated with the carbon backbone of the polymer, which is common to them all. Yet, there is strong evidence to suggest that the states responsible for charge transfer are the side-groups of the polymer.

The evidence for the hypothesis that contact charging of an insulator is determined by some electron energy level associated with it has been strongly reinforced by investigations into the relationship between the contact charging of an insulator and its chemical nature. Correlations between contact charging and chemical properties were noticed by the early investigators, notably Shaw,[183] whose work on insulator-insulator contacts is also relevant to metal-insulator contacts. His specimens included a number of alums, and he noticed that the order of these alums in a triboelectric series correlated with the order of the electronegativity of their metallic constituents. He also found that, on the whole, basic materials tended to charge positive and acidic ones negative. Similar correlations were found by Rudge[189, 190] and Medley.[191]

c) *Mechanism of Charge Transfer*

Harper[171] has indicated three main ways in which charge can transfer from one body to another: by transfer of electrons, transfer of ions, and transfer of material carrying charge. There is a good deal of evidence-for example, the variation of charge with metal work function, and its correlation with the chemical properties of the insulator-to suggest that charge transfer is often due to electrons. However, other mechanisms may be important in special circumstances.

Electron Transfer. When a metal touches an insulator, electrons may pass from the metal into empty states in the insulator (or from occupied insulator states into the metal). Insulator states may be of several kinds; the Bloch states of the conduction and valence bands; localized states due to impurities; and localized states intrinsic to the surface.

Calculations of the amount of charge transfer to an insulator have in general been of two kinds; most commonly, it is assumed that the insulator and the metal come into thermodynamic equilibrium and that the charge transfer is such as to bring the Fermi level of the metal and the Fermi level of the insulator into coincidence. Alternatively, the amount of charge on the insulator surface may be assumed to be limited by the process by which electrons transfer; for example, electrons may tunnel into localized states near to the surface of the insulator and the total charge transferred may then be limited by the distance that electrons can tunnel.

In general, a calculation of the charge transferred during contact is not sufficient to predict the charge separation observed in a contact charging experiment, for charge may redistribute itself after the surfaces are separated.

Insulators are characterized by a large forbidden energy gap.[192] The electronic structure of polymers is of particular interst because their contact charging is large and has been extensively studied. For polyethylene there is a general consensus that the conduction band edge is within about 1 eV of the vacuum level (probably slightly above it) and that the top of the valence band is about 8 eV below the vacuum level.

The energy bands in polymers, like those of covalent solids, are very wide (several electron-volts) but in polymers the broadening is due to interactions within the polymer molecule rather than to interactions between neighbouring molecules; intermolecular interactions are in fact very small.[193-195]

This weak interaction has an important bearing on the question of states within the energy gap; polymers are at least partly amorphous, and in an amorphous material the band states are known to spread into what would, in a single crystal, be the energy gap.[196] If the interactions between neighbouring molecules are weak, as in a Van der Waals solid like polyethylene, the band edges will be only very slightly smeared out, and no states will occur near mid-gap.

When a metal and insulator are in contact, empty states in the insulator which are more than about an electron-volt above the metal Fermi level, or full states more than an electron-volt below, cannot contribute significantly to the contact electrification. The Fermi level of metals is typically 4 or 5 eV below the vacuum level, so the valence and conduction bands of polyethylene, and probably most other insulators, cannot be responsible for their charging by metals. The fact that virtually all insulators do charge when contacted by metals implies that they have electron energy levels within their energy gap, due either to impurities and imperfections or to surface states. It has been difficult to test this conclusion because it is not easy to prepare most insulators in so pure a form that there are a negligible number of electron states in their energy gap. Recently, however, Cottrell, Reed, and Rose-Innes[197] have prepared specimens of very pure solid rare gases. These specimens probably had a negligible number of states within the gap; and indeed these "ideal" insulators did not charge when contacted by metals.

Little is known about electron states in the forbidden gap of polymers. It is suspected that electron traps occur as a result of various kinds of defects, such as chain folding and branching,[198] carbonyl groups,[199] cavities and entanglements,[198] unsaturated bonds,[198,200,201] and molecular oxygen,[198] but it is difficult to obtain firm evidence about the energies of such traps. A great deal of empirical information is available from thermally stimulated current (TSC) and other measurements, and some of this information is given in Table 2. The TSC technique, however, only gives information about traps which are less than about 2 eV below the conduction band, because most organic polymers cannot withstand the temperature necessary to release electrons from deeper traps. Unfortunately, traps within 2 eV of the conduction band are probably too high above any metal's Fermi energy to be involved in contact charging by metals. Nevertheless, it is useful to know that bulk traps in polymers can occur in densities up to about 10^{23} m^{-3}, because if deeper traps also occur at such densities they can certainly account for contact charging. It should be kept in mind, however, that the TSC technique of determining trap depths is based on the assumption that electrons are thermally released into the conduction band, whereas in polymers the thermally stimulated current may well be due to the hopping of electrons from one trap to another, a process which is greatly assisted by molecular motions and therefore, by a temperature rise.[208,209]

TABLE 2 Some Experimental Data on Densities and Energies of Traps in Polymers

Polymer*	Technique	Order of magnitude of trap density (m^{-3})	Trap Energy (eV below conduction band)	Reference
PE	TSC	10^{22}	–	202
PC	U.V. excitation	–	Band 0·5 to 1	203
PET	TSC	10^{22}	0·5 and 0·85 discrete	204
PE	Hopping conduction	10^{19}–10^{28}	~1eV	200, 207
PS, PE, PET, PMMA	X-ray induced conduction	10^{22}–10^{26}**	Exponential distribution	205
PS, PE, PP, PVF, PVC, PTFE	TSC	10^{21}–10^{22}	1–2eV, discrete	199
PET, PC	Breakdown field	5×10^{21}–5×10^{22}	–	206

* Abbreviations: PE = Polyethylene; PC = Polycarbonate; PET = Polyethyleneterephthalate; PS = Polytyrene; PP = Polypropylene; PMMA = Polymethylmethacrylate; PTFE = Polytetrafluoroethylene; PVF = Polyvinylfluoride; PVC = Polyvinylchloride.
** Upper limits.

Contact charging may be sensitive to the nature of the chemical groups present in the insulator; this suggests that these groups act as donor or acceptor sites. Lowell has studied this point in some detail.[210] The contact charging of polyethylene doped with octadecanol showed that the -OH groups in polyethylene matrix acted as electron donors. For octadecanol concentrations up to about 25 wt% the charge density increased approximately linearly with the density of donors. However, only a small fraction of the -OH groups close to the surface were involved in contact charging, a fact, not understood. A theory of electron states in polymers based on this idea, and with contact charging in mind, has recently been proposed by Duke and Fabish.[211] It is also important to not that in the model of Duke and Fabish the existence of localized electron energy levels deep in the energy gaps is an inherent property of polymers with certain side groups, it does not depend on the presence of impurities.

The proposal of Duke and Fabish, that electron states in a polymer are spread over a wide range of energy, is of great interest. Certain features of contact electrification can be understood if the electron states in the insulator are spread over a range of 1 eV or more. Duke and Fabish suggest that the variation brought about by polarization effects is of this order. In passing, it is worth noting that the electron states are not significantly broadened by mutual interaction, because electrons which are present in the insulator as a result of contact to a metal are normally too far apart to perturb one another appreciably. A charge density of 10^{-4} C/m^2 implies that the electrons are at least 10^{-7} m apart on average, and the interaction energy between them is only $\sim 10^{-2}$ eV.

An electron state of particular interest in polymers is the *free radical*. Free radicals may be present in polymers; they are sometimes introduced in manufacture, and in addition, they may be generated when a metal is pressed against a polymer, because carbon-carbon bonds of the polymer chain may be broken when the polymer is deformed. It is quite likely that free radicals might act as electron acceptors and thus, participate in contact charging,[212] but there is little evidence about this.

Surface States. States deep within in the bulk of an insulator are unlikely to play any part in contact charging because they are inaccessible to electrons from the contacting metal.[213] However, bulk states which happen to lie very close to the surface can communicate with a contacting metal because electrons can tunnel short distances into the insulator.[155,174] There may, in addition, be states specifically associated with the surface. These true surface states may themselves be divided into two kinds: extrinsic surface states are associated with impurities on the surface, whereas intrinsic surface states, where they exist, are present on a perfectly clean (e.g. freshly cleaved) surface of the pure and perfect insulator.

Extrinsic surface states may, of course, be present on the surface on any insulator; for example, charged impurity atoms (ions). Intrinsic surface states, on the other hand, are probably present (at energies relevant to contact charging) only on particular kinds of insulator. To see this is so, we need only to recall that the electron states of the solid arise from the energy levels of the constituent atoms, shifted and broadened by interactions. In a covalent solid, the interactions may be sufficiently strong to cause hybridization, so that a given atomic level is associated with states both in the valence band and in the conduction band. If we regard an atom at the surface of a covalent solid as intermediate between an isolated atom and an atom in the bulk, we might expect such an atom to have electron states whose energy is around mid-gap. Such states may also be interpreted as "dangling bonds" (a surface atom of silicon, for example, has only three of its four available bonds satisfied); these states are called "Shockley states".

In an ionic solid, the energy states (bands) may be regarded as arising from the orbitals of the isolated ions, shifted and perturbed by interactions. Generally speaking, the interactions are weak because the orbitals do not overlap very much, and again we may regard a surface ion as intermediate between a bulk and an isolated ion. It is therefore, possible that the energy of the orbitals of a surface ion might lie in the energy gap, but because the interactions are weak, we would not expect surface states of this kind to lie very far from the band edges. Such surface states, called "Tamm states", may be though of as arising from the difference in electron affinity of surface and bulk ions.

In molecular solids, interactions between molecules are very weak, and intrinsic surface states will not occur except very close to the band edges. This picture suggests, therefore, that the presence or absence of intrinsic surface states well within the energy gap depends very much on the nature of the material, i.e., whether it is covalent, ionic, or molecular. Calculations[214,215] bear this out, showing that states deep in the forbidden gap are likely to be found only in covalently bonded materials, and direct experiment[216-218] has confirmed that deep surface states are present on covalent but not on ionic surfaces.

Very few experiments can be said to reveal the influence of an identified surface state on contact charging. Hays[219,220] has shown that exposure to ozone increases the charging of polyolefins by mercury, presumably because of new chemical groups formed at the polymer surface, and Bauser[152] has reported that the contact charging of anthracene is strongly affected by the presence on its surface of anthraquinone.

Information about the electron states in solids can be obtained from photoemission experiments. The relationship between contact charging and the energy of electron levels has been studied for polymers[221, 222] and anthracene.[167] Photoelectrons have a limited range in solids, so electrons photoemitted from solids give information about states very close to, or on, the surface.

Kittaka and Murata[221, 222] have investigated the role of surface states in the contact charging of polymers by comparing contact charging and photoemission experiments. They find that there is no sharp threshold energy for photoemission; nevertheless, a significant photocurrent appears for photon energies greater than about 4eV. This energy is comparable to the work function of common metals, and is in accord with the experimental fact that polymers tend to charge negatively against metals of small work function and positively against metals of larger work function. Kittaka and Murata have confirmed that, in polymers, there are empty states at energies less than 4eV below the vacuum level; they showed that photoemission occurs at lower photon energies if the polymer has been previously exposed to low energy electrons (from a hot filament) which fill the empty states near to the surface. They also showed that the onset of photoemission can be shifted to lower photon energies by pre-irradiation with short-wavelength light, and suggest that this treatment fills shallow, previously empty, levels with electrons excited from deeper states.

An important question about the contact charging of a given material is whether it is an intrinsic property of the material-that is, attributable to bulk or intrinsic surface states-or whether it is due to adventitious impurities on its surface (extrinsic surface states). In principle, this question may be answered by preparing an uncontaminated surface by cleaving or cutting the material[223] in a vacuum, to avoid oxidation or other contamination from the atmosphere. In the case of polymers and other soft insulators the question is more easily investigated by measuring the charge on the material after contacting it with differently shaped metal contactors; a spherical metal contactor makes contact essentially with the pre-existing surface of the insulator, whereas a pointed (conical) contactor digs into the insulator and thus creates fresh surface. Using this technique, Cottrell et al.[224] has shown that the contact charging of several polymers (Teflon, PET, PVC, and unoxidized polyethylene or polypropylene) is not caused by extrinsic surface states; the charge density was the same for both kinds of metal contactor. On the other hand, polyethylene which has been exposed for a long time to the atmosphere acquires a greater charge density from the spherical contactor than from the conical one, showing that exposure to the air generates extrinsic surface states, as Hays[219, 220] has suggested.

Thickness of Charge Layer. Contact charging has been attributed, at one extreme, to a very thin layer of charge in surface states and, at the other, to charge extending several hundred ångstroms into the bulk. It would clearly be of great help if the thickness of the charge layer at the insulator surface could be determined by direct experiment. A possible method of doing this is to measure how the charge transfer is altered when an electric field is applied across the metal-insulator interface.[225] The greater the depth to which contact charge penetrates, the greater should be the effect of an applied electric field.

A number of workers have measured the effect of electric fields on contact charging. Sometimes[226, 227] the electric field has a complicated effect, and it is probable that in some cases, at least, electrical conduction in the "insulator" influences the results. But in other cases,[163, 219, 220] its effect can be described in a simple way: consider, for the sake of being definite, a flat sheet of insulator, one side of which is in contact with an earthed metal sheet and the other side contacted by a metal plate to which a voltage V is applied. It is found that the charge transferred to the insulator, in addition to the ordinary contact charge (V = 0), is CV, where C is approximately equal to the capacitance between the contacting plate and the ground plane. As Hays[219, 220] has pointed out, this is exactly what one would expect of a sample with a high density of surface states. So it appears plausible that the contact charging of the materials studied in these experiments is controlled by a high density of surface states. Yet, if that were so, it would be difficult to see why the charge density is so small.

Finally, it is important to point out the dangers of applying the above analysis uncritically. A value of the charge-layer thickness may be deduced from observations of the effect of a field on contact charging only if it is certain that the field acts in the way envisaged above, that is by shifting the energy levels in the insulator relative to the metal Fermi level. In practice other phenomena can also occur and may cause confusion. Thus, when an electric field is applied to an insulator such as a polymer a bulk polarization is induced which may persist for a long time after the field is removed. Many methods of measuring the charge on the insulator will not distinguish this polarization charge from the true contact charge. The polarization charge can be larger than the contact charge, even in apparently non-polar materials such as polyethylene and Teflon. It is therefore, important to design the experiment in such a way as to avoid this error. This requires some care. A similar difficulty arises if the "insulator" is in fact slightly conducting. An electric field will in that case cause a current to flow between the "insulator" and a metal touching it. This will alter the charge transfer but in a way quite unrelated to the mechanisms envisaged above. The experiments of Lowell[225] show that it is not possible to estimate the depth of penetration of charge from just simple observations of the effect of an electric field on contact charging.

Williams et al.[228] have invented a promising method of obtaining information about the depth of charge penetration into insulators. They made use of the fact that fluorinated polymers cause positive charge to transfer to almost any contacting material; moreover, if a fluorinated polymer is blended with another polymer, the fluorinated polymer tends to be concentrated at the surface. Williams and his colleagues studied blends of polydimethylaminoethyl methacrylate (which we shall call N) with polyhexafluoroisopropyl methacrylate (which we shall call P). They found, using ESCA, that the concentration of P near the polyblend surface increased rapidly with increasing proportion of P, until the proportion of P reached 2%; the surface composition then saturated, showing no further change as the proportion of P to N in the blend increased. It seems, then, that P segregates at the surface until the proportion reaches 2%, but when the proportion of P exceeds 2% the excess of P is distributed through the bulk. Contact electrification studies of the samples of P-N blends were very revealing. When an insulator contacted such samples it acquired charge which depended strongly on the proportion of P, as long as this proportion was less than 2%; but no further change in the contact charge occurred when the proportion of P increased beyond 2%.

This result, together with the ESCA analysis described above, suggests that charge can only transfer to states very near to the surface, and that states deeper in the insulator play no part in contact charging. On the other hand, measurement of the charge transferred to a metal touching a polyblend sample suggested a quite different conclusion. The charge transfer continued to vary with P-concentration well beyond the value of 2% at which the surface composition saturates. This indicates that, for metal contacts, states in the bulk as well as states near to the surface take part in charge exchange. This experiment does not give the actual depth into which electrons can penetrate; nevertheless, it indicates the bulk states may participate in contact charging.

To summarize, the experimental results seem to show that either true surface states or bulk states in insulators may accept contact charge, the role of each kind of state depending on circumstance. However, experimental methods for determining the depth of the charge penetration are either not very reliable or of limited applicability and more research is needed into this important aspect of contact charging.

Back-Flow of Electrons. When a metal touches an insulator, charge is transferred because of total free energy of the system is thereby reduced. If the energy of an electron trap in the insulator is less than the Fermi energy of the metal, electrons will pass (if they can) from the metal into the trap. Typically, we may expect the energy of the system to be reduced by ~1 eV when an electron passes from the metal to the trap. If now the metal is removed from the insulator, the excess charge will produce an electric field in the space between the insulator and the metal, and work must be done to separate them. Consequently, separating the metal from the insulator raises the free energy of the system, and the system is no longer in equilibrium, because its free energy would be reduced if electrons should return to the metal. The only reason that they do not do so is the existence of an energy barrier. Static charging is therefore a non-equilibrium phenomenon (irrespective of whether or not thermodynamic equilibrium exists during the contact).

There are three distinct ways in which charge can redistribute itself as the surfaces are separated. If one body rolls or slides on the other, charge may redistribute by electrical conduction; charge may also be redistributed by electrons tunnelling between the separating surfaces; and if the experiments are carried out in air, sparks may occur. In experiments on static charging sliding or rolling is easily eliminated, and sparks can be avoided by working in a vacuum. But tunnelling cannot be circumvented and is therfore, the most important mechanism from a fundamental point of view.

Back-Tunnelling. The calculation of electron tunnelling between separating metal and insulator may be illustrated as follows. An insulator acquires charge in surface states whose energy is Δ below the Fermi level of the contacting metal. If the metal and the insulator surfaces are separated, there will be an electric field σ/ε_0 between them, where σ is the charge density on the insulator. Therefore, the energy of the electrons will now be $\Delta - e\sigma z/\varepsilon_0$ below the Fermi level, where z is the separation between the metal and insulator. If z is small, there is no possibility of tunnelling from the insulator to the metal, because the states of appropriate energy in the metal are full. However, when z exceeds a value z_m given by

$$z_m = \frac{\varepsilon_0 \Delta}{\sigma e},$$

5.46

the trap lies above the Fermi level of the metal and an electron in the trap can tunnel into the empty states of the metal. To estimate the charge which transfers by tunnelling, one needs to calculate the tunnelling rate. As a rough approximation, it is assumed that charge transfer by tunnelling is very rapid as long as z is less than a critical value z_c (and bigger than z_m), but becomes negligible for $z > z_c$. There are two possibilities: either $z_m < z_c$, in which case there will be virtually no tunnelling, or $z_m > z_c$, in which case tunnelling starts at separation z_m and stops at z_c. By hypothesis, tunnelling is very rapid for $z_m < z < z_c$. Consequently, tunnelling will be just rapid enough to keep the surface state energy equal to the metal Fermi energy: if the energy of the surface state rises above the Fermi energy, a strong tunnelling current reduces the charge on the insulator surface until the surface state falls back to the Fermi level, and the tunnelling current falls again.

To obtain the effect of back-tunnelling on the contact charge we note that, if the density of states on the insulator surface is N, so that $\sigma = Ne$ during contact, the condition $z_m > z_c$ for tunnelling to occur during separation may be written (from Eq. 5.46)

$$N > \varepsilon_0 \Delta / (e^2 z_c).$$

5.47

If this condition is satisfied, the charge remaining on the insulator after separation is

$$\sigma = \varepsilon_0 \Delta / (e z_c),$$

5.48

since, till cut-off at $z = z_c$, the charge on the insulator is such as to keep the traps opposite the Fermi level.

This simple model predicts that, if the insulator has a low density of electron traps ($N < \varepsilon_0 \Delta / e^2 z_c$, see Eq. (5.47), the contact charge would be independent of Δ (i.e., would be the same for different metals), but proportional to N. For larger values of N, the charge density is independent of N [Eq. (5.48)], but because of the dependence on Δ, it varies linearly with the metal work function. It is reasonable to suppose z_c to be of the order of 1 nm; if we take $\Delta = 0.1$ eV, Eq. (5.47) is satisfied if $N > 10^{16}$ m^{-2}, corresponding to $\sigma \gtrsim 10^{-3}$ C/m^2. However, the charge densities commonly observed are typically an order of magnitude or more smaller than this, so it appears that back-tunnelling is probably not important in most contact charging experiments. A more detailed calculation of tunnelling between metals and insulators and its role in contact charging is given by Lowell.[229]

Ion Transfer. A number of authors[183, 230-235] have suggested that contact charge may be due to the transfer of ions from one surface to the other. However, the overall electrical effect of a positive ion being transferred from a surface cannot be distinguished from an electron transferred to that surface to neutralize the ion. In the case of metal-insulator contacts, at least, the latter is more plausible.

The most vigorous recent advocate of ion transfer has been Kornfeld.[236, 237] He asserts that insulators generally contain a net internal charge because of charge defects in the crystal lattice (there is direct evidence for this in alkali halides);[238] this internal charge is compensated by ions on the surface. (These ions are attracted to the surface from the atmosphere, which is always slightly ionized.) Kornfeld suggests that because different surfaces have different affinities for a given ion there will in general be a transfer of ions from one surface to the other when two ion-coated surfaces are touched together. He claims that it is possible to explain in this way how surfaces of the same material may charge each other, and how the sign of the charge transferred to one surface when it is rubbed by another may eventually change as rubbing continues – a phenomenon noted for example by Shaw and Jex,[239] as well as in Kornfeld's work.

It is difficult to accept Kornfeld's mechanism as the usual cause of contact charging. There is almost overwhelming evidence that electron transfer is the dominant cause when one of the contacting materials is a metal. Moreover, there is some evidence that the charging of one insulator by another can be predicted from knowledge of the charging of each of the insulators by metals; this suggests that charge transfer between two insulators is also attributable to electrons, but the situation is not as clear as for metal-insulator contacts. It is true that Kornfeld's model can explain his experimental observations rather neatly; but none of his experiments could justifiably be said to provide a critical test of his model.

Pyroelectric insulators[171, 240] are of particular interest in connection with ionic mechanisms of charge transfer. These materials have, below a certain temperature, a permanent dipole moment whose direction can easily be reversed by "poling"–that is, cooling the sample from a high temperature in an electric field of the appropriate direction. The dipole moment of a pyroelectric material generates an external electric field and the material will, if it can, collect ions from its surroundings until the external field is zero. Thus, pyroelectric materials are normally coated with a dense layer of ions whose sign is known and can be reversed by poling. The dipole moment may be very large and the ion layer consequently very dense-much more so than on an ordinary insulator. Robins and his colleagues[241, 242] have made use of pyroelectric insulators in an attempt to establish whether or not compensating ions on insulator surfaces may play a part in the contact charging of insulators by metals. If they do, the contact charging of a compensated pyroelectric surface should be strongly dependent on the direction of the specimen's polarization. Robins et al.[242] showed that this is in fact so. Nevertheless, in spite of this result, it is probable that the contact charging of their materials is not a consequence of the surface ion layer; for the charging of a pyroelectric surface which has not been compensated by externally supplied compensating ions is also strongly dependent on the polarization direction.[243] It appears that the contact charging is influenced by the polarization of the pyroelectric but not by the presence of compensating ions. Since ions are likely to be present in smaller numbers on the surfaces of other insulators, it is probable that they are insignificant in the contact charging of insulators by metal.

Other considerations might apply if water is present. Water may influence contact charging in a less direct way, that is by increasing the conductivity of the insulator. The charge transferred in a single normal contact is unlikely to be affected; but if contacts are repeated the enhanced conductivity of the insulator may help the charge build up to a large value and if sliding occurs, an increased conductivity may be expected to reduce the total charge transferred by enhancing back-flow.

Surface Ion Flow. Further experimental work directed toward the problem of ion flow across the bare surface of the polymer might in principle give insight into the stability of charges trapped at the air-polymer interface. Baum and Lewis have deposited very low energy ions on PET surfaces and have demonstrated that the resulting patch of charge is extremely stable, showing little or no lateral motion.[244] Ions of either sign are equally firmly bound, and charged patches of opposite signs show very little tendency to recombine, despite the attractive Coulomb field. Unfortunately, estimating the magnitude of the transverse field is not easy since most electric flux lines run to the ground plane behind the specimen.

Consequently, ions formed by capturing electrons (or holes) at the polymer-metal interface are also liable to be strongly bound to the polymer. However, humid conditions will lead to a modest surface conductivity and, hence, to a spreading of the charge.

Bulk Ion Diffusion. Ions should be able to pass relatively freely through insulators, as long as there are no specific electrostatic interactions between the ion and the host matrix.[245,246] The experimental measurements of carrier mobility do not agree well with the diffusion coefficients of neutral molecules, while on the theoretical front, the polaron theory of carrier transport suggests that the electrostatic interactions are quite important.

Other experimental work using liquid electrodes shows that ions do penetrate into plastics. One group of experiments related to the treeing problem shows that water and saline solutions entered polycarbonate[247] and even hydrophobic plastic such as PE.[248] Whether the ions penetrated roughly uniformly across the surface or progressed preferentially down cracks, dislocations, and interfacial areas was not revealed by the study. However, the onset of treeing points to preferential motion along regions of mechanical distortion. Another, long-standing work on iodine injection and ion injection into polyethylene,[249–251] is undergoing further investigation.[252,253] Interpretation of this set of experiments has been based on the premise that injection of ions occurs uniformly across the area of the electrodes and is not significantly disturbed by inhomogeneities in the material. An undiscussed problem concerns plasticization of the material by the liquid. Certainly, bulk liquids in contact with the polymer will cause plasticization to a greater or lesser degree, depending on the chemical nature of the liquid and its compatibility with the polymer. Nevertheless, it does not follow that individual ions, present in low concentration, can cause plasticization within their own locality. When ion exchange can occur at the liquid-polymer interface (for example, in the water-polyester system[253]) or when hydrogen bonding encourages proton transport, accepting the idea that ion injection is an easy process is fairly natural.

A further problem, just now emerging, is whether the electrode material itself migrates into the polymer. Metallic ions migrate from the solid chlorides into PVF_2 foils,[254] and there is some evidence for inward diffusion from conventional metal electrode films.[255,256]

Back-Flow of Charge By Thermionic Emission of Ions. If we believe that ions transfer from one surface to another in contact with it, we should consider whether they can transfer back when the surfaces are separated. Tunnelling of ions is unlikely to be significant (because of their large mass) but ions might cross from one surface to another by thermionic emission.[235]

It is difficult to discuss back-transfer quantitatively, because we have very little knowledge of, for example, the binding energies U_1 and U_2. However, we may make some progress with the help of plausible assumptions. First, we note that if charge on the insulator surfaces is stable after separation then the binding energies U_2 and U_1 must be so large that thermionic emission does not occur for large z. When the surfaces are close together, the barrier to emission from one to the other will be lowered so that ion transfer can occur. If we assume that the long-range part of the potential is due to the image force, the barrier for separation z will be lower than for $z = \infty$ by an amount of the order of $e^2/4\pi\varepsilon_0 z$. If this is to be appreciable (say $\sim 0\cdot 1\ U_2$, where we assume $U_2 \sim 1$ eV), z must be less than 10^{-8} m. Thus, the rate of ion transfer will be significant only for

$$z \gtrsim 10^{-8}\ \text{m}. \tag{5.49}$$

But, in addition to this upper limit, there will usually be a lower limit for z: for ions to transfer in significant numbers, the energy difference $U_2 - U_1$ must change significantly, say by $0\cdot 1$ eV. The change in $U_2 - U_1$ caused by the field $E = \sigma/\varepsilon_0$ between the surfaces is $\sigma z/\varepsilon_0$ eV; so charge transfer will not begin until

$$z \gtrsim 0\cdot 1\varepsilon_0/\sigma. \tag{5.50}$$

We have already established that charge transfer can only occur for $z < 10^{-8}$ m. Thus, if there is to be any significant transfer of ions during separation

$$0\cdot 1\varepsilon_0/\sigma \gtrsim 10^{-8}\ \text{m}. \tag{5.51}$$

So back-transfer by thermionic emission only becomes possible for charge densities in excess of 10^{-4} m^{-2}, and it seems likely that backtransfer of a large fraction of the charge will require even higher charge densities.

Material Transfer. There is no doubt that the contact of two bodies can result in the transfer of material from one to the other; not only "foreign" matter such as dust particles, but actual pieces of the two bodies themselves.

Surface analysis by ESCA[257] has shown that when polymers and metals are brought into contact some of the metal transfers to the polymer and some of the polymer to the metal. Material transfer is of possible significance to contact charging if the number of transferred atoms per unit area exceeds the charge density (in units of e per unit area) observed in contact charging. While the amount of material transferred cannot be estimated very precisely, it is quite clear that this condition is easily met.[246] When metals slide over polymers very large amounts of polymer may transfer to the metal.[258]

Charge transfer will occur as a result of material transfer if the transferred material carries charge. It is, in fact, quite likely to do so because conditions at the surface of a material are in general not the same in the interior and, as a result, the surface may carry a layer of charge. For example, charge may reside in the surface states of a semiconductor and be compensated by charge of the opposite sign distributed in the interior. Again, metals are usually coated with oxide which in general carries a net charge compensated by charge in the underlying metal.

It seems to us that contact charging is in general too reproducible and systematic to be attributed to so capricious a process as material transfer. Moreover, there is evidence that even in those cases where material transfer has been shown to take place, it is not the primary cause of charge transfer; Salanek et al.[257] showed that large amounts of material were transferred in the first contact of a metal and a polymer, but that the second and subsequent contacts did not appreciably increase the amount of material transferred. Consequently, if a metal charges a polymer because of material transfer, one would expect charge transfer to be possible only if the two materials have not previously been in contact. However, it is found[259] that the same region of a polymer surface may be repeatedly charged to roughly the same extent by repeated contacts with a metal (the charge on the surface being removed between contacts). Thus, it is unlikely that material transfer is an important primary cause of contact charging. That is not to say, however, that it is not sometimes an important factor; for it is clear that transfer of large amounts of material will tend to reduce net charge transfer. In the limit where a thick layer of the insulator is transferred to the surface of the metal, one might expect no net charge trnasfer at all, the charge originally transferred across the interface being carried in a neutral dipole layer on the metal surface. Levy et al.[260] observed material transfer between textile filaments that they rubbed together; they also found that charge transfer steadily diminished as rubbing continued, and they ascribed this decrease to the material transfer.

Perhaps the most plausible exception to the rule that material transfer is not a cause of charge transfer occurs in the charging of insulators by liquid mercury. It is very easy to transfer oxides and other impurities from the surface of mercury to another surface contacting it; Harper[171] has reviewed evidence of anomalous behaviour in mercury, and has suggested that material transfer might account for it. On the other hand, contacting mercury to polyethylene[219, 220] charges the polymer to much the same extent as contacts with other metals;[159] furthermore, the contact charging of polyethylene can be increased by oxidizing the polymer, and this increase is the same whether contacts are to mercury[219, 220] or to other metals.[261] So in the case of polyethylene at least, there is no evidence that charging by mercury is different from charging by other metals.

d) *Simulation of Contact Charging of Polymers by an Analogue Model.*

Contact charging of polymers depends on the mechanisms of charge transfer and storage on the surface and in the bulk. Charge storage and charge transport in polymers are discussed in terms of an electron energy level system[262, 263] with localized band-gap levels, i.e. localized traps for electrons or holes. Within this concept, the density and the energetic situation of localized levels both on the surface and in the bulk are responsible for the electrostatic charging of polymer solids. Using this concept, Fuhrmann et al.[264-267] have developed an analogue computer model to show how experimental parameters among others may affect the measured charging. This model correlates polymer charging with such parameters as contact ratio, contact frequency, work function of the contacting metal, band bending of polymers which results from the injected excess charge carriers, the influence of the electric field pattern within the polymer due to the electric space charge, and energy level of the polymer band gap states and barrier heights between these levels. Contact charging of polymers under a wide variety of conditions was simulated by an analogue computer using a simple kinetic model for charge injection, charge storage and dissipation on the surface and in the bulk of polymers.

e) *Insulator-Insulator Contacts*

Most of the recent work on contact charging has concentrated on the problem of metal-insulator contacts. Contacts between two insulators have not been much studied, and relatively little is known about them. A topic which has dominated the subject of contact charging of two insulators until quite recently is the question of whether or not a "triboelectric series" exists? Then there is the apparent paradox of an insulator transferring charge to a nominally identical one.

Comparison Between Metal-Insulator and Insulator-Insulator Contacts. There is some experimental evidence to suggest that insulator insulator charging is caused by the same basic mechanism as metal insulator charging. Davies[165] found that the charge transfer between two insulators can be predicted, up to a point, from knowledge of the charge acquired by each of the insulators on contact to metals. Davies assumed that the charge on his insulators, due to contact with metals, is such as to bring the Fermi levels of one of the metal and the insulator into coincidence. Using his measurements of metal-insulator charging to deduce a "Fermi lelel" for each insulator, he found that the charge transfer between two insulators is correlated with their "Fermi levels", the sign of the charge transfer being consis tent with the hypothesis that electrons pass from the insulator with the higher "Fermi level" to that with the lower. This experiment is important; without it, one might suppose the charging of an insulator by a metal occurs by one mechanism, whereas the charging of an insulator by another insulator occurs by a quite different mechanism, such as ion transfer. Davies' experiment shows that this is not so.

Duke and Fabish[268] have likewise extended their theory of metal insulator charging to the case of insulator-insulator contacts. They assert that charge transfer between a metal and an insulator is due to tunnelling of electrons between the metal and those states in the insulator is due to tunnelling of electrons between the metal and those states in the insulator which are within a narrow range of energy ("window") near the metal Fermi level. In the case of insulator-insulator contacts they propose that the mechanism is essentially the same, but that the "window" is much wider because the strong energy-dependence of the insulator density of the matrix element is offset by the strong energy-dependence of the insulator density of the states. With this modification, they find that the charge transfer between two polymers can be predicted from the density of states in each, which they deduce from metal-insulator charge transfer measurements. The broad conclusion from this, as from Davies' experiment[165] must be that insulator-insulator charging is governed by the same mechanisms as metal-insulator charging.

It is important to point out that all of the above work has been carried out on organic polymers. Very little is known about other kinds of insulators, though some work by Challande[269] suggests that the conclusions of Davies mentioned above may apply to NaCl and sapphire as well.

Contact Charging of Identical Insulators. From symmetry considerations, one does not expect charge transfer when identical insulators are brought into contact. However, it is a common experience that nominally identical insulators may charge one another when they are rubbed together.[270,271] Apparently it has not been established whether mere touching, as opposed to rubbing, can cause charge transfer.

Henry[270] has pointed out that a degree of asymmetry is often present when two objects are rubbed together, so there is nothing paradoxical about the mutual charging of identical bodies by rubbing. The simplest example is that of a rod drawn across a second rod in the manner of a bow on a violin string; the rubbed area of the "bow" is drawn out along a line, whereas the "string" is rubbed on a single spot. Henry[270] found that the charges on the rods reversed when the "rubbed" rod became the "rubber", confirming that the charge transfer is due to asymmetry in the manner of rubbing. It may be that this asymmetry causes a temperature difference between the contacting surfaces, the "spot" on the one rod becoming hotter than the "line" on the other. Temperature difference may cause charge transfer by a kind of Thomson effect. If this is in fact the mechanism of charge transfer one would expect the magnitude of the charge transfer to depend on the speed of rubbing, but this has not been tested.

Ice is a particularly important example of contact charging of similar insulators. Charge transfer between ice and ice is of great importance in clouds. The electrification of ice crystals by collision with each other is thought to play a crucial role in the development of the strong electric fields which culminate in lightning. It is well established that charge transfer between two samples of ice can occur as a result of a temperature difference; the charge transfer is due to protons and is caused by a Thomson effect. After contact, the colder sample contains a higher density of protons and is positively charged.

f) *Triboelectric Series*

A question which has been the subject of much study since very early times, is whether insulators can be ranked in an order (a triboelectric series, see Chapter 1, Table 1.1) such that a material higher up the series (that is, near the positive end) will always charge positive when touched or rubbed with a material lower down, towards the negative end. It is certainly plausible that such a series should exist. Indeed, a triboelectric series must exist if one particular mechanism (e.g. electron transfer) is always responsible for contact charging, and the experiments of Davies[165] and Duke and Fabish[268] strongly suggest that at least some polymers and metals should form a triboelectric series.

Though a group of materials can usually be arranged into a triboelectric series, Shaw and Jex[239] point out that this is not always possible; "rings" rather than "series" may occur. For example, they found that silk charges glass negative, and glass charges zinc negative, but zinc charges silk negative. Another anomaly, apparent in several triboelectric series[182, 212, 232] is the very different position occupied by rough and smooth samples of the same material, notably glass. This may be connected with frictional heating; insulators have been charged by rubbing in most experiments on triboelectric series, and it is known that vigorous rubbing may result in a charge transfer different in sign from that produced by touching or gentle rubbing.[272, 273] Therefore, it may be that a material's place in a series may be changed not only by changes in its physical condition, such as smoothness, but also by the details of the contact. The observation that all materials cannot be arranged in one unique and self-consistent triboelectric series suggests that there are several different mechanisms of contact charging, such as electron transfer and free-radical generation by rubbing; but it is not clear whether the anomalies described above reflect a diversity of charge transfer mechanisms or merely minor changes of one single mechanism (such as might be induced by heat due to rubbing).

g) *Electrostatic Properties and Chemical Structure*

Recent work has provided impressive evidence that in polymers charging is governed by the chemical nature of the sidegroups attached to the carbon-chain backbone.[274-278] Gibson et al.[279-286] have studied this question in some detail. Thus, linear free energy relationships between the magnitude of triboelectric charging for amorphous polymeric and polycrystalline monomeric aromatic organic solids and the Hammett substituent constants became available.[281, 287, 288] In aromatic systems the substituents alter the energy levels of the π-orbitals associated with the aromatic nucleus. This in turn affects triboelectric charging.

For a series of poly(olefins) of the following structure:

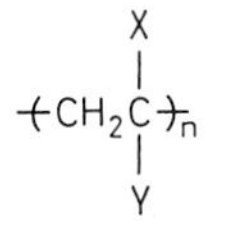

$$\left(CH_2 \underset{\underset{Y}{|}}{\overset{\overset{X}{|}}{C}} \right)_n$$

X = H	X = CH_3
Y = C_6H_5	Y = C_6H_5
= COOH	= COOH
= Cl	= Cl
= CN	= CN
= OH	= OCOCH_3
= OCOCH_3	

a number of correlations were found.[281] A quantitative relationship between triboelectric charging and molecular structure by means of correlation with gas (ionization potential) and solution phase (σ_1 constants) properties was demonstrated. Conformation, tacticity and morphology were found to be second order effects. The preservation of the ordering of relative energy levels from gas to solution to solid states for organic molecules thus allows prediction and control of the molecular level of relative triboelectric charging based on gas and solution phase properties.

In another study the manipulation of the triboelectric charging properties of a copolymer was undertaken by a systematic chemical modification.[284]

$$\text{-(CH-CH}_2\text{)}_m \text{-(C-CH}_2\text{)}_n \text{-(C-CH}_2\text{)}_0$$

with pendant groups:
- on first unit: C_6H_5
- on second unit (CH_3, CO, NH, $(CH_2)_6$, R)
- on third unit (CH_3, $COO(CH_2)_4H$)

R = NH₂   R = NHCOFerrocenyl
= OH   = OCOC₆H₄OCH₃
= O-DYE   = OCOC₆H₅
= H   = OCOC₆H₄Cl
= NHCOC₆H₄OCH₃   = OCOC₆H₄NO₂
= NHCOC₆H₄NO₂

R = NH_2 R = $NHCOFerrocenyl$
= OH = $OCOC_6H_4OCH_3$
= $O\text{-DYE}$ = $OCOC_6H_5$
= H = $OCOC_6H_4Cl$
= $NHCOC_6H_4OCH_3$ = $OCOC_6H_4NO_2$
= $NHCOC_6H_4NO_2$

Some of the major conclusions that were drawn from this study were:

1. Conversion of an alkyl ester to an alkyl amide results in an enhanced positive charging capacity.
2. Using R = H as a reference the presence of amino or hydroxyl groups results in enhanced positive charging ability (amino group leads to greater positive charging than hydroxyl).
3. The triboelectric charging of polymers is made more negative by acylation of amine and hydroxyl groups.
4. Substituents on aromatic rings influence the charging as follows:
   • methoxy derivative charges more positively than the nitro derivatives;
   • nitration results in diminished positive charging; and
   • bromination gives similar results to nitration, but not as pronounced.

Thus, chemical modification provides control of triboelectric charging properties by kinetic control of the extent of reaction.

h) Surface Analysis by a Triboelectric Charging Technique

The sensitivity of triboelectrification to the presence of foreign species on the surface also offers the opportunity for its utilization in analytical techniques for surfaces. Thus, the technique has been used to detect surface contamination and chemical alterations of surfaces.[285]

Surface Contamination. A solid solution of bis(4-diethylamino-2-methylphenyl)phenylmethane (1) and bisphenol-A polycarbonate (2) was prepared and examined for its triboelectric properties. The relevant data are summarized in Table 3.

As can be seen from the data, beads exposed to (1) became strongly negatively charged. Furthermore, compound (1) or some product thereof was picked up by the polycarbonate from the exposed beads because when clean beads came in contact with the polycarbonate subsequently, they charged to a more negative value than when coming in contact with a clean polycarbonate.

TABLE 3 Effect of Exposure to (1) on the Charging of Metal Beads vs Fresh Polycarbonate Film

Beads	Bead Charge (nC/g)		
	Clean Beads	Beads Exposed to (1)	Clean Beads on Exposed Polycarbonate
100-μm Steel Beads	−1.64±0.13	−2.86±0.15	−2.10±0.16

Detection of Chemical Reactions. Triboelectric charging is known to vary with the chemical nature of the two contacting bodies. Therefore, in principle, any chemical changes that take place at the surface are detectable by a change in the triboelectric properties. Several examples of such chemical changes are illustrated.

Thermal Treatment. Heating of a film of styrene-methacrylate methacrylamide terpolymer, containing a blocked diisocyanate, at 185°C for different periods of time showed that the triboelectric charge of the film varied by more than an order of magnitude in a 12 min. reaction time period.

Oxidation of Polystyrene. The amount of negative charge acquired by the polystyrene film aged in dry air in a dry box and absence of ultraviolet light increased by a factor of 50% over 350h.

Oxidation of Polyethylene. Exposure of branched polyethylene either to air or ozone increased the negative charging capacity of the film tenfold.

Oxidation of Coal. Virgin coal charges positively and with increasing exposure time to air at 350°C became less positive and then negative.

Photochemical Transformation. A patented process uses photochemical surface reaction as an imaging system.[289] It is based upon the change in triboelectric charging capacity between light struck and non-photolyzed areas of the surface. Surface coverage by the photoactive species can be as low as 0.2 mg per square foot or about one monolayer!

Sulfonation of Polystyrene. A very brief sulfonation of freestanding polystyrene film surface resulted in a dramatic increase in the positive charging capacity of the film from 0.2 nC/g for the virgin polystyrene to 15 nC/g for 1 monolayer sulfonated sample.

Conclusion. The triboelectric charging technique can be used for mass transfer measurements, changes in molecular structure, and any changes at or near the surface. It has the additional advantages, of being simple, requiring relatively little sample, and being nondestructive.

i) Contact Charging of Ideal Insulators

Although this book treats polymeric materials from the most insulating to the most conducting-superconducting, no ideal polymeric insulators or superconductors have been prepared as yet. Thus, it was of interest to mention that there exists at least one family of ideal insulators-the rare gases.[290]

Solidified rare gases form very simple insulators whose atoms are held together by weak van der Waals forces. The electronic structure of these solids is comparatively well understood.[291] The energy gap is large compared with metal work functions and the bottom of the conduction band is close to the vacuum level. The spherical atoms retain their complete and stable complement of s and p electrons. In these solids there are no intrinsic surface states, no dangling bonds. Because the interatomic forces are weak, crystal defects such as vacancies or dislocations should not introduce localized electron states deep in the forbidden gap.

Pure, solidified rare gases are therefore, excellent ideal insulators with which to test simple theories of contact charging.

The rare gas solids that were tested for contact charging were: neon, argon, krypton, and xenon with gold, cadmium, and aluminum as metals. For all of these combinations, *no contact charging* (any contact charge density had to be less than 10^{-6} C/m) could be detected. When these materials were doped, contact charging was detectable. The following were the main results:

1. When metal spheres of Au, Al and Cd were pressed against sheets of solid Ar, Ne, Kr, and Xe at 6K, there was no detectable contact charging. Thus, the contact charging, if any, had to be less than 10^{-6} C/m^2 or less than 1 electronic charge per 10^6 surface atoms.
2. If Ar was doped with the electronegative molecules, Cl_2 and O_2, significant charge transfer occurred, the doped insulator acquiring negative charge from the metals with a peak charge density of 10^{-4} C/m^2, similar to that commonly observed on polymers.
3. If the added impurities were not electronegative (CO, CO_2, and CH_4) no charging occurred. Weak charging was found with N_2.

Summary. Pure solidified rare gases are not charged when contacted by metals, i.e. they do not undergo contact charging. This confirms the simple theory of electron transfer from a metal to an ideal insulator. The ideal insulator will acquire contact charge if it is doped with electronegative molecules.

The results are in qualitative agreement with a simple model of contact charging in which negative charging of an insulator is due to electrons occupying states in the energy gap which are associated with electron accepting impurities.

j) Conclusions

There is a great deal of experimental evidence that the charge acquired by an insulator, when contacted by a metal, can be attributed to electron transfer; moreover, the amount of charge transferred appears to be governed by the energy difference between the metal Fermi level and some energy level in the insulator. When contacts are made repeatedly the charge is commonly found to increase with the number of contacts. It is possible that repeating the contact allows charge to penetrate to the interior of the insulator, for example, by electrical conduction between successive contacts; but even if electrons can penetrate to the bulk of the insulator in this or some other way, they will not necessarily occupy the electron states of the insulator in the way demanded by equilibrium thermodynamics.

If, as seems likely, contact charge does not penetrate deep into an insulator, the charge must reside in surface states or in bulk states which are so close to the surface that electrons may tunnel directly between them and the metal. In polymers, these states may be an orbital of a molecular group attached to the carbon chain. If an empty (acceptor-like) state is to participate in contact charging, its energy must lie below the metal Fermi level; correspondingly, a donorlike state must lie above the Fermi level. The orbitals of isolated molecular groups (e.g. the benzene ring of polystyrene) do not meet these conditions. But Duke and Fabish have suggested that, when the molecule is incorporated in a polymer, energy shifts may occur which are large enough to allow the orbitals to take part in charge exchange. Moreover, the energies may be broadened to cover a range of energy ~ 1 eV, and this provides a natural explanation of the dependence of contact charge on metal work function. However, an alternative explanation of this fact is possible: the transferred charge sets up an electric field which shifts the position of energy levels in the insulator relative to the metal Fermi level, and eventually prevents further transfer of charge. This second explanation is not plausible if the experimental estimates of the magnitude of the charge density are correct, for the field would not be strong enough to cause appreciable energy shifts. But, we have seen that uncertainty about the area of true contact prevents us being confident about the true charge density; a reliable way of determining the true charge density is urgently required. Moreover, the question of whether back-tunnelling occurs during separation cannot be finally answered until the charge density can be reliably determined. Present evidence suggest that back-tunnelling does not usually occur to an appreciable extent.

5.3   EXPERIMENTAL TECHNIQUE AND DATA

5.3.1   Steady-State Conduction

a) *Waiting Period*

After a voltage step is applied, the current decays to a steady or quasi-steady value. How long this takes depends on the temperature, time, material, and electric field, but delays of a few hours may well be needed to establish a semblance of steady-state conditions at room temperature.[119] While adequate precautions are usually observed, some examples in the literature show use of a 60-s delay, which is quite inappropriate as a measure of conductivity. Also, examples of measurements taken under temperature cycling show considerable thermal hystersis. These results may provide interesting qualitative information, but they must be discounted when reliable data are needed to determine the conduction mechanism.

b) *Conditioning*

The matter of conditioning is also a serious problem. Experimenters often find that they cannot obtain reproducible results unless they provide an initial running-in period for each specimen. Specific procedures vary from material to material and from laboratory to laboratory, but they may take the form of a temperature cycle, a long period under voltage followed by a discharge, a period of holding the specimen under vacuum, or some combination of these treatments. There is no systematic study of conditioning for any polymer, but the generally accepted ideas are that conditioning anneals out any mechanical strains or structural defects incurred during manufacturing and handling, that it discharges any static electrification present in the starting material, and that it eliminates volatile fractions retained from the polymerization process.

c) *Electrode Application*

To obtain precise measurements, electrodes should be applied to the specimen in a well-defined way. In this respect, mechanical contacts such as those used in commercial test sets are not satisfactory, since they necessarily enclose an irregular air or vacuum layer between the metal and the polymer. Silver paint and colloidal graphite electrodes may give rise to solvent plasticization of the adjacent polymer. Evaporated metal electrodes are the most attractive proposition, even though questions may arise about the detailed nature of the contact. Assuming that proper attention has been paid to prior conditioning, to the decay of transients, and to the making of proper contacts, one can make meaningful steady-state measurements.

d) *Typical Values of Conductivity*

The most obvious features of steady-state conduction at low fields are that it is ohmic and that it shows an Arrhenius temperature dependence. Typical values of conductivity range

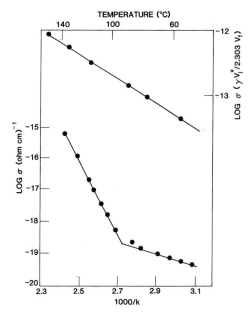

Fig. 5.8. The lower curve shows two regions of activated conduction, with a knee at T_g (left ordinate). The material is PS. Dividing out by the free volme, V_f produces a straight line. V_i^* is the activation volume and γ is a numerical constant of order unity (right ordinate). The orginal data are from Ref. 292.

from 10^{-20} $(\Omega cm)^{-1}$ at room temperature to 10^{-4} $(\Omega cm)^{-1}$ at 150°C, as is illustrated in Fig. 5.8. Also shown in the figure is a change of slope that occurs at the glass-transition temperature T_g. This change is identical to the change in the curve of free volume against temperature,[292] so dividing by the free volume removes the knee, as is also shown in the figure. It has been suggested that this is overwhelming evidence in favor of an ionic mechanism in the three polar polymers studied in detail [PS, poly(methyl methacrylate) (PMMA), and a polyester], but there is really no reason for excluding an electronic mechanism. Conductivity in low-density polyethylene (LDPE), high-density polyethylene (HDPE),[293] and PET[294] jumps abruptly by a factor of 10 when these polymers are melted.

e) Semicrystalline Polymers

The morphology of semicrystalline polymers has a strong effect on their conductance. In PET[295] and other polymers,[296] the amorphous regions appear to conduct 10 times better than the crystalline regions. Detailed studies of the effect of crystallite size are less conclusive.[297] One very interesting correlation coming out of this work, which is also followed by PE, is the so-called compensation rule or Meyer-Neldel rule relating the pre-exponential σ_0 in the conductivity to the activation energy for conduction, ΔH. We have

$$\sigma = \sigma_0 \exp\left(-\frac{\Delta H}{kT}\right) \tag{5.52}$$

and

$$\sigma_0 = \sigma_{00} \exp(B\Delta H), \tag{5.53}$$

where σ_{00} and B are constants. Surprisingly, the data for diverse polymers lie on roughly the

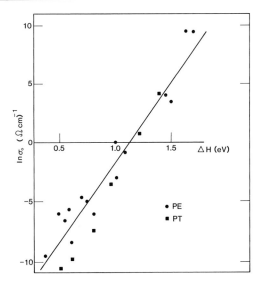

Fig. 5.9. A compensation rule plot, showing a correlation between activation energy Δ and the pre-exponential conductivity σ_0. The original data are for PE[298] and PET.[296]

same curve, as is shown in Fig. 5.9. While the classic hopping mechanism contains an implicit correlation between the energy and the pre-exponential, it is not of the form found empirically. The explanation of this experimental finding remains obscure, and whether this correlation is followed in other polymers remains to be seen.

f) Single Crystals of Polymers

Very little work has been done on single crystals of polymers. The evidence points to highly conductive, nonlinear properties that are strongly dependent on the contact material.[299, 300] The large conductance of isolated PE crystals suggests that the crystalline portion of bulk PE should conduct strongly. The evidence just cited contradicts this, so one must assume that the transfer of charge carriers from the amorphous to the crystalline regions is inhibited. This is difficult to understand considering the interpenetration of molecular chains from one region to the next.

g) Pressure Effect

Since low-field conductivity is closely correlated with free volume, it should also be correlated with pressure. Studies using tensile stress indicate that there is indeed an activation volume V^*, which is proportional to the mechanical compliance.[301] Apart from some work on irradiated plastics, this approach does not seem to have been followed up, although piezo-stimulated currents are now being examined in polar materials.[302] At much higher stresses (3×10^{10} Pa) under shock conditions, conductivity increases by more than 10 orders of magnitude, except in specimens thinner than 1 mm.[303] Presumably, some drastic phase change occurs above 4×10^8 Pa, the limit of the piezostimulated current work.

h) Thickness, Electrode Material, and Ambient Medium

In the ohmic regime, one expects the conductivity to be independent of thickness and independent of the electrode metal. Actual measurements to confirm these features are somewhat sparse, but the thickness dependence[304] and independence from electrode material seem to be obeyed.[305,306] Finally, we note that the ambient medium may affect the conduction properties. Changes in going from air to electrolyte surroundings have been observed, but their full implications in the ohmic region have not yet been explored, particularly in the context of air and vacuum ambients.[57]

i) Nonlinear Conduction

The onset of nonlinear currents occurs at fields of about 10^5 V cm^{-1}. The corresponding current densities vary sharply with field and range from 10^{-4} to 10^{-7}. The data are most often fitted to the Poole-Frenkel equation or one of its variants, and typically one obtains an activation energy W of about 1 eV and a measured Poole-Frenkel coefficient β_m in the correct range,[307]

$$\frac{1}{2} \beta_{PF} = \beta_s \gtrsim \beta_m \gtrsim \beta_{PF}. \qquad\qquad 5.54$$

At least for PET, the β_m values tend to favor the lower end of this inequality and thus suggest the intervention of an uncompensated donor or acceptor. The value of W is much lower than the reputed barriers to injection, and this rules out the Schottky mechanism.

On the basis of the sinh law, the deviation from a linear J-V characteristic yields the jump distance a. With this model, a comes to 7 nm in PET,[308] and in PVC it is 1 nm below Tg and increases to 5 nm above Tg.[309] In some cases, variations in conductance are associated with the electrode materials, so a Schottky process is probably involved.[310] In yet other cases, the thickness and voltage dependence are consistent with space-charge-limited currents, which implies that carriers can be freely supplied by the source electrode.

j) Conclusion

The steady-state experimental work can be summarized by saying that, in general, there is no single class of behavior for a given polymer. The ohmic region does not give much information about the nature of carrier concentration. In the region of higher fields, conduction may be due to several mechanisms; different specimens of the same polymer may respond in different ways because of different impurities, morphologies, heat treatments, electrodes, and so on. Hence each case must be taken separately.

5.3.2   Transient Conduction

The typical transient current after application or removal of a step voltage consists of a decaying current approximately following the Curie-von Schweidler power law, t^{-n}. A current density of 10^{-10} A cm^{-2} at a time of 1 s and a field of 10^5 V cm^{-1} is representative. In the majority of cases, the charging and discharging transients obey the superposition principle. Correlating the decay curves with the dielectric loss measurements establishes that in many cases the effect is wholly dipolar, with a wide distribution of relaxation times.[311]

Careful analysis of PET data using isochronal analysis,[312] Fourier transforms of dielectric data,[313] and pyroelectric studies[36] has established that there is no charge storage in this material at applied fields up to 6×10^5 V cm^{-1}. Some doubt remains about the time span up to 1 s. If any charging occurred on this time scale, however, the general rule that charge loss occurs in a different manner from charge storage ensures that the field configurations would remain different in the charge and discharge phases even long after the charge had vanished; the remaining polarization would reflect this prior situation and the superposition principle would be violated, contrary to observation. Annealing causes additional complications, and in PET this takes the form of increasing crystallization at elevated temperatures. At room temperature, nonlinear response and failure of the superposition principle have been seen in the incremental response at high standing fields ($E > 1.2$ MV cm^{-1}) and even at moderately large field increments (0.2 MV cm^{-1}) applied on top of smaller standing fields.[307]

Charge injection is not easy to establish, either from the steady-state current or from the transient response. Variations with electrode material and nonlinear response may occur without space-charge effects because they may simply arise from emission-limited or extraction-limited processes adjacent to the electrodes. In some cases, however, the effect of injected charge can be seen from the discharge of the dielectric. Thus, fields in excess of 1 MV cm^{-1} insert enough charge into PE to alter the apparent (but not the real) breakdown strength.[314] The charge, however, is almost entirely discharged within a few tens of microseconds, so it is not observable on the time scales usually employed in conduction work. For PET, the storage time is approximately 1 min.[315] It is apparent that high fields are needed to give significant injection. This is supported by some TSC work, which also exhibits charge storage in PET for polarizing fields above 1 MV cm^{-1} and temperatures exceeding $-40°C$.[316] The temperature threshold and the fact that aluminum injects only electrons whereas gold does not inject at all both point to a Schottky mechanism. A further deduction from this work is that elevated temperatures are needed if the charges are to fall into the deeper traps. This rather curious aspect should be more fully explored.

5.3.3 Radiation-Induced Conduction

Under the influence of light or ionizing radiation, enhanced currents may flow in polymers. In the infrared region, a transient current is followed by a reversed transient of the same shape when the illumination is extinguished. Initial experiments, carried out with a time resolution of 1 s, revealed that the current response is linear in the light intensity, linear in the electric field, and not very sensitive to wavelength. Further work established that this effect is pyroelectric in origin.[317] Upon illumination, the charge ΔQ transferred in the external circuit is

$$\Delta Q = - A(P)T\, \Delta T,   \qquad 5.55$$

where A is the area, (P) is the mean value of the polarization across the thickness of the specimen, T is the expansion coefficient in the thickness direction, and ΔT is the temperature increase in the specimen. Typical values for PET are $\Delta Q = 20$ pC, A = 5 cm^2, T = 1.5 x 10^{-4} deg^{-1}, $\Delta T = 10$ K, and (P) = 2.7 nC cm^{-2}. These results refer to an applied field of 3×10^5 V cm^{-1} followed by short-circuiting for 90 min and by white-light illumination of an intensity of 3 mW cm^{-2}. The remaining polarization corresponds to a dielectric increment $\Delta\varepsilon' = 0.1$. Comparison with the dielectric constant of $\varepsilon' = 3$ shows that we are dealing with a relatively small part of the total dielectric response. The magnitude of the effect decays with time, in step with the remanent polarization.[316] The results depend strongly on the specimen's electrical and thermal history.

On a much shorter time scale, infrared illumination does, in fact, reveal details of the trapped-charge distribution.[31, 318] The thermal equilibration time between the front and back of a typical specimen made of plastic film is about 10 ms. Observations made on faster time scales will consequently reflect the inhomogeneous expansion of the dielectric. If the applied field is significant, the effect is overridden by the change in the specimen's capacitance. The sheet of charge at depth $\times$ in the material induces a charge density q on the front electrode of magnitude

$$q = \varrho dx\, \frac{x}{\ell}.   \qquad 5.56$$

If we assume that light passes through the transparent front electrode and the transparent polymer and is absorbed at the back electrode, only this electrode will warm up. The adjacent polymer will expand first, and the induced charge on the front electrode will change, giving rise to a current in the external cirucit of

$$ I = A \frac{dq}{dt} = + \varrho dx \frac{x}{\ell^2} \frac{d\ell}{dt}. \qquad 5.57 $$

Clearly, in an actual experiment, one must consider a distribution of charge density $\varrho(x)$ across the whole thickness ℓ and must take into account the time evolution of the thermal expansion. Both can be done either by decomposition into Fourier components[318] or by analog modeling.[31] If the illumination is kept on, the expansion will eventually become essentially uniform. As a result, the trapped charge will give rise to a net charge flow of zero in the external circuit, $\int I dt \, 0$, leaving only the polarization component to contribute to the measured charge flow.

The original hope in the infrared work was that illumination would empty the relatively shallow traps (1 eV or less deep) to give first a transient current related to the amount of trapped charge and then an enhanced steady current caused by the enforced change in the trapping ratio ϑ. While PSC experiments have been proposed for insulator systems and the theory exists,[319, 320] the polymers do not respond in this way. Either shallow traps do not exist in adequate concentration or they are not optically active. This result is not fully consistent with the TSC experiments on polymers containing trapped charge.[316]

a) Near-Ultraviolet Range

In the near-ultraviolet range, there are many reports of photoconductance phenomena. Photoinjection occurs with fairly well defined thresholds for carriers of one sign and some-times of both signs[321] near 3 eV, and the yield conforms to the Onsager prediction. The barrier heights clearly do not directly follow the work function of the electrode material.[322] In addition, although one-exciton dissociation has been invoked to account for correspond-ence between the photocurrent and the optical absorption in the energy range of 4 to 5 eV,[323] biexcitonic annihilation must be ruled out since the current is linearly dependent on light intensity. Time-dependent effects[324] and changes with the ambient atmosphere add to the complications that abound in this field.[325] Temperature effects have hardly been studied, but there is evidence of thermal activation, with a change of slope at T_g.[326] The field dependence is nonlinear at fields above 10^5 V cm^{-1}, as is implicit in an Onsager mechanism, but linear at low fields,[327] where yield is essentially independent of field and carrier transport dominates the current-voltage characteristic. The continuing difficulty of interpretation is illustrated by recent observations of field and wavelength dependences of the photocurrent in poly(2-chloro-p-xylylene).[328] Here, Fowler plots and field-enhanced injection suggest a wide-band polymer, but some aspects of the results are better accounted for by narrow conduction bands together with surface-state effects that do not, however, dominate the injection process. The only test of this situation is to measure the currents at both electrodes and to discard the data if they are unequal.[327]

Obviously, the near-ultraviolet response is extremely complex. At best, we can give some figures as a very rough guide to the magnitude of the effect: at a field of 10^5 V cm^{-1}, with an illumination intensity of 10 mW cm^{-2}, the nominal steady-state current density is 1 pA cm^{-2}. The absolute efficiency of carrier production is hard to estimate, but it could be approximately 10^{-3} at this field.[321]

b) Vacuum-Ultraviolet Range

In the vacuum-ultraviolet range, the photocurrent rises sharply at the intrinsic absorption edge at $h\nu = 8$ eV.[329–331] However, these data have not been tested against theoretical yield curves of the form of Eq. (5.45), so there is as yet no test of whether the experimental work is consistent with the presumed band structure. Furthermore, the current measurements are always uncertain in that they refer to the product of a generation probability and a drift term.

c) *Nonpenetrating Radiation*

Nonpenetrating radiation can induce a conductive layer in the dielectric close to the bombarded surface during irradiation. The layer, acting as an injecting electrode in many polymers, then carries a space-charge-limited current to the counterelectrode. This system has been used in the indirect measurement of slow mobilities and has been reviewed recently.[332] Because of the industrial importance of electrets, fairly detailed analyses have been made and correlated with experimental results.[47,333] Charge builds up in the dielectric at a depth corresponding to the range of the primary beam. The range is progressively reduced under the influence of the field of the charge already deposited, but this effect is mitigated by leakage through both irradiated and nonirradiated regions.[333,334] The flow of space-charge-limited current into the nonirradiated region also may occur in the formation of corona-charged electrets, thus accounting for the trapped charge lying well beyond the range of either bombarding ions or secondary electrons in these films.

If pulsed radiation is used, carrier mobilities can be deduced from the time-dependent currents.[64,335] The presently reported values of $\mu\tau \approx 10^{-9}$ cm^{2}V^{-1} in PE are deduced from the saturation of transported charge versus field; that is,

$$Q_m = Q_{exc}w \left[\frac{1 - \exp\left(-\dfrac{\ell}{W}\right)}{\ell} \right], \qquad\qquad 5.58$$

where

$$w = \mu\ell E . \qquad\qquad 5.59$$

Here, Q_m is the measured charge, Q_{exc} is the amount of excited charge, and w is the carrier range. We have assumed that excitation takes place close to the front electrode. What mobility and lifetime appear in the range w is something of a question, but presumably one should use a free-carrier mobility μ_0, and then τ is the lifetime to shallow trapping. Also, only if the drift currents (on the time scale of 1 s) are analyzed properly in terms of multiple trapping kinetics can one judge whether the field dependence of the apparent mobility was due to the measurement or whether there is an underlying field dependence of the true mobility.[336,337]

d) *Penetrating Radiation*

By using penetrating radiation, one can in principle measure the RIC in the material if the dose-enhancement effects caused by the adjacent high atomic number electrodes are taken into account.[136,338] The results are anomalous unless stored charge is removed, and doses of 200 Gy seem adequate for this purpose.[339] Given these precautions, the conductivity of a great many substances is linear in dose rate and for a diversity of materials is much the same, lying within a couple of orders of magnitude of

$$\frac{\sigma}{\dot\gamma} \cong 10^{-15} \, (\Omega \text{ cm})^{-1} \text{ Gy}^{-1}\text{s} \qquad\qquad 5.50$$

for a range of dose rates covering 10^{-6} Gy s^{-1} to 10^{12} Gy s^{-1}[133,340] This is of the form predicted from Eqs. (5.41) and (5.42), although the reason for the relative insensitivity to the insulator's chemical nature is not clear. This prompt conductivity is also relatively insensitive to temperature.[341]

e) *Three Complications*

However, there are three complications with radiation-induced conductivity. First, the conductivity exhibits a delayed component, which continues after the ionizing radiation has been turned off. It is generally agreed that the delayed conductivity becomes progressively less important as the temperature falls.[142, 342] In addition, both magnitude and decay rate vary strongly with the current before termination of the irradiation. This delayed conductivity can be represented empirically by a hyperbolic relation

$$\frac{I_0}{I} = 1 + bn_0t,$$
                                                                                              5.61

where I_0 and I are the initial current and the current at time t, respectively; t is the time following the end of irradition, n_0 is the initial carrier concentration; and b is an apparent bimolecular rate constant. Since the steady current I_0 is linear in the dose rate, at least at dose rates exceeding ~1 Gy s^{-1}, but Eq. (5.61) is still obeyed,[341, 343] the system does not follow a bimolecular recombination, and the equation represents a convenient classification scheme and not a model of the decay process.

The second complication arises at low dose rates, less than about 1 Gy s^{-1}. The steady-state response in many polymers at this range is higher than the value extrapolated from the linear range Eq. (5.60) with an appropriate value of the constant, and one finds a power law dependence with exponent z < 1, which is itself somewhat temperature dependent. Associated with this phenomenon are a slow rise in conductivity when the irradiation is turned on and an even slower decay when it is turned off. The decay is still of the hyperbolic form. It is clear that the steady-state conductivity under these conditions follows the free-volume curve, showing a break at the glass-transition temperature T_g,[344] although here too a numerical comparison has not yet been carried out. Both risetime and decay time get shorter as the dose rate increases until the rise is essentially instantaneous and unobservable under the high dose rate conditions discussed earlier. The changes in these time constants and the sublinear response suggest interband bimolecular recombination, and the early explanations, along these lines, invoked an exponential trap distribution to account for z > 1/2.[142, 143] However, direct electron-hole recombination does not occur even at very high dose rates, and alternative models should be considered.[134, 141] Since the correct explanation is not yet available, all numerical values now given for mobilities and trap densities should be regarded with caution.

The final complication concerns the absorption currents that flow when voltage is applied under radiation conditions.[345] There are features in the current in addition to the dark absorption current plus the steady-state RIC. These features have been explained on the basis of a Maxwell-Wagner polarization in a hetergeneous system, but they might equally well derive from a dipolar response arising from a field redistribution caused by unequal RIC in the amorphous and crystalline regions, or they could simply be manifestations of the delayed RIC, which is of overrriding importance at the low dose rates used. The dissipation factor shows somewhat analogous features.[346]

5.3.4   Detection of Trapped Charge

Conduction is accompanied by trapping of charge, so one way of determining some features of the conduction mechanism is to inspect the charge distribution after the conduction phase. Shallowly trapped charges will, of course, detrap and discharge quite quickly, so only deeply trapped charges remain for interrogation. As a rough rule of thumb, charges shallower than 0.5 eV are not available at room temperature.

An adaption of the technique using optical sensing permits one to follow variations of charge density on a time scale of a few milliseconds.[347] Probably the most useful system is the transient pyroelectric method, which involves deconvolution of the charge distribution from a signal compounded from this charge distribution and from the time and position-dependent thermal expansion of the specimen.[31,348] The method is nondestructive, but the deconvolution may not be unique. A traveling shock wave can provide the same information in more direct form,[34,349] but with the penalties of more complex equipment and poorer spatial resolution, of about 5 μm.

The charge distribution can be determined by destructive electrical techniques. A measurement of surface voltage followed by total discharge gives the location of the centroid.[350,351] More detailed information, with a depth resolution of 1 μm, can be obtained by using an electron beam of progressively increasing energy to sweep through the specimen to greater and greater depths.[32] A coarse method of analysis consists of the sectioning technique, in which successive slices of the specimen are dropped into a Faraday cup and their charge is measured directly. The slices may be cut from the bulk[352] or they may be sheets taken from a stack forming a thick specimen.[353] In either case, false results may arise because of surface charges created during separation. It is also possible to estimate the depth of the charge centroid during electron beam charging, by measuring the currents on both the front and back faces of the specimen.[354]

Optical methods of detection are attractive in that they are noncontacting and do not normally disrupt the electric field within the specimen. The obvious optical technique is to release trapped charges using light of the appropriate quantum energy under an applied field and to measure the resulting drift current. While successful with inorganic crystals, this PSC method has not proved useful in polymers, although the reasons for this failure are not understood. Another approach is to measure the optical absorption of the filled trap. This is a well-known tool in the field of radiation chemistry, and the color center in organic glasses at 77 K has been exhaustively studied.[15,21,24,355] The same center occurs in PE[21,356,357] and absorbs in the near-infrared region. Unfortunately, this trapped electron is thermally unstable and does not exist at room temperature. Deeper traps have not been detected, either because they do not exist, because they are not optically active, or most likely because their abosrption cross section is so small that the absorption at the existing trapped charge densities is below the resolution limits of the recording equipment.

The Raman effect has been used to find the field distribution in PE.[33] It appears possible to obtain a field resolution of 5 kV cm^{-1} against a mean field of 150 kV cm^{-1}. Another method is to use the Stark effect. Since that experiment requires good optical quality and is operated at helium temperatures, it probably cannot be extended to polymers.[358]

Electron spin resonance (ESR) studies of polymers show trapped electrons at 77 K following gamma irradiation.[21] However, the trapped electrons no longer exist at room temperature.[21] There is some suggestion that ionic species are formed.[359]

There is a wealth of purely free radical and oxidation phenomena,[360] paralleling the more familiar low-temperature work, but there are also ESR signals that correlate strongly with the TSC response. Since x-ray irradiation does not produce these particular signals, it is clear that they are induced only by charged-particle bombardment. Clearly, this requires further investigation.

Under favorable conditions, a trapped charge gives rise to pyroelectric, piezolelectric[361], and electrostrictive[362] responses. One can also find capacitance changes at high fields, and these are ascribed to charge injection.[363] Because all these methods are indirect, involve an averaging of some sort over the charge distribution, and are usually outweighed by polar effects, they do not provide the detailed spatial information that is really needed.

5.3.5   Conducting Particle-Loaded Polymers

Polymers are frequently loaded with carbon black to obtain a weakly conducting material . that maintains the virtues of light weight, low cost, and ease of molding. The main features to be expected are a conductance that increases with the concentration of the carbon black, the onset of nonohmic conduction when the field at the ends of the particles exceeds the threshold for thermionic or field emission, and an abrupt change to a conducting system when the percolation limit is reached. In a general way, these theoretical predictions are met with both carbon black dispersions and metallic powders. The metallic powders do not form a random dispersion but tend to coat the polymer grains. In this case, the transition to metallic conduction occurs when there is roughly monolayer coverage of the polymer grains. The concentration at which this occurs varies strongly with the ratio r_m/r_p, where r_m and r_p are the mean radii of the metallic and polymer grains, respectively. The experimental results are quite close to the value predicted by a simple geometrical calculation.[364, 365]

At the other extreme, what is probably an intimate dispersion of carbon black in the insulating matrix has been obtained by making a carbon black/wax/styrene butadiene rubber (SBR) ternary mixture.[366] Above the melting point of the wax, these mixtures show a large resistivity, which falls with frequency and also falls sharply with increasing dc voltage. Below the wax melting point, the resistance is low and only weakly dependent on voltage. The capacitance is large at low temperatures, about 1000 times the vacuum capacitance of the test cell, but falls abruptly and becomes frequency dependent beyond the melting point.

At a more practical level, polymers with a small percentage of carbon show an ohmic response and superposition of charging and discharging transients up to 10^4 V cm^{-1}.[367] At higher fields, this response goes over first into a V-I characteristic that has been interpreted as space-charge limited[50] and then to a field emission type of behavior.[368] Since the interpretation of nonohmic conductance curves may be ambiguous, these assignments of mechanism may not be completely correct, but the general trend is clear.

5.3.6   Surface Conduction

The leakage of charge across the surface of an insulator may be as important as the transport through the bulk, but it appears that the surface conduction has been studied much less thoroughly. Consequently, our knowledge is more rudimentary. At high fields and under atmospheric conditions, surface conduction takes place by means of polluted regions of the surface. While this explanation is of great technical importance to power utilities, it does not reflect the underlying electrical properties of the dielectric surface. Measurements of surface transport fall into three basic groups. In the first group, a charge put onto the surface by ion bombardment forces the surface to be conducting. In the second group, the dielectric is held in a humid atmosphere, and the transport across the wetted dielectric is measured. Finally, in some experiments, the dry and reputedly clean polymer is studied.

a) *Ion Bombardment*

In the first group of measurements, if the net beam current density (allowing for secondary emission and backscattering) is J_c and the surface potential is $V(x)$, then the current balance equation becomes[369]

$$J_s(x + dx) - J_s(x) - J_b x = J_c x, \qquad\qquad 5.62$$

where J_b is the bulk current density and J_s is the surface current density. If a bulk conductivity σ and a surface conductivity σ_s are assumed, then

$$-\sigma_s \frac{d^2V}{dx^2} + \frac{\sigma V}{d} = J_c, \qquad 5.63$$

which has simple exponential solutions. The assumption made here that the bulk current flow is normal to the surface is reasonable for films that are thin in comparison with their width. The experimental data agree tolerably well with the analysis and give a ratio for PTFE of $\sigma_s/\sigma = 20$ cm.

The absolute values of σ and σ_s could not be found. The edge effect, which is marked, could be accounted for by adding a correction length of approximately 10d to the insulator at $\times = 1$. Whether this means that the surface conductance was a factor of 10 smaller in the y direction or whether this signals the need for a full two-dimensional analysis in the vicinity of the edge was not determined. By using an interdigitated array for the lower electrode, it is possible to separate out the bulk and surface components.[370] In this work, the surface conduction was shown to depend on both relative humidity and electrical history. Whether the surface conductivity is the same both with and without the bombardment has not been investigated.

b) *Humid Atmosphere*

Measurements made in the presence of water vapor indicate a strong dependence of surface conductance on relative humidity. A reduction by four orders of magnitude for a change from 40 to 90% relative humidity is typical for many polymers.[371-375] Values of σ in the range of 10^{-10} to 10^{-16} $(\Omega cm)^{-1}$ are typical. Oxidation of the surface increases water adsorption and conductivity, while average tangential fields exceeding 1 kV cm^{-1} lead to nonlinear current-voltage characteristics.[372] The conductivity is an exponential function of the thickness of the adsorbed layer,[373] although deviations may occur below monolayer coverage. When relative humidity is changed, equilibration times appear to be approximately 10 s.

c) *Clean, Dry Polymers*

Measurements on clean, dry polymers have been carried out both as an adjunct to the humidity-dependence tests[372,373,375] and independently. Surface conductivities are reported from 10^{-17} $(\Omega cm)^{-1}$ for PTFE to below 10^{-19} $(\Omega cm)^{-1}$ for PE. Immediately, a problem arises: the bulk and surface conductances become comparable, and it is necessary to evaluate the separate contributions to the total current in a surface cell. These evaluations, in turn, require an evaluation of the electrostatic field under conditions of mixed bulk and surface conduction. Even with bulk conduction alone, calculation of the field pattern is nontrivial, and large corrections (sometimes one or two orders of magnitude) are required to reduce the apparent conductivity to a true bulk value.[376,377] A highly conductive surface, like those in the water-covered systems, will show a nearly uniform voltage gradient. A wholly insulating surface has an infinite field next to the sharply terminated electrodes,[378] while free injection from one electrode onto the surface gives a space-charge-limited current,[379] with a quadratic voltage dependence,

$$I = V^2 \mu_s \frac{(\varepsilon' + 1)\varepsilon_0}{\ell^2 \pi}. \qquad 5.64$$

In this equation, μ_s is the surface mobility, while the dielectric constant appears in the form $(\varepsilon' + 1)$ to account for the presence of air on one side of the surface and polymer on the other. The tangential field across the surface will generally be quite nonuniform. This must be allowed for in reducing experimental observations to physical parameters of the material, but the appropriate corrections have not been applied in practice.

Clearly, there is some difficulty in reconciling the fact that purely polar processes cannot account for surface charging[378] with the observation that the discharging current, ascribed largely to perimeter flow in tetrafluoroethylene hexafluoropropylene copolymer (FEP), exhibits the classic dipolar absorption peaks.[380] The problem needs to be understood because surface spreading can contribute to dielectric loss,[381,382] and it undoubtedly is important in the charging of polymers during extrusion.[383] It also affects the edge corrections applied in high-precision dielectric constant measurements.

5.3.7   Thermoelectric Power in Polymers

Some attempts have been made to measure the thermoelectric power (Seebeck coefficient) α_s in polymers.[384–386] The magnitude of α_s is ~ 2 mV K^{-1}, corresponding to a carrier activation energy of ~ 1 eV. The sign of α_s gives the sign of the carrier. It is positive in PET at high temperatures, suggesting protonic conduction, negative in PVC, and quite variable in a number of nylons. The experiments are difficult to carry out, and the data are too few to make useful comparisons with conduction results.

5.3.8   Electroluminescence in Polymers

Electroluminescence has been found in several polymers. In PET at 3 MV cm^{-1}, recombination between free carriers and either carriers or trapped charges of the opposite sign can be discarded as a model, because the number of light quanta put out exceeded the number of countercharges that could be held in the material.[387] The light production was consistent with a model of impact excitation by hot electrons in the region of the cathode and was associated with nondestructive breakdown. In work at lower fields, ranging up to 8×10^5 V cm^{-1}, and under ac excitation, several diverse polymers yielded a light output B of the form[388]

$$ B \sim \exp\left[-\frac{A}{V}\,\Theta V^{1/2} \right], \qquad\qquad 5.65 $$

where the coefficient Θ is close to β_{PF}/kT. Although this suggests field injection and Poole-Frenkel transport, the fields are somewhat low for regular field emission. A study of TSL and isothermal luminescence of PE at 77 K showed that the light output reflected the detrapping of charges.[389] The charges themselves could be broken into upfield and downfield groups, which exhibited different decay rates and reversed their roles as the field was reversed.

5.3.9   Noise in Polymers

Only a few studies of noise in polymers exist. PS, PE, and PET have shown quite similar flicker noise, with a spectral power that varied with frequency as f^{-m}, $1.3 < m < 1.7$, and was proportional to the square of the dc current.[390] This noise appeared only close to the breakdown point. It was associated with conducting channels, since raising the standing current artificially by ultraviolet illumination did not raise the noise level. Secular variations in the noise spectra were thought to be due to local annealing of sensitive spots. Noisy signals observed during discharge of electrets[391] were attributed to microdischarges of some sort. The currents seen before the onset of oscillation also appear to be noisy.[61] Microphony in cables seems to be associated with triboelectric charging at the conductor-polymer interface or with piezoelectric effect.[392] In either case, the noise is triggered by mechanical disturbance and does not reflect the fundamental noise properties of the material.

5.4   CONCLUSIONS

A number of problems were discussed in this review. One was the role of ions, including the conditions leading to easy injection and the discrepancy between ionic mobilities and the diffusion coefficients of comparable neutral molecules. In particular, the penetration of water and of metallic ions from metal electrodes may have a considerable bearing on prebreakdown conditions.

Another problem has to do with electron beam injection. A polymer that has a low enough RIC in the irradiated volume will carry SCLC in the nonirradiated material, with low current densities corresponding typically to a mobility of 10^{-12} cm^2 V^{-1}s^{-1}. When these materials are not irradiated, why do they show an ohmic region followed by a bulk high-field region that is not SCLC? There is no significant electrode dependence in many cases, so the carrier supply is adequate at the contacts to carry the required current densities.

Still another problem has to do with free volume and conductivity. The connection between them needs to be explored from the theoretical point of view, particularly to establish definitive facts that will distinguish between electronic and ionic conduction. This would be especially pertinent to heavily plasticized plastics.

Ever-present are the problems of proper identification of traps, particularly those operating at and above room temperature, and proper modeling of radiation-induced conductivity, for which existing models of the delayed effects are inadequate. Involved with both problems is the apparent change in cross section and in energy depth of traps in some materials evidenced by temperature effects[393] and field-dependent effects.[394]

High-field and prebreakdown regions present considerable difficulties in interpretation, and further effort is required to understand the transport mechanisms and the effects of charge storage. In particular, attention should be paid to the Onsager models rather than to the variously modified Pool-Frenkel calculations.

Surface conduction and surface charge spread require attention. Although behavior under humid conditions can be reasonably related to the absorbed water, the action of antistatic agents appears to be a black art.[395, 396] The question of whether semicrystalline polymers can be understood by the theories of composite materials remains unanswered. Finally, while the photoconductive properties of many polymers in the near-ultraviolet range are partially understood in terms of barrier heights, many of their other experimental details are inconsistent with current models.

PART 2. SYNTHETIC METALS

5.5   INTRODUCTION

During the 1960s the first synthetic metals [materials with conductivity $> 1 \ (\Omega cm)^{-1}$] were synthesized. The first molecular compounds found to possess metal-like conductivity were the tetracyano and tetraoxalatoplatinates, the so-called Krogman salts.[397, 398] These square planar complexes contained stacks of PtX_4 or IrX_4 ($X = CN$ or C_2O_4) units based on a chain of central platinum or iridium atoms. This conductivity originates from the overlap of the 5-d_{zz} orbitals between neighboring platinum (iridium) complexes, which forms a conduction band. In potassium cyanoplatinate (Fig. 5.10) the weak d_σ-d_σ metal-metal bonds are strengthened by removing one-third of the electrons from the 5-d_{zz} antibonding orbitals by bromine oxidation:

$$K_2Pt(CN)_4 \xrightarrow{\ Br_2\ } K_2Pt(CN)_4Br_{0.3} \cdot 2.3H_2O.$$

This reaction results in a fractional oxidation level of 2.3 giving the compound $K_2Pt(CN)_4Br_{0.3} \cdot 2.3H_2O$ (KCP) with equivalent platinum atoms. In effect, it is a polymerization because the decrease in interplanar distance from 0.335 to 0.289 nm gives a bonded chain of metal atoms that now forms a conduction band five-sixths full. The conductivity, which increases on oxidation from 10^{-7} to $10^2 \ (\Omega cm)^{-1}$ is metallic and highly anisotropic, being 10^5 times more parallel than perpendicular to the metal-metal chain. Thus, KCP is a one-dimensional metal and shows a metal-insulator transition at about 100 K, below which the conductivity is very low. In this case the phase change might be due to an asymmetric location of the potassium or bromide ions in the lattice.[399–401]

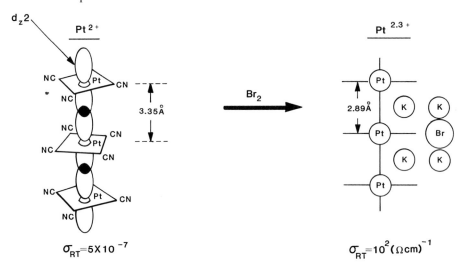

Fig. 5.10. Potassium cyanoplatinate and its bromine oxidation to a fractional oxidation level.

Two basic requirements must be met for electrical conductivity in these types of chain compounds. First, a sufficient interaction or overlap of molecular orbitals is needed to allow the formation of delocalized wave functions. Second, the delocalized molecular orbitals must be only partially filled so that electrons can move almost freely throughout the crystal lattice.

The extended electronic states needed for proper overlap can be found both in the p- and d-orbitals of hetero atoms and in the π-electron systems of unsaturated organic molecules. However, the conducting polysilanes do not fit these basic requirements. Although a microscopic conduction model has not been worked out as yet "sigma bond conjugation" has been proposed for high conductivity in these materials.

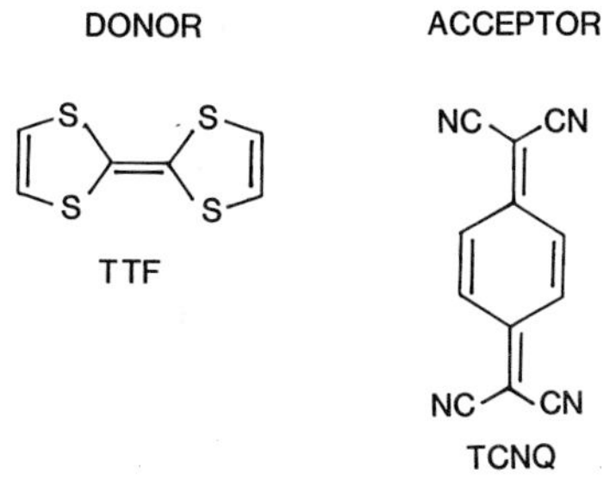

DONOR   ACCEPTOR

TTF   TCNQ

Fig. 5.11. Tetrathiofulvalene (TTF) and tetracyanoquinodimethane (TCNQ).

Charge-transfer complexes were the next class of molecular substances found to possess electrical conductivity. Tetrathiofulvalene (TTF), tetracyanoquinodimethane (TCNQ), seen in Fig. 5.11, and their derivatives are the most extensively studied of the charge-transfer complexes. A segregated stack of TTF and TCNQ molecules with partial charge transfer between them has a conductivity, $\sigma > 10^3$ $(\Omega cm)^{-1}$ at 300 K, which increases on cooling to 60 K. Below 60 K, the conductivity of the TTF-TCNQ decreases to the semiconducting region and undergoes a metal-insulator transition. The first charge-transfer complex found to have electrical conductivity but not to undergo this transition was HMTSF-TCNQ; its conductivity is $\sigma > 10^3$ $(\Omega cm)^{-1}$ down to extremely low temperatures.[402]

The conjugated polymers are the third major class of molecular conductors. The first example to be discovered was the inorganic polymer poly(sulfur nitride), shown in Fig. 5.12. Polycrystalline compactions of poly(sulfur nitride) are known to be highly conducting from the work in 1964 of Chapman et al,[403] who concluded that the material was a semiconductor. Nine years later, work by others showed that single crystals of the material possess metallic conductivity [1730 $(\Omega cm)^{-1}$] along the polymer chain axis.[404]

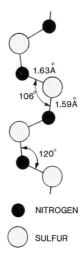

1.63Å

106°

1.59Å

120°

● NITROGEN

○ SULFUR

Fig. 5.12. Poly(sulfur nitride), $(SN)_n$. Source is Ref. 611.

At about this same time, major advances were made with a purely organic polymeric system–polyacetylene. As far back as 1971 Shirakawa and Ikeda reported the generation of free-standing poly-acetylene films for their spectroscopic studies.[405] The interest in poly-acetylene and its derivatives "exploded" in 1977 when Shirakawa et al[406] and Chiang et al[407] transformed a semiconducting polyacetylene film by doping it with chlorine, bromine, iodine, and arsenic pentafluoride to the metallic regime, $\sigma = 56$ $(\Omega cm)^{-1}$ for AsF_5.

Modern research, development, and applications of conducting polymers are characterized by two themes: 1. materials, and 2. models. The first theme involves materials-development activities aimed at combining the desirable properties of polymers (low cost, light weight, moldabililty, and mechanical flexibility, for example) with the acceptable electrical behavior characteristic of semiconductors or metals. The second theme involves construction of microscopic models of charge transport and establishment of the relationships between molecular architecture and the electrical properties of polymers; it is aimed at systematizing the preparation of polymeric materials of specified conductivity and greater crystallinity and orientational order to test them.

The achievement of tailored electrical properties of polymers is pursued in three ways. The first approach consists of modifying the intrinsic bulk properties of polymers by processing, especially by pyrolysis. In this approach, acceptable electrical properties are developed by altering the chemical composition or structure of the initial material. The second approach focuses on altering the properties of polymers at the molecular level by controlled incorporation of molecular dopants that may or may not form charge-transfer complexes with the host polymer. This approach is analogous to that used to control the electrical properties of commerically important crystalline semiconductors such as silicon and GaAs. It is called molecular doping because it consists of diffusing isolated molecular dopants (AsF_5, I_2, or cesium electride, for example) into polymers. The third and most common approach is to attain the desired conductivity by incorporating macroscopic pieces of conducting material (metal flakes, carbon-black particulates, or carbon fibers, for example) into host polymers to form conducting composites. It is the traditional approach in the preparation of conducting polymers and is used today in the fabrication of nearly all commercial products based on conductive polymers.[408] A strategy popular before 1970 was the synthesis of highly conjugated polymers in an attempt to prepare intrinsic semiconductors with small energy gaps.[409,410] Because this strategy usually led to intractable and impure materials, it is not pursued much today. On the other hand, materials-development activities on conduction composites are extensive. For example, moldable polymers loaded with carbon black are used in video disks.[411] Their applications in large-area thick-film electronics are increasing[412] as is their use as antistatic agents.[413] Moreover, composite materials suitable for shielding against electromagnetic interference are being examined intensively.[414-416]

However, the focus of most current research is on the molecular doping of polymers to produce acceptable electrical properties. This technique has been utilized commercially for nearly a decade in photoconductors for electrophotographic copying machines[417-419] and has been applied in iodine-doped polyvinylpyridine electrodes for commercial lithium-iodine pacemaker batteries.[420] It has also been proposed as a suitable vehicle for the fabrication of low-cost photovoltaic cells.[421,422]

Perhaps the most significant aspect of current work on molecularly doped polymers is the construction and critical evaluation of microscopic models of the conduction prosesses, for the models reveal that semiconducting polymers are not polymeric semiconductors in the same sense as are well-known inorganic network semiconductors like silicon.[423-425] Thus, the physical concepts that underlie materials design criteria remain in a state of rapid development.

5.6   BASIC CONSIDERATIONS

5.6.1   Specific Electrical Conductivity

The specific electrical conductivity of a solid, σ $(\Omega\text{cm})^{-1}$, is defined as the current i (in amperes), flowing through 1-cm cube of the material under unit electrical potential:

$$V = Ri, \text{ where } R = L/\sigma A \qquad\qquad 5.66$$

where the sample length is L (cm), its area is A (cm^2), and the potential is V (V).

For simplicity, specific conductivity may be treated as a scalar, thereby presuming that the induced current flows parallel to the imposed field. The specific conductivity σ is related to two basic parameters, the charge carrier density n (cm^{-3}) and the charge carrier mobility μ (cm^2/Vs), and in this case σ may be expressed as:

$$\sigma = \sum_i q_i n_i \mu_i, \qquad\qquad 5.67$$

where q_i is the charge on the ith species. With polymeric materials, each parameter n_i or μ_i may be ambience-sensitive, potential-sensitive, and influenced by the precise conditions of fabrication.

"Ambience-sensitive" means that, in addition to being temperature-sensitive, both number and mobility may be sensitive to the precise experimental conditions, that is, to lattice spacing, sample preparation, and ambient atmosphere (such as moisture or the electron-accepting and -donating properties of the surrounding gas). The mobility μ is a vector and is therefore direction-sensitive. The number of charge carriers is a pure number,

$$n_i = n_i(V,T,B), \mu_i = \mu_i(V,T,B,z), \qquad\qquad 5.68$$

where B indicates ambience and z indicates direction. The relationship however, is defined only for good, single-crystal samples. The influence of crystalline-amorphous phase boundaries, and interfaces in general, may lead to large deviations from ideal behavior.

Thus, all phenomena that affect parameters such as lattice spacing, adsorption equilibrium, potential distribution, dipole orientation, and molecular species can affect electrical conductivity. Typically, first- and second-order phase transitions, chemical degradation, dipole alignment and molecular motion, charge-carrier trapping and detrapping, impurities, and electrodes have been shown to affect electrical measurements in polymers.

5.6.2   Experimental Conductivity

Phenomenologically, a value for conductivity is obtained by measuring the current flowing through a piece of material and using the sample dimensions to calculate σ from

$$\sigma = \frac{i\,L}{V\,A} \qquad\qquad 5.69$$

where L (cm) is the sample length, A (cm^2) is its area (cross section), and V is the potential across the material. Hence, the dependence of either the number of carriers or the carrier mobility on the potential will be shown by a potential dependence of σ as defined above.

The type of electrical conductivity measurement reported in the literature usually involves a simple measurement of current as a function of time, temperature, ambient atmosphere, and potential. Attempts are then made to relate the conductivity to physical processes thought to be occurring in the polymer. Until recent years, there have been few attempts to study, for example, charge-carrier mobility as an independent variable.

Frequently, electrical conductivity varies exponentially with temperature, is a function of time, and may vary with electrical field:

$$\sigma = \sigma_0 \exp - (E_\sigma/kT) = f(\text{time}) = Ag(E).\qquad\qquad 5.70$$

Changes in E_σ, the "activation energy" of conduction, are often observed near glass-transition temperatures. Since the conductivity is made up of terms relating to both the number and the mobility of the charge carriers, any prediction regarding the conduction process that does not recognize these dependencies is meaningless. As more mobility measurements have been carried out, it has become recognized that the motion of the charge carriers is an activated process. Thus, the simple assumption that polymers can be described in terms similar to those used for crystalline, covalent semiconductors has been seriously questioned.

5.6.3   Polymeric Solid State

The molecular nature of polymeric materials distinguishes them from covalent crystalline semiconductors.[423, 424] In the solid state, organic molecules retain their identity and interact weakly as molecular entities through van der Waals or electrostatic forces. In a linear polymer, for example, the electron-electron interactions within a given macromolecular chain are much stronger than those between chains. Electrons experience a nonperiodic and time-varying potential even within an isolated macromolecule because of the many internal conformations that the macromolecule can assume. In addition, in most polymers, the macromolecules are not packed into perfect single crystals. Thus, the two central structural distinctions between polymers, and familiar covalent crystalline semiconductors are the polymers' molecular character and their lack of periodic long-range order.

The combined influence of molecularity and disorder can lead to profound differences between the fundamental physical phenomena that occur in traditional covalent network semiconductors and those that are characteristic of organic materials. The molecular character of polymers makes electronic motion along the individual macromolecules one-dimensional. Reduced dimensionality implies that, even if polymeric materials were perfectly periodic crystalline solids, their electronic properties could be governed by certain types of collective ground states, called Fermi surface instabilities, which characteristically occur in one- and sometimes two-dimensional systems.[426] This concept is relevant in considering the properties of unsaturated-backbone polymers, for example, polyacetylene, which in pure form would exhibit metallic behavior in the absence of an alternating-bond-length backbone geometry.

However, as a direct consequence of the well-known Peierls instability[427] of one-dimensional coupled electron-phonon systems, the distortion of the backbone lattice which produces the bond alternation also creates a gap exactly at the Fermi surface and thus changes a would-be metal into a semiconductor. The occurrence of disorder in polymers leads to the concept that even the intrinsic electronic states in these materials may be localized.[412, 424, 428] In such a case, intrinsic activated-charge mobilities should be observed, in contrast to the case of traditional energy-band semiconductors for which intrinsic carrier mobilities decrease with increasing temperature as T^{-n}, $n > 0$. In addition, the consequences of disorder are enhanced as the dimensionality of the system is reduced.[429] Therefore, although organic polymers seem to exhibit transport and optical properties analogous to those of crystalline network semiconductors, the interpretation of these properties and the design principles for electronic materials involve different physical phenomena in the two cases.

5.7   CHARGES IN POLYMERS

5.7.1   Relaxation

When a charge is injected into a polymer, it induces changes in the electronic charge density and atomic positions both on the molecular site that it occupies (intramolecular relaxation) and on neighboring molecular sites (intermolecular relaxation). This phenomenon, called relaxation, leads to a lowering of the energy of the composite system (added charge plus polymer) by an amount called the relaxation energy E_r. The relaxation energy is defined for an injected charge, for example, a molecular ion, as the difference between the ground-state energy of the ion and the Hartree-Fock molecular-orbital eigenvalue, which corresponds to the free-ion state. Both intramolecular and intermolecular contributions to the relaxation energy can be large for polymers: $E_r(intra) \cong E_r(inter) \cong 1$–$2$ eV.[424, 430] Therefore, molecular anions or cations in polymers are about 2–4 eV more stable than would be predicted on the basis of the corresponding molecular orbitals.

The intermolecular contributions depend on the local atomic structure near the injected charge. For example, a surface charge exhibits only about 60% of the bulk relaxation energy because of the absence of polarizable neighboring species outside the condensed phase.[431] More generally, local variations in the composition and structure of polymers cause spatial fluctuations in the site energies of charges in these materials. For intrinsic-charge states, the magnitude of these fluctuations may be inferred by analyzing the width of either valence-electron photoemission lines[424, 430] or contact charge-exchange spectra.[428] Such fluctuations are important because they create localized molecular-ion states in polymers.[423, 431] In particular, intrinsic localized molecular-ion states may be involved in the contact charge-exhange behavior of pendant-group polymers,[432] and extrinsic localized molecular-ion states dominate the transport properties of molecularly doped polymers.[433]

The average values of intermolecular contributions to the relaxation energy depend on the dielectric response of the medium. If the medium is characterized by a dielectric function, the intermolecular relaxation energies can be defined in terms of the normal modes of the medium's dielectric response to external electromagnetic fields. This procedure has been applied in detail for poly(2-vinylpyridine),[430] in which there are three types of dielectric normal modes called longitudinal polymerization fluctuations. They are $\omega_t \sim 10^{-3}$ s^{-1}, the torsional or backbone modes; $\omega_{IR} \sim 10^{13}$ s^{-1}, the infrared modes; and $\omega_v \sim 10^{15}$ s^{-1}, the valence-electron modes. The interaction of each of these polarization-fluctuation normal modes with an injected charge and the interaction of this charge with the intramolecular normal modes of the molecule on which it resides contribute to the relaxation energy. All of these diverse types of modes must be included in microscopic models of the electronic properties of polymers, because each type exerts a distinct and characteristic influence on each of the three experimentally accessible measures of electronic motion in the material, that is, on photoemission, ultraviolet absorption, and electron transfer.

5.7.2   Localization

The local or extended nature of charges in polymers is determined by competition between electron-phonon coupling leading, via Peierls mechanism, to change localization and/or fluctuations in the local site energies, which also tend to localize the charges, and the hopping integrals for intersite charge transfer, which tend to delocalize the charges. The fluctuation-induced localization concept can be defined more precisely by considering the motion of an injected charge along a polymer chain; the chain's site energy is ε_n for the site labeled n, and its hopping integral to neighboring sites is V_n. If the chain were perfectly periodic, then all the ε_n and V_n would be equal: $\varepsilon_n = \varepsilon$, $V_n = V$ for all n. In this case, the energies E(k) and eigenfunctions $\psi_k(x)$ of the injected charge are given by

$$E(k) = \varepsilon + 2 V \cos (ka), \qquad\qquad 5.71$$

$$\psi_k(x) = \exp (ikx)u_k(x), \text{ and} \qquad\qquad 5.72$$

$$k = \pi s/Na. \qquad\qquad 5.73$$

Here, a designates the spacing between the N periodic sites along the chain, s is an integer, and $u_k(x)$ is a periodic function of x with period a. Equations (5.71)–(5.73) define the traditional Bloch states $\psi_k(x)$, which are characteristic of a one-dimensional periodic polymer chain. These states are delocalized or extended; that is, the injected charge has a finite probability $|\psi(na)|^2 \sim N^{-1}$ of being on any of the sites along the chain. In band models of transport in polymers, these extended states are occupied by the mobile carriers, which exhibit a finite mobility μ and lead to a finite conductivity σ.[4,410,428] The number of these states per unit energy, which is called the one-electron density of states p, is indicated schematically in Fig. 5.13a.

The disorder along the macromolecular chains in real polymers renders this periodic chain model unrealistic. In particular, both the site energies ε_n and the hopping integrals V_n form distributions whose qualitative features can be inferred from spectral and transport measurements on specific materials. Although the detailed analysis is complicated, the qualitative features can be indicated in terms of a mean site energy ε; a root mean square (rms) deviation from the mean,

$$\Delta = \sqrt{[(\varepsilon_n - \varepsilon)^2]AV;} \qquad\qquad 5.74$$

and a mean hopping integral V. Variations in the site energies from the mean, which are described by Δ, are called diagonal disorder, whereas analogous variations of the hopping integrals are called off-diagonal disorder. Similarly, variations caused by local time-independent fluctuations in composition or structure are said to arise from static disorder, whereas variations generated by thermal vibrations or longitudinal polarization fluctuations are said to arise from dynamic disorder. All sources of disorder must be considered in order to determine the localized or extended character of the electronic states associated with charges in polymers, and these sources are described by choosing suitable distributions of ε_n and V_n.

In the nearest-neighbor hopping model, charges are localized-for example, they form molecular cations or anions within the solid-if $\Delta > czV$. Here, z is the coordination number of the presumably identical molecular sites, and c is a dimensionless number of the order of unity, which depends on both the connectivity (dimensionality) of the molecular system and the extent of off-diagonal disorder.[424,429,430] The quantity zV is the one-electron bandwidth W. Typically, $c \equiv 2.5$ for isotropic three-dimensional systems, 1.5 for two-dimensional systems, and zero for one-dimensional systems. Different classes of polymers exhibit systematically distinct ranges of Δ and V. In typical pendant-group and molecularly doped polymers, $0.1 \text{ eV} \leq \Delta \leq 1 \text{ eV}$, and $V \leq 0.1 \text{ eV}$ for motion along the polymeric backbone of pendant-group polymers, and $V \ll 0.1$ eV for hopping between different macromolecular chains. Therefore, Δ czV is clearly satisfied for these materials, and charges form intrinsic pendant-group polymers or extrinsic molecularly doped polymers with local molecular-ion states. In polymers with larger hopping integrals within the individual macromolecular chains (polyacetylene, polyethylene, and polyphenylene, for example) Δ is less than V for motion along the chain. Even if interchain hopping were neglected, injected charges still would be localized in these materials because c = 0 for one-dimensional systems. However, if strong interchain hopping occurs, the polymer can become two- or three-dimensional, depending on the packing of the macromolecular chains. Such chain interactions are thought to occur in polymers that exhibit metallic conductivity. Poly(sulfur nitride) $(SN)_n$ and heavily doped polyacetylene are examples.[434, 435] These materials constitute important intermediate cases in which the electronic states available for charges are neither completely extended ($\Delta = 0$) nor completely localized (the Fermi glass model). The nature of these states is indicated in Fig. 5.13b. States near the edges of the bands that would exist if $\Delta = 0$ are localized, whereas those near the center of these bands remain extended. The energy that separates these two states is the mobility edge E_c. Figure 5.13 indicates how the localized states penetrate into the band and into the forbidden gap with increasing static diagonal disorder Δ until all the states have been localized and the gap has completely disappeared when $\Delta \gg cW$. This disordered semiconductor model[436] is somewhat of a simplification of electron behavior in nonperiodic solids, but it permits a systematic interpretation of experiments on molecularly doped conducting polymers.

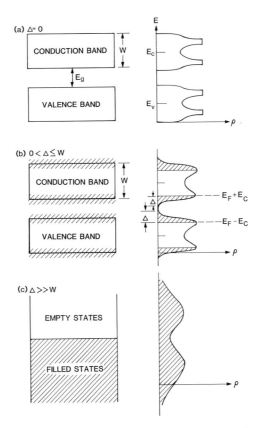

Fig. 5.13. Schematic indication of the consequences of static diagonal disorder [when $\Delta \neq 0$, in Eq. (5.74)] on the localization of one-electron states in a nominally three-dimensional undoped polymeric solid. The symbol ϱ designates the one-electron density of states. (a) $\Delta = 0$ describes the traditional energy-band model. (b) $\Delta < W$, where W is the one-electron bandwidth, describes the localization of electronic states at the edges of the band but not the center. E_c is the mobility edge and E_f is bulk electrochemical potential. States close to the band centers are extended, whereas those further removed are localized. The shaded areas indicate localized states. (c) $\Delta \gg W$ describes the situation in which all electronic states are localized and the concept of energy bands has lost its meaning (the Fermi glass model). For the quasi-one-dimensional polymers the band structure peaks at the band gap. Source is Ref. 436.

5.7.3 Insulator-Metal Transitions

The molecular doping approach to conducting polymers involves inserting molecular dopants into nominally semiconducting or insulating materials to form charge-transfer complexes with the macromolecular chains. Common dopants are p-tetracyanoquinodimethane (TCNQ), AsF_5, and I_2. All of these compounds are acceptors; that is, each extracts electrons from the host polymer to form a molecular anion, such as $TCNQ^-$ or I_3^-. The central issues in describing electrical transport in the doped polymers are the nature, density, and mobility of the charges produced by the charge-transfer process. It must be determined whether the mobile carriers are the excess electrons on the molecular anions, positive holes induced by the charge transfer on the otherwise undistorted macromolecular chains, or some type of structural defect associated with deformations of the polymer macromolecules induced by the charge-transfer process.

As the concentration c of dopant increases, the wave functions of these carriers overlap and broaden into impurity bands. At low dopant concentrations, the states in these bands are completely localized, as indicated in Fig. 5.13c. As long as the bulk electrochemical potential E_F lies within the localized-state region of the impurity band, the material remains a semiconductor with vanishing conductivity at zero temperature. If the coulumb interactions between electrons are neglected, the impurity band is precisely half full for a single dopant species. As the concentration of dopant continues to increase, so does the average interimpurity hopping integral V. Consequently, since Δ is roughly constant, there exists a concentration c_0 above which $\Delta > czV$ is no longer satisfied, and the electronic states at the center of the impurity band, where E_F lies, become extended as indicated in Fig. 5.13b. At this concentration, the conductivity becomes metallic and is nonzero at zero temperature. Hence, the semiconductor experiences an insulator-metal transition as a function of increasing dopant concentration. Two additional phenomena complicate this simple model. First, the interactions between two electrons on the same dopant site cannot be neglected. If two electrons occupy the same dopant site, the second has an energy $E_i + U$, where E_i is the energy of the first electron. At low concentrations, or $c \ll c_0$, charge neutrality requires the $E_F = E_i + U/2$. Therefore, two impurity bands form with increasing c; one is completely full, that is, centered at E_i, and one is completely empty, that is, centered at $E_i + U$. Hence, as c increases, both bands broaden and their centers merge until, at $c \gg c_0$, they become a single band when $U(c) \ll V(c)$. If this refinement is included in the model, the insulator-metal transition occurs when E_F is equal to the mobility edge E_c of the upper band.[437] The second phenomenon is compensation; that is, the occurrence of charge transfer when more than one type of dopant is introduced. Introduction of a second dopant varies the value of E_F within the first dopant's impurity bands.

The disordered semiconductor model suggests two possible mobile charge carriers: the excess charges on the dopants, such as the electrons on $TCNQ^-$, and those on the polymer macromolecules, which at low temperatures and dopant concentrations are localized by the electrostatic potentials of the charged dopants. Which of these charges actually becomes mobile depends on both the relative energies of the impurity-band states emanating from the charged dopants and the intrinsic carrier states emanating from the polar macromolecules. The one detailed calculation reported, for polyacetylene doped with AsF_5^-, AsF_6^-, SbF_6^-, and PF_6^- suggests that the observation of an insulator metal transition in this system depends on the occurrence of mobile carriers on the dopant molecules.[438] However, molecularly doped conducting polymer systems have not yet been subjected to the degree of scrutiny required to identify the nature of the mobile carriers unambiguously. The disordered semiconductor model's main contributions to understanding transport in molecularly doped polymers are three predictions: (1) Disorder should produce localized intrinsic charge carriers, that is, activated mobilities and conductivities, in undoped polymers. (2) Only localized intrinsic and extrinsic carriers should exist at low doping levels. (3) Insulator-metal transitions are expected at doping levels sufficiently high that the chemical potential E_F can access delocalized states associated with the electron motion characteristic of the impurity doped polymer macromolecules.

The consequences of the quasi-one-dimensional character of the polymer molecules also must be considered. This topological feature of polymers can affect the nature of insulator-metal transitions in them because it renders the macromolecules particularly deformable upon charge transfer. In a variety of wide band-gap semiconductors, such as alkali halides, charges injected from dopants, contacts, or vacancies often induce local deformations of the host material.[439-441] This is expected to be the case in certain charged macromolecules. In particular, injected charges create (because of electron-phonon coupling) local bond-length distortions, which generate intrinsic localized states in the semiconductor band gap of the uncharged material.[442-444] These states correspond to the familiar polarons and color centers in conventional semiconductors and insulators.[440,441] In quasi-one-dimensional systems such as macromolecules, they assume a particular form that can be readily understood from the nature of these entities' ground states.

5.7.4 Fermi Surface Instabilities

In certain circumstances, macromolecules exhibit collective ground states induced by the interaction of their valence electrons with each other or with the molecular motions of the macromolecular chains (i.e. phonons). These collective ground states may be either super-conducting or semiconducting.[445] Superconducting behavior has been observed only in poly-(sulfur nitride),[444] whereas many unsaturated backbone materials, for example, polyacety-lene and the polydiacetylenes, are thought to exhibit collective semiconducting ground states.

Polyacetylene illustrates the nature of the semiconducting, collective ground states. Figure 5.14a depicts an infinite, planar $(CH=CH)_n$ macromolecule. Each carbon atom has associated with it three bonding (σ) electrons and one π-electron in a p_z orbital, which is oriented normal to the plane of the macromolecule. The σ-electrons fill three bonding bands with energies well below the electrochemical potential E_F. If all the bond lengths were equal and electron-electron interactions were neglected, polyacetylene would be metallic in character because the π-electrons would fill their energy band only halfway. Hence, E_F would lie in the center of this band, as indicated in Fig. 5.14b. Two phenomena can alter this metallic behavior. Electron-electron interactions can lead to electronic charge densities with lower symmetry than the $(CH=CH)_n$ macromolecular chain, or the chain can distort and lower its symmetry. The latter seems to occur primarily in polyacetylene (in other systems it is the electron-phonon interaction), leading to the energy bands indicated in Fig. 5.14c.[446] The $(CH=CH)_n$ macromolecule has experienced a metal-insulator transition from a metallic to a collective semiconducting ground state characterized by a regular pattern of alternating bond lengths and an electron charge density that is periodic with the period $a_s + a_d$ rather than with the equal-bond-length period $a_s = a_d = a$.

This tendency towards self-induced metal-insulator transitions is a general feature of one-dimensional systems[425] and is characteristic of the behavior of $(CH=CH)_n$ upon molecular doping. The generality of the phenomenon is the result of the instability of one-dimensional metals with regard to symmetry-reducing distortions, which render them semi-conductors. In the Hartree-Fock approximation, a one-dimensional metal is never stable. Rather, ground states with reduced-symmetry charge densities (charge-density waves), spin densities (spin-density waves), or bond orders (bond-order-alternation waves) always exhibit decreased energies and frequently compete with each other in a one dimensional system.[426,447] These reduced-symmetry collective ground states are called Fermi surface instabilities. If the model is extended to encompass electron-phonon (intermolecular)

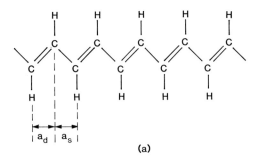

(a)

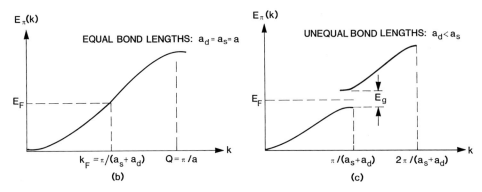

(b)   (c)

Fig. 5.14. Schematic indication of the structure of (a) transpolyacetylene and the energy momentum relations characteristic of the π-electrons normal to a planar periodic $(CH=CH)_n$ macromolecule for (b) equal bond lengths and (c) alternating double and single bonds. The symbols a_s and a_d designate the projections along the axis of the molecule of the single- and double-bond lengths, respectively. E_g denotes the magnitude of the electronic energy gap caused by alternating the single- and double-bond lengths. Source is Ref. 446.

interactions as well as electron-electron interactions, two new classes of reduced symmetry collective ground states must be considered: superconducting and Peierls semiconducting states. A Peierls transition is a metal-insulator transition in which the reduced symmetry of the electronic charge density (the charge-density wave) is accompanied by a corresponding symmetry-reducing distortion of the atomic geometry.[426] Thus, the bond alternation in $(CH=CH)_n$ is merely a special case (dimerization) of a Peierls transition, and the bond-distorted $(CH=CH)_n$ semiconductor is an example of a Peierls semiconductor.

The period of an electronic-charge-density wave (CDW) or a spin-density wave (SDW) depends explicitly on the amount of charge. For a given CDW, the valence-electron charge density as a function of position x is given by

$$\varrho_{CDW}(x) = \varrho_0 + \varrho_1 \cos (qx + \Phi) \qquad\qquad 5.75$$

The period q of the charge-density wave is related to the number n of electrons per unit length on the macromolecular chain by $q = \pi n$. The phase Φ is arbitrary. Moreover, the magnitude of semiconducting-energy gap depends on n approximately as

$$E_g = c_1 n^2 \exp [-c_2 n] , \qquad\qquad 5.76$$

in which c_1 and c_2 are appropriate constants.[426] Therefore, doping $(CH=CH)_n$ with molecular dopants should not generate mobile carriers on the macromolecular chain, but should alter the period of the electronic CDW and the magnitude of the one-electron energy gap. Although this behavior does not seem to occur in molecularly doped $(CH=CH)_n$, these considerations illustrate that the mobile carriers induced in a Peierls or CDW semiconductor by charge-transfer complex formation can be drastically different from those predicted by the semiconductor model, because the charge transfer distorts the charge-density waves on the polymer macromolecules and, hence, can alter the macromolecular geometry by means of electron-phonon interactions.

Such behavior is observed in several crystalline organic semiconductors.[448] However, dopants in $(CH=CH)_n$ seem to induce localized charged defects that, at low temperatures and doping concentrations, are bound to the charged dopant species that produced them.

5.8   CHARGE TRANSPORT IN DOPED CONJUGATED POLYMERS

5.8.1   Introduction

The past few years have witnessed an enormous growth of interest in nonlinear excitations corresponding to intrinsic defects in quasi-one-dimensional condensed-matter systems.[449-451] One of the most celebrated examples is the linear conjugated polymer trans-polyacetylene, $(CH=CH)_n$. Here, both microscopic coupled electron-phonon[444, 452-460] and phenomenological[461-463] models have shown that the double degeneracy of the ground state allows kinklike solitons to exist. The model of Su, Schrieffer, and Heeger,[444, 451] improving on the earlier work of Pople and Walmsley,[464] used simple Hückel theory and elastic energy arguments.[465] The model seems to fit much of the optical, infrared, and magnetic data.

Apart from the possible implications[449-451] for transport properties, doping mechanisms, and the observed metal-insulator transition in $(CH=CH)_n$, the kink solitons, with their unconventional spin and charge assignments,[444, 452] have stimulated theoretical work on the existence and role of "fractional charge"[466-470] in both solid-state systems and field-theory models.[471-473]

Furthermore, Bishop and Campbell predicted on analytic grounds the existence of polarons in trans $(CH=CH)_n$ and of polarons and bipolarons in cis $(CH=CH)_n$.[474] The work of Brazovskii and Kirova[472] and Su and Schrieffer[475] complemented this prediction.

A new development occurred in 1979 with the discovery that poly(p-phenylene), PPP, could be doped to conductivity levels quite comparable with those obtained in the polyacetylene system.[471] This discovery demonstrated the nonuniqueness of the polyacetylene system and paved the way for the discovery of several new polyaromatic-based conducting polymer systems. These polyaromatics now include poly(p-phenylene sulfide),[472, 473] polypyrrole,[476] polythiophene,[477] polyquinoline,[478, 479] polyquinoxaline and pyrrones.[480, 481] The PPP system was also important theoretically, since the generally similar experimental behavior of PPP and polyacetylene[482] cast doubt on the doping and transport theories that were highly specific to polyacetylene. Thus, many other organic polymer systems show very much the same experimental results as polyacetylene (high conductivity, growing infrared and near-infrared absorption, and anomalous magnetic susceptibility) but are unable to support topological (i.e. kink) solitons because they do not have degenerate ground-state structures, however, polaron-solitons are still possible, as discussed below, and provide a natural framework for the wider class of conjugated conducting polymers.[476]

5.8.2   Defects in Conjugated Polymers

Most of the theoretical work in the conducting polymers area has been concentrated on neutral and charged defects on the polymer chains. This work is not reviewed here; rather, we give a general picture on doping and carrier transport, applicable to all conducting polymers, and compare polyacetylene and poly(p-phenylene) for illustration. This is taken from the work of R. R. Chance et al.[483] in which greater detail may be found.

a) *Polarons, Bipolarons, and Solitons*

The charged defects that could be formed when polyacetylene or PPP is ionized by an electron acceptor are: polarons (radical cations), bipolarons (dications), and charged sol-itons (cations), shown in Fig. 5.15.[483] Most of the work reported in the literature is con-cerned with solitons, both neutral (radical) and charged. This work dates back to Pople and Walmsley, who recognized that a radical on a polyacetylene backbone could migrate isoenergetically along the polyacetylene chain by quantum mechanical bond flipping because the structures on either side of the defect have the same energy.[484] This idea was extended and promoted by Campbell and Bishop in the language of field theory to explain much of the interesting physics of the polyacetylene system.[471, 472] A major new addition was that the radical defects were extended over about 15 C-C bonds. Of special interest was the possibility of charge transport via charged solitons. This idea was appealing because of the experimental observation of spinless transport, that is, the ESR measurement of a spin concentration too low to account for the observed conductivity level.[485] However, the same experimental observation has been made for PPP.[486] PPP cannot support kink solitons since the structures on either side of the charged defect do not have the same energy, as is illustrated in Fig. 5.15 for the cation defect on PPP. The benzoid structure to the left of the defect is significantly lower in energy than the quinoid structure to the right. Thus, the kink soliton energy explanation of doping and transport is unappealing because it lacks generality to the numerous conducting polymer systems other than polyacetylene.

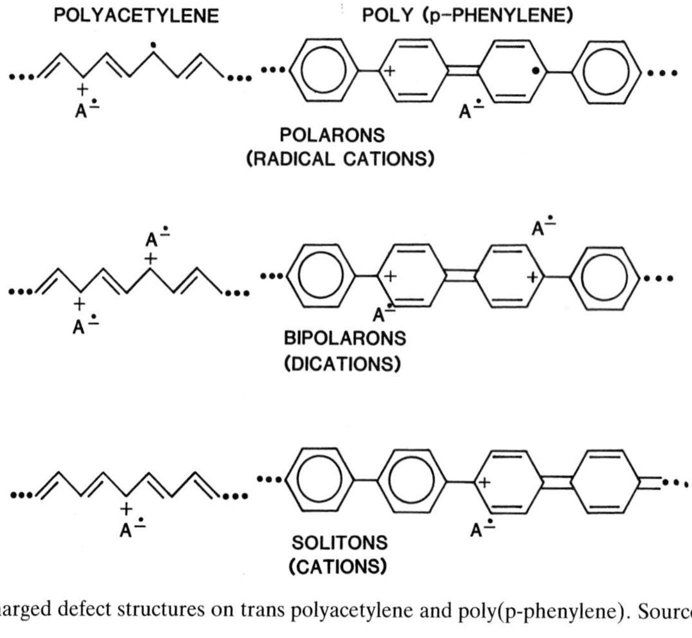

Fig. 5.15. Charged defect structures on trans polyacetylene and poly(p-phenylene). Source is Ref. 483.

What defect structures are expected on removal of one electron from a conjugated polymer, such as PPP or polyacetylene? The work of Bishop and Campbell had shown that the one-electron ionization of trans $(CH=CH)_n$ would produce a polaron and that any kind of "confinement" force-either the lack of degeneracy as in cis $(CH=CH)_n$ or some interchain effects-would mean that the two-electron ionization would produce a bipolaron.[474] Thus, the ionization event in PPP should produce a polaron with a structure like that shown in Fig. 5.15. In fact, this has been shown to be true for polyacetylene, in which the defect pair is strongly bound in forming a polaron.[487,488] Calculations using the Hückel theory and a construction very similar to that used by Su et al.[444,452] predict that ionization of either polyacetylene or PPP yields a polaron. Also, in both polyacetylene and PPP two polarons will interact to produce a bipolaron (Fig. 5.15), but with an activation barrier dependent on defect concentration.[487,488] Once polarons have interacted to form bipolarons in polyacetylene, the charged defects can move essentially independently as charged solitons. However, the dopant counter ions would tend to pin the charged defects near the ionization site. In PPP, the bipolaron would remain as a well-defined entity since the two charged defects are bound because of the nondegenerate ground state.

b) Spinless Transport

How can one get spinless transport in these systems? In the PPP case the only likely possibility is the bipolaron species depicted in Fig. 5.15. Spinless transport in polyacetylene has been attributed to charged solitons,[444,452] but this assignment has immediate limitations when interchain transport is considered. Disorder in the polyacetylene system certainly requires that interchain transport be facile for efficient carrier migration. Consider an infinite polyacetylene chain containing one charged soliton with a neighboring, defect-free chain, as depicted in Fig. 5.16. This soliton cannot jump to the next chain because the reorganization of bond lengths that would follow such a jump requires an infinitely large activation barrier. The soliton mechanism is also unattractive for finite chains because the soliton cannot jump isoenergetically in that case. Kivelson's model for interchain transport gets around these problems by requiring a neutral soliton on the next chain.[489] This model is applicable only at very low doping levels, since any neutral solitons present in polyacetylene (trapped between cross links) would be immediately ionized on further doping. Thus, Kivelson's model has limited applicability and cannot address the problem of spinless transport observed at doping levels as high as 2%.[485] In any case, Kivelson's theory ignores the fact that a neutral and a charged soliton form a bound state, a polaron, with a binding energy of about 0.3 eV.[487,488]

These problems are eliminated by a model having two solitons (a bipolaron) on an infinite chain. The soliton pair can jump to the next chain isoenergetically and with a reasonable activation barrier. The jump probability $P(x)$ for two solitons separated by x carbon atoms will contain the elements

$$P(x) = F(x) \, Q_1(x) \, Q_2(x) \,, \qquad 5.77$$

where $F(x)$ is the Franck-Condon factor (the square of the vibrational overlap for the jump); $Q_1(x)$ is the probability of finding a second charged soliton at a site $\times$ carbon atoms from the first charged soliton on a single chain; and $Q_2(x)$ is the probability of finding a suitable (unoccupied) site on the next chain to receive the x-length bipolaron. $F(x)$ should decrease rapidly as $\times$ increases. $Q_1(x)$ should peak at roughly $1/C$, where C is the concentration of solitons, because of coulombic repulsion between solitons of like charge. $Q_2(x)$ is derivable from $Q_1(x)$ and leads to saturation of the spinless (bipolaron) contribution to the conductivity at high C. This contribution σ_{++} can be computed by integrating Eq. (5.77) over x and multiplying the result by C:

$$\sigma_{++} = C \int P(x) \, dx \,. \qquad 5.78$$

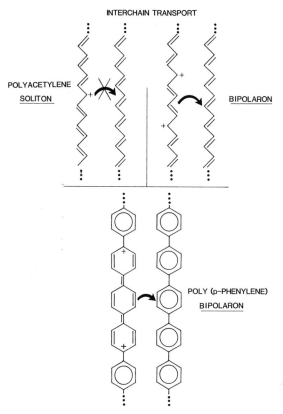

Fig. 5.16. Schematic illustration of interchain transport in polyacetylene and poly(p-phenylene). Source is Ref. 483.

c) *Computer Simulations*

Chance et al. have modeled this process and computed conductivity-versus-C curves that are very similar to those obtained experimentally, as seen in Fig. 5.17.[483] At low C, few soliton pairs will have sufficiently small $\times$ for transport to take place because of the F(x) term; that is, F(x) at the peak in the $Q_1(x)$ distribution will be small. As C increases, σ will increase superlinearly since the peak in $Q_1(x)$ will shift to lower $\times$ values where F(x) is larger. At still larger C values, σ will level off and eventually will decrease because the value of the $Q_2(x)$ term will be small: few sites will now be available for accepting the bipolaron. Thus, the net qualitative result from this model is an S-shaped curve for the spinless bipolaron contribution to the conductivity.

For PPP, the situation is quite different. In that case, the two charged defects making up the bipolaron are bound. The calculations indicate that the bipolaron will extend over about five rings in PPP (although any coulombic effects are ignored).[487, 488] Thus, in this treatment the bipolaron is a well-defined entity of limited spatial extent in PPP, so both the F(x) term and the $Q_1(x)$ term become constants. Therefore, the spinless contribution to the conductivity will rise in proportion to C, eventually becoming saturated and decreasing when the Q_2 term becomes small. No experimental data for conductivity versus doping level exist for PPP-the problem being the inhomogeneity of the doping process. There is some experimental indication of the existence of bipolarons in AsF_5-doped PPP.[490]

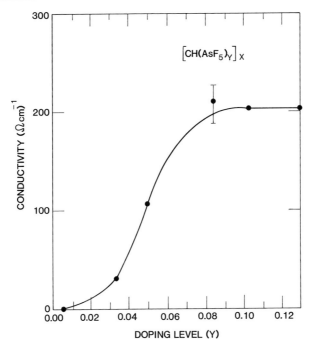

Fig. 5.17. Conductivity versus doping level for AsF$_5$ doping of polyacetylene. Source is: Y. W. Park et al., J. Chem. Phys. *73*, 946 (1980).

d) *Bipolaron Transport*

Bipolaron transport offers a reasonable explanation for spinless transport in polyacetylene and PPP. The model is not specific to polyacetylene in that it does not require a degenerate ground state. The model for charge transport via bipolarons in PPP is applicable to a broad range of conducting polymer systems.

Application of this model assumes that the observation of spinless transport is reliable; the evidence for this is strong but not universally accepted.[485] In particular, Epstein et al. suggest that in the I$_2$ doping of polyacetylene both magnetic and electrical data can be adequately explained by a model based on variable range hopping of electrons not polarons.[491] Their model, which requires a finite density of states at the Fermi level, is based on the theoretical work of Mele and Rice, who argue that a finite density of states will be induced at the Fermi level by disorder.[492] Thus, although the question is not entirely resolved, the experimental evidence still favors spinless transport.

5.8.3 Summary

The following qualitative picture of the doping and transport process applies generally to all conducting polymer systems. First, if the dopant is an acceptor, it ionizes the chain to produce a polaron (radical cation). This polaron is pinned to the ionization site and does not contribute significantly to conductivity. As more dopant is added, the chain is ionized further and a higher concentration of polarons is formed. Also, the polarons can be further ionized to produce a bipolaron (dication), since a polaron is more easily ionized than a polyacetylene chain. As the polaron concentration increases, polarons interact to produce bipolarons, which are uncorrelated charged solitons in polyacetylene and correlated dications in PPP and other cases. The bipolarons transport the charge by moving along the chains and by interchain hopping and are responsible for the observed spinless conductivity. At still higher doping levels, little is left of the original polymer's electronic structure; geometric distortions caused by the charged defects overlap spatially along the polymer chain and eliminate the energy gap between occupied and unoccupied states.[493] At this point, conventional conductivity involving carriers with spin sets in.

5.9 PREPARATION OF CONDUCTING POLYMERS

5.9.1 Introduction

The field of synmetals remains an active area of fundamental research that spans experimental and theoretical solid-state physics and organic and polymer synthetic chemistry. The variety of new conducting polymeric solids continually being discovered is rich. The area of synthesis is extremely fast moving and competitive. Here, we summarize the major types of synthesis techniques used to generate the most studied conducting polymers and list representative examples in each case. We mention only those polymers whose conductivity exceeds 1 $(\Omega cm)^{-1}$ as representing symmetals, although polymers with conductivities less than 1 $(\Omega cm)^{-1}$ are often called "conducting" in the literature.

The major techniques used to synthesize conducting polymers (polymers with conjugated backbones) are of four types:

1. Pyrolysis
2. Ziegler-Natta catalysis
3. Electrochemical synthesis
4. Condensation polymerization.

By far the two most important techniques are (1) addition reactions, like Zielger-Natta catalysis, in which all the atoms present in the monomer are also incorporated into the polymer, and (2) condensation reactions in which a small molecule such as water is eliminated from the monomer in the process of forming the polymeric material. So far, Ziegler-Natta catalysis has received the most attention from experimentalists, but we think condensation polymers will become more important in the future.

5.9.2 Pyrolysis

Polymer pyrolysis is the oldest way to generate conducting organic materials. This approach to the preparation of a conducting polymer consists of eliminating heteroatoms, (halogens, oxygen, and nitrogen, for example) from the polymer by heating it to form an extended aromatic structure eventually approaching that of graphite. Graphite is a prototypical synthetic metal when treated with certain dopants. Pyrolysis probably increases charge-carrier mobilities by producing extended conjugation and increases the number of charge carriers by forming free radicals, which can act as donors to form hole carriers (cations) or as acceptors to form electron carriers (anions). The product of polymer pyrolysis can be powder, film, or fiber, depending on the form and nature of the starting polymer and the pyrolysis conditions.

a) *Polyacrylonitrile*

One extensively studied system is polyacrylonitrile (Fig. 5.18). Pyrolysis occurs in three stages. The first stage, achieved by heating at 200–300°C in the presence of oxygen, results in closure of six-membered rings by formation of conjugated imino functionalities.[494–496] The second stage, achieved by heating above 300°C in an inert atmosphere, results in dehydrogenation of the backbone, which leads to a fully conjugated ladder polymer structure. Extended planar graphite structures probably form above 600°C by loss of NH_3 or HCN.[496–499] Conductivity is controlled by temperature in the third stage. Heating at 400–500°C can produce conductivities of 10^{-12}–10^{-3} $(\Omega cm)^{-1}$. The third stage, carried out in the presence of $AlCl_3$ at 900°C, produces black Orlon, with a conductivity of 20 $(\Omega cm)^{-1}$.[496, 500–502] Pyrolysis conditions can be varied to yield films or fibers. If solutions of polyacrylonitrile are treated with metal salts and then pyrolyzed, the resultant polymer is metal-doped.[500–503] For example, use of silver salts before pyrolysis at about 650°C yields a thermoplastic with a conductivity of 100 $(\Omega cm)^{-1}$.[503]

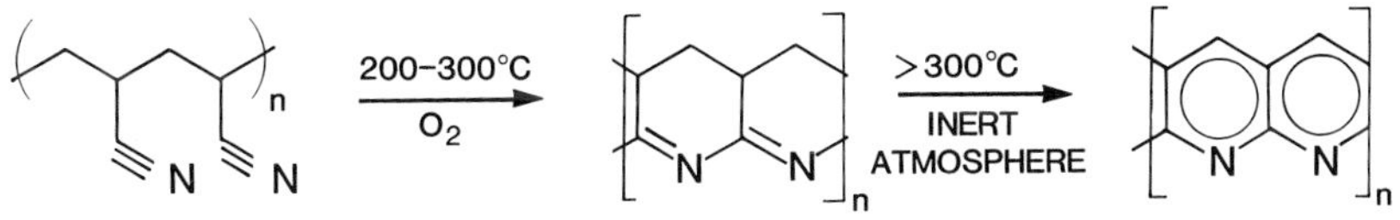

Fig. 5.18. Polyacrylonitrile system.

b) *Kapton*

Kapton, or poly(N,N'-bis(p,p'-oxydiphenylene)pyromellitimide), has also been studied

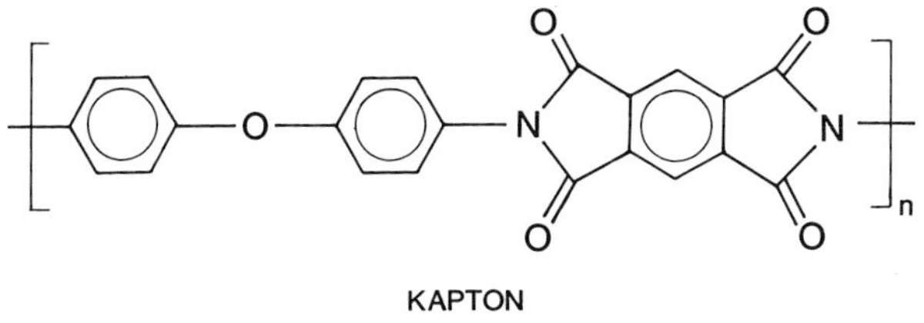

KAPTON

extensively. Vacuum pyrolysis proceeds in three stages.[504, 505] Stage one occurs at about 600°C and results in loss of CO and intramolecular cyclization to small aromatic systems. After the first stage, the conductivity remains in the semiconductor range. The second stage occurs at about 700°C and results in formation of larger aromatic structures exhibiting conductivities of about 10^{-7} $(\Omega cm)^{-1}$ or greater. The third stage occurs at 800°C; at this temperature, more extended, network aromatic graphitic structures of high conductivity [about 20 $(\Omega cm)^{-1}$] form.

The evolution of free-radical sites during pyrolysis is shown by ESR.[504, 506] The line width decreases at higher temperature, indicating increased delocalization.[506] Interaction of the free radicals with acceptors can lead to formation of "holes" (positive ions) by electron loss from the polymer. Donor interaction with the free radicals can convert the free radicals to negative ions.

c) *Other Polymers*

Pyrolysis of other polymers yields materials with conductivities in excess of $1(\Omega cm)^{-1}$. Examples are given in Table 5.4.

Table 5.4 Conductivities of Pyrolyzed Polymers

Polymer	Conductivity, $(\Omega cm)^{-1}$	Ref.
Polyynes	2	507–511
Preoxidized polydivinylbenzene	~100	512
Ion-exchange resins containing		
Ni, Al, Na, Ca or Th	~100	513–516
Polyacrylonitrile + Ag salt	~100	503
Phenanthrene/pyromellitic anhydride		
(PAQR) polymers	~100	503

d) Pyrolysis Stages

Pyrolysis of organic polymers has been sorted into component reactions depending on temperature:[517]

Stage 1 (<350°C):	Loss of volatile adsorbed species.
Stage 2 (350–600°C):	Single C-C bonds, C-Cl, C-I, C-Br, and C-O bonds broken with formation of condensed aromatics and free radicals.
Stage 3 (>600°C):	Loss of H_2 from aliphatic portions, yielding larger condensed aromatic plates with fewer free-radical sites.

This scheme is consistent with x-ray,[518] infrared,[517,519] and ESR[520,521] measurements on a variety of polymeric substrates. Thus, most polymers, when pyrolyzed, give electrically conductive materials; the only variables are the precise temperature, the yields, and the physical form of the product.

5.9.3 Ziegler-Natta Catalysis

From the early 1960s until the late 1970s, little work was reported on conducting polymers. Interest in polyacetylene and polyacetylene derivatives increased immensely in 1977 when Shirakawa et al.[522] and Chiang et al.[407] transformed a semiconducting polyacetylene film to the metallic regime, $\sigma(300\ K) = 560\ (\Omega cm)^{-1}$ for AsF_5. Since that time many catalysts and dopants as well as the polymerization of various acetylene derivatives have been studied.[523] Of the catalysts, the Ziegler-Natta catalyst [Ti(O-n-C_4H_9)$_4$-Al(C_2H_5)$_3$] system in its various modifications is by far the most used even today. It yields free-standing films as well as foams, partially oriented stretched films, composites, and powders depending on the experimental procedure used; all the generated materials, however, have been insoluble and infusible.

a) Shirakawa-Type Ziegler-Natta Catalyst System

Shirakawa's method of making silvery polycrystalline films of $(CH=CH)_n$ using a Ziegler-Natta catalyst is the most widely used and best characterized process.[524,525] Other synthesis methods proposed by Showa Denko K. K., Aldissi, Hocker, Wnek, Meyer, and Toray Industries also use such a catalyst but with variations in the general procedure.

For a typical Shirakawa catalyst system, 15 mmol Ti(OC_4H_9)$_4$ (as bought) are added to 60 ml toluene (distilled and stored under N_2) with hypodermic syringes; 30 ml of this solution is placed in a Schlenk-type flask attached to a vacuum line cooled by a dry-ice/

methanol mixture and evacuated. Once the temperature is constant, $CH \equiv CH$ is added. Formation of $(CH = CH)_n$ film begins immediately and may be interrupted by evacuation of the flask. The catalyst solution under the film is removed by hypodermic syringe, and the film is washed with toluene or hexane until it is colorless. After the film is blown dry by N_2 for a minute at room temperature, it is stored at -30°C in N_2.

The reaction is typically carried out in the temperature range -100°C to 180°C with toluene as the solvent below 80°C and n-hexadecane above 80°C. Diethyl ether, anisole, and hexane have been used as solvents on occasion, but there is no indication of which solvent was used below -70°C.[525] The chain configuration and color depend on the polymerization temperature. At temperatures below -70°C, nearly all the material was reddish cis-$(CH = CH)_n$ (as determined by IR), and at temperatures above 150°C it was nearly all bluish trans-$(CH = CH)_n$. At room temperature, the material was a purplish mixture (Table 5.5).

The choice of catalyst and the concentration are both critical. The effectiveness of various transition metal acetoacetonates (acac) tried with $Al(C_2H_5)_3$ was ranked as $Ti > V > Cr > Fe > Co > Mn$. Furthermore, only the soluble catalyst systems like $Ti(OC_4H_9)_4$-$Al(C_2H_5)_3$, $Ti(acac)_3$-$Al(C_2H_5)_3$, or $Cr(acac)_3$-$Al(C_2H_5)_3$ formed uniform films. The best combination was $Ti(OC_4H_9)_4$-$Al(C_2H_5)_3$, with Al/Ti 3–4 and a minimum concentration of $Ti(OC_4H_9)_4 = 3$ mmol/l. When very low catalyst concentrations were used, a precipitate formed and became a flock or powder.[526] When some of the toluene-precipitate solution was spread on glass and the solvent was evaporated, a golden-tinted shiny film remained; when the toluene was replaced by benzene and the solution was freeze-dried, a fluffy powder resulted. When a higher catalyst concentration was used, a swollen mass or gel filled all the solution. Washing this mass left a black solid. The solid would not reabsorb the solvent to reform the gel, but it could be pressed between mirror polished plates to form a shiny film. Additionally, replacing the toluene by benzene and freeze-drying the solution left a porous gel that could be pressed to form a film. At and above the critical concentration, a film formed on the catalyst solution. The initial film was so dense that $CH \equiv CH$ would not easily diffuse through it; thus, the diffusion process was the rate-determining step. Films produced this way can range in thickness from 10^{-5} to 0.5 cm depending on the $CH \equiv CH$ pressure and the reaction time; they can be free standing or on a substrate.[526] When they are grown on glass, the side next to the glass is shiny and silvery; the other side is grey or black, but it can be polished with a cloth to resemble the glass side. The films may be grown in situ on glass slides, electron micrograph grids, etc., by placing the catalyst solution on the chosen substrate and exposing it to $CH \equiv CH$.[527]

TABLE 5.5 Cis and Trans Contents of Polyacetylenes Prepared at Various Temperatures[a, b]

Polymerization temperature (°C)	Cis content (%)	Trans content (%)
150	0.0	100.0
100	7.5	92.5
50	32.4	67.6
18	59.3	40.7
0	78.6	21.4
−18	95.4	4.6
−78	98.1	1.9

[a] Catalyst: $Ti(OC_4H_9)_4$-$Al(C_2H_5)_3$; Al/Ti 4; 10 mmol/l
[b] Source is Ref. 525

b) *Typical Conductivities of Doped Polyacetylenes*

Doping polyacetylene can increase its conductivity by as much as 12 orders of magnitude and alter its electrical, optical, and magnetic properties. The doping can be either p-type (oxidative), done with bromine, iodine, AsF_5, SbF_6, $HClO_4$, H_2SO_4, $(NO)(PF_6)$, or $Ag(ClO_4)$; or n-type (reductive), done with lithium, sodium, or potassium. Stretch-aligned ($l/l_0 = 3$) trans-polyacetylene doped with AsF_5 may reach room temperature conductivity as high as 3200 $(\Omega cm)^{-1}$. Some typical conductivities of polyacetylenes are listed in Table 5.6.

TABLE 5.6 Dopant Concentration and Conductivity for $(C_2H_2)_n$[523]

Species	Conductivity at 25°C $(\Omega cm)^{-1}$	Ref
cis-$(C_2H_2)_n$	1.7×10^{-9}	a
trans-$(C_2H_2)_n$	4.7×10^{-5}	a
cis-$[CHI_{0.25}]_n$	3.6×10^2	b
cis-$[CHI_{0.30}]_n$	5.5×10^2	a
$[CHI_{0.24}]_n$ prepared with $Ti(CH_2\text{-}C_6H_5)_4$	20	c
trans-$[CHI_{0.22}]_n$	3.1×10^2	b
I_2-doped LDPE/(C_2H_2)(2 wt%)	5	d
cis-$[CH(IBr)_{0.15}]_n$	4×10^2	a
trans-$[CH(IBr)_{0.12}]_n$	1.2×10^2	b
cis-$[CH_{1.01}AsF_5OH)_{0.11}]_n$	7×10^2	a
cis-$[CH(AsF_5)_{0.03}]_n$	1.2×10^2	a
trans-$[CH(AsF_5)_{0.03}]_n$	1.2×10^2	b
trans-$[CH(AsF_5)_{0.06}]_n$	1.7×10^2	e
trans-$[CH(AsF_5)_4]_n$ ($l/l_0 = 3$)	3.2×10^3	f
cis-$[CH_{1.1}(AsF_6)_{0.1}]_n$	7×10^2	a
cis-$[CH(SbF_6)_{0.05}]_n$	4×10^2	a
$[CH(SbF_5)_4]_n$ made with $Ti(CH_2\text{-}C_6H_5)_4$	10	c
cis-$[CH(SbCl_5)_{0.022}]_n$	2	a
cis-$[CH(SO_3F)_4]_n$	7×10^2	a
cis-$[CH_{1.058}(PF_5OH)_{0.011}]_n$	3×10^1	a
cis-$[CH(H_2SO_4)_{0.106}(H_2O)_{0.297}]_n$	1.2×10^3	a
cis-$[CH(HClO_4)_{0.127}(H_2O)_{0.297}]_n$	1.2×10^3	a
$[CH(AgClO_4)_{0.018}]_n$	3	g
cis-$[Li_{0.30}(CH)]_n$	2×10^2	a
cis-$[Na_{0.21}(CH)]_n$	2.5×10^1	a
trans-$[Na_{0.25}(CH)]_n$	8×10^2	b
cis-$[K_{0.16}(CH)]_n$	5×10^1	a

a. A. G. MacDiarmid and A. J. Heeger, Synth. Metals *1*, 101 (1979/1980).

b. J. A. Butcher, Jr., J. Q. Chamber, and R. M. Pagni, J. Am. Chem. Soc. *100*, 1013 (1978).

c. M. Aldissi, C. Linya, J. Sledz, F. Schue, L. Giral, J. M. Fabre, and M. Rolland, Polymer *23*, 243 (1982).

d. M. E. Galvin and G. E. Wnek, Polym. Prepr. *23(1)* 99 (1982).

e. G. E. Wnek, J. Polym. Sci., Polym. Lett. Edn. *17*, 779 (1979).

f. M. A. Druy, C. H. Tansg, N. Brown, A. J. Heeger, and A. G MacDiarmid, J. Polym. Sci., Poly. Phys. Edn. *18*, 429 (1980).

g. T. C. Clarke and G. B. Street, Synth. Metals *1*, 119 (1979/80).

5.9.4 Electrochemical Synthesis

Conducting polymers can also be prepared by electrochemical polymerization accompanied by simultaneous oxidation. The most prominent example of a conducting polymer prepared by this technique is polypyrrole. Films prepared by the stoichiometric electropolymerization of pyrrole itself in the presence of an electrolyte solution of tetraethyl ammonium tetrafluoroborate have conductivities in the range of 40 to 100 $(\Omega cm)^{-1}$.[528, 529] Earlier, black films of an oxypyrrole had been prepared by anodic oxidation of pyrrole on platinum in a dilute sulfuric acid solution.[530] These brittle films were reported to have conductivities of 8 $(\Omega cm)^{-1}$.

A combination of chemical and electrochemical analysis showed the structure of polypyrrole prepared in tetraethyl ammonium tetrafluoroborate electrolyte to be[529]

$$C_{4.00}H_{3.44}N_{0.87}(BF_4)_{0.26-0.30}$$

However, the exact chemical composition depends on the preparation conditions. The evidence that the polymerization occurs at the α-carbons comes primarily from the oxidative degradation studies of chemically prepared polypyrroles or pyrrole blacks, which lead predominantly to pyrrole-2,5-dicarboxylic acid. Also, the fact that α-substituted pyrroles do not undergo this type of polymerization, but β-substituted pyrroles do, suggests that α-substitution blocks the polymerization process.[531]

Film Preparation. A careful study of the various factors in electrochemical preparation has allowed one to optimize growth conditions so that the properties of conductivity, adherence, morphology and feasibility can be varied.

Typical polymerization cell geometry is illustrated in Figure. 5.19.[529] It consists of a single-compartment, two-electrode electrochemical cell with an evaporated platinum electrode and the counter electrode consisting of gold wire tightly wrapped around a glass microscope slide. The plane-parallel cell arrangement was necessary to insure uniform thickness over the film. Typically, the cell may contain 0.1 M Et$_4$NBF$_4$, and 0.006 M pyrrole in 99% aqueous CH$_3$CN. The cell is under galvanostatic control. The cell current is increased linearly with time over a period of 3 min from zero to its final value. The final current density is usually set at 1 mA cm^{-2}, although values ranging from 0.5 to 1.5 mA cm^{-2} may be used. Once the final current density is reached, little further change in the cell potential is noted, indicating that the film being deposited continues to conduct. The platinum electrode gradually darkens as the polypyrrole overlayer thickens. Films up to 50 μm thick are prepared in this manner. These films adhere well to the platinum, but they can be removed intact from the surface of the metal, by careful peeling.

The electrode material, solvent, electrolyte, oxygen content, water content, current density, and current-density history all influenced the properties of the films and could be controlled in the electrochemical environment.[529] Thus, polymerization onto platinum electrodes resulted in smoother, better adhering films than polymerization onto tin oxide electrodes. Intrinsic silicone electrodes yielded very poor, nonuniform films. Films grown from

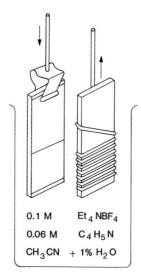

0.1 M   Et$_4$NBF$_4$

0.06 M   C$_4$H$_5$N

CH$_3$CN   + 1% H$_2$O

Fig. 5.19. The single-compartment, two-electrode cell. Source is Ref. 529.

acetonitrile had a higher conductivity than those grown from aqueous solutions. Preparations from solutions of deoxygenated organic solvents yielded films of somewhat higher conductivity, 30 and 100 $(\Omega cm)^{-1}$ and less variability. The water content in aprotic organic solvents proved useful in controlling adhesion. The absence of water produced very poorly adhering, nonuniform films, and increased amounts of water improved adhesion. (Too great adhesion can make removing the film from the electrode difficult.) Excessive current densities yielded films having very rough surfaces. A gradual increase of current from zero to its final value improved the films' adhesion and morphology.

5.9.5 Condensation Polymerization

Condensation polymerization is an extremely varied and extensive field of polymerization techniques and structures. It is as large as the field of organic chemistry. Instead of trying to treat the whole subject even in general terms, we discuss here only the polymerization reactions that have led to the few conducting polymers that have been studied. Although only a few have been studied, we think this area will be the source of many of the future synmetals. We review the synthesis of the following polymers:

a) Poly(p-phenylene)
b) Poly(p-phenylene sulfide)
c) Polyquinolines
d) Polyquinoxalines
e) Pyrrones.

a) *Poly(p-phenylene)*

Polyarylenes in general and poly(p-phenylene) in particular have been prepared by a variety of methods including

1. Oxidative polymerization of aromatic compounds.
2. Coupling of aromatic halogen compounds.
3. Condensation of aromatic nuclei via organometallic reagents.
4. Cycloaliphatic materials as precursors.
5. Decomposition of diazonium salts.

Because polymers of this type display enhanced thermal stability, considerable effort has been expended in optimizing their synthesis. All of the synthesis methods have one major problem: chain-growth terminating side reactions leading to low molecular weight or cross linked materials, or both. We give some details of the two most effective and optimized methods for synthesizing poly(p-phenylene) and only refer to the original reports of the other methods.

Oxidative Polymerization of Benzene. One of the most effective techniques consists of using a benzene-aluminum chloride-cupric chloride system at 35°C:[532, 533]

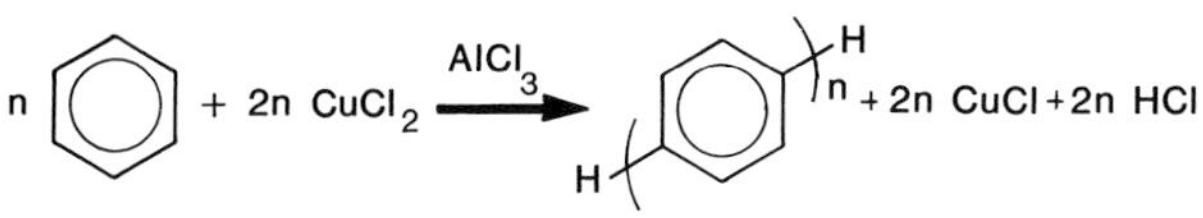

The polymer yield attains an almost quantitative value at an $AlCl_3$-$CuCl_2$ molar ratio of 2:1.[533] The molecular weight is also affected by solvent concentration and temperature.[534] Investigations of the scope of the reaction showed that benzene can also be polymerized with the aid of molybdenum pentachloride,[535] ferric chloride,[536, 537] or molybdenum oxotetrachloride,[538] but the products possess a greater degree of structural irregularity.[535, 536]

The concept of cationic propagation and dehydrogenation has been invoked to explain the polymerization of benzene in the aluminum chloride-cupric chloride system, as shown in Fig. 5.20.[532] Indeed, the concept provides a plausible working hypothesis.

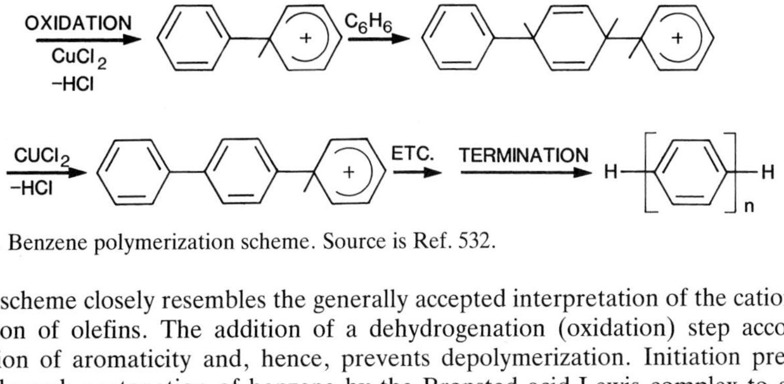

Fig. 5.20. Benzene polymerization scheme. Source is Ref. 532.

This scheme closely resembles the generally accepted interpretation of the cationic polymerization of olefins. The addition of a dehydrogenation (oxidation) step accounts for restoration of aromaticity and, hence, prevents depolymerization. Initiation presumably occurs through protonation of benzene by the Bronsted acid-Lewis complex to give a σ-complex (benzonium ion). The involvement of a Bronsted acid cocatalyst has been established for the ferric chloride-benzene polymerization[539, 540] and for many olefin systems.[541] Coupling of the σ-complex with benzene monomer to give a new substituted benzonium ion is analogous to the propagation in the olefin system. The relatively high temperature of about 30°C required to polymerize benzene, as compared with temperatures as low as -100°C at which olefins polymerize rapidly, could be due to the stability (low reactivity) of the delocalized benzonium ion. Alternatively, the high temperature may be necessary for the oxidation of the cyclohexadiene units that prevents reversibility of the propagation step. The hypothesis that the cyclohexadiene units are converted to aromatic structures during the reaction is supported by the observation that 1,4-cyclohexadiene is readily transformed to benzene by aluminum chloride-cupric chloride-cuprous chloride, aluminum chloride-cuprous chloride,[533] ferric chloride[536], and molybdenum pentachloride.[535] The loss of a proton or a bimolecular reaction involving either hydrogen chloride or traces of complexed water can terminate the reaction.

Coupling of Dihalobenzenes. Two well-known coupling reactions of haloaromatics are noted in the organic chemistry literature from the late 1890s. One is known as the Ullman reaction, in which the catalyst is copper:[542]

$$I-\langle\bigcirc\rangle-I \xrightarrow[200°C]{Cu} X-[\langle\bigcirc\rangle]_n-X$$

X = I or H

The other is the Wurtz-Fittig reaction, in which the catalyst is sodium or potassium:[543]

$$Cl-\langle\bigcirc\rangle-Cl \xrightarrow{Na} Cl-[\langle\bigcirc\rangle]_n-Cl$$

The temperature required for the Ullman synthesis is commonly about 200°C, although, depending on the reactivity of the aryl halide, it may be as low as 100°C or as high as 300°C. Other metals, such as silver, may also be used in place of copper and give equally good results.

Although the Ullman synthesis is used primarily to prepare oligophenylenes, it has been used also to prepare higher polyphenyls. For example, the use of p-dibromobenzene and activated copper powder in benzene at 250°C generated dibromopoly-p-phenylene:[544]

$$Br-\langle\bigcirc\rangle-Br \xrightarrow[C_6H_6/250°C]{Cu°} Br-[\langle\bigcirc\rangle]_n-Br$$

The Wurtz-Fittig reaction has received considerably less attention than the Ullman reaction presumably because of higher amounts of unwanted side reactions. Nevertheless, the Wurtz-Fittig reaction has been applied to polyphenylene synthesis rather extensively. A typical preparation consists of treating p-dichlorobenzene with sodium or sodium potassium alloy to produce poly(p-phenylene), a tan powder, that is soluble only in aromatic solvents and does not melt when heated to 550°C.[443, 545] Molecular weight measurements and chlorine analysis point to an average molecular weight of 2600.

Condensation of Aromatic Nuclei via Organometallic Reagents. Higher poly(p-phenylenes) may be produced when the mono-Grignard derivative of a dihalobenzene is decomposed in the presence of catalytic amounts of a polyvalent metal chloride:[546, 547]

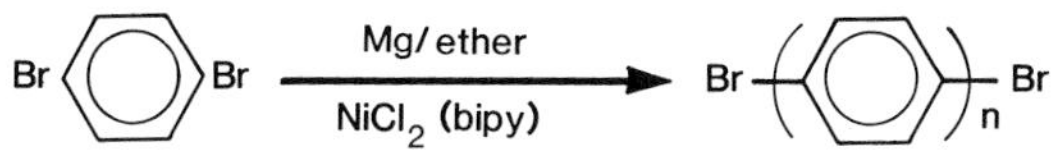

Cycloaliphatic Materials as Precursors. A very early synthesis technique for poly(p-phenylene) initiated by Marvel et al in 1959 involved the dehydrogenation of poly(1,3-cyclohexadiene). The polymerization of 1,3-cyclohexadiene with a Ziegler-Natta catalyst (tri-isobutyl aluminum-titanium tetrachloride) under a variety of conditions provided a polymer having a regular 1,4-structure with a molecular weight of about 10,000. Aromatization of the polymer by either bromination or chlorination, followed by pyrolysis or by treatment with chloranil in boiling xylene for 48 h, provided excellent yields of poly(p-phenylene):[548-551]

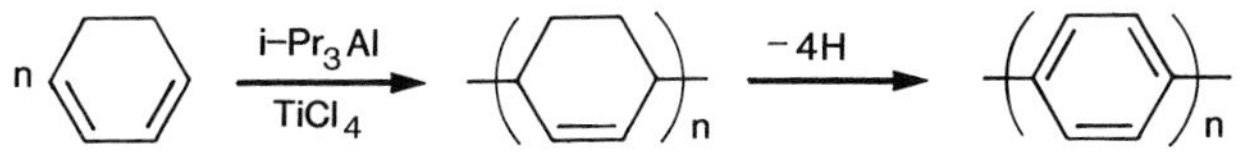

Decomposition of Diazonium Salts. In the Gatterman reaction, diazonium salts decompose in the presence of powdered copper. When this reaction is applied to the deamination of benzidine-3,3'-dicarboxylic acid via its diazonium salt, it generates poly(phenylenes) having carboxylic acid groups attached to the benzene rings. Thermal treatment of these alkali soluble polymers produces poly(p-phenylenes).[552-554]

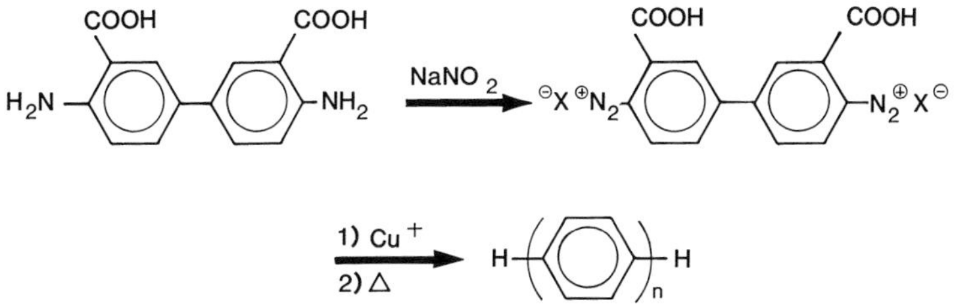

b) *Poly(p-Phenylene Sulfide)*

The methods for preparing poly(p-phenylene sulfide) can be divided into electrophilic and nucleophilic reactions. One of the oldest electrophilic reactions is the Friedel-Crafts reaction of sulfur with benzene:

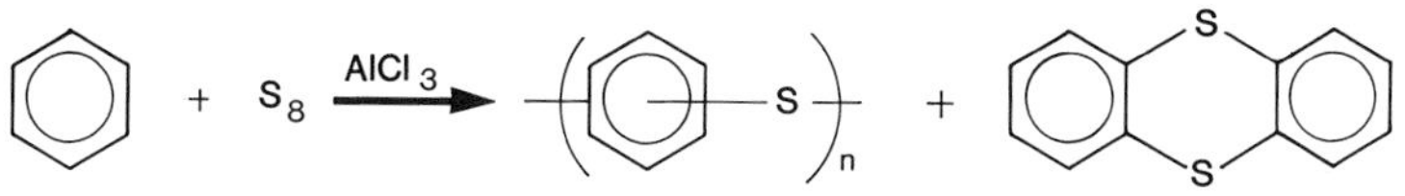

Thianthrene (A) in this reaction is always formed as a by-product and the yields of the polymeric product can be as high as 80%.[555,556] As an alternative procedure, sulfur chlorides can be used instead of sulfur. Although the electrophilic reactions described are simple, it is the nucleophilic substitutions that are used commercially.

Macallum Polymerization. One of the most thoroughly studied and used reactions, Macallum reaction, involves treating halobenzenes with sulfur and sodium carbonate in a sealed container at 275–360°C.[557,558]

The product of this reaction is determined by the aryl/sulfur ratio. Some modifications of this procedure are possible. One of these is to prereact the sulfur and sodium carbonate or to replace the product of the reaction with sodium sulfide to which a small amount of sulfur has been added.[556] Another modification is to replace the halobenzene with an aryl tetrazonium salt using sodium sulfide as the sulfur source.

Self-Condensation of Metal Halothiophenoxides. Another general procedure consists of self-condensation of metal halothiophenoxides

where X = F, Cl, Br, I, or $N_2^+X^-$ and M = Cu, Li, Na, or K. The reactions are conducted at 200–250°C under nitrogen in the solid state, in a slurry, or in pyridene,[559-563] and the yields can be quantitative. The reactivity order of the halogens is I > Br > F ~ Cl and that of the metal cations is Cu^+ ~ Li^+ > Na^+ > K^+. Silver salts have also been used.[564] Although the preferred method is to use metal salts of p-halothiophenoxides, the m-halothiophenoxides[565] and two-component systems such as dithiohydroquinone and dihalobenzene can also be polymerized.[561, 562]

c) Polyquinolines

A particularly exciting development in the field of electrically conducting polymers is the emergence of conducting, soluble, high-temperature polymers as a broad class of materials. We describe here the synthesis of the first three classes of such materials: polyquinolines, polyquinoxalines, and pyrrones.

High-molecular-weight, soluble, poly-2,6-(4-phenyl)quinoline was prepared using an acid-catalyzed Friedlander synthesis:[566]

Structural variants such as poly-2,6-[4-(4'-chlorophenyl)quinoline] and poly-2,6-[4-(4'-methoxyphenyl)quinoline] were synthesized similarly, except that 4-chlorophenylacetonitrile and 4-methoxyphenylacetonitrile were substituted for phenylacetonitrile.

All of the free-standing films were doped by treating them with solutions of sodium or potassium naphthalide or anthracide using either THF or dimethoxyethane as the solvent. The conductivities obtained for the three quinolines were as follows:[567]

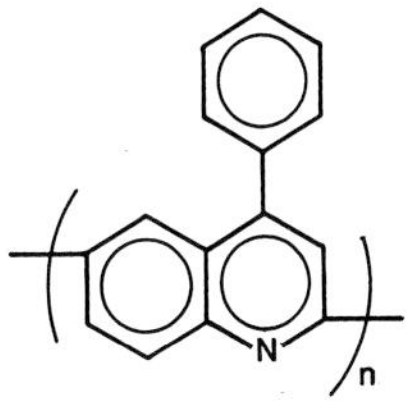

50 $(\Omega \text{cm})^{-1}$

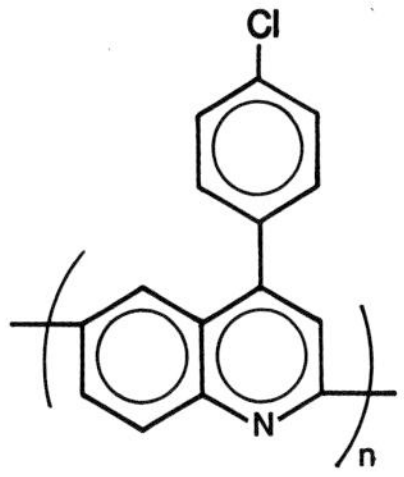

1.3 $(\Omega \text{cm})^{-1}$

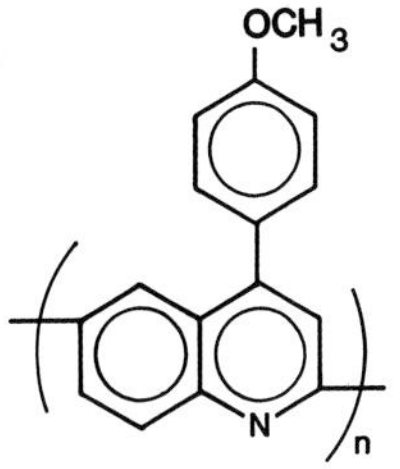

4.5 $(\Omega \text{cm})^{-1}$

Similar work on polyquinolines by another group was reported at about the same time.[568] This group reported the conductivities of three polyquinolines, only two of which had moderate conductivities as fibers: poly-2,6-(4-phenyl)quinoline, σ 11 $(\Omega \text{cm})^{-1}$ and

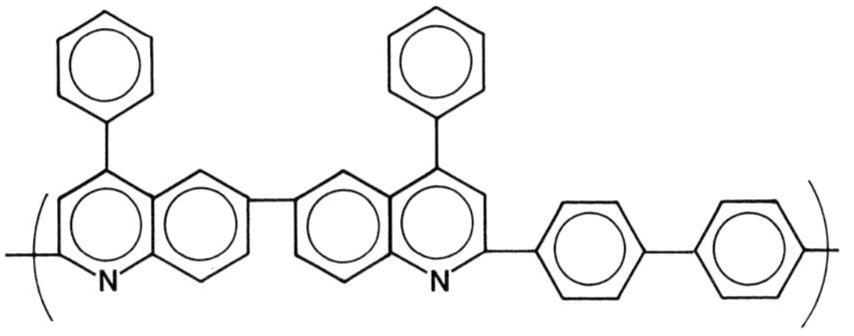

8 $(\Omega \text{cm})^{-1}$

d) Polyquinoxalines

The synthesis of the first reported conducting polyquinoxaline consisted of a condensation reaction between 3,3'-diaminobenzidine and para-bis(phenylglyoxalyl) benzene.[569,570]

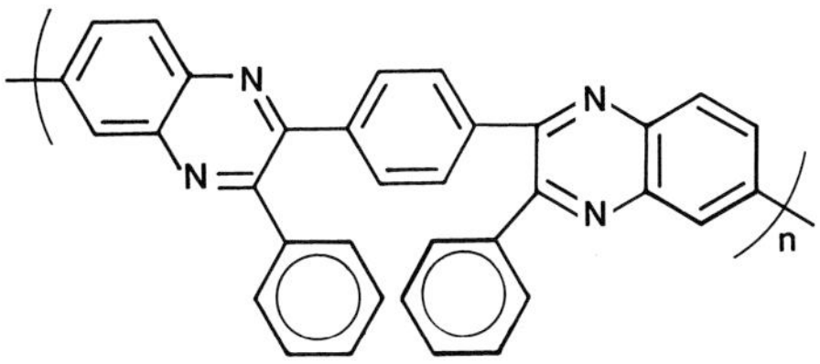

Para-bis(phenylglyoxalyl) benzene was prepared according to the literature procedure.[571,572] The polymer was prepared by adding the para-bis(phenylglyoxalyl) benzene powder (10.27 g, 0.03M) to a stirred (high-speed blender) slurry of 3,3'-diaminobenzidine (5.36 g, 0.025M) in a 1:1 mixture of m-cresol and xylene (40 ml). Additional solvent (13 ml) was used to wash down the residual tetracarbonyl reactant, and the mixture was stirred at room temperature for 16 h. For viscosity determination, a portion of the solution was poured into methanol in a high-speed blender, and the resulting precipitated solid was boiled in methanol and dried at 130°C in a vacuum oven overnight. Typical inherent viscosity in sulfuric acid was 2.0 dl/g. The conductivity obtained using cesium electride or cesium ceside as the dopant at 6 wt% was 20 $(\Omega cm)^{-1}$.[569]

e) *Pyrrones*

At least three pyrrones have been n-doped to conductivities as high as 20 $(\Omega cm)^{-1}$.[481,569] Their structures are:

PYRRONE I

PYRRONE II

PYRRONE III

The synthesis procedures for the three pyrrones are as follows.

Pyrrone 1. Pyromellitic dianhydride (from Princeton Chemical Research) was sublimed through a fiberglass fabric onto a cold finger in a sublimator at 200°/0.05 mm. A colorless sublimate, mp 286–287°C was obtained.

3,3'-Diaminobenzidine (from Burdick and Jackson Laboratories, Inc.) was recrystallized from a 2:1 mixture of water and acetonitrile after treatment with charcoal to yield a light-tan powder, mp 176°C, after vacuum drying for 2 days.

Dimethylacetamide (from E. I. duPont de Nemours and Co., Inc.) was received under N_2 and was distilled from pyromellitic dianhydride before use. The polymer was prepared by adding 95 ml of dimethylacetamide solution of pyromellitic dianhydride (12.9 g in 100 ml, 0.04M) to a stirred, hot (about 60°C) dimethylacetamide solution of 3,3'-diaminobenzidine (8.56 g in 100 ml, 0.04M) in a preheated high-speed blender under N_2. After 30 min of stirring, the remaining 5 ml of the dimethylacetamide solution of pyromellitic dianhydride was added. Stirring and heating were continued for 1 h, and then the polymer dope was separated by centrifuging. The supernatant solution was decanted and stored under N_2 in a refrigerator. The intrinsic viscosity of the polymer dope was 1.0 dl/g in dimethylacetamide.

Pyrrone 2. Tetraaminobenzene tetrahydrochloride (from Burdick and Jackson Laboratories, Inc.) was purified by dissolving it in the minimum amount of water, treating it with charcoal and reprecipitating it with concentrated hydrochloric acid. Since 1,2,4,5-tetraaminobenzene is extremely susceptible to air oxidation, polymers from this tetramine were prepared using the tetrahydrochloride salt. Dimethylformamide was purified by distillation from phosphorus pentoxide.

The polymer was prepared by adding a dimethylformamide solution of pyromellitic dianhydride (4.36 g in 40 ml, 0.04M) dropwise to a stirred slurry of tetraaminobenzene tetrahydrochloride in dimethylformamide and pyridine (5.68 g, 0.02M; 35 ml DMF and 6.5 ml pyridine) in a high-speed blender under N_2. The stirring was then continued for half an hour. The polymer was precipitated with aqueous ethanol and washed with acetone to remove pyridine hydrochloride. It was then redissolved in dimethylformamide or hexamethylphosphoramide for intrinsic viscosity determination and film casting. Typical intrinsic viscosity in dimethylformamide was 0.60 dl/g.

Pyrrone 3. The preparation of the benzimidazobenzophenanthroline-type Pyrrone 3 was described by Arnold and Van Densen in 1969.[573] The starting materials are naphthalene-1,4,5,8-tetracarboxylic acid and 2,3,5,6-tetraaminobenzene. The polymer films are prepared from methanesulfonic acid solutions by filtration, casting, or spraying techniques.

5.10 CONDUCTING POLYMERS WITH SPECIAL PROPERTIES

In this section we summarize the latest and most significant advances in conducting polymeric materials, processes, and properties reported in the literature. The summaries are presented in random order. However, we think that a scientific or technological progress in any one of these areas will have great impact on the field of conducting polymers in general.

5.10.1 The First Soluble Polymers

The first soluble polyacetylene, polybenzene, polynaphthalene, and polyanthracene were generated in AsF_3 solution with AsF_5 as the polymerization initiator.[574] A solubilized form of polyacetylene generated by grafting polyacetylene onto a polyisoprene carrier polymer had been reported in 1983.[575]

5.10.2 Direct Synthesis of Oriented Polyacetylene Films From Acetylene Gas.

Acetylene was polymerized on the faces of biphenyl crystals containing dissolved Ziegler-Natta catalyst to give oriented films of $cis(CH = CH)_n$.[576]

5.10.3 Soluble Conducting Poly(acetylene)/Poly(styrene) and Poly(acetylene)/Poly(isoprene) Block Copolymers.

Soluble, conducting, block copolymers were prepared by first preparing the anionic (n-butyllithium) carrier block, and then reacting it with tetrabutoxytitanium in toluene and using the reaction product to initiate the polymerization of acetylene and, thus, to form a diblock copolymer having conductivities of $1–10(\Omega cm)^{-1}$,[577] when doped with I_2 or AsF_5.

Similar, but nonconducting styrene-acetylene block copolymers were described by G. E. Wnek at the Los Alamos National Laboratory Workshop on Synthetic Metals, Los Alamos, New Mexico, in August 1983.

5.10.4 Water Stable p-Doped Polyacetylene

Polyacetylene can be doped electrochemically with $NaAsF_6$ in 52% aqueous HF to the metallic regime without the inclusion of oxygen.[578] Conductivities achieved were 10–100 $(\Omega cm)^{-1}$.

5.10.5 Conducting Polyaniline

Aniline has been converted to an oxidized, conducting form of polyaniline by using ammonium persulfate in hydrochloric acid.[579] The polymer was doped to conductivity as high as 10 $(\Omega cm)^{-1}$ by adding various acids in water solution. The possible chemical structures are:

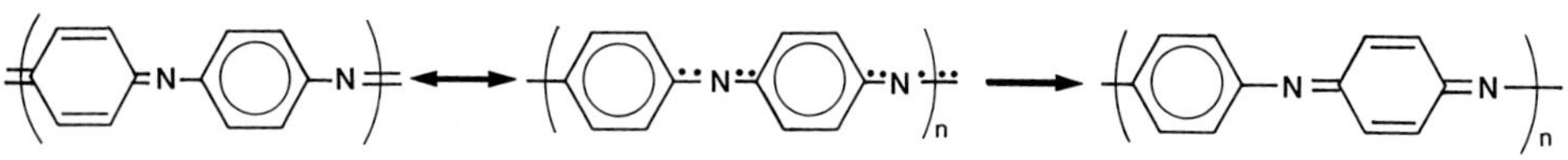

5.10.6 Polyacetylene at High Pressures

The optical response of trans-polyacetylene has been studied at pressures up to 150 kbar.[580] From the absorption edge position versus pressure, three main regions have been identified: (1) a *stability* region, 0–50 kbar, where a reversible red-shift of the absorption edge occurs; (2) a *reactive* region, 50–80 kbar, where irreversible behavior begins; and (3) a *transformation* region, above 80 kbar, where a material transparent to visible light is formed. Raman spectra suggest that the polymer's identity is maintained throughout the investigated pressure range. The drastic change in optical properties is attributed to the generation of cross-links with consequent reduction of the average undisturbed chain length.

5.10.7 Doped Conducting Polymers via Radiation Field

Irradiation of polyacetylene, polythiophene, poly(phenylquinoline) and poly(p-phenylene sulfide) in an SF_6 or BF_3 atmosphere with γ-rays and an electron beam increased conductivity more than 3 orders of magnitude in polythiophene + SF_6, more than 6 orders of magnitude in poly(p-phenylene sulfide) + SF_6, more than 5 orders of magnitude in poly(p-phenylene sulfide) + BF_3, and more than 4 orders of magnitude in poly(phenylquinoline) + SF_6.[581, 582]

5.10.8 Chiral Metals: Synthesis and Properties of a New Class of Conducting Polymers

The synthesis of complexes incorporating either chiral polymer backbones, chiral dopants, or chiral solvating ligands for dopant ions has been reported.[583] The chiral complexes had conductivities as high as 50 $(\Omega cm)^{-1}$; however, the conductivities depended strongly on the structural nature of the complexes. A few chiral ammonium and phosphonium ions prepared from readily available, optically active precursors were electrochemically inserted into polyacetylene films with the following results:

$$-\text{(CH} \rightarrow_X^{\ominus} + R^*N^{\oplus}(CH_3)_3 \longrightarrow -[(CH)_X^{\ominus} R^*N^{\oplus}(CH_3)_3]_n$$

5.10.9 Conductivity Anisotropy in Oriented, High-Molecular Weight Polyphenylene Vinylene

High-molecular-weight films, fibers, and foams of poly(p-phenylene vinylene) have been prepared via poly(p-xylene-α-dimethylsulfonium chloride) by thermal elimination of $(CH_3)_2S$ and HCl:[584]

Doped stretched samples possessed a pronounced anisotropy of conduction proportional to the draw ratio. AsF_5-doped stretched films have shown conductivities as high as $500\ (\Omega cm)^{-1}$.

5.10.10 Polypyrrole n-Alkylsulfates and n-Alkylsulfonates with Layered Structure

Electrochemically prepared polypyrrole films from aqueous solutions of sodium n-alkylsulfates, sodium n-alkylsulfonates, or disodium 1,10-decanedisulfonate possessed conductivities as high as $160\ (\Omega cm)^{-1}$.[585] The films had good mechanical properties and environmental stability.

5.10.11 Amorphous Polyacetylene by Reverse Diels-Alder Reaction Process

In 1980 a novel and elegant synthesis of polyacetylene was described by Edwards and Feast.[586,587] The approach involved synthesis of the monomer 7,8-bis(trifluoromethyl)-tricyclo[4,2,2,0$^{2.5}$]deca-3,7,9-triene (I), which was easily prepared in 80% yield from hexa-fluorobut-2-yne and cyclooctatetraene. A metathesis ring-opening polymerization of I with $WCl_6 \cdot (C_6H_5)_4Sn$ (1:2) and $TiCl_4 \cdot (C_2H_5)_3Al$ as catalysts yielded a soluble polymer (II). This polymer decomposed spontaneously on standing in the dark under an atmosphere of dry N_2, yielding a black material with a metallic luster (III). Analytical infrared and Raman spectroscopic data are in agreement with the known data on trans-polyacetylene. The reaction sequence is outlined below.

The polyacetylene film had a density of 1.05 g/cm^3, a dc conductivity of about 10^{-7} $(\Omega cm)^{-1}$ and, when doped with iodine, a conductivity of about 10 $(\Omega cm)^{-1}$ for a composition of $(CHI_{0.27})_n$.

5.10.12 Polyacetylene-Polypyrrole Composite

Polypyrrole electropolymerized onto polyacetylene gave a composite film with conductivity as high as 40 $(\Omega cm)^{-1}$ and with excellent air and water stability for up to 40 days.[588]

5.10.13 Single-Fiber Poly(acetylene)

Fibers were synthesized by the reverse Diels-Alder process by first growing the fibers from a solution of the prepolymer and then converting them into polyacetylene single fibers of diameters 1–100 μm and more than 1 cm long.[589] These fibers appear to be entirely trans-polyacetylene with a density of 1.06 g/cm^3 and a conductivity in the undoped material of 10^{-7} to 10^{-8} $(\Omega cm)^{-1}$.

5.10.14 Polymerization of Acetylene in Liquid Crystal Solvent

Highly oriented polyacetylene has been synthesized using nematic liquid crystals as the polymerization solvent.[590,591]

5.10.15 Intrinsically Conducting Polymers-Poly(Metal Tetrathiooxalates).

Various transition metal ions have been coordinated with conjugated ligands to synthesize polymers with metal ions within the main chain.[592] Ligands such as tetrathiosquarate, tetrathionaphthalene, and tetrathiafulvalene tetrathiolate have been used. The tetrathiooxalate complexed with nickel ions gave linear poly(nickel tetrathiooxalate) oligomers with conductivities as high as 20 $(\Omega cm)^{-1}$.

5.10.16 Environmentally Stable, Soluble, and Conducting Poly(3,3'-N-Methyl-carbazoyl)

The synthetic procedure consists of first preparing a Grignard reagent, which reacts with a nickel catalyst to form an intermediate diorganonickel complex. The complex is subsequently cross-coupled with the halogenated monomer.[593]

Alternatively, 3,6-dibromo-N-methylcarbazole has been simultaneously polymerized and doped in liquid iodine. The iodine-doped material is indefinitely stable in air at room temperature and has a conductivity of 5 $(\Omega cm)^{-1}$.

5.10.17 Electrically Conductive Phthalocyanine Materials

One approach to enforcing stacking architecture in metallomacrocyclic (i.e. phthalocyanine) conductors is by covalently linking the charge-carrying molecular units in a cofacial orientation.[594] Conductive polymer fibers are also formed by combining phthalocyanine with Kevlar-29 material and doping with, for example, iodine.[595]

5.10.18 Conductive Polysilanes

A wide series of dialkyl and alkyl,aryl substituted polysilanes has been synthesized by a Sandia National Laboratories group.[596] These materials have been found to be extremely good photoconductors and can be p-doped (I_2, AsF_5) to metallic conductivity. This is a novel class of polymeric metallically conducting materials in which there is no conjugated backbone.

5.11 SUPERCONDUCTING POLYMERS

5.11.1 Historical Review

Little in 1964 first suggested the possibility of high-temperature superconductivity in a long, quasi-one-dimensional macromolecule having certain specific side chains-cyanine dyes.[597] Figure 5.21 shows the macromolecule's proposed structure.

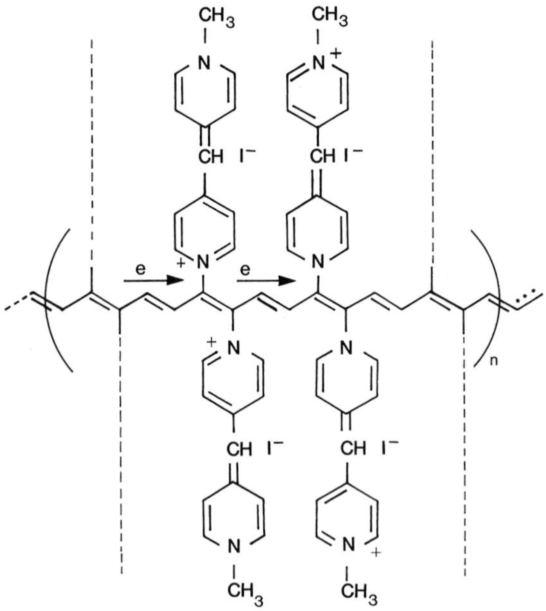

Fig. 5.21. A model for an organic superconductor according to Little.[594]

In this model the virtual oscillations of electronic charge in the side chains could lead to an attractive interaction between electrons moving along the central spine of the molecule. High T_c is predicted in the exciton mechanism because the characteristic energy of the mediating particle, or exciton, is large $(M/c \cdot m)^{1/2}$ where M and m are respectively ionic and electronic masses.

So far, no one has made this polymer. The nearest approach is that of Liepins et al., in which the conjugated polymaleonitrile backbone was used with three types of pendant groups: cyanine, merocyanine, and a diazo.[598,599] Figure 5.22 shows their synthesized structures.

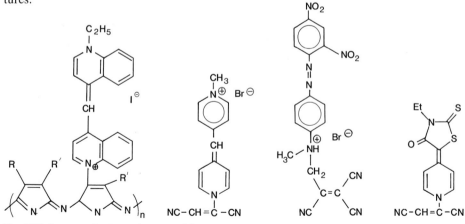

Fig. 5.22. Superconducting polymer models.

The three types of polymers were isolated as dark brown to black solids with a metallic luster. The dc room-temperature conductivities on pellets of compacted powders were from

10^{-8} to $10^{-12}(\Omega cm)^{-1}$. The samples were tested for superconductivity down to a temperature of 1.50 K and none was found. In retrospect, it is unfortunate that the materials were not tested to lower temperatures.

Little's calculations and their implications have been criticized severely on the theoretical grounds that the long-range order necessary for superconductivity could not exist in a one-dimensional molecule.[600,601] Despite this, an extensive search for superconductivity in organic systems began. It eventually led to discovery of the first highly conducting anisotropic organic crystal:tetrathiafulvylene-tetracyanoquinodimethane charge transfer salt (TTF-TCNQ) in the early 1970s.[602] However, this crystal was not superconductive, and below 53 K it exhibited Fröhlich-Peierls metal-to-insulator transition,resulting from the electron-phonon coupling.[603,604] Many other similar charge-transfer salts were subsequently discovered.[605]

In parallel with developments in the field of quasi-one-dimensional organic metals, intense interest in the possibly low-dimensional conducting systems led to investigations of a number of polymer systems with high conductivity potential. The obvious chemical and structural anisotropy of polymers immediately suggested that a conducting polymer might have the highly anisotropic electrical properties seen in quasi-one-dimensional conducting crystals such as KcP^{606} and TTF-TCNQ.[605]

The significant development was the discovery of superconductivity in the first polymeric material-poly(sulfur nitride), $(SN)_n$. Polycrystalline compactions of $(SN)_n$ were known to be highly conducting from the work of Chapman et al,[607] who had concluded that the material was a semiconductor. In 1973 Walatka et al.[404] reported results of electrical measurements on single crystals of $(SN)_n$. The metallic conductivity along the polymer chain axis observed by these authors stimulated extensive research into the properties of the material. With the discovery of superconductivity in $(SN)_n$ crystals by Greene, Street, and Suter,[608] the investigation of $(SN)_n$ and the search for other highly conducting polymers rapidly developed.

Thus, the discoveries of Heeger et al[602] and Greene et al[608] stimulated a worldwide interest in highly conducting compounds. Soon the first organic charge-transfer complex, $(TMTSF)_2PF_6$ or tetramethyltetraselenafulvalene phosphorous hexafluoride was synthesized. It is superconductive under pressure: T_c 0.9 K at 12 kbars.[609,610]

Subsequently, a whole family of charge-transfer complexes, including ClO_4^-, ReO_4^-, AsF_6^-, SbF_6^-, and TaF_6^-, was synthesized. Among this family, the first organic charge-transfer complex, the perchlorate, was found to be superconducting at ambient pressure.

Equally feverish activity was going on in the area of poly(sulfur nitride). Attempts to synthesize chemical analogs of $(SN)_n$ have not been successful. However, work on modifying its electronic properties has been extensive. The polymer has been oxidized by several reagents in several laboratories with interesting results.[611-613] For example, the bromine-oxidized material $(SNBr_{0.4})_n$ exhibits the highest conductivity of any polymeric material synthesized so far: about $40,000(\Omega cm)^{-1}$.

The search for superconductivity in two-dimensional polymeric systems has been going on since the early 1950s. The most prominent example is graphite. The discovery of superconductivity in graphite in 1965 generated little excitement, however, presumably because of the very low transition temperatures found: 0.020 to 0.55 K.

Biological polymers also have been studied. There are certainly numerous well-known examples of biological semiconductors, and the possibility of superconduction in the DNA double helix, for example, has been considered. We summarize what little information exists on biological superconductivity in Sec. 5.11.4.

5.11.2 Polysulfur Nitride, (SN)$_n$

A detailed review on various aspects of polysulfur nitride has been published by W. D. Gill et al. recently.[614] Here we will present a summary of that review.

a) Synthesis of (SN)$_n$

Both films and crystals of (SN)$_n$ have been prepared by the thermal pyrolysis of S_4N_4 to S_2N_2 in the course of trying to remove excess sulfur from S_4N_4 by passing its vapors over silver wool.[615] The silver wool acts as a catalyst in the conversion of S_4N_4 to S_2N_2.[616,617] As the crystal structure of S_2N_2 reveals, the square planar S_2N_2 molecules are ideally arranged for a solid-state polymerization to (SN)$_n$.[618] Burt's paper (Ref. 615) provides the basis of techniques used today to prepare (SN)$_n$ crystals for investigation of the compound's electrical properties. All of these techniques emphasize the importance of the purity of the intermediate S_2N_2 crystals and careful temperature control during their slow solid-state polymerization.[619–621] Labes et al. have also investigated crystal growth techniques involving photoinitiation of polymerization of solution-grown S_2N_2 crystals.[622,623]

Films have been prepared by two techniques, pyrolysis of S_4N_4 and direct heating of (SN)$_n$.[624–626] Films in which the (SN)$_n$ chain direction is ordered can be prepared by deposition on Mylar treated to provide a series of parallel scratches on the surface.[627]

b) Structure of (SN)$_n$

Burt in 1910 characterized (SN)$_n$ as a polymer[615] on the basis of its complete insolubility. However, it was not until 1956 that Goehring and Voigt first investigated its structure and suggested a zig-zag geometry for the chain.[628] Douillard showed that this geometry was incorrect and advanced what has proved to be essentially the correct chain structure.[629] A preliminary crystal structure obtained from electron diffractions[630] by using this chain geometry was later refined by x-ray diffraction[618] and confirmed by neutron diffraction.[631] This structure is shown in Fig. 5.23. The unit cell contains two almost flat chains, which are centrosymmetrically related but translationally inequivalent.

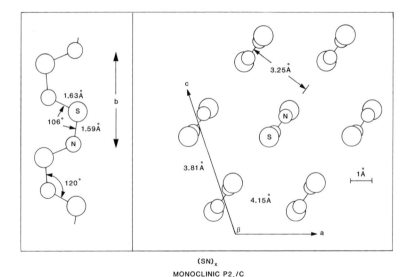

(SN)$_x$

MONOCLINIC P2$_1$/C

Fig. 5.23. The structure of (SN)$_x$ crystals. Source is Ref. 618.

The inequivalent chains alternate along the c-axis, whereas equivalent chains are adjacent along the a-axis. The chains all lie in the $10\bar{2}$ plane where equivalent chains alternate. This $10\bar{2}$ plane is an easy cleavage plane. The shortest interchain bonds are tabulated in Table 5.7. Comparison of the bond lengths with the corresponding van der Waals diameters (VDW) suggests that interactions between the chains are weak relative to the bonding within the chains.

TABLE 5.7 Interchain Distances in $(SN)_n$[618]

Shortest Separation	Within $(10\bar{2})$ Plane Å	Between $(10\bar{2})$ Planes Å	VDW (Å)
S-S	3.48	3.72	3.70
N-N	3.35	3.37	3.15
S-N	3.26	3.40	3.35

c) Normal Conductivity and Superconductivity

Conductivity and thermoelectric power measurements have strongly suggested that $(SN)_n$ is metallic to 4.2 K in the direction parallel to the $(SN)_n$ chains in the crystal structure. Strong anisotropy was observed for conductivity parallel and perpendicular to the fiber axis of the crystals, which coincides with the $(SN)_n$ chain axis. This anisotropy led to early speculation that $(SN)_n$ was a quasi-one-dimensional conductor. However, the persistence of metallic conductivity to very low temperatures, where a Peierl's transition to the insulating state would be expected for a one-dimensional system, suggested that the fibrous nature of $(SN)_n$ crystals might be dominating the observed conductivity anisotropy.

The discovery of superconductivity in $(SN)_n$ dramatically verified the compound's metallic properties. The discovery also marked the first observation of superconductivity in a polymer and the first observation of superconductivity at ambient pressure in a material containing no metallic elements. The superconductivity experiments suggest that $(SN)_n$ is a bulk, Type II superconductor but that crystal perfection strongly affects its superconductivity.

The effect of improved crystal perfection on the conductivity properties is shown in Fig. 5.24. The maximum conductivity increased from 1000 $(\Omega cm)^{-1}$ to about 4000 $(\Omega cm)^{-1}$ and the resistivity ratio π_{RT}/π_{4K} increased from about 3 to 250.[632] The superconductivity transition temperature T_c also increased from 0.26 to 0.35 K. The quadratic dependence of resistivity on temperature observed with the best crystals suggested to Chiang et al that instead of the usual electron-phonon scattering processes, electron-electron Umklapp scattering between electronic and hole pockets of the Fermi surface is dominant in $(SN)_n$.[633]

Early, unsuccessful attempts to observe a Meissner effect in $(SN)_n$ crystals left some doubt as to whether the observed superconductivity was a bulk effect.[634] However, a broad hump in the specific heat indicative of the expected BCS anomaly was observed.[635] Recent observations of the Meissner effect have verified the model of $(SN)_n$ as a bulk, weakly coupled filamentary Type II superconductor.[636,637] A number of interesting problems related to superconductivity in $(SN)_n$ still need to be resolved. They include the pressure dependence of T_c which increases strongly with pressure to about 8 kbar where a sudden decrease in T_c apparently signals a change in phase;[638,639] the absence of superconductivity in $(SN)_n$ films,[640-643] and the absence of a superconducting gap in tunneling experiments.[644]

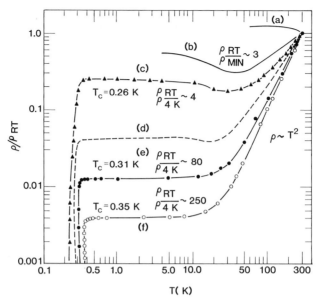

Fig. 5.24. Temperature dependence of the resistivity of $(SN)_n$ crystals: (a) $(SN)_n$ pellets; (b) crystals from Walatka; (c) crystals from Street; (d),(e),(f) crystals grown by the technique described by Street and Greene.[631] Source is Ref. 614.

Full understanding of the temperature dependence of the critical magnetic field and its strong anisotropy is lacking.[645]

d) Optical Properties

The optical properties of $(SN)_n$ crystals have been measured by several groups, and the measurements have played an important role in our understanding of the intrinsic properties.[646-648] The calculated optical conductivity σ_{opt} 2.5×10^4 $(\Omega cm)^{-1}$ is about 10 times greater than the measured dc conductivity. Optical reflectivity with the E-vector perpendicular to the b-axis showed weak structure in reflectivity and is interpreted to be a strongly damped plasma edge at $h\nu_p$ 2.4 eV with τ 3×10^{-16} s. The observations of this perpendicular reflectivity edge was the first experimental evidence that $(SN)_n$, although strongly anisotropic, should not be regarded as a quasi-one-dimensional metal. This conclusion is also supported by electron energy loss experiments[649] and by magnetoresistance anisotropy[650] and is in good agreement with the three-dimensional orthogonalized-plane-wave (OPW) band-structure calculations.[651,652]

e) Other Physical Properties

A broad range of experimental techniques have been applied to $(SN)_n$ to measure both its lattice and electronic properties. The experiments include specific heat,[653,654] inelastic neutron scattering,[655] infrared reflectance, Raman scattering,[656-658] x-ray,[659-661] ultraviolet photoemission,[662,663] magnetoresistance,[650, 664,665] Hall effect,[665] and junction properties.[666-668]

From the electronic contribution to specific heat, Harper et al[653,654] obtain a value for the Fermi level density of states of 0.14 states/eV-spin-molecule in excellent agreement with band-structure predictions. The temperature dependence of the lattice contribution to the specific heat is characteristic of a solid with quasi-one-dimensional binding forces. From infrared reflectance, Raman, and neutron-scattering results, Stolz et al.[656, 657] estimate that the interchain force constants are about 10 times smaller than the intrachain force constants.

Several measurements of the galvanomagnetic properties of $(SN)_n$ crystals have been reported. Beyer et al.[650] measured the magnetoresistance anisotropy at 4.2 K and compared it with the anisotropy derived from the calculated plasma tensor of Grant et al.[652] A negative magnetoresistance dominated the measurements at low magnetic fields. At higher fields a quadratic positive magnetoresistance was observed with a 3:1 ratio of parallel to transverse mobility anisotropy, in reasonable agreement with the calculated value of 5.7. The b-axis mobilities are about 600 cm^2/V-s and 400 cm^2/V-s for holes and electrons, respectively. The scattering time of 1.5×10^{-13} s corresponds to a mean free path of about 700 Å along the b-axis. Kahlert and Seeger have observed the Hall effect for an $(SN)_n$ crystal, which gave a value of the effective carrier density n_{eff} 3.2 x 10^{21} cm^{-3} in excellent agreement with band-structure results.[665]

Junction properties measured by Scranton et al. have shown the interesting result that $(SN)_n$ is more electronegative than gold: it produces large Schottky barriers on contact with n-type semiconductors.[666, 667] A practical utilization of this property in Schottky barrier solar cells has been investigated by Cohen and Harris.[668]

f) Chemical Modifications of $(SN)_n$

Introduction. The discovery of superconductivity in crystals of $(SN)_n$ motivated intensive efforts in several laboratories to synthesize analogous compounds. Much of this work is focussed on efforts to produce $(SeN)_n$ from the known compound Se_4N_4 by routes similar to those described for conversion of S_4N_4 to $(SN)_n$.[632] These efforts have not been successful. Similarly unsuccessful attempts have also been made to produce $(SCN)_n$.[669] Oligomeric analogs of $(SN)_n$ such as 1,9-diaryl-pentasulfurtetranitride have been prepared, but they showed no evidence of conductivity despite an increasing red shift of the ultraviolet-visible absorption with increasing chain length that indicated extensive electron delocalization along the chain. Attempts to make even longer chain oligomers were not successful.[670]

Halogen Modifications. In 1976 Bernard et al. reported the formation of an intercalation compound of $(SN)_n$ and bromine.[671] Independently Street and Gill surveyed a large number of potential intercalates and found that the halogens Br_2, I_2, ICl, and IBr all increased the conductivity of $(SN)_n$.[613, 672] The bromine derivatives are the most extensively studied because they show the highest conductivity.

The simplest preparative technique for brominating $(SN)_n$ is exposure to dry bromine vapor. On exposure $(SN)_n$ crystals change color from gold to blue-black and expand in directions perpendicular to the chain axis. Exposure to the vapor pressure of bromine at room temperature leads to a composition $(SNBr_{0.5})_n$, which on pumping in vacuum (10^{-5} torr) at room temperature for 1 h gives a final composition of $(SNBr_{0.4})_n$. At this composition the crystal has expanded by approximately 50% in volume perpendicular to the chain axis. The flotation density increases from 2.32 g/cm^3 to 2.65 g/cm^3. Virtually any composition of lower bromine content can be obtained by heating a sample of $(SNBr_{0.4})_n$ in vacuum for various periods of time. However, the $(SNBr_{0.4})_n$ composition appears to have the best electrical properties and has been most extensively studied. It is important to brominate with vapor because $(SN)_n$ reacts with liquid bromine yielding significant amounts of a side product $S_4N_3Br_3$.[673]

A different preparative route involves direct bromination of the $(SN)_n$ precursor molecule S_4N_4.[674, 675] Exposure to bromine vapor causes S_4N_4 crystals to turn black and expand rapidly, thereby destroying their external habit. After removal of free bromine the remaining, conductive black powder has the composition $(SNBr_{0.4})_n$. Infrared,[676] Raman,[677, 678] thermal analysis,[676] and mass spectrometry[679] all indicate that this material is the same as that obtained by bromination of $(SN)_n$ crystals; however, it is even more structurally disordered. The mechanism of this ring-opening reaction is unknown. Both ICl and IBr vapors also react readily with S_4N_4 to form conducting solids.[674, 675, 680]

Considerable effort has gone into studies of the molecular nature of the intercalated halogens in $(SN)_n$ derivatives. In graphite, bromine is present in the form of weakly ionized Br_2.[681] In $(SN)_n$, however, Raman spectroscopy indicates a much more complex situation.[677, 678, 682, 683] Two strong Raman fundamentals are observed at 150 cm^{-1} and 230 cm^{-1}. The band at 150 cm^{-1} has been assigned without ambiguity to the symmetric stretch of the tribromide ion Br_3^-. The band at 230 cm^{-1} can be assigned to the asymmetric stretch of the same Br_3^- ion or to the stretching frequency of Br_2 downshifted from its 325-cm^{-1} frequency in the gas phase by its strong association with the $(SN)_n$ lattice. Macklin et al. examined the infrared absorption of brominated $(SN)_n$ and found no evidence for the 230-cm^{-1} peak that would be expected to be infrared active for the asymmetric stretch of a linear Br_3^- ion.[684] On this basis it is concluded that both Br_2 and Br_3^- molecular species are present in brominated $(SN)_n$. From the polarization dependence of the Raman peaks, the Br_2 and Br_3^- appear to be oriented with their axes parallel to the $(SN)_n$ chains. Extended x-ray Absorption Fine Structure studies are also consistent with this orientation and indicate that similar concentrations of Br_2 and Br_3^- species are present in the $(SNBr_{0.4})_n$ crystals.[685, 686] Magnetic susceptibility measurements show the absence of paramagnetic species such as Br_2^-.[687]

Copolymerization. A more recent modification effort involved the synthesis of various SN copolymers.[688–690] Both the various types of comonomers and the length of the $(SN)_n$ segments were studied. Studies included the comonomer units:

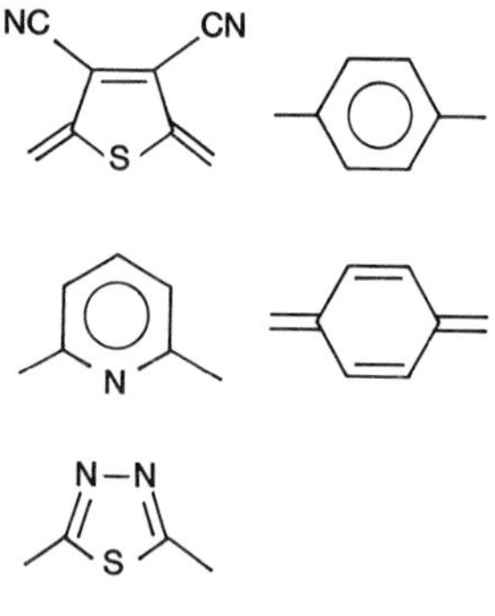

All of the copolymers were obtained as highly colored or black materials insoluble in common laboratory solvents. The undoped materials have conductivities in the range of 10^{-16} to 10^{-5} $(\Omega cm)^{-1}$, and doping with bromine has produced conductivities as high as 10^{-3} $(\Omega cm)^{-1}$.

5.11.3 Graphite

Graphite represents polymers with a high degree of two-dimensional order. As far as its electronic properties are concerned, graphite lies on the border of metallic behavior and its conductivity has been explained in terms of nearly touching, narrow valence and conduction bands.[691–694]

The first search for superconductivity in graphite intercalation compounds was conducted in 1952, and none was found at temperatures as low as 1.25 K.[695] Superconductivity was found in intercalation compounds of graphite with alkali metals in 1965.[696] The chemical formulas corresponded to C_8A, where A was K, Rb, or Cs. The layer structure of graphite was preserved, and the alkali-metal atoms were lying in layers alternating with the graphite carbon layers. The observed transition temperatures (in K) were:

	T_c
Cs-graphite	0.020–0.135
Rb-graphite	0.023–0.151
K-graphite	up to 0.55

The transition temperatures varied with the quality of the graphite and the details of the treatment procedure. The alkali metals and the pyrolytic graphite used in the experiments were tested separately down to 0.011 K and were not superconducting.

Recently, interest in the superconducting properties of these compounds has increased, and different values for the T_c of several compounds have been reported.[697–701] Superconductivity has been observed also in compounds other than alkali metal. Examples of compounds and their T_c's are: $KHgC_8$ amalgam, 1.9 K;[702] stage-two $RbHgC_8$ amalgam, 1.46 K;[703,704] stage-one $KHgC_4$, 0.7–0.9 K;[701] stage-one $RbHgC_4$, 0.99 K;[701] stage-one $KTl_{1.5}C_4$, 2.7 K;[705] and stage-two $KTl_{1.5}C_8$, 2.45 K.[705] Among very recent results reported on a number of pseudoternary compounds are $KTl_{1.35}Hg_{0.15}C_4$ with a T_c 2.55 K and $KHg_{0.9}Pb_{0.1}C_8$ with a T_c 1.73 K.[706]

The above results suggest that examination of other types of intercalants not only in graphite but also in other lamellar compounds such as boron nitride should lead to finding higher T_c's.

5.11.4 Biological Polymers

Deoxyribonucleic acid (DNA) has a structure resembling Little's superconductor model but although the poly(sugar phosphate) backbone is periodic, the pendant pyrimidine and purine bases are placed aperiodically. Use of a periodic DNA model has shown that the delocalized π-electrons from the bases might pair if they interacted with the σ-electrons functioning as the polarizable side-chain electrons of Little's model.[707] Moreover, in the case of the DNA double helix the polarization of the π- and σ-electrons in one chain might give an attractive interaction between the π-electrons of the other chain and result in electron pairing.[707,708] This should lead to enhanced conductivity if not superconductivity in some regions of DNA.

There is support for the view that certain parts of nerve fiber having a high concentration of cholesterol are superconductive at physiological temperatures.[709,710] Halpern found that the diamagnetism of the sodium salts of cholic, desoxycholic, lithocholic, and cholanic acids changed abruptly at 30, 60, 130, and 277 K, respectively. These transitions are thought to be superconducting in small domains dispersed in the bulk insulating matrix.[711] Goldfein has now shown that the transitions are electronic in nature because there is no change in the atomic lattice structure.[712] He also finds that the four bile acid salts obey the empirical rule of Matthias, which applies to superconducting transition-metal alloys; that is, T_c is proportional to the average number of valence (outer shell) electrons per atom.[713] This suggests high-temperature superconducting regions in these compounds.

Proteins certainly show semiconductivity, which increases dramatically with the degree of hydration, but the conduction mechanism is not known. Possibly in the water layer next to the polymer chain a dopant species ordering occurs that leads to an increased conduction. Evidence now appearing suggests that proteins also may show superconductivity. For example, a magnetic field of 600 G increases the diamagnetic susceptibility of a 0.01% aqueous solution of lysozyme by a factor of 10^4 times that expected for ordinary diamagnetic materials.[714] An increase in field to 800 G destroys the effect by what appears to be a room-temperature Meissner effect. Small superconductive regions attached to each enzyme molecule may be formed by some process involving water. These regions may cluster together and lead to the enormous increase in diamagnetism. So far no high conductivity or superconductivity has been observed as a bulk property in biopolymers. However, these compounds may hold the clue to the specification for a true superconducting polymer.

5.11.5 Other Structures

Since the discovery of superconductivity in $(SN)_n$ polymer, a search for superconductivity in other isoelectronic structures has been going on. One of the first modifications to be investigated was the substitution of selenium for sulfur in the polymer structure. Synthesis of $(SeN)_n$ was attempted without success.[632]

On the basis of the self-consistent field (SCF)-tight-binding MO theory, the isoelectronic structure $(SCH)_n$ should be a metallic conductor.[715] No attempt to synthesize it appears to be reported.

Another isoelectronic structure under study at Los Alamos involves phosphorus: $(S\overset{\circ}{P}R)_n$, where R is hydrogen or methyl.[716] As there is no precedent for phosphorus compounds of this type, new synthetic procedures are being developed for their synthesis.

5.11.6 Conclusion

The work on organic polymeric superconduction is relatively recent, but it has already demonstrated that the first step must be to understand the organic metallic state. The second step involves unraveling the relationship between charge-carrier mobility and the supermolecular structure of polymers. Progress will be slow until we understand this relationship. Then, as the third step chemists will have a more logical way of selecting structures that are likely to exhibit superconductivity.

5.12 MOLECULAR ELECTRONICS

5.12.1 Introduction

The tremendous improvements in reliability, compactness, versatility, and range of electronic circuitry that widespread use of solid-state devices has brought constitute a major technological advance. Within biological systems, however, some tasks that are performed by solid-state devices in electronic applications are performed, instead, by organic molecules; such tasks include storage and transfer of both energy and electrons.

The fundamental limits to semiconductor-chip density, already in view, have prompted forward-looking corporations and individuals to start thinking about molecular chemical circuits. By entering the molecular world, it becomes possible, in principle, to produce circuit elements a thousand times smaller than those achieved with conventional semiconductors. Smaller circuit elements would lead to a quantum leap in computational density with faster and cheaper switching networks. These vastly higher computational densities are needed in complex simulations, pattern recognition, interactive computer graphics, context-dependent analysis, and artifical intelligence.[717–723]

At present, the highest-density semiconductor chip on the market contains about 450,000 transistors in an area 4 mm square, with spacing between elements of about 1.5

microns. By means of new materials such as gallium arsenide and advanced lithographic techniques for etching circuits with beams of electrons or ions, it may ultimately be possible to produce semiconductor chips four times denser, with a spacing of 0.2 micron. Below this size, however, semiconductor circuits would have a finite probability of tunneling between adjacent devices, causing a loss of information. An even greater limitation on further microminiaturization is the tendency of closely packed computing elements to overheat unless superconducting switches such as Josephson junctions are used.

The suggestion to try synthetic electronic devices based on organic molecules (molecular electronics) was first disclosed in 1972.[724] A full account of the conceptual ideas in organic memory devices and molecular rectifiers became available in 1974.[724-727]

There are two possible approaches to building carbon-based chips. The first approach involves building a digital carbon-based chip in which synthetic organic polymer molecules would serve as the wires and binary switches, initiating the function of silicon components by turning the flow of electrons on and off. The second approach involves building an analog carbon-based chip, which would employ protein molecules such as enzymes as the computing elements. Since enzymes are three-dimensional structures and have many possible conformational states, they are theoretically capable of graded responses and entirely new forms of computation.

5.12.2 Molecular Rectifiers

A reasonable first step is to examine the potential use of molecules as components of electronic circuitry by checking the current-voltage characteristics of a single molecule acting as a rectifier. Common solid-state rectifiers are based on the use of p-n junctions. An organic molecule, to show rectifier properties, should have roughly the properties of a p-n junction. By the use of substituent groups on aromatic systems, it is possible to increase or decrease the π-electron density within the organic molecule and therefore to create relatively electron-poor (p-type) or electron-rich (n-type) molecular subunits. Those substituents classified as electron withdrawing (that is, showing positive Hammett constants[728]) will cause their aromatic subunit to become relatively poor in π-electron density, thus raising the electron affinity and making the subunit a good electron acceptor. Conversely, electron-releasing substituents will increase the π-electron density, thereby lowering the ionization potential and rendering the subunit a good electron donor.[729-731]

The so-called charge-transfer salts, show high electronic conductivity and spin susceptibility because of donor-acceptor transfer of electrons.[732] This electron motion suggests that a rectifier can be built in which electrons could pass from a cathode to an acceptor site or from a donor site to an anode, but not in the other direction. If, however, the electronic systems of the donor and acceptor molecular subunits are allowed to interact strongly with one another, a single donor level will exist on the time scale of any laboratory experiment.[733, 734] Therefore, the donor and acceptor sites should be effectively insulated from one another for the device to function. They can be insulated by placing a σ-electron system between the donor and acceptor π-subunits. A rectifier molecule based on the popular acceptor tetracyanoquinodimethane (TCNQ) and the donor tetrathiofulvalene (TTF) is shown in Fig. 5.25.[724]

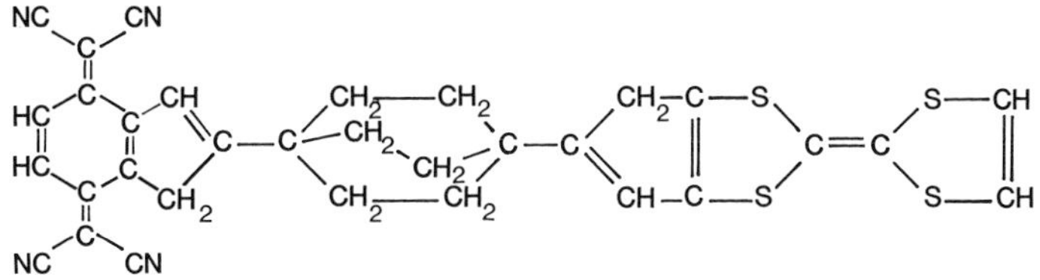

Fig. 5.25. An example of a rectifier molecule.

In this case, the methylene (-CH$_2$CH$_2$-) bridge is triple rather than single to help ensure molecular rigidity. Its purpose is to make the π-levels of the donor and acceptor sites essentially noninteracting on the time scale of electronic motion to or from the electrodes. Such a molecule should show rectifier properties, with the electron current passing only from right to left in the molecule or from left to right along the system:

cathode $\rightarrow$ acceptor $\rightarrow$ donor $\rightarrow$ anode.

5.12.3 Organic Memory Device

The next more complicated level in molecular devices can be represented by a memory element.[726] The device may be based, for example, on two types of organic molecules:[724]

These molecules would constitute a monomolecular film with the molecules in a perpendicular orientation to the attached electrodes. An energy profile across the film (45–100 Å) would have first and second minimum energy levels and an interposed maximum energy level. On application of an electric field or optical and thermal energy, electrons would tunnel from the first to the second minimum energy level, producing a detectable current. Modifying these molecules by substitution could introduce a third minimum and a second maximum energy level. The modified molecules would require energy application above a higher threshold value for electron transfer, and thus would permit a nondestructive memory reading. Additional modifications may involve the use of both lasers to raise the energy level of the transmitted electrons and attached photoelectrically active films to increase the electrical conduction on application of light.

5.12.4 Soliton Switching

A still higher level of complexity is represented by devices involving soliton switching, soliton logic, soliton valving, and soliton memory elements among others.[735] On a microscopic scale a soliton is a nonlinear structural disturbance that moves in one (and perhaps higher) dimensions like a "particle." Associated with this pseudoparticle are a definite energy, momentum, and velocity. Davydov[736, 737] postulated in 1976 that a soliton traveling thousands of angstroms down an α-helix might be the signal transport mechanism associated with bond breaking in ATP. The bond energy associated with that phenomenon is only four times the thermal background and normally would be lost in the thermal background before traveling far. Accordingly, soliton transport is associated with the motion of a disturbance moving without energy loss. In the α-helix the motion of this "solitary" wave is necessarily linked to the stretching of the polypeptide amide bond (-CO-NH-) through its dipole moment.

In conjugated systems the corresponding dipole moment may be absent; however, single-double bond rearrangement is possible, and it presumably provides the necessary mechanism for soliton propagation. A schematic drawing illustrates the mechanism necessary for soliton propagation. In Fig. 5.26, the soliton is moving from left to right. At its center is a moving "phase" or "domain" boundary with respect to the conjugation. Note that plus- and minus-charged solitons exist as well as radical solitons and that the disturbance at the soliton center is much larger than is suggested in the figure. The passage of a soliton through a conjugated system generally results in the exchange of single and double bonds. This effect will play a major role in soliton switching, as discussed below.

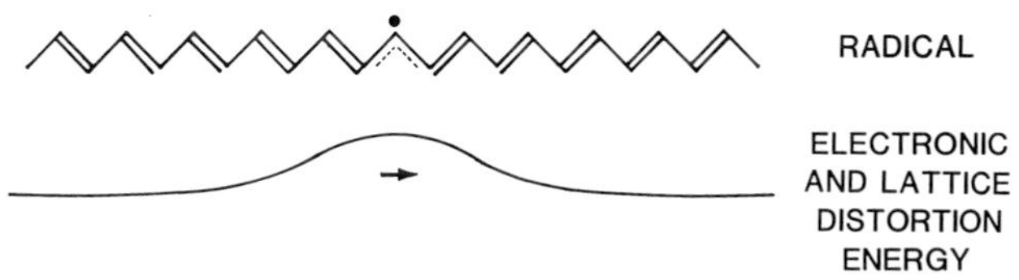

Fig. 5.26. The motion of a radical soliton in a conjugated system is associated with the motion of a "Phase boundary" or "kink" between ordered single-double bond domains. Source is Ref. 733.

The "push-pull" disubstituted olefin 1,1-N,N-dimethyl-2-nitroethenamine is of special interest because it can be photoactivated to undergo an electron transfer from the amine nitrogen to the nitrooxygen.[738] At the same time there is a conformational change involving the olefinic double bond:[738]

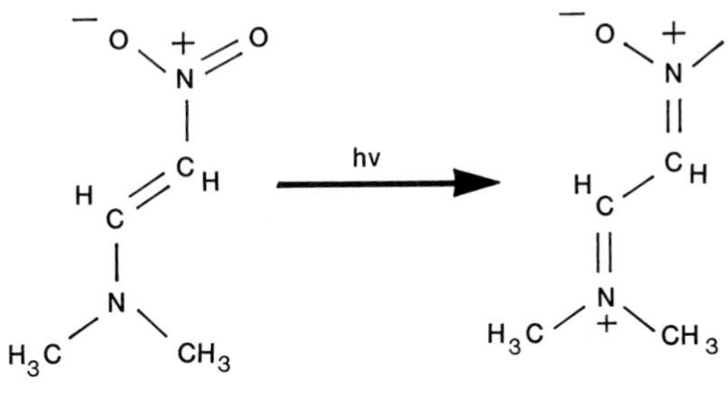

Now, assume that the double bond is part of a larger polyacetylene chain, as indicated in Fig. 5.27.[735] Under polarized photoactivation it should still undergo electron transfer. However, if a soliton has passed down the polyene chain, the photoactivation process can no longer take place. The soliton has switched off the internal charge-transfer reaction. Thus, the absorption spectra of the push-pull olefin can serve also as a detector for passage of the soliton.

Soliton logic, soliton valving, and soliton memory elements all involve still higher levels of molecular structural complexity. They have been discussed in a Molecular Electronic Devices Workshop.[735]

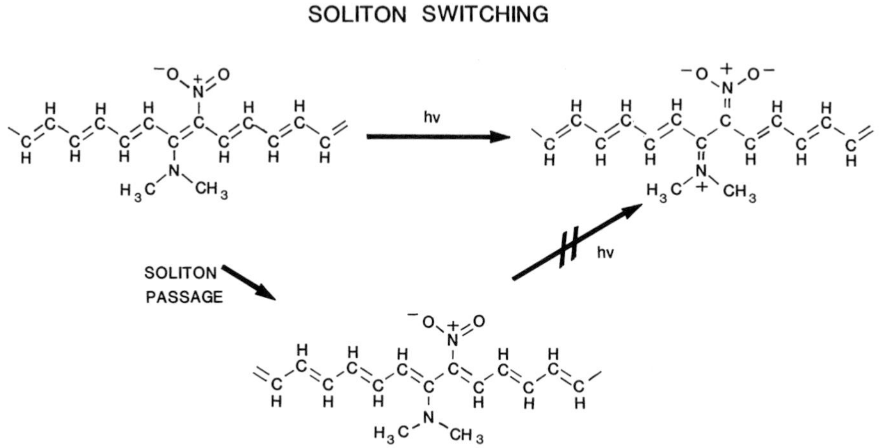

SOLITON SWITCHING

Figure 5.27. A push-pull disubstituted olefin imbedded in trans-polyacetylene can (a) be switched off by the propagation of a soliton or (b) be used as a soltiton detector. Source is Ref. 735.

5.13 BIOELECTRONICS

5.13.1 Introduction

Bioelectronics or biotechnical electron devices, or simply biochips, have generated a large amount of interest recently.[739–743] The beginnings of the conceptual phase of bioelectronics can be traced to the mid-1970s and more specifically to two events: (1) the 1978 National Science Foundation sponsored workshop on "Opportunities for Microstructures Science and Engineering,"[744] and (2) two patents on "Microsubstrates and Methods for Making Micropattern Devices," issued to McAlear and Wehrung, also in 1978.[745, 746] Since 1979, the Naval Research Laboratory has been publishing annual reports on electroactive polymers.[747, 748] Molecular electronic devices workshops have also been held since 1981,[749, 750] and an interesting report on conformational switching in molecular electronic devices has been published.[751] More recently the National Science Foundation cosponsored with University of California at Los Angeles, the first "International Conference on Chemically Based Computing," which in effect put the biochip on the scientific agenda worldwide.[752] The main objectives of the Conference were to define the basic problems of biochip design and fabrication as well as the applications for which such devices might be used. The consensus of the Conference was that a great deal more work is needed at the fundamental level before development can begin.

5.13.2 Organized Molecular Components

Since there is as yet no consensus on the optimal type of molecular switching system or any concrete design for a biochip, discussion of all possible means of organizing molecular components into functional circuits is in order. Only in that way is there a hope of testing the feasibility of the organized molecular components approach. Thus, several approaches have been discussed and some may be worked on. The three major approaches are: (1) molecular self- assembly, (2) modular chemical synthesis, and (3) molecular films. The ideas discussed here are those presented in the patents and workshops mentioned in Sec. 5.13.1.

a) *Molecular Self-Assembly*

The molecular self-assembly is a four-billion-year-old idea that occurs in the nature continually.[749] At the molecular scale, functional systems are constructed molecule by molecule and are driven by thermodynamics and the unique chemical properties of the individual molecules. The proof for self-assembly of extremely complex functional systems is life itself. The biochemical organization of living cells is very different from what would be desirable in a molecular electronic device, but molecular biology and biochemistry offer a model upon which to base the development of self-organizing systems. Furthermore, the new techniques of recombinant DNA and genetic engineering now offer the tools required to fabricate self-assembling molecular devices with electronic properties.

Self-assembly is characteristic of biomolecules. All the genetic information required to produce any organism is encoded in DNA. The DNA molecule is a linear polymer of four nucleotides or bases: adenine (A), cytosine (C), guanine (G), and thymine (T). The genome or complete DNA sequence of a small virus contains several thousand bases in a single linear molecule, while the genomes of higher organisms such as man contain several billion bases. DNA is actually a double-stranded polymer. Its two strands run in opposite directions and their sequences are self-complementary. A base in one strand can form hydrogen bonds with the base opposite it in the other strand according to a pairing rule where A pairs with T and C pairs with G. A short stretch of double-stranded DNA can be represented as follows:[751]

5'....ACCTTGATGCTCCTGGCACAGATGAGGAAAATCTCTCTTTTCTCCT ...3'
3'....TGGAACTACGAGGACCGTGTCTACTCCTTTTAGAGAGAAAAGAGGA ...5'

If the two strands are physically separated and then mixed together in solution under appropriate conditions, they will perfectly reestablish the original pairing for their entire length. This conformation is thermodynamically the most stable and therefore arises spontaneously. This is what is meant by self-assembly.

At this time we do not know what protein assemblages might serve the functions of the well-known diodes, transistors, conductors, and resistors. More importantly, however, proteins could provide the structural backbone for molecular electronic devices. Proteins could be designed to recognize and bind electronically functional molecules in the same manner that enzymes recognize and specifically bind their substrates. Different proteins bearing different functional molecules could then self-assemble to bring these molecules together in precise orientation and covalently link them where necessary. This process could be repeated with a diverse array of functional proteins, building up a two-dimensional organic crystal containing a complex electronic circuit.

It may be possible to "borrow" the structure of existing biomolecules that can be modified to function electronically. For example, many biomolecules chelate specific metal ions and incorporate them into their structures. Certain porphyrins can bind a single atom of iron, magnesium, zinc, nickel, cobalt, or copper. These porphyrins can in turn be bound to proteins as in hemoglobin. Using this basic strategy, it may be possible to design a protein that would assemble itself into a long tubular structure with many metal-containing porphyrin groups stacked along the axis of the tube. With the proper molecular structure it might be possible to overlap the orbitals of adjacent metal atoms and thereby form a linear conductor.

b) *Modular Chemical Synthesis*

In modular chemical synthesis, molecule-sized fragments would be added to a substrate in a highly controlled fashion.[753] An array of molecular computing elements would be grown on a semiconductor surface by reactions that would add only one subunit at a time to specific sites on the substrate. The reactions would occur in a special cell, with the flow of reagents regulated by automated control valves. Different solutions would be introduced, reacted, and rinsed away for each layer, and specialized areas of the chip would be structured through laser-catalyzed reactions. A series of such reactions would therefore build up molecular wires, insulating regions, and switching or memory elements. Ultimately, macroscopic contacts to the outside world would be synthesized on the outer surface of the device.

An advantage of modular synthesis is that many identical parallel processors would be fabricated through the same sequence of chemical reactions. However, the requirements of this technique greatly exceed the current state of the synthetic laboratory. On the other hand, such control at the molecular level is possible in biological systems such as living cells, which routinely perform this kind of microengineering.

c) *Molecular Films*

The molecular-film approach is the least futuristic of the three, and most of the tools of assembly are available. It involves designing ordered molecular films that will then direct the protein components of a biochip to self-assemble in the appropriate spatial patterns.[745, 746, 754] The basic knowledge for preparing molecular films was developed in the 1930s by Langmuir and Blodgett.[755]

Using the Langmuir/Blodgett (LB) technique, it is possible to build up multilayer films that incorporate different molecules including proteins in each layer. Thus, for example, light-absorbing and light-emitting dyes have been incorporated with LB films, and optically driven molecular switches may be possible by this technique.[756] McAlear and Wehrund have built laminates of protein monolayers on glass and then used lithographic and cytochemical methods to create microscopic conducting surfaces to which molecular switches might be attached.

5.13.3 Genetic Engineering

Of the methods discussed so far genetic engineering is the most futuristic; however, it is also one of the most active research areas today.[749] Newly developed techniques in molecular biology, specifically recombinant DNA technology, DNA sequencing, and oligonucleotide synthesis now make it possible to engineer precisely the genetic information of living cells. Genes from widely different organisms can be combined into a single host cell. The regulatory sequences in the DNA can be manipulated to control the expression of the encoded protein products. By *de novo* chemical synthesis, totally artificial DNA sequences for proteins not found in nature can be created. This technology may now be applied to bioelectronics, initially by modifying the DNA sequences that specify natural proteins, and later by synthesizing entirely new genes that code for purely artificial proteins with novel properties.

However, before genes that code for new proteins are synthesized, we must learn the basic rules that govern how a protein's linear amino acid sequence determines its three-dimensional folding pattern. Research in this area is still rudimentary, and no one knows for sure how many years it will take to have this knowledge at hand.

The basic premise in this approach to fabrication of molecular electronic devices was that proteins with required catalytic and/or structural properties could be synthesized. This, in turn, rests on the ability to predict the three-dimensional folding of a protein from the primary sequence of amino acids-knowledge we still do not have. Thus, the ultimate goal for the biological fabrication of a molecular computer is still very much a dream.

5.13.4 Conclusion

Bioelectronics is still largely pure theory, but so were many other technologies in the past. A large amount of basic research is still needed; however, to cite an old Chinese proverb: "A journey of a thousand miles starts with the first step."

5.14 MOLECULAR ELECTRONICS RESEARCH GROUPS

1. Bell Laboratories
   600 Mountain Ave.
   Murray Hill, NJ 07974–20070
2. Ajinomoto Co., Inc.
   Central Research Laboratories
   1 Suziki-cho, Kawasaki-ku
   Kawasaki, 210
   Japan
3. Carnegie-Mellon University
   Center for Molecular Electronics
   Schenley Park
   Pittsburgh, PA 15213
4. Genex Corp.
   6110 Executive Blvd.
   Rockville, MD 20852
5. Gentronix Laboratories, Inc.
   7503 Standish Place
   Rockville, MD 20855
6. IBM Corp.
   Thomas J. Watson Research Center
   Yorktown Heights, NY 10598
7. Max-Planck Institute
   D-3400 Goettingen
   Federal Republic of Germany
8. Microelectronics Center of North Carolina
   Research Triangle Park, NC 27709
9. University of Mississippi
   Department of Chemistry
   University, MS 38677
10. Naval Research Laboratory
    Chemistry Division, Code 6175
    4555 Overlook Ave.
    Washington, DC 20375
11. University of Warwick
    Department of Physics
    Coventry CV4 7AL
    England

5.15 REFERENCES

PART I

1. C. Kittel, *Introduction to Solid State Physics,* 5th ed., John Wiley & Sons, Inc., New York (1976).
2. N. W. Ashcroft and W. Mermin, *Solid State Physics,* Holt, Rinehart and Winston, New York (1976).
3. L. E. Lyons and J. C. Mackie, Proceedings of the Chemical Society, p. 71 (1962).
4. F.Gutmann and L. E. Lyons, *Organic Semiconductors,* Wiley, New York (1967).
5. N. F. Mott and R. W. Gurney, *Electronic Processes in Ionic Crystals,* Oxford Press, London (1940).
6. L. E. Lyons, in *Physics and Chemistry of the Organic Solid State,* Vol. I, D. Fox, M. M. Labes, and A. Weissberger, Eds. Interscience Press, New York (1963).
7. R. H. Partridge, J. Chem. Phys. *52,* 2485 (1970).
8. M. R. Philpott, J. Chem. Phys. *63,* 485 (1975).
9. P. J. Baldwin, Ph.D. thesis, University of London (1975).
10. N. A. Cade and W. Young, J. Phys. C *12,* 819 (1979).
11. R. Bartnikas and R. M. Eichhorn, Eds., *Engineering Dielectrics, IIA,* ASTM Special Technical Publication 783, Philadelphia (1983), Chapter 3.
12. W. Shockley and W. T. Read, Phys. Rev. *87,* 835 (1952).
13. References to early work are given by K. Fox, Am. J. Phys. *45,* 871 (1975).
14. M. R. Belmont, Thin Solid Films *28,* 149 (1975).
15. T. Kumura, K. Fueki, P. Narayana, and L. Kevan, Can. J. Chem. *55,* 1940 (1977).
16. M. Nishida, J. Chem. Phys. *66,* 2760 (1977), and corrigendum, ibid *67,* 4786, (1977).
17. L. Kevan, International J. Radiation Physics and Chemistry *6,* 297 (1974).
18. A. Sumi, and Y. Toyozawa, J. Phys. Soc. Jpn. *35,* 137 (1973).
19. E. A. Silnish, Phys. Status Solidi A *3,* 817 (1970).
20. M. Tachiya and A. Mozumder, J. Chem. Phys. *61,* 3890 (1974).
21. R. M. Keyser, K. Tsuji, and F. Williams, in *The Radiation Chemistry of Macromolecules,* Vol. I, M. Dole, Ed., Academic Press, New York (1972).
22. H. Y. Wang and J. E. Willard, J. Chem. Phys. *69,* 2964, (1978).
23. Y. Toyozawa in *Phonons and Excitons,* C. G. Kuper and G. D. Whitfield, Eds., Oliver and Boyd Press, Edinburgh (1963).
24. J. E. Willard, Science *180,* 553, (1973).
25. A. E. Blake, A. Charlesby, and K. J. Randle, J. Phys. D *7,* 759 (1974).
26. J. H. Ranicar and R. J. Fleming, J. Polym. Sci. Polym. Phys. Ed. *10,* 1979 (1972).
27. T. Nishitani, K. Yoshino, and Y. Inuishi, Jpn J. Appl. Phys. *14,* 721 (1975).
28. P. Kelly, M. J. Laubitz, and P. Braunlich, Phys. Rev. B *4,* 1960 (1971).
29. R. J. Fleming and L. F. Pender, Phys. Rev. B *18,* 5900 (1978).
30. L. F. Pender and R. J. Fleming, J. Phys. C *10,* 1571 (1977).
31. R. E. Collins, Rev. Sci. Instrum. *48,* 83 (1977).
32. G. M. Sessler, J. E. West, D. A. Berkley, and G. Morgenstern, Phys. Rev. Lett. *38,* 368 (1977).
33. M. Latour, and G. Donnet, J. Electrostat. *8,* 81 (1979).
34. P. Laurenceau, J. Ball, G. Dreyfus, and J. Lewiner, Comptes Rendus, Academie des Sciences, *283B,* 135 (1976).
35. R. H. Partridge, J. Poly. Sci. Part A. *3,* 2817 (1965).
36. M. M. Perlman, J. Electrochem. Soc. *119,* 892 (1972).
37. B. Cantaloube, G. Dreyfus, and J. Lewiner, J. Polym. Sci., Polym. Phys. Ed. *17,* 95 (1979).
38. A. Reiser, M. W. B. Lock, and J. Knight, Trans. Faraday Soc. *65,* 2168 (1969).
39. H. J. Wintle J. Appl. Phys. *43,* 2927 (1972).
40. I. P. Batra, K. K. Kanazawa, and H. J. Wintle, J. Appl. Phys. *43,* 719 (1972).
41. E. A. Baum, T. J. Lewis, and R. Toomer, J. Appl. Phys. D *10,* 2525 (1977).
42. H. von Seggern, J. Appl. Phys. *50,* 7039 (1979).
43. R. Elsdon, and F. R. G. Mitchell, J. Phys. D *9,* 1445 (1976).
44. P. J. Lock in *Elektrostatische Aufladung,* Dechema Verlag, Frankfurt, (1974), pp. 87–93.
45. D. K. Davies, Conference on Static Electrification, London 1967, (Proceedings, Institute of Physics and the Physical Society), pp. 29–36.
46. L. M. Beckley, T. J. Lewis, and D. M. Taylor, J. Phys. D *9,* 1355 (1976).
47. B. Gross, G. M. Sessler and J. E. West, J. Appl. Phys. *45,* 2841 (1974).

48. B. Gross, G. M. Sessler, and J. E. West, J. Appl. Phys. *47*, 968 (1976).
49. J. Chutia, and K. Barua, J. Phys. D *13*, L9 (1980).
50. H. St-Onge, IEEE Trans. Electr. Insul. *EI-150*, 350 (1980).
51. G. Stetter, Kolloid Z. Z. Polym. *215*, 112 (1967).
52. A. Many and G. Rakavy, Phys. Rev. *126*, 1980 (1962).
53. H. Sodolski, J. Phys. C *12*, 3717 (1979).
54. Y. Kaahwa, Physics Status Solidi A *55*, K197 (1979).
55. B. I. Sazhin, V. P. Shuvaev, and V. B. Budtov, Vysokomol. Soedin. Ser. A *12*, 2393 (1970).
56. T. Mizutani and M. Ieda, J. Phys. D *12*, 291 (1979).
57. T. J. Lewis and D. M. Taylor, J. Phys. D *5*, 1664 (1972).
58. G. T. Jones and G. T. Lewis, Symp. Faraday Soc. *9*, 192 (1971).
59. J. H. Renicar and R. J. Fleming, J. Polym. Sci. Part A-2 *10*, 1321 (1972).
60. R. Goffaux, Bulletin Scientifique de l'Association des Ingenieurs Electriciens de l'Institut Electrotechnique Monefiore (Belgium) *88*, 299 (1975).
61. A. Toureille, J. Appl. Phys. *47*, 2961 (1976).
62. L. Brehmer and M. Pinnow, Phys. Status Solidi A *50*, K239 (1978).
63. D. K. Davis and P. J. Lock, J. Electrochem. Soc. *120*, 266 (1973).
64. E. H. Martin and J. Hirsch, J. Appl. Phys. *43*, 1001 (1972).
65. J. Kyokane, S. Harada, K. Yoshino, and Y. Inuishi, Jpn J. Appl. Phys. *18*, 1479 (1979).
66. T. Nishitani, K. Yoshino, and Y. Inuishi, Jpn J. Appl. Phys. *15*, 931 (1976).
67. B. Gross, G. M. Sessler, H. von Seggern, and J. E. West, Appl. Phys. Lett. *34*, 555 (1979).
68. R. A. Moreno, and B. Gross, J. Appl. Phys. *47*, 3397 (1976).
69. M. M. Perlman, T. J. Sonnonstine, and J. A. St. Pierre, J. Appl. Phys. *47*, 5016 (1976).
70. B. N. Ganguly, Phys. Rev. B *12*, 1275 (1975).
71. D. M. Taylor and T. J. Lewis, J. Phys. D *4*, 1346 (1971).
72. W. D. Gill in *Photoconductivity and Related Phenomena*, J. Mort and D. M. Pai, Eds., Elsevier Press, Amsterdam (1976).
73. M. Pollak, Philos. Mag. *36*, 1157 (1977).
74. J. Noolandi, Phys. Rev. B *16*, 4474 (1977).
75. K. W. Kehr and J. W. Haus, Physica *93A*, 412 (1978).
76. L. F. Pender and R. J. Fleming, Department of Physics, Monash University, Clayton, Australia, private communication, 1977.
77. R. E. Barker, Pure and Apl. Chem. *46*, 157 (1976).
78. T. Tanaka and J. H. Calderwood, J. Phys. D *7*, 1295 (1974).
79. K. Yatsuhashi, K. Kamisako, and H. Sasabe, Rep. Prog. Polym. Phys. Jpn *20* (1977).
80. K. Hayashi, K. Yoshino, and Y. Inuishi, Jpn J. Appl. Phys. *14*, 39 (1975).
81. A. V. Vannikov, Sov. Phys. Solid State *9*, 1068 (1967).
82. S. Matsumoto and K. Yahagi, Jpn J. Appl. Phys. *12*, 930 (1973).
83. J. Hirsch and E. H. Martin, J. Appl. Phys. *43*, 1008 (1972).
84. R. C. Hughes in *Second International Conference on Electrophotography*, D. R. White, Ed., Society of Photographic Scientists and Engineers, Washington, D. C. (1974), pp. 147–151.
85. J. J. O'Dwyer, *The Theory of Electrical Conduction and Breakdown in Solid Dielectrics*, Oxford University Press, London (1973).
86. M. A. Lampert, and P. Mark, *Current Injection in Solids*, Academic Press, New York (1970).
87. N. F. Mott and E. A. Davis, *Electronic Processes in Non-Crystalline Materials*, Oxford University Press, London (1971).
88. W. E. Spear, Adv. Phys. *23*, 523 (1974).
89. W. Paul, Thin Solid Films *33*, 381 (1976).
90. V. Ambegaokar, B. I. Halperin, and J. S. Langer, Phys. Rev. B *4*, 2612 (1971).
91. G. E. Pike, Phys. Rev. B *6*, 1572 (1972).
92. D. J. Jeffrey, Proc. R. Soc. London, Ser. A *335*, 355 (1973).
93. G. K. Batchelor and R. W. O'Brien, Proc. R. Soc. London A *355*, 313 (1977).
94. W. W. Mullins, J. Appl. Phys. *50*, 6754 (1979).
95. P. Hedvig, *Dielectric Spectroscopy of Polymers*, Hilger Press, Bristol (1977), p. 282.
96. L. K. H. van Beek, Prog. Dielectr. *7*, 69-114 (1967).
97. J. R. Macdonald, J. Chem. Phys. *61*, 3977 (1974).
98. M. J. Sparnay, Trans. Faraday Soc. *53*, 306 (1957).
99. T. M. Hayes, and D. D. Thornburg, J. Phys. C *6*, 450 (1973).

100. R. Coelho V. K. Agarwal, and R. Haug, J. Phys. D *10,* 1943 (1977).
101. J. Lindmayer, J. Reynolds, and C. Wrigley, J. Appl. Phys. *34,* 809 (1963).
102. M. A. Lampert and F. Edelman, J. Appl. Phys. *35,* 2971 (1964).
103. W. Mehl, J. M. Hale, and F. Lohmann, J. Electrochem. Soc. *113,* 1166 (1966).
104. P. Mark and W. Helfrich, J. Appl. Phys. *33,* 205 (1962).
105. A. Rosental and A. Sapar, J. Appl. Phys. *45,* 2787 (1974).
106. J. Mort and P. Nielsen, Phys. Rev. B *5,* 3336 (1972).
107. P. N. Murgatroyd, Phys. Status Solidi A *8,* 259 (1971).
108. D. F. Barbe, J. Phys. D *4,* 1812 (1971).
109. H. P. Schwob and D. F. Williams, J. Appl. Phys. *50,* 2638 (1979).
110. H. H. Poole, Philos. Mag. *34,* 341 (1917).
111. R. M. Hill, Philos. Mag. *23,* 59 (1969).
112. G. Vincent, A. Chantre, and D. Bois, J. Appl. Phys. *50,* 5484 (1979).
113. M. R. Belmont, Thin Solid Films *60,* 341 (1979).
114. J. Antula, J. Appl. Phys. *43,* 4663 (1972).
115. K. K. Thornber, Solid-State Electron. *21,* 259 (1978),
116. W. B. Nottingham in *Handbuch der Physik, 21,* S. Flugge, Ed., Springer Verlag, Berlin (1956), pp. 1-175.
117. P. N. Murgatroyd, Phys. Status Solidi A *6,* 217 (1971).
118. D. L. Fulfrey, A. H. M. Shousha, and L. Young, J. Appl. Phys. *41,* 2838 (1970).
119. M. E. Baird, Rev. Mod. Phys. *40,* 219 (1968).
120. R. H. Walden, J. Appl. Phys. *43,* 1178 (1972).
121. H. J. Wintle, J. Non-Cryst. Solids *15,* 471 (1974).
122. H. J. Wintle, IEEE Trans. Electr. Insul. *EI-120,* 424 (1977).
123. S. Uemura, J. Polym. Sci. Polym. Phys. Ed. *10,* 2155 (1972).
124. J. R. Macdonald, J. Chem. Phys. *54,* 2026 (1971).
125. R. Meaudre and G. Mesnard, Rev. Phys. Appl. *7,* 213 (1972).
126. W. Brenig in *Amorphous and Liquid Semiconductors,* J. Stuke and W. Brenig, Eds. Taylor and Franciss Press, London (1974), pp. 31-47.
127. N. Kumar and J. Heinrichs, J. Phys. C *9,* 2331 (1976).
128. D. M. Pai, J. Appl. Phys. *46,* 5122 (1972).
129. P. J. Melz, J. Chem. Phys. *57,* 1694 (1972).
130. R. R. Chance and C. L. Braun, J. Chem. Phys. *64,* 3573 (1976).
131. P. M. Borsenberger and A. I. Ateya, J. Appl. Phys. *50,* 909 (1979).
132. J. K. Baird, V. E. Anderson, and S. A. Rice, J. Chem. Phys. *67,* 3842 (1977).
133. T. J. Ahrens and F. Wooten, IEEE Trans. Nucl. Sci. NS-230, 1268 (1976).
134. L. Weave, J. K. Shultis, and R. E. Faw, J. Appl. Phys. *48,* 2762 (1977).
135. B. L. Beers, IEEE Trans. Nucl. Sci. *NS-240,* 2429 (1977).
136. A. R. Frederickson, IEEE Trans. Nucl. Sci. *NS-240,* 2532 (1977).
137. B. Gross, IEEE Trans. Nucl. Sci. *NS-250,* 1048 (1978).
138. A. C. Papadakis and P. N. Keating, British J. Appl Phys. *16,* 613 (1965).
139. D. K. Nichols and V. A. van Lint, IEEE Trans. Nucl. Sci. *NS-130,* 119 (1966).
140. M. Schott, Mol. Cryst. *5,* 229 (1969).
141. E. L. Frankevich and B. S. Yakovlev, Int. J. Radiat. Phys. and Chem. *6,* 281 (1974).
142. J. F. Fowler, Proc. R. Soc. London A., *236,* 464 (1956).
143. A. Rose, RCA Rev. *12,* 362 (1951).
144. R. P. Dahiya and V. K. Mathur, J. Phys. D *7,* 1512 (1974).
145. M. D. Tabak and M. E. Scharfe, J. Appl. Phys. *41,* 2114 (1970).
146. P. Braunlich, Phys. Status Solidi *21,* 383 (1967).
147. R. J. Powell, J. Appl. Phys. *41,* 2424 (1970).
148. H. Seki, Phys. Rev. B *2,* 4877 (1970).
149. E. O. Kane, Phys. Rev. *127,* 131 (1962).
150. J. N. Murrel in *Symposium on Electrical Conductivity in Organic Solids,* H. Kallmann and M. Silver, Eds. Interscience Press, New York (1971), pp. 127–145.
151. J. Lowell and A. C. Rose-Innes, Adv. in Physics *29,* 947 (1980).
152. H. Bauser, Dechema Monographs *72,* 11 (1974).
153. W. Ruppel, Dechema Monographs *72,* 321 (1974).
154. J. Fuhrmann, J. Electrostat. *4,* 109 (1977).

155. D. K. Donald, J. Electrochem. Soc. *115*, 270 (1968).
156. P. E. Wagner, J. Appl. Phys. *27*, 1300 (1956).
157. D. K. Davies, *Static Electrification*, Institute of Physics Conference Series, No. 4, p. 29 (1967).
158. F. Nordhage and G. Backstrom, *Static Electrification*, Institute of Physics Conference Series, No. 27, p. 84 (1975).
159. J. Lowell, J. Phys. D *9*, 1571 (1976).
160. H. T. M. Haenen, J. Electrostat. *2*, 151 (1976).
161. A. Wahlin and G. Backstrom, J. Appl. Phys. *45*, 2058 (1974).
162. D. K. Davies in *1973 Annual Rep. Conf. Elec. Ins. Diel. Phenomena*, National Academy of Sciences – National Research Council, Washington D. C., p. 1.
163. J. A. Medley, Br. J. Appl. Phys. *4*, suppl. 2, 528 (1953).
164. D. K. Davies, J. Phys. *D2*, 1533 (1969).
165. D. K. Davies, Adv. Stat. Electrification *1*, 10 (1970).
166. G. A. Cottrell, J. Phys. *D11*, 681 (1978).
167. S. Kittaka and Y. Murata, Jap. J. Appl. Phys. *18*, 295 (1979).
168. C. Weaver, J. Mangaly, and T. Robson, Proceedings of the 3rd International Conference on Static Electricity, Grenoble.
169. K. P. Homewood and A. C. Rose-Innes, *Static Electrification*, Institute of Physics Conference Series, No. 48, p. 233 (1979).
170. R. Elsdon and F. R. G. Mitchell, J. Phys. *D9*, 1445 (1976).
171. W. R. Harper, *Contact and Frictional Electrification*, University Press, Oxford (1967).
172. A. Kasai and J. Nishi, Dechema Monographs *72*, 419 (1974).
173. T. J. Fabish, H. M. Saltsburg, and M. L. Hair, J. Appl. Phys. *47*, 930 (1976).
174. T. J. Fabish, H. M. Saltsburg, and M. L. Hair, J. Appl. Phys. *47*, 940 (1976).
175. J. Fuhrmann and J. Kurschner, J. of Electrostatics *10*, 115 (1981).
176. J. Fuhrmann and R. Hofmann, Proc. 1st Int. Conf. Conduct. Breakdown Solid Dielectrics, p. 71 (1983).
177. J. Fuhrmann and R. Hofmann, IEEE Trans. Electrical Insulation *EI-190*, 187 (1984).
178. K. P. Homewood and A. C. Rose-Innes, J. Phys. D, Appl. Phys. *15*, 2283 (1982).
179. K. P. Homewood, J. Lowell, and A. C. Rose-Innes, Inst. Phys. Conf. Ser. No. 66, p. 225 (1983).
180. J. Lowell, J. of Electrostatics *14*, 149 (1984).
181. J. Lowell, J. Phys. D, Appl. Phys. *17*, 1859 (1984).
182. S. P. Hersh and D. J. Montgomery, Text Res. J. *25*, 279 (1955).
183. P. E. Shaw, Proc. Royal Soc. *94*, 16 (1917).
184. R. G. C. Arridge, Br. J. Appl. Phys. *18*, 1311 (1967).
185. I. I. Inculet and E. P. Wituschek, *Static Electrification*, Institute of Physics Conference Series, No. 4, p. 37 (1967).
186. F. Nordhage and G. Backstrom, J. Electrostat. *3*, 371 (1971).
187. R. F. Challande, Adv. Stat. Electrification *1*, 156 (1970).
188. S. Kittaka and Y. Murata, 16th Conference of the Electrostatic Society, Osaka, Japan (1971).
189. W. A. D. Rudge, Lond. Edinb. Dubl. Phil. Mag. *25*, 481 (1913).
190. W. A. D. Rudge, Proc. Roy. Soc. *A90*, 256 (1914).
191. J. A. Medley, Nature (London) *171*, 1077 (1953).
192. N. F. Mott and R. W. Gurney, *Electronic Processes in Ionic Crystals*, Clarendon Press, Oxford (1940).
193. J. E. Falk and R. J. Fleming, J. Phys. *C6*, 2954 (1973).
194. J. E. Falk and R. J. Fleming, J. Phys. *C8*, 627 (1975).
195. W. L. McCubbin and D. C. Gurney, J. Chem. Phys. *43*, 983 (1965).
196. N. F. Mott and E. A. Davies, *Electronic Processes in Non-Crystalline Materials*, Clarendon Press, Oxford (1971).
197. G. A. Cottrell, C. Reed, and A. C. Rose-Innes, *Static Electrification*, Insitute of Physics Conference Series, No. 48, p. 249 (1979).
198. I. Bousted and A. Charlesbury, Proc. Roy. Soc. *A316*, 291 (1970).
199. M. M. Perlman, J. Electrochem. Soc. *119*, 892 (1972).
200. D. K. Davies and P. J. Lock, J. Electrochem. Soc. *120*, 266 (1973).
201. M. M. Perlman and S. Unger, J. Phys. *D5*, 2115 (1972).
202. K. Amakawa and Y. Inuishi, Jap. J. Appl. Phys. *12*, 755 (1973).

203. J. D. Brodribb, D. M. Hughes, and T. J. Lewis, *Electrets, Charge Storage and Transport in Dielectrics*, M. M. Perlman, ed., Electrochemical Soc., London (1973).
204. R. A. Cresswell and M. M. Perlmann, J. Appl. Phys. *41*, 2365 (1970).
205. J. F. Fowler, Proc. Roy. Soc. *236*, 464 (1956).
206. G. M. Sessler and J. E. West, J. Appl. Phys. *43*, 922 (1972).
207. P. J. Lock, Dechema Monographs *72*, 87 (1974).
208. J. H. Ranicar and R. J. Fleming, J. Polym Sci. *10*, 1979 (1972).
209. G. Sawa, M. Kawale, D. C. Lee, M. Ieda, Jap. J. Appl. Phys. *13*, 1547 (1974).
210. J. Lowell, J. Phys. D, Appl. Phys. *12*, 2217 (1979).
211. C. B. Duke and T. J. Fabish, Phys. Rev. Lett. *37*, 1075 (1976).
212. J. Henniker, Nature (London) *196*, 474 (1962).
213. J. Lowell, J. of Electrostatics *8*, 161 (1980).
214. W. Shockley, Phys. Rev. *56*, 317 (1939).
215. S. G. Davison and J. D. Levine, Solid St. Phys. *25*, 1 (1970).
216. E. H. Rhoderick, *Metal Semiconductor Contacts*, University Press, Oxford (1978).
217. S. Kurtin, T. C. McGill, and C. A. Mead, Phys. Rev. Lett. *22*, 1433 (1969).
218. T. C. McGill and C. A. Mead, J. Vac. Sci. Technol. *11*, 935 (1974).
219. D. A. Hays, Dechema Monographs *72*, 95 (1974).
220. D. A. Hays, J. Chem. Phys. *61*, 1455 (1974).
221. Y. Murata, Jap. J. Appl. Phys. *18*, 1 (1979).
222. S. Kittaka and Y. Murata, Jap. J. Appl. Phys. *18*, 575 (1979).
223. B. C. O'Neil and T. R. Foord, *Static Electrification*, Institute of Physics Conference Series, No. 27, p. 104 (1975).
224. G. A. Cottrell, J. Lowell, and A. C. Rose-Innes, J. Appl. Phys. *50*, 374 (1979).
225. J. Lowell, J. Phys. D, Appl. Phys. *14*, 1513 (1981).
226. I. I. Inculet and W. D. Greason, *Static Electrification*, Institute of Physics Conference Series, No. 11, p. 23 (1971).
227. J. Fuhrmann, Colloid Polymer Sci. *254*, 129 (1976).
228. M. W. Williams, C. J. Auclair, G. P. Caesar and J. M. Short, Conference Record 10th Annual Meeting of the IEEE Industry Applications Society, Atlanta (1975).
229. J. Lowell, J. Phys. D, Appl. Phys. *12*, 1541 (1979).
230. H. R. Harper, Soc. Chem. Ind. Monographs *14*, 115 (1961).
231. W. J. Dunning, Soc. Chem. Ind. Monographs *14*, 127 (1961).
232. P. S. Henry, J. Text. Inst. *48*, 5 (1957).
233. P. S. Henry, Br. J. Appl. Phys. *4*, Suppl. 2, S6 (1957).
234. F. R. Ruckdeschel and L. P. Hunter, J. Appl. Phys. *46*, 4416 (1976).
235. F. R. Ruckdeschel and L. P. Hunter, J. Appl. Phys. *48*, 4898 (1977).
236. M. I. Kornfeld, J. Phys. *D9*, 1183 (1976).
237. M. I. Kornfeld, Soviety Phys. Solid St. *11*, 1306 (1969).
238. M. I. Kornfeld, Soviety Phys. Solid St. *10*, 1904 (1969).
239. P. E. Shaw and C. S. Jex, Proc. Roy. Soc. *118*, 97 (1928).
240. M. I. Kornfeld, Soviety Phys. Solid St. *16*, 211 (1974).
241. E. S. Robins, Ph.D. thesis, University of Manchester, 1977.
242. E. S. Robins, A. C. Rose-Innes, and J. Lowell, Static Electrification, Institute of Physics Conference Series, No. 27, p. 115 (1975).
243. E. S. Robins, J. Lowell, and A. C. Rose-Innes, J. Electrostat. *8*, 153 (1980).
244. E. A. Baum and T. J. Lewis, 1975 Conference on Static Electrification, London, Institute of Physics, pp. 130–140.
245. R. A. Huggins and J. M. Huggins, Macromolecules *10*, 889 (1977).
246. R. E. Barker, Pure and Appl. Chem. *46*, 157 (1976).
247. H. E. Bair, G. E. Johnson, and R. Merriweather, J. Appl. Phys. *49*, 4976 (1978).
248. D. W. Auckland and R. Cooper, Proc. Inst. Electr. Eng. *122*, 860 (1975).
249. D. W. Swan, J. Appl. Phys. *38*, 5051 (1967).
250. B. I. Sazhin, V. P. Shuvaev, and V. B. Budtov, Vysokomol. Soedin. Ser. A *12*, 2393 (1970).
251. T. J. Lewis and D. M. Taylor, J. Phys. D *5*, 1664 (1972).
252. G. T. Jones and G. T. Lewis, Symp. Faraday Soc. *9*, 192 (1971).
253. H. Sodolski, J. Phys. C *12*, 3717 (1979).
254. S. Osaki and Y. Ishida, J. Polym. Sci. Polym. Phys. Ed. *11*, 801 (1973).

255. Y. Segui, Bui Ai, C. Bagnol, J. Pistre, Y. Danto, and A. S. Barriere, J. Appl. Phys. *50*, 2973 (1979).
256. C. A. Hogarth and T. Iqbal, Thin Solid Films *51*, L45 (1978).
257. W. R. Salanek, A. Paton, and D. T. Clark, J. Appl. Phys. *47*, 144 (1976).
258. C. M. Pooley and D. Tabor, Proc. Roy. Soc. *A329*, 251 (1972).
259. J. Lowell, J. Phys. *D10*, L233 (1977).
260. J. B. Levy, J. H. Wakelin, W. J. Kauzmann, and J. H. Dillon, Text. Res. J. *28*, 897 (1958).
261. J. Lowell, J. Phys. *D10*, 65 (1977).
262. H. Krupp, Physical Models of the Static Electrification of Solids, Static Electrification, 1971, Inst. Phys. Conf. Ser. No. *11*, p. 1 (1971).
263. J. Fuhrmann, Coll. Polym. Sci. *254*, 129 (1976).
264. M. Hennecke, R. Hoffmann, and J. Fuhrmann, J. of Electrostatics *6*, 15 (1979).
265. J. Kurschner and J. Fuhrmann, J. of Electrostatics *14*, 73 (1983).
266. J. Kurschner, J. Fuhrmann, and H. J. Streibel, J. of Electrostatics *14*, 83 (1983).
267. J. Fuhrmann and H. J. Streibel, Inst. Phys. Conf. Ser. No. 66, p. 145 (1983).
268. C. B. Duke and T. J. Fabish, J. Appl. Phys. *49*, 315 (1978).
269. R. F. Challande, C. r. hebd Seanc. Acad. Sci. Paris, *266*, 649 (1968).
270. P. S. H. Henry, Br. J. Appl. Phys. *4*, 531 (1951).
271. P. E. Shaw, Proc. Phys. Soc. *39*, 180 (1927).
272. V. E. Gonsalves, Text. Res. J. *24*, 1 (1954).
273. E. Zimmer, Kunstoffe *60*, 465 (1970).
274. B. V. Derjaguin, Y. P. Toporov, I. N. Aleinikova, J. Colloid Interface Sci. *54*, 59 (1976).
275. I. Shinohara, F. Yamamoto, H. Anzai, and S. Endo, J. Electrostat. *2*, 99 (1976).
276. M. W. Williams, C. J. Auclair, G. P. Caesar, and J. M. Short, Conference Record 10th Annual Meeting of the I.E.E.E. Industry Applications Soc. Atlanta (1975).
277. P. J. Cressman, G. C. Hartmann, J. E. Kuder, F. D. Saeva, and D. Wychick, J. Chem. Phys. *61*, 2740 (1974).
278. B. R. Vijayendran, J. Colloid Interface Sci. *64*, 514 (1978).
279. H. W. Gibson, J. Am. Chem. Soc. *97*, 3832 (1975).
280. H. W. Gibson and F. C. Bailey, Chem. Phys. Lett. *51*, 352 (1977).
281. H. W. Gibson and F. C. Bailey, Can. J. Chem. *53*, 2162 (1975).
282. H. W. Gibson and F. C. Bailey, J. Chem. Soc. Chem. Comm. 815 (1977).
283. H. W. Gibson, F. C. Bailey, and J. Y. C. Chu, J. Polym. Sci. Polym. Chem. Ed. *17*, 777 (1979).
284. H. W. Gibson, F. C. Bailey, J. L. Mincer, and W. H. H. Gunther, J. Polym. Sci. Polym. Chem. Ed. *17*, 296 (1979).
285. H. W. Gibson, J. M. Pochan, F. C. Bailey, Anal. Chem. *51*, 483 (1979).
286. J. M. Pochan, H. W. Gibson, F. C. Bailey, and D. F. Hinman, J. Electrostatics *8*, 183 (1980).
287. H. W. Gibson and F. C. Bailey, J. Chem. Soc. Perkin Trans II, p. 1575 (1976).
288. P. J. Cressman, G. C. Hartmann, J. E. Kuder, F. D. Saeva, and D. Wychick, J. Chem. Phys. *61*, 2740 (1974).
289. J. G. McNally, U. S. Pat. 3,748,128 (1973).
290. G. A. Cottrell, C. E. Hatto, C. Reed, and A. C. Rose-Innes, J. Phys. D, Appl. Phys. *17*, 989 (1984).
291. B. Sonntag in *Rare Gas Solids*, Vol. II, chap. 17, M. L. Klein, and J. A. Venables, eds., Academic Press, New York (1977).
292. T. Miyamoto and K. Shibayama, J. Appl. Phys. *44*, 5372 (1973).
293. M. Kosaki, M. Yoda, and M. Ieda, J. Phys. Soc. Jpn *31*, 1598 (1971).
294. F. S. Smith and C. Scott, Br. J. Appl. Phys. *17*, 1149 (1966).
295. H. Sasabe, K. Sawamura, S. Saito, and K. Yoda, Polym. J. *2*, 518 (1971).
296. B. I. Sazhin and G. N. Podosenova, Sov. Phys. Solid State *6*, 1755 (1965).
297. S. N. Kolesov, N. P. Balaban, V. A. Putintsev, and I. S. Kolesov, Vysokomol. Soedin. Ser. B *18*, 5 (1976).
298. G. Sawa, M. Ieda, and K. Kotagawa, Electron. Lett. *10*, 50 (1974).
299. A. van Roggen, Phys. Rev. Lett. *9*, 368 (1962).
300. G. Senecal and J. S. Ham, J. Appl. Phys. *42*, 2714 (1971).
301. R. E. Barker, P. S. Marshall, and R. C. Tsai, 1971 *Annual Report, Conference on Electrical Insulation and Dielectric Phenomena*, National Academy of Sciences-National Research Council, Washington, D.C. (1972), pp. 65–73.

302. Bui Ai, P. Destruel, Hoang The Giam, and R. Loussier, Phys. Rev. Lett. *34*, 84 (1975).
303. A. R. Champion, J. Appl. Phys. *43*, 2216 (1972).
304. J. H. Kallweit, Kunstoffe *47*, 651 (1957).
305. A. E. Binks and A. Sharples, J. Polym. Sci. A-2 *6*, 407 (1968).
306. V. Adamec, Z. Ange. Phys. *29*, 291 (1970).
307. A. Pillonet and G. Asch, Comptes Rendus, Academie des Sciences, B., *273*, 432 (1971).
308. L. E. Amborski, J. Polym. Sci. *62*, 331 (1962).
309. M. Kosaki, K. Sugiyama, and M. Ieda, J. Appl. Phys. *42*, 3388 (1971).
310. D. Kiessling and B. Mundorfer, Plastik and Kautschuk *16*, 348 (1969).
311. J. Vanderschueren and A. Linkens, J. Appl. Phys. *49*, 4195 (1978).
312. D. K. DasGupta and K. Jyner, J. Phys. D *9*, 829 (1976).
313. J. R. Hanscomb and Y. Kaahwa, J. Phys. D *11*, 725 (1978).
314. A. Bradwell, R. Cooper, and B. Varlow, Proc. Inst. Electr. Eng. *118*, 247 (1971).
315. R. Cooper, B. R. Varlow, and J. P. White, *Conference on Dielectric Materials, Measurements and Applications*, I.E.E., London (1975), pp. 209–212.
316. K. Kojima, A. Maeda, Y. Takai, and M. Ieda, Jpn J. Appl. Phys. *17*, 1735 (1978).
317. H. J. Wintle and J. Turlo, J. Appl. Phys. *50*, 7128 (1979).
318. B. Andress, P. Fischer, and P. Rohl, Prog. Colloid Polym. Sci. *62*, 141 (1977).
319. D. J. DiMaria, F. J. Feigl, Phys. Rev. B *9*, 1874 (1974).
320. J. D. Brodribb, D. O'Colmain, and D. M. Hughes, J. Phys. D *8*, 856 (1975).
321. S. Sapieha and H. J. Wintle, Canadian J. Phys. *55*, 646 (1977).
322. T. Mizutani, Y. Takai, T. Osawa, and M. Ieda, J. Phys. D *9*, 2253 (1974).
323. Y. Takai, T. Osawa, T. Mizutani, and M. Ieda, J. Polym. Sci. Polym. Phys. Ed. *15*, 945, (1977).
324. H. J. Wintle, J. Polym. Sci. Polym. Phys. Ed. *12*, 2135 (1974).
325. L. A. Vermeulen, H. J. Wintle, and D. A. Nicodemo, J. Polym. Sci. A-2 *9*, 543 (1971).
326. T. Mizutani, T. Ueno, Y. Takai, and M. Ieda, Jpn J. of Appl. Phys. *12*, 757 (1973).
327. J. D. Comins and H. J. Wintle, J. Polym. Sci Polym. Phys. Ed. *10*, 2259 (1972).
328. Y. Takai, K. Ishii, T. Mizutani, and M. Ieda, J. Phys. D *12*, 601 and 1409 (1979).
329. O. M. Sorokin and V. A. Blank, Sov. Phys. Solid State *11*, 2141 (1970).
330. K. J. Less and E. G. Wilson, J. Phys. *6*, 3110 (1973).
331. M. Ofran, N. Oron, and A. Weinreb, Mol. Cryst. Liq. Cryst *6*, 415 (1970).
332. D. M. Taylor, Int. J. Radiat. Phys. Chem. *13*, 209 (1979).
333. B. Gross, J. Dow, and S. V. Nablo, J. Appl. Phys. *44*, 2459 (1973).
334. D. M. Taylor, J. Phys. D *9*, 2269 (1976).
335. K. Yoshino, J. Kyokane, T. Nishitani, and Y. Inuishi, J. Appl. Phys. *49*, 4849 (1978).
336. F. W. Schmidlin, Phys. Rev. B *16*, 2362 (1977).
337. J. Noolandi, Phys. Rev. B *16*, 4466 (1977).
338. W. L. Chadsey, IEEE Trans. Nuc. Sci. *NS-210*, 235 (1974).
339. R. E. Leadon, C. E. Mallon, and B. A. Green, IEEE Trans. Nuc. Sci. *NS-200*, 126 (1973).
340. H. J. Wintle, Br. J. Radiol. *33*, 706 (1960).
341. F. N. Coppage, IEEE Trans. Nuc. Sci. *NS-120*, 147 (1965).
342. R. H. Bartlett, G. A. Fulk, R. S. Lee, and R. C. Weingart, IEEE Trans. Nucl. Sci. *NS-220*, 2273 (1975).
343. H. E. Boesch and A. S. Hill, IEEE Trans. Nucl. Sci. *NS-160*, 124 (1969).
344. S. E. Vaisberg, V. P. Sichkar, and V. L. Karpov, Vysokomol. Soedin. Ser. A *13*, 2502 (1971).
345. V. Adamec, J. Polym. Sci. A-2 *6*, 1241 (1968).
346. V. Adamec, Nature *200*, 1196 (1963).
347. E. A. Balik, J. Appl. Phys. *43*, 302 (1972).
348. R. E. Collins, J. Appl. Phys. *47*, 4804 (1976).
349. P. Laurenceau, G. Dreyfus, and J. Lewiner, Phys. Rev. Lett. *38*, 46 (1977).
350. H. J. Wintle, J. Appl. Phys. *42*, 4724 (1971).
351. G. M. Sessler, J. Appl. Phys. *43*, 408 (1972).
352. B. Gross, Conference on Static Electrification (Proceedings of the Institute of Physics and the Physical Society), London, 1971, pp. 33–43.
353. Z. Croitoru, Rev. Gen. Electr. *68*, 489 (1959).
354. B. Gross, G. M. Sessler, and J. E. West, J. Appl. Phys. *48*, 4303 (1977).
355. K. K. Ametov, G. F. Novikov, and B. S. Yakovlev, Int. J. Radiation Phys. Chem. *10*, 43–49 (1977).

356. R. H. Partridge in *The Radiation Chemistry and Macromolecules*, M. Dole, Ed., Academic Press, New York (1972).
357. R. H. Partridge, J. Chem. Phys. *52*, 1277 (1970).
358. S. J. Sheng and D. M. Hanson, J. Appl. Phys. *45*, 4954 (1974).
359. D. Campbell, Polym. Lett. *8*, 313 (1970).
360. G. Dreyfus, J. Lewiner, and M. Legrand, Phys. Rev. B *20*, 1720 (1979).
361. G. Dreyfus and J. Lewiner, J. Electrochem. Soc. *120*, 1083 (1973).
362. J. Fuhrmann, Kolloid Z. Z. Polym. *250*, 1075 (1972).
363. H. Sakamoto and K. Yahagi, Jpn J. Appl. Phys. *19*, 253 (1980).
364. R. P. Kusy and D. T. Turner, Nature (London) Phys. Sci. *229*, 58, (1971).
365. A. Malliaris and D. T. Turner, J. Appl. Phys. *42*, 614 (1971).
366. F. Bueche, J. Polym. Sci. Polym. Phys. Ed. *11*, 1319 (1973).
367. H. St-Onge, IEEE Trans. Electr. Insul. *EI-110*, 20 (1976).
368. L. K. H. van Beek and B. I. C. F. van Pul, J. Appl. Polym. Sci. *6*, 651 (1962).
369. N. J. Stevens, C. K. Pruvis, and J. Staskus, IEEE Trans. Nucl. Sci. *NS-250*, 1304 (1978).
370. B. T. McClure and A. Contolatis, *1976 Annual Report, Conference on Electrical Insulation and Dielectric Phenomena*, National Academy of Sciences-National Research Council, Washington, D.C., 1978, pp. 469–475.
371. N. Gibson, and F. C. Lloyd, Br. J. Appl. Phys. *16*, 1619 (1965).
372. G. Sawa and J. H. Calderwood, J. Phys. C *4*, 2313 (1971).
373. Y. Awakuni and J. H. Calderwood, J. Phys. D *5*, 1038 (1972).
374. J. B. Jordan, R. Saint-Arnaud, and P. Le-Phan, *1976 Annual Report, Conference on Electrical Insulation and Dielectric Phenomena*, National Academy of Sciences-National Research Council, Washington, D.C., p. 296–301 (1978).
375. R. F. Field, General Radio Experimenter *20*, (2–3), 6 (1945).
376. S. Hirota, J. Appl. Phys. *50*, 3003 (1979).
377. H. J. Wintle and T. C. Chapman, J. Appl. Phys. *51*, 3435 (1980).
378. T. C. Chapman and H. J. Wintle, J. Appl. Phys. *51*, 4898 (1980).
379. J. A. Geurst, Phys. Status Solidi *15*, 107 (1966).
380. P. J. Atkinson and R. J. Fleming, J. Phys. D *13*, 625 (1980).
381. L. Frenkel, J. Res. Nat. Bur. Stand. A *68*, 185 (1964).
382. P. J. Atkinson and R. J. Fleming, J. Phys. D *13*, 655 (1980).
383. D. M. Taylor, T. J. Lewis, and T. P. T. Williams, J. Phys. D *7*, 1756 (1974).
384. R. J. Fleming and J. H. Ranicar, J. Macromol. Sci. Chem. *B4*, 1223 (1970).
385. S. P. Hersh and P. L. Grady, *Elektrostatische Aufladung*, Dechema Verlag, Frankfurt, p. 251 (1974).
386. H. J. Goldsmid and J. R. Hanscomb, J. Phys. C *11*, L657 (1978).
387. H. Bassler, G. Vaubel, K. Rasskopf, and K. Reinke, Zeitschrift für Naturforschung A *26*, 814 (1971).
388. W. A. Hartman and H. L. Armstrong, J. Appl. Phys. *38*, 2393 (1967).
389. A. E. Blake and K. J. Randle, J. Phys. D *10*, 759 (1977).
390. L. F. Pender and H. J. Wintle, J. Appl. Phys. *50*, 361 (1979).
391. B. Gross, G. M. Sessler, and J. E. West, Appl. Phys. Lett. *24*, 351 (1974).
392. E. P. Fowler, Proc. Inst. Electr. Eng. *123*, 1043 (1976).
393. G. M. Sessler and J. E. West, J. Appl. Phys. *50*, 3328 (1979).
394. G. Sawa, M. Dawade, and M. Ieda, J. Appl. Phys. *44*, 5397 (1973).
395. P. H. Ong and J. van Turnhout, *Elektrostatische Aufladung*, Dechema Verlag, Frankfurt (1974), pp. 104-124.
396. E. L. Zichy, *Elektrostatische Aufladung*, Dechema Verlag, Frankfurt (1974), pp. 147-161.

PART 2

397. K. Krogmann, Angew. Chem. Internat. Edn. *8*, 35 (1969).
398. M. J. Minot and J. H. Perlstein, Phys. Rev. Lett., *26*, 371 (1971).
399. R. Comes, M. Lambert, H. Launois, and H. R. Zeller, Phys. Rev. (B) *8*, 571 (1973).
400. R. Comes, M. Lambert, H. Launois, and H. R. Zeller, Phys. Status Solidi (B), *58*, 587 (1973).
401. J. M. Perlstein, M. J. Minot, and V. Walatka, Mater. Res. Bull. *7*, 309 (1972).

402. D. Bloor, Chem. in Brit. *19,* 725 (1983).
403. D. Chapman, R. J. Warn, A. G. Fitzgerald, and A. D. Yoffe, Trans. Faraday Soc. *60,* 294 (1964).
404. V. V. Walatka, M. M. Labes, and J. H. Perlstein, Phys. Rev. Lett. *31,* 1139 (1973).
405. H. Shirakawa and S. Ikeda, Polym. J. *2,* 231 (1971).
406. H. Shirakawa, E. J. Louis, A. G. MacDiarmid, C. K. Chiang, and A. J. Heeger, J. Chem. Soc. Chem. Commun. 578 (1977).
407. C. K. Chiang, C. R. Fincher, Jr., Y. W. Park, A. J. Heeger, H. Shirakawa, E. J. Louis, S. C. Gau, and A. G. MacDiarmid, Phys. Rev. Lett. *39,* 1098 (1977).
408. A. R. Blythe, *Electrical Properties of Polymers,* Cambridge University Press, Cambridge, United Kingdom (1979), pp. 123–132.
409. A. Rembaum in *Encyclopedia of Polymer Science and Technology,* N. M. Bikales, Ed., Interscience Publishers, New York (1969), Vol. 11, pp. 318–337.
410. H. Meier, *Organic Semiconductors,* Verlag Chemie, Weinheim, West Germany (1974).
411. L. Fox, RCA Rev. *39,* 116 (1978).
412. G. Keitel, Macroelectronic Manufacturing and Testing, 32 (Oct. 1980).
413. J. M. Crosby and J. E. Theberge, Mater. Eng. 29 (Feb. 1980).
414. D. E. Davenport, Org. Coat. Plast. Chem. *43,* 740 (1980).
415. D. M. Bigg and E. J. Bradbury, Org. Coat. Plast. Chem. *43,* 746 (1980).
416. R. M. Simon, Soc. Plast. Eng. Tech. Pap. *26,* 207 (1980).
417. W. L. Dulmage, W. A. Light, S. J. Marino, C. D. Saltzberg, D. L. Smith, and W. J. Staudenmayer, J. Appl. Phys. *49,* 5543 (1978).
418. R. M. Schaffert, IBM J. Res. Dev. *15,* 75 (1971).
419. R. F. Wolter, J. Appl. Photogr. Eng. *4,* 151 (1978).
420. S. Yoshimurea in *Molecular Metals,* W. E. Hatfield, Ed., Plenum Publishing Corp. New York, (1979), pp. 471–489.
421. V. Y. Merritt, IBM J. Res. Dev. *22,* 353 (1978).
422. D. L. Morel, Mol. Cryst. Liq. Cryst. *50,* 127 (1979).
423. C. B. Duke and L. B. Schein, Physics Today *33* (2), 42 (1980).
424. C. B. Duke, Mol. Cryst. Liq. Cryst. *50,* 63 (1979); Org. Coat. Plast. Chem. 42, 446 (1980).
425. C. B. Duke, *Proc. 1980 IEEE International Symposium on Circuits and Systems,* IEEE, Piscataway, NJ, (1980), pp. 20–21.
426. P. M. Chaikin, Ann. N.Y. Acad. Sci. *313,* 128 (1978).
427. R. E. Peierls, *Quantum Theory of Solids,* Clarendon Press, Oxford (1955).
428. T. J. Fabish, Crit. Rev. Solid State Mater. Sci. *8,* 383 (1979).
429. N. F. Mott and E. A. Davis, *Electronic Processes in Non-Crystalline Materials,* Clarendon Press, Oxford, United Kingdom, (1971).
430. C. B. Duke, W. R. Salaneck, T. J. Fabish, J. J. Ritsko, H. R. Thomas, and A. Paton, Phys. Rev. B *28,* 5717 (1978).
431. C. B. Duke, Surface Sci. *70,* 674 (1978).
432. C. B. Duke and T. J. Fabish, J. Appl. Phys. *49,* 315 (1978).
433. W. D. Gill in *Photoconductivity and Related Phenomena,* J. Mort and D. M. Pai, Eds., Elsevier North-Holland, Inc., Amsterdam, The Netherlands (1976), pp. 304–334.
434. G. B. Street and W. D. Gill in *Molecular Metals,* W. E. Hatfield, Ed., Plenum Publishing Corp. New York (1979), pp. 301–326.
435. A. G. MacDiarmid and A. J. Heeger in *Molecular Metals,* W. E. Hatfield, Ed., Plenum Publishing Corp. New York, (1979), pp. 161–186.
436. P. W. Anderson in *Ill-Condensed Matter,* R. Balian, R. Maynard, and G. Toulouse, Eds., North-Holland Publishing Company, Amsterdam, The Netherlands (1979), pp. 162–261.
437. N. F. Mott, *Metal-Insulator Transitions,* Taylor and Francis Ltd., London, United Kingdom (1974), Chap. 6.
438. R. V. Kasowski, E. Caruthers, and W. Y. Hus, Phys. Rev. Lett. *44,* 676 (1980).
439. S. D. Druger and R. S. Knox, J. Chem. Phys. *50,* 3143 (1969).
440. D. Emin, Adv. Phys. *22,* 57 (1973).
441. C. Kittel, *Introduction to Solid State Physics,* 2nd ed., John Wiley & Sons, Inc., New York (1959), Chaps. 17–18.
442. J. A. Pople and J. H. Walmsley, Mol. Phys. *5,* 15 (1962).
443. M. J. Rice, Phys. Rev. *71A,* 152 (1979); M. J. Rice and E. J. Mele, Solid State Commun. *35,* 487 (1980).

444. W. P. Su, J. R. Schrieffer, and A. J. Heeger, Phys. Rev. Lett *42*, 1698 (1979).
445. V. J. Emery in *Highly Conducting One-Dimensional Solids,* J. T. Devresse, R. P. Evrard, and V. E. van Doren, Eds., Plenum Publishing Corp. New York (1979), pp. 247–303.
446. C. B. Duke, A. Paton, W. R. Salaneck, H. R. Thomas, E. W. Plummer, A. J. Heeger, and A. G. MacDiarmid, Chem. Phys. Lett. *59*, 146 (1978).
447. D. Caxes, L. Salem, and C. Tric, J. Poly. Sci. Part C *29*, 109 (1970).
448. J. B. Torrance, Ann. N.Y. Acad. Sci. *313*, 210 (1978).
449. A. R. Bishop and T. Schneider, Eds., *Solitons in Condensed Matter Physics,* Springer, Berlin (1978).
450. J. Bernasconi and T. Schneider, Eds., *Physics in One Dimension,* Springer, Berlin (1981).
451. L. Alcacer, *The Physics and Chemistry of Low Dimensional Solids,* Reidel, Dordrecht (1980).
452. W. P. Su, J. R. Schrieffer, and A. J. Heeger, Phys. Rev. B *2*, 2099 (1980).
453. A. Kotani, J. Phys. Soc. Jpn. *42*, 408 and 416 (1977).
454. S. A. Brazovskii, Zh. Eksp. Teor. Fiz. Pis'ms Red. *28*, 656 (1978); [JETP Lett. *28*, 606 (1978).
455. S. A. Brazovskii, Zh. Eksp. Teor. Fiz. *78*, 677 (1980); [Sov. Phys. JETP *51*, 342 (1980).
456. H. Takayama, Y. R. Lin-Liu, and K. Maki, Phys. Rev. B *21*, 2388 (1980).
457. J. A. Krumhansl, B. Horovitz, and A. J. Heeger, Solid State Commun. *34*, 945 (1980).
458. B. Horovitz, Solid State Commun. *34*, 61 (1980).
459. B. Horovitz, Phys. Rev. Lett. *46*, 742 (1981).
460. B. Horovitz, Phys. Rev. B *22*, 1101 (1980).
461. M. J. Rice, Phys. Lett. *71A*, 152 (1979).
462. M. J. Rice and J. Timonen, Phys. Lett. *73A*, 368 (1979).
463. M. J. Rice and E. J. Mele, Chem. Scr. *17*, 21 (1981).
464. J. Pople and S. Walmsley, Trans. Faraday Soc. *58*, 441 (1962).
465. L. Salem, *Molecular Orbital Theory of Conjugated Systems,* Benjamin, NY (1966).
466. R. Jackiw and C. Rebbi, Phys. Rev. D *13*, 3398 (1976).
467. R. Jackiw and J. R. Schrieffer, Nucl. Phys. B *190*, 253 (1981).
468. W. P. Su and J. R. Schrieffer, Phys. Rev. Lett. *46*, 738 (1981).
469. M. J. Rice and E. J. Mele, Phys. Rev. B *25*, 1339 (1982).
470. S. Kivelson and J. R. Schrieffer, Phys. Rev. B *25*, 6447 (1982).
471. D. M. Ivory, G. G. Miller, J. M. Sowa, L. W. Schacklette, R. R. Chance, and R. H. Baughman, J. Chem. Phys. *71*, 1506 (1979).
472. R. R. Chance, L. W. Shacklette, G. G. Miller, D. M. Ivory, J. M. Sowa, R. L. Elsenbaumer, and R. H. Baughman, J. Chem. Soc. Chem. Commun. 348 (1980).
473. J. F. Rabolt, T. C. Clarke, K. K. Kanazawa, J. R. Reynolds, and G. B. Street, J. Chem. Soc. Chem. Commun. 347 (1980).
474. A. R. Bishop and D. K. Campbell in *Nonlinear Problems: Present and Future,* A. R. Bishop, D. K. Campbell, B. Nicolaenko, eds., North Holland Publ. Co., Amsterdam (1982), p. 195.
475. W. P. Su and J. R. Schrieffer, Proc. Nat. Acad. Sci. *77*, 5526 (1980).
476. K. K. Kanazawa, A. F. Diaz, R. H. Geiss, W. D. Gill, J. F. Kwak, J. A. Logan, J. F. Rabolt, and G. B. Street, J. Chem. Soc. Chem. Commun. 854 (1979).
477. A. F. Diaz, J. Crowley, J. Bargon, G. P. Gardini, and J. B. Torrance, J. Electroanal. Chem. *121*, 355 (1981).
478. Y. S. Papir, V. P. Kurkov, and S. P. Current, in Extended Abstracts Electrochemical Society Meeting, San Francisco (1983) p. 820.
479. S. E. Tunney, J. Suenaga and J. K. Stille, Macromolecules *16*(8), 1398 (1983).
480. R. Liepins and M. Aldissi, "Electride Doping of Soluble High Temperature Polymers," Symposium on Order in Polymer Materials, GTE Labs, Inc., August 1983.
481. Oh-Kil Kim, J. Poly. Sci., Poly. Lett. Ed. *20*, 663 (1982).
482. L. W. Shacklette, R. R. Chance, D. M. Ivory, G. G. Miller, and R. H. Baughman, Synth. Met. *1*, 307 (1979).
483. R. R. Chance, D. S. Boudreaux, H. Eckhardt, R. L. Elsenbaumer, J. E. Frommer, J. L. Bredas, R. Silby, Quantum Chemistry of Polymers-Solid State Aspects, p. 221 (1984).
484. J. A. Pople and S.H. Walmsley, Mol. Phys. *5*, 15 (1982).
485. D. Moses, A. Denenstein, J. Chen, A. J. Heeger, P. McAndrew, T. Woerner, A. G. MacDiarmid, and Y. W. Park, Phys. Rev. B *25*, 7652 (1982).
486. M. Peo, S. Roth, K. Dransfeld, B. Tieke, J. Hocker, H. Gross, A. Grupp, and H. Sisel, Solid State Comm. *35*, 119 (1980).

487. J. L. Bredas, R. R. Chance, and R. Silbey, Mol. Cryst. Liq. Cryst. *77*, 319 (1982).
488. J. L. Bredas, R. R. Chance, and R. Silbey, Phys. Rev. B *26*, 5843 (1982).
489. S. Kivelson, Phys. Rev. Lett. *46*, 1344 (1981).
490. G. Crecelins, M. Stamm, J. Fink, and J. J. Ritsko, Phys. Rev. Lett. *50*, 1498 (1983).
491. A. J. Epstein, H. Rommelmann, R. Bigelow, H. W. Gibson, D. M. Hoffmann, and D. B. Tanner, Phys. Rev. Lett. *50*, 1866 (1981).
492. E. J. Mele and M. J. Rice, Phys. Rev. B *15*, 5397 (1981).
493. J. L. Bredas, B. Themans, J. M. Andre, R. R. Chance, D. S. Boudrequx, and R. Silbey, Proc. Int. Conf. Conducting Polymers, Les Arcs (1982); J. Phys. Colloq. 373 (1983).
494. J. Manassen and J. Wallach, J. Am. Chem. Soc. *87*, 2671 (1965).
495. J. Gallard, T. Laederich, R. Salle, and P. Traynard, Bull. Soc. Chim. Fr. *2204* (1963).
496. N. Grassie and J. C. McHeill, J. Polym. Sci. *17*, 707 (1958).
497. O. Vohler, P. L. Reiser, R. Martina, and D. Overhoff, Angew. Chem. *82*, 401 (1970).
498. L. K. H. van Beek, J. Appl. Polym. Sci. *9*, 553 (1965).
499. P. J. Goodhew, A. J. Clarke, and J. E. Bailey, Mat. Sci. Eng. *17*, 3 (1975).
500. A. V. Topchiev, M. A. Geiderich, V. A. Kargin, B. A. Kreuzel, B. E. Davydov, L. S. Polak, and I. M. Kustanovich, Dokl. Acad. Nauk. SSSR *128*, 312 (1959).
501. A. A. Berlin, A. M. Dubinskaya, and U. S. Moshkovskii, Vysokomol. Soedin. *6*, 1938 (1964).
502. A. V. Vlasov, P. Y. Glazunov, V. L. Morozov, I. I. Patalakh, L. S. Polak, B. L. Tselin, and R. S. Rafikov, Dokl. Akad. Hauk. SSSR *158*, 141 (1964).
503. H. Pohl in *Modern Aspects of the Vitreous State*, J. D. Mackenzie, Ed., Butterworths, London, UK, (1962), Vol. 2, p. 72.
504. A. Rembaum, J. Polym. Sci. Part C (29), 157 (1970).
505. S. D. Bruck, Polymer *6*, 319 (1965).
506. H. B. Brom, Y. Tomkiewicz, A. Aviram, A. Broers, and B. Sunners, Solid State Comm. *26*, 135 (1950).
507. L. I. Kotlyarevskii, L. B. Fisher, A. A. Dulov, A. A. Slinkin, and A. M. Rubinstein, High Mol. Comp. USSR *4*, 174 (1962).
508. M. Hatano, S. Kambara and S. Okamoto, J. Chem. Soc. Japan, Ind. Chem. Sec. *65*, 716 (1962).
509. A. V. Topchiev, J. Polym. Sci. Part A-1, 591 (1963).
510. V. V. Korshak, V. I. Kasatochkin, A. M. Sladkov, J. P. Kudrjawzew and K. Usenbaev, Dokl. Akad. Nauk, SSSR *136*, 1342 (1961).
511. V. V. Korshak, S. L. Sosin, and A. M. Sladkov, J. Polym. Sci. Part C (4), 1315 (1963).
512. F. H. Winslow, W. O. Baker, and W. A Yager, J. Am. Chem. Soc. *77*, 4751 (1955)
513. H. A. Pohl, *Proceedings of the Fourth Conference on Carbon*, Pergamon, London (1960), p. 241.
514. H. A. Pohl and J. P. Laherrere, ibid, p. 259.
515. H. A. Pohl and J. P. Laherrere, *Proceedings of the Princeton University Conference on Semiconduction in Molecular Solids*, Ivy-Curtie Press, Princeton, New Jersey (1960), p. 93.
516. J. P. Laherrere and M. A. Pohl, "Semiconduction in Aluminum Doped Pyropolymers," Plastics Laboratory Technical Report 570, Princeton University Press, Princeton (1960).
517. M. I. Pope, *Papers of the Conference on Industrial Carbon and Graphite*, London, Great Britian (1966), p. 474.
518. R. Diamond and P. B. Hirsch, *Industrial Carbon and Graphite*, Society of Chemical Industry, London, Great Britian (1957), p. 197.
519. R. A. Durie and J. Szewczyk, *3rd International Conference on Coal Science*, Valkenburg, The Netherlands (1959).
520. M. Becher and H. F. Mark, Angew. Chem. *73*, 637 (1961).
521. H. W. Holden and J. C. Robb, Fuel *39*, 485 (1960).
522. H. Shirakawa, E. J. Louis, A. G. MacDiarmid, C. K. Chiang, and A. J. Heeger, J. Chem. Soc. Chem. Commun. 578 (1977).
523. A. M. Saxman, R. Liepins, and M. Aldissi, Prog. Polym. Sci. *11* (1/2), 57 (1985).
524. H. Shirakawa and S. Ikeda, Japan. Pat. No. 32,581 (1973).
525. T. Ito, H. Shirakawa, and S. Ikeda, J. Polym. Sci., Polym. Chem. Ed. *12*, 11 (1974).
526. H. Shirakawa and S. Ikeda, Synth. Metals *1*, 175 (1979/1980).
527. A. G. MacDiarmid and A. J. Heeger, Synth. Metals *1*, 101 (1980).
528. A. F Diaz, K. K. Kanazawa, and G. P. Gardini, J. Chem. Soc., Chem. Commun. 635 (1979).
529. K. K. Kanazawa, A. F. Diaz, W. D. Gill, P. M. Grant, G. B. Street, G. P. Gardini, J. F. Kwak, Synthetic Metals *1*, 329 (1980).

530. A. Dall'Olio, G. Dascola, V. Varacca, and V. Bocche, C. R. Acad. Sci., Sec. C267, *433* (1968).
531. G. P. Gardini, Adv. Heterocycl. Chem. *15*, 67 (1973).
532. P. Kovacic and A. Kyriakis, J. Am. Chem. Soc. *85*, 454 (1963).
533. P. Kovacic and J. Ozlomek, J. Org. Chem. *29*, 100 (1964).
534. P. Kovacic and L. C. Hsu, J. Polymer Sci. *4*, 5 (1966).
535. P. Kovacic and R. M. Lange, J. Org. Chem. *38*, 968 (1963).
536. P. Kovacic and F. W. Koch, J. Org. Chem. *28*, 1864 (1963).
537. K. N. Rao and S. K. Dayal, Indian J. Appl. Chem. *39*, 45 (1966).
538. M. L. Larson and F. W. Moore, Inorg. Chem. *5*, 801 (1966).
539. P. Kovacic and C. Wu, J. Polymer Sci. *47*, 45 (1960).
540. P. Kovacic, F. W. Koch, and C. E. Stephan, J. Polymer Sci. Part A, *2*, 1193 (1964).
541. D. C. Pepper in *Friedel-Crafts and Related Reactions*, G. A. Olah, Ed., Wiley-Interscience, New York (1964), Vol. II, p. 1293.
542. G. K Noren and J. K. Stille, Macromol. Revs. *5*, 385 (1971).
543. G. A. Edwards and G. Goldfinger, J. Poly. Sci. *16*, 589 (1955).
544. A.A. Berlin, J. Polym. Sci. *55*, 621 (1961).
545. G. Goldfinger, J. Polym. Sci. *4*, 93 (1949).
546. T. Yamamoto, Y. Hayaski, and A. Yamamoto, Bull. Chem. Soc. Jap. *51*, 2091 (1978).
547. S. K. Taylor, S. G. Bennett, I. Khoury, and P. Kovacic, J. Polym. Sci., Polym. Lett. Eds. *19*, 85 (1981).
548. C. S. Marvel and G. E. Hartzell, J. Am. Chem. Soc. *41*, 448 (1959).
549. G. LeFebvre and F. Dawans, J. Polym. Sci. *2*, 3277 (1964).
550. P. E. Cassidy, C. S. Marvel, and S. Ray, J. Polym. Sci. *3*, 1553 (1965).
551. D. A. Frey, M. Hasegawa, and C. S. Marvel, J. Polym. Sci. *1*, 2057 (1963).
552. A. A. Berlin and V. P. Parini, Izv. Vyssh. Uchebn. Zaved. Khim. Khim. Tekhnol. *1*, 122 (1958).
553. A. A. Berlin and V. P. Parini, Izv. Akad. Nauk SSSR, 1674 (1959).
554. A. A. Berlin, V. I. Liogonkii, and V. P. Parini, J. Polym. Sci. *55*, 675 (1961).
555. C. Friedel and J. M. Crafts, Ann. Chim. Phys. *14*(6), 433 (1888).
556. N.G. Gaylord, *Polyethers, in High Polymers Series*, Vol. XIII, Part III, Interscience Publisher, New York (1962).
557. A. D. Macallum, J. Org. Chem. *13*, 154 (1948).
558. A. D. Macallum, U.S. Patent No. 2,513,188 (June 27, 1950) and No. 2,538,941 (January 23, 1951).
559. R. W. Lenz, C. E. Handlovits, and H. A. Smith, J. Polym. Sci. *58*, 351 (1962).
560. R. W. Lenz, C. E. Handlovits, and W. K. Carrington, Belgian Patent No. 613,003 (July 23, 1962).
561. H. A. Smith and C. E. Handlovits, "Phenylene Sulfide Polymers," Technical Documentary Report ASD-TRD-62–322 (March 1962).
562. H. A. Smith and C. E. Handlovits, ASD-TDR-62–372, Report Conf. High Temperature Polymer Fluid Research, Dayton, Ohio, 1962.
563. C. C. Price and S. Tsunawaki, J. Org. Chem. *28*, 1867 (1963).
564. S. Tsunawaki and C. C. Price, J. Polym. Sci. Part A *2*, 1511 (1964).
565. D. Schulze, Z. Chem. *5*(I), 19 (1965).
566. J. K. Stille, Macromolocules *14*, 870 (1981).
567. Y. S. Papir, V. P Kurkov, and S. P. Current, "Synthesis and Chemical Doping of New Tractable Electrically Conducting Polymers," Abstract No. 543, The Electrochemical Soc. Inc., Annual Meeting, San Francisco, May 8–13, 1983.
568. S. E. Tunney, J. Suenaga, and J. K. Stille, Macromolecules *16*, 1398 (1983).
569. R. Liepins and M. Aldissi, Mol. Cryst. Liq. Cryst. *105*, 151 (1984).
570. P. M. Hergerother, Appl. Polym. Symp. No. 22, 57 (1973).
571. W. Wrasidlo and J. M. Augl, J. Polym. Sci. Part A-1 *7*, 3393 (1969).
572. W. Wrasidlo and J. M. Augl, J. Polym. Sci. Part B *7*, 281 (1969).
573. F. E. Arnold and R. L. VanDeusen, Macromolecules *2*, 497 (1969).
574. M. Aldissi and R. Liepins, J. Chem. Soc., Chem. Commun. 255 (1984).
575. F. S. Bates and G. L. Baker, Macromolecules *16*, 704 (1983).
576. T. Woerner, A. G. MacDiarmid, and A. J. Heeger, J. Polym. Sci., Polymer Lett. Ed. *20*, 305 (1982).
577. M. Aldissi, J. Chem. Soc., Chem. Commun. 1347 (1984).

578. R. B. Kauer, A. G. MacDiarmid, and R. J. Mammone in "Polymers in Electronics," T. Davidson, Ed., ACS Symposium Series No. 242, American Chemical Society (1984).
579. A. G. MacDiarmid, J. C. Chiang, M. Halpern, W. S. Huang, S. L. Mu, N. L. D. Somasiri, W. Wu, and S. I. Yaniger, Mol. Cryst. Liq. Cryst. *121,* 173 (1985).
580. A. Brillante, K. Syassan, M. Hanfland, and J. Hecker, paper presented at the International Conference on the Physics and Chemistry of Low-Dimensional Synthetic Metals, Abano Terme, Italy, June 17–22, 1984.
581. K. Yoshino, S. Hayashi, K. Kaneto, J. Okube, T. Moriya, T. Matsuyama, and H. Yamaoka, paper presented at the International Conference on the Physics and Chemistry of Low-Dimensional Synthetic Metals, Abano Terme, Italy, June 17–22, 1984.
582. R. Liepins, A. Nyitray, and R. Jahn, unpublished results.
583. R. L. Elsenbaumer, H. Eckhardt, Z. Iqbal, J. Toth, and R. H. Baughman, Mol. Cryst. Liq. Cryst. *118,* 111 (1985).
584. D. R. Gagnon, J. O. Capistran, F. E. Karasz, and R. W. Lenz, Polymer Preprints Am. Chem. Soc. Div. Polym. Chem. *25*(2), 284 (1984).
585. W. Werner, M. Monkenbusch, G. Wegner, Makromol. Chem., Rapid Commun. *5,* 157 (1984).
586. J. H. Edwards and W. J. Feast, Polymer *21,* 595 (1980).
587. D. C. Bott, C. K. Chai, J. H. Edwards, W. J. Feast, R. H. Friend, and M. E. Horton, J. Phys. Colloq. C3, suppl. No. 6 *44,* C3 (1983).
588. G. Ahlgren and B. Krische, J. Chem. Soc., Chem. Commun. 946 (1984).
589. G. Leising, Polymer Commun. *25,* 201 (1984).
590. K. Araya, A. Mukoh, .T Narahara, H. Shirakawa, Chemistry Letters 1141 (1984).
591. M. Aldissi, J. Poly. Sci., Poly. Lett. Ed. *23,* 167 (1985).
592. J. R. Reynolds, J. C. W. Chien, F. E. Karasz, C. P. Lillya, Polymer Preprints *25*(2), 242 (1984).
593. S. T. Wellinghoff, Z. Deng, J. Reed, and J. Racchini, Polymer Preprints *25*(2), 238 (1984).
594. T. J. Marks, Science *227,* 881 (1985).
595. T. Inabe, J. F. Lomax, J. W. Lyding, C. R. Kannewurf, T. J. Marks, Macromolecules *17*(2), 262 (1984).
596. John Ziegler, personal communication, October 1985.
597. W. A. Little, Phys. Rev. A *134,* 1416 (1964).
598. R. Liepins, C. Walker, H. A. Fairbanks, P. Lawless, and R. Mueller, Polymer Preprints *11,* 1048 (1970).
599. R. Liepins and C. Walker, I&EC Prod. Res. Dev. *10,* 401 (1971).
600. R.A. Ferrel, Phys. Rev. Lett. *13,* 330 (1964).
601. P.C. Hohenberg, Phys. Rev. *158,* 383 (1967).
602. A. J. Heeger and A. F. Garito, in *Low Dimensional Cooperative Phenomena,* H. J. Kellan, Ed., Plenum Publishing Corp., New York (1975).
603. H. Fröhlich, Proc. Poy. Sec. *A223,* 296 (1954).
604. R. E. Peierls, *Quantum Theory of Solids,* Oxford University Press, London (1955).
605. A. J. Berlinsky, Contemp. Phys. *17,* 331 (1976).
606. H. R. Zeller, *In Festkörper Problems XIII, Advances in Solid State Physics,* Pergamon Press, Vieweg (1973).
607. D. Chapman, R. J. Warn, A. G. Fitzgerald, and A. D. Yoffe, Trans. Faraday Soc. *60,* 294 (1964).
608. R. L. Greene, G. B. Street, and L. J. Sutter, Phys. Rev. Lett. *34,* 577 (1975).
609. K. I. Bechgaard, C. S. Jacobsen, K. Mortensen, H. J. Pedersen, and N. Thorup, Solid State Commun. *33,* 1119 (1980).
610. D. Jerome, A. Mazaud, M. Ribault, and K. J. Bechgaard, J. Phys. Lett. *41,* L-95 (1980).
611. C. Bernard, A. Herold, M. Lelaurain, and G. Robert, C. R. Acad. Sci. *C283,* 125 (1976).
612. G. B. Street, W. D. Gill, R. H. Geiss, R. L. Greene, and J. J. Mayerle, J. Chem. Soc., Chem. Commun. 407 (1977).
613. W. D. Gill, W. Bludan, R. H. Geiss, P. M. Grant, R. L. Greene, J. J. Mayerle, and G. B. Street, Phys. Rev. Lett. *38,* 1305 (1977).
614. W. D. Gill, T. C. Clarke, and G. B. Street, Appl. Phys. Comm. *2*(4), 211 (1982–83).
615. F. P. Burt, J. Chem. Soc. 1171 (1910).
616. R.D. Smith, J. Chem. Soc. Dalton Trans. 478 (1979).
617. M. Goehring and D. Voigt, Naturwissenschaften *40,* 481 (1953).
618. M. J. Cohen, A. F. Garito, A. J. Heeger, A. G. MacDiarmid, C. M. Mikulski, and M. S. Saran, J. Amer. Chem. Soc. *98,* 3844 (1975).

619. G. B. Street, H. Arnal, W. D. Gill, P. M. Grant, and R. L. Greene, Mater. Res. Bull. *10,* 877 (1975).
620. C. M. Mikulski, P. J. Russo, M. S. Saran, A. G. MacDiarmid, A. F. Garito, and A. J. Heeger, J. Amer. Chem. Soc. *97,* 6358 (1975).
621. H. Kahlert and B. Kundu, Mat. Res. Bull. *11,* 967 (1976).
622. M. M. Labes, P. Love, and L. F. Nichols, Chem. Rev. *79,* 1 (1979).
623. P. Love, H. I. Kao, G. H. Myer, and M. M. Labes, J. Chem. Soc. Chem. Commun. 301 (1978).
624. R. L. Patton, Ph.D. Thesis, University of California, Berkeley (1969).
625. C. Hsu and M. M. Labes, J. Chem. Phys. *61,* 4640 (1974).
626. E. J. Louis, A. G. MacDairmid, A. F. Garito, and A. J. Heeger, J. Chem. Soc. Chem. Commun 426 (1976).
627. A. A. Bright, M. J. Cohen, A. F. Garito, A. J. Heeger, C. M. Mikulski, and A. G. MacDiarmid, App. Phys. Lett. *26,* 612 (1975).
628. M. Geohring and D. Voigt, Z. Anorg. Allg. Chem. *285,* 181 (1856).
629. A. Douillard, Ph.D. Thesis, Claude Bernard University, Lyon, France (1972).
630. M. Boudeulle, Crystal Structures Commun. *4,* 9 (1975).
631. G. Heger, S. Klein, L. Pintschovious, and H. Kahlert, J. Solid State Chem. *23,* 341 (1978).
632. G. B. Street and R. L. Greene, IBM J. Res. Dev. *21,* 99 (1977).
633. C. K. Chiang, M. J. Cohen, A. F. Garito, A.J. Heeger, C. M. Mikulski, and A. G. MacDiarmid, Solid State Commun. *18,* 1351 (1976).
634. R. H. Dee, A. J. Berlinsky, J. F. Carolan, E. Klein, N. J. Stone, B. G. Turrell, and G. B. Street, Solid State Commun. *23,* 303 (1977).
635. L. F. Lou and A. F. Garito, unpublished information.
636. R. H. Dee, D. H. Dollard, B. G. Turrell, and J. F. Carolan, Solid State Commun. *24,* 469 (1977).
637. Y. Oda, H. Takenaka, H. Nagano, and I. Nakada, Solid State Commun. *32,* 659 (1979).
638. W. H. G. Muller, F. Baumann, G. Dammer, and L. Pintschovius, Solid State Commun. *25,* 119 (1978).
639. L. R. Bickford, R. L. Greene, and W. D. Gill, Phys. Rev. B *17,* 3525 (1978).
640. F. DeLaCruz and H. J. Stolz, Solid State Commun. *20,* 241 (1976).
641. R. J. Soulen and D. B. Utton, Solid State Commun. *1,* 105 (1977).
642. W. Beyer, W. D. Gill, and G. B. Street, Solid State Commun. *27,* 343 (1978).
643. C. J. Adkins. J. M. D. Thomas, and M. W. Young, J. Phys. C Solid State Phys. *13,* 3427 (1980).
644. P. M. Chaikin, P. K. Hasma, and R. L. Greene, Phys. Rev. B *17,* 179 (1978).
645. L. J. Azevedo, W. G. Clark, G. Deutscher, R. L. Greene, G. B. Street, and L. J. Sutter, Solid State Commun. *19,* 197 (1976).
646. P. M. Grant, R. L. Greene, and G. B. Street, Phys. Rev. Lett. *35,* 1743 (1975).
647. A. A. Bright, M. J. Cohen, A. F. Garito, A. J. Heeger, C. M. Mikulski, P. J. Russo, and A. G. MacDiarmid, Phys. Rev. Lett. *34,* 206 (1975).
648. L. Pintschovius, H. P. Geserich, and W. Moller, Solid State Commun. *17,* 477 (1975).
649. C. H. Chen, J. Silcos, A. F. Garito, A. J. Heeger, and A. G. MacDiarmid, Phys. Rev. Lett. *36,* 525 (1976).
650. W. Beyer, W. D. Gill, and G. B. Street, Solid State Commun. *23,* 577 (1977).
651. W. E. Rudge and P. M. Grant, Phys. Rev. Lett. *35,* 1799 (1975).
652. P. M. Grant, W. E. Rudge, and I. B. Ortenburger, *Lecture Notes in Physics,* Vol. 165, *Organic Conductors and Semiconductors,* Springer-Verlag, Berlin (1977).
653. J. M. E. Harper, R. L. Greene, P. M. Grant, and G. B. Street, Phys. Rev. B *15,* 539 (1977).
654. R. L. Greene, P. M. Grant, and G. B. Street, Phys. Rev. Lett. *34,* 89 (1975).
655. L. Pintschovius, H. Wendel, and H. Kahlert, in *Lecture Notes in Physics, Organic Conductors and Semiconductors,* L. Pal, G. Gruner, A. Janossy, and J. Solyom, Eds., Springer-Verlag, Berlin (1977), p. 589.
656. H. J. Stolz, A. Otto, and L. Pintschovius, *Proceedings of the 3rd International Conference on Light Scattering Solids,* Campinas, Brazil, July 1975, edited by M. Balkanski, R. C. C. Leite, and S. P. S. Porto, Eds. Flammarion Sciences, Paris (1976), p. 736.
657. H. J. Stolz, H. Wendel, A. Otto, L. Pintschovius, and H. Kahlert, Phys. Status Solidi B *78,* 277 (1976).
658. H. Temkin and D. B. Fitchen, Solid State Commun. *19,* 1181 (1976).
659. L. Ley, Phys. Rev. Lett. *35,* 1976 (1975).

660. P. Mengel, P. M. Grant, W. E. Rudge, B. H. Schechtman, and D. W. Rice, Phys. Rev. Lett. *35*, 1803 (1975).
661. W. R. Salaneck, J. W. Lin, and A. J. Epstein, Phys. Rev. B *13*, 5574 (1976).
662. E. E. Koch and W. D. Grobman, Solid State Commun. *23*, 49 (1977).
663. P. Mengel, I. B. Ortenburger, W. E. Rudge, and P. M. Grant, in *Lecture Notes in Physics, Organic Conductors and Semiconductors,* L. Pal, G. Gruner, A. Janossy, and J. Solyom, eds., Springer-Verlag, Berlin (1977), p. 591.
664. K. Kaneto, M. Yamamoto, K. Yoshino, and Y. Inuishi, Solid State Commun. *26*, 311 (1978).
665. H. Kahlert and K. Seeger, *Physics of Semiconductors, Pro. 13th Int. Conf. Rome,* F. G. Fumi, Ed., Tipographa Mares, Rome (1976).
666. R. A. Scranton, J. Appl. Phys. *48*, 3838 (1977).
667. R. A. Scranton, J. S. Best, and J. O. McCaldin, J. Vac. Sci. Technol. *14*, 930 (1977).
668. M. J. Cohen and J. S. Harnis, Jr., Appl. Phys. Lett. *33*, 812 (1978).
669. V. A. Starodub, V. P. Babiichuk, V. P. Batulin, I. V. Krivoshei, and N. V. Mansya, Phys. Status Solidi A *59*, K231 (1980).
670. J. Kuyper and G. B. Street, J. Amer. Chem. Soc. *99*, 7848 (1977).
671. C. Bernard, A. Herold, M. Lelaurain, and G. Robert, C. R. Acad. Sci. *C283*, 125 (1976).
672. G. B. Street, W. D. Gill, R. H. Geiss, R. L. Greene, and J. J. Mayerle, J. Chem. Soc. Chem. Commun. 407 (1977).
673. G. Wolmerhauser and G. B. Street, Inorg. Chem. *17*, 2685 (1978).
674. G. B. Street, R. L. Bingham, J. I. Crowley, and J. Kuyper, J. Chem. Soc. Chem. Commun. 464 (1977).
675. M. Akhtar, C. K. Chiang, A. J. Heeger, and A. G. MacDiarmid, J. Chem. Soc. Chem. Commun. 846 (1977).
676. G. B. Street, S. Etemad, R. H. Geiss, W. D. Gill, R. L. Greene, and J. Kuyper, Ann. NY Acad. Sci. *313*, 737 (1978).
677. H. Temkin and G. B. Street, Solid State Commun. *25*, 455 (1978).
678. H. Temkin, D. B. Fitchen, W. D. Gill, and G. B. Street, Ann. NY Acad. Sci. *313*, 771 (1978).
679. R. D. Smith and G. B. Street, Inorg. Chem. *17*, 941 (1978).
680. M. Akhtar, C. K. Chiang, A. J. Heeger, J. Milliken, and A. J. MacDiarmid, Inorg. Chem. *17*, 1539 (1978).
681. J. J. Song, D. D. L. Chung, P. C. Eklund, and M. S. Dresselhaus, Solid State Commun. *20*, 1111 (1976).
682. Z. Iqbal, R. H. Baughman, J. Kleppinger, and A. G. MacDiarmid, Ann. N.Y. Acad. Sci. *313*, 775 (1978).
683. Z. Iqbal, R. H. Baughman, J. Kleppinger, and A. G. MacDiarmid, Solid State Commun. *25*, 469 (1978).
684. J. Macklin, G. B. Street, and W. D. Gill, J. Chem. Phys. *70*, 2425 (1979).
685. H. Morawitz, W. D. Gill, P. M. Grant, G. B. Street, and D. Sayers, *Lecture Notes in Physics I,* S. Barisic et al., Eds., Springer, Berlin (1979).
686. H. Morawitz, P. Bagus, T. C. Clarke, W. D. Gill, P. M. Grant, and G. B. Street, Synthetic Metals *1*, 267 (1980).
687. J. C. Scott, J. D. Klick, and G. B. Street, Solid State Commun. *28*, 723 (1978).
688. G. Wolmershauser, R. Jotter, and T. Wilhelm, J. Phys. Colloq. C3, Suppl. No. 6, *44*, June 1983.
689. O. J. Scherer, G. Wolmershauser, and R. Jotter, Z. Naturforsch. *37B*, 432 (1982).
690. G. Wolmershauser, J. Fuhrmann, R. Jotter, T. Wilhelm, and O. J. Scherer, Mol. Cryst. Liq. Cryst. *118*, 435 (11985).
691. P. R. Wallace, Phys. Rev. *71*, 622 (1947).
692. G. H. Kinchin, Proc. R. Soc. London, Ser. *A217*, 9 (1953).
693. R. R. Haering and P. R. Wallace, Phys. Chem. Solids *3*, 253 (1957).
694. J. C. Slonczewski and P. R. Weiss, Phys. Rev. *109*, 272 (1958).
695. G. Henning and L. Meyer, Phys. Rev. *87*, 439 (1952).
696. N. B. Hannay, T. H. Geballe, V. T. Matthias, K. Andres, P. Schmidt, and D. MacNair, Phys. Rev. Lett. *17*(7), 225 (1965).
697. J. Poitrenand, Rev. Phys. Appl. *5*, 275 (1970).
698. M. Kobayashi and I. Tsujikawa, J. Phys. Soc. Jpn. *46*, 1945 (1979).
699. Y. Koike, H. Suematsu, K. Higuchi, and S. Tanuma, Solid State Commun. *27*, 623 (1978).
700. Y. Koike, H. Suematsu, K. Higuchi, and S. Tanuma, J. Phys. Chem. Solids *41*, 1111 (1980).

701. S. Tanumna, Y. Iye, and Y. Koike in *Physics of Intercalation Compounds*, L. Pietronero and E. Tosatti, Eds., Springer Series in Solid State Science, Vol. 38, Berlin (1981).
702. M. G. Alexander, D. P. Goshorn, D. G. Onn, D. Guerard, P. Lagrange, and M. E. Makrini, Synth. Met. *2*, 203 (1980).
703. L. A. Pendrys, R. Wachnik, F. L. Vogel, P. Lagrange, G. Furdin, M. E. Makrini, and A. Herold, Solid State Commun. *38*, 677 (1981).
704. M. G. Alexander, D. P. Goshorn, D. Guerard, P. Lagrange, M. E. Makrini, and D. G. Onn, Solid State Commun. *38*, 103 (1981).
705. F. L. Vogel, R. Wachnik, and L. A. Pendrys, in *Physics of Intercalation Compounds*, L. Peitronero and E. Tosatti, Eds, Springer Series in the Solid-State Sciences, Vol. 38, Berlin (1981).
706. L. A. Pendrys, R. A. Wachnik, and F. L. Vogel, Synthetic Metals *5*, 277 (1983).
707. J. Ladik, G. Biczo, and J. Redly, Phys. Rev. *188*, 710 (1969).
708. J. Ladik and A. Bierman, Phys. Lett. A *29*, 636 (1969).
709. F. W. Cope, Physiol. Chem. and Phys. *3*, 403 (1971).
710. F. W. Cope, Physiol. Chem. and Phys. *6*, 405 (1974).
711. E. H. Halpern, "High Temperature Non-metallic Superconductors," Naval Shipyard Research and Development Report 3917, Annapolis, Maryland (1973).
712. S. Goldfein, Physiol. Chem. and Phys. *6*, 261 (1974).
713. J. M. Blatt, *Theory of Superconductivity*, Academic Press, New York (1964).
714. N. A. G. Ahmed, J. H. Calderwood, H. Fröhlich, and C. W. Smith, Phys. Lett. A *53*, 129 (1975).
715. T. Yamabe, K. Tanaka, A. Imammera, H. Kato, and K. Fukui, Bull. Chem. Soc. Jpn, 50(4)0, 798 (1977).
716. R. Liepins and L. Caudle, unpublished results, 1984.
717. N. Angier, Discover, p. 76 (May 1982).
718. H. F. Schaefer, Ann. Rev. Phys. Chem. p. 261 (1976).
719. F. L. Carter in *Nonlinear Electrodynamics in Biological Systems*, Plenum Publ. Corp., New York, p. 243 (1984).
720. F. L. Carter in *Computer Applications in Chemistry*, Elsevier, Amsterdam, p. 225 (1983).
721. F. L. Carter, *Physica 10D*, Elsevier, Amsterdam, p. 175 (1984).
722. D. W. G. Byatt, Electronics and Power, p. 351 (May 1979).
723. J. E. Lisman, *Proceedings of the National Academy of Sciences*, p. 3055 (May 1985).
724. A. Aviram and P. E. Seiden, U.S. Patent Application No. 258,639, June 1, 1972; U.S. Patent 3,833,894, September 3, 1974.
725. A. Aviram and M. A. Ratner, Bull. Chem. Phys. Soc. *19*, 341 (1974).
726. A. Aviram, P. E. Seiden, and Fr. Demande, 2,186,701, Feb. 15, 1974.
727. A. Aviram and M. A. Ratner, Chem. Phys. Lett. 29(2)0, 277 (1974).
728. J. Hine, *Physical Organic Chemistry*, McGraw-Hill, New York (1962).
729. G. Briegleb, *Elektronen Donator Acceptor Komplexe*, Springer, Berlin (1961).
730. H. A. Benesi and J. H. Hildebrand, J. Am. Chem. Soc. *71*, 2703 (1949).
731. R. S. Mulliken and W. B. Person, *Molecular Complexes*, Benjamin Co. Inc., New York, (1969).
732. P. L. Nordio, A. Soos, and H. M. McConnell, Ann. Rev. Phys. Chem. *17*, 237 (1966).
733. J. E. Harriman and A. H. Maki, J. Chem. Phys. *39*, 778 (1963).
734. R. Hoffmann, Accounts Chem. Res. *4*, 1 (1971).
735. F. L. Carter, Ed., *Molecular Electronic Devices*, Marcel Dekker, New York (1982).
736. A. S. Davydov and N. I. Kisluka, Phys. Stat. Sol. *59*, 465 (1973).
737. A. S. Davydov and N. I. Kisluka, Sov. Phys. JETP *44*, 571 (1976).
738. A. Hazell and A. Mukhopadhyay, Acta Crystallog. *B36*, 747 (1980).
739. R. Dietz, Engineering, p. 16 (January 1985).
740. J. H. McAlear and J. M. Wehrung, "The Biochip Now, 2000 A.D. and Beyond," U.S. Department of Commerce Report No. DS2002, p. 51 (August 1984).
741. B. J. Tucker, High Technology, p. 36 (February 1984).
742. J. vanBrunt, Bio/Technology *3*, 209 (1985).
743. T. Hogg and B. A. Huberman, *Proceedings of the National Academy of Sciences*, p. 6871 (November 1984).
744. J. M. Ballantine, Ed., "NSF Workshop on Opportunities For Microstructures Science and Engineering," Cornell University Press, Ithaca, New York (1978).
745. J. H. McAlear and M. M. Wehrung, U.S. Patent No. 4,103,064, July 25, 1978.
746. J. H. McAlear and M. M. Wehrung, U.S. Patent No. 4,103,073, July 25, 1978.

747. L. B. Lockhart, Jr., Ed., "The NRL Program on Electroactive Polymers-The First Annual Report," Naval Research Laboratory, Washington, D.C. (1979).
748. R. B. Fox, Ed., "The NRL Program on Electroactive Polymers-The Second Annual Report," Naval Research Laboratory, Washington, D.C. (1980).
749. K. M. Ulmer in "Proceedings of the Molecular Electronic Devices Workshop," F. L. Carter, Ed., Naval Research Laboratory, Washington, D.C., March 23–24, 1981.
750. F. L. Carter, Ed., "Proceedings of the Second International Workshop on Molecular Electronic Devices," Naval Research Laboratory, Washington, D.C. (April 13–15, 1982).
751. F. L. Carter, Ed., "Progress in Concepts of Conformational Switching and Molecular Electronic Devices," Report 1982, NRL-MR-4717. (AD-A110752).
752. F. E. Yates and M. Conrad, co-chairmen, "The International Conference on Chemically Based Computing," National Science Foundation and UCLA, Santa Monica, CA, October 1983.
753. F. L. Carter in "Proceedings of Winter School on Electroactive Polymers," P. Bernier, Ed., Font. Romen, France, January 3–10, 1982.
754. J. H. McAlear and J. M. Wehrung, ibid.
755. A. Barlow, Ed., *Langmuir-Blodgett Films,* Elsevier Sci. Pub. Co., New York (1980).
756. H. Kuhn, Pure Appl. Chem. 53 (11), 2105 (1981).

Chapter 6

ELECTRICAL PARAMETERS OF POLYMERS IN SUMMARY

6.1   INTRODUCTION

The four key parameters – dielectric constant ε, tangent of dielectric loss angle $\tan\delta$, dielectric strength, and electrical conductivity σ – of the electrical properties of polymers have been discussed separately in Chapters 2–5. Here, we discuss their correlations, point out significant conclusions, and rank top polymeric materials according to their properties.

In Appendices 1–7 we have collected the available data on dielectric constants, dissipation factor, dielectric strength, arc resistance, electrical conductivity, water vapor permeability, and water absorption in various polymers.

6.2   CORRELATIONS OF THE FOUR KEY ELECTRICAL PARAMETERS

The conductivity in insulating polymers depends chiefly on the mobility of very small quantities of impurity ions and electrons. In metallically conducting polymers, it is related to the quantity of doping material used, which in turn determines the extent of oxidation (p-doping) or reduction (n-doping) of the polymer. The primary charge carriers are thought to be polarons, and their mobilities are thought to be less than the speed of sound.

The dielectric constant and the dielectric loss depend chiefly on the behavior of the molecular chains and their supermolecular structures. Superficially, it would seem that the conductivity and dielectric constant and dielectric loss are mutually independent quantities. But as has been shown empirically, relationships among them are very close indeed.[1] Correlations that have been shown to exist are as follows:

1. Conductivity correlates with low-frequency (below 100 Hz) dielectric constant. Conductivity increases with increasing ε. The interpretation of this relationship is that, the higher the ε, the more charge carriers there are likely to be and, as a result, conductivity will increase.[1]

2. The mobility of charge carriers χ has a very good correlation with the mean velocity of the Brownian movement of polymer chain segments. For α relaxation of dipole chain segments, the latter is proportional to the reciprocal of relaxation time τ. The relationship between χ and τ is[2,3]

$$\chi(T,P) \, [\tau(T,P)]^x = \text{constant,} \qquad\qquad 6.1$$

where x is a constant, T is temperature, and P is pressure. Of course, this relationship holds true only for T above the glass-transition temperature, where the amorphous region of polymers is similar to a liquid phase in its properties. The χ, however, is not an intrinsic parameter of a polymer, because it depends upon the presence of accidental charge carriers.

3. A correlation between ε, tan δ, and ϱ_v with dielectric strength E_B is also possible. It is well known that breakdown depends on interactions among the electric field, particles, and atoms in a polymer. However, this phenomenon is very complicated and impossible to solve exactly using quantum theory even for the simplest of atomic structures. Thus, for the evaluation of a phenomenon as complex as dielectric breakdown, one starts with the empirical data, utilizing the microscopic effects and results already well known.

The dielectric breakdown is affected by such factors as the intrinsic properties of a polymer, the environment, and the testing procedure. Assuming that we can keep the environmental and testing conditions constant, then the intrinsic properties of a polymer are the main variable.

We can postulate that when the average kinetic energy of charge carriers in the polymer reaches the polymer's level of ionization energy, electrons may be emitted from the polymer molecule and destruction of the polymeric dielectric will commence. The average kinetic energy (K.E.) of charge carriers under the electric field is proportional to the product of the internal field strength E_i and the mean free path λ, and is equal to

$$\text{K.E.} = E_i \lambda e \,, \qquad\qquad 6.2$$

where e is the charge of the electron. If E_i is estimated from the Mosotti field,

$$E_i = \left(\frac{\varepsilon + 2}{3}\right) E_e = \left(\frac{\varepsilon + 2}{3}\right) \frac{U_e}{d}, \qquad\qquad 6.3$$

where ε is the dielectric constant of the polymer, d is the thickness of polymeric dielectric, and E_e and U_e are external field strength and external voltage applied, respectively. Then, the minimum energy from the charge carriers to start ionization U_i is

$$U_i = K.E. = E_i \lambda e = \frac{\lambda}{3d} \, eU_e(\varepsilon + 2). \qquad 6.4$$

Since

$$U_i = V_i e , \qquad 6.5$$

where V_i is the ionization potential of the polymer, then

$$U_e = \frac{V_i}{\dfrac{\lambda}{3d}(\varepsilon + 2)}, \qquad 6.7$$

or

$$U_e = f\left[V_i, \frac{\lambda}{3d}, (\varepsilon + 2)\right], \qquad 6.8$$

But the dielectric strength E_B is related to U_e, ϱ_v and tan δ. Then

$$E_B = f\left[V_i, \frac{\lambda}{3d}, (\varepsilon + 2), \varrho_v, \tan \delta\right], \qquad 6.9$$

The mean free path is the cubic root of free volume V_f. From Eq. (6.1), since χ is related to ϱ_v, and τ is related to V_f, ϱ_v is also a function of V_f. Hence we can drop λ from Eq. (6.8), and convert it to

$$E_B = f \, [V_i, \varepsilon, \varrho_v, \tan \delta]. \qquad 6.10$$

The physical significance of Eq. (6.10) is that E_B is a function of ε, tan δ, and ϱ_v. This empirical relationship can be checked with actual experimental data such as is listed in Table 6.1.[4] These data come from 19 samples of polymers of quite different nature. When these data are treated with nonlinear equations on a computer, the following relationships can be deduced:

$$E_B = A + B \log \frac{\varrho_v T_g}{\varepsilon \tan \delta}, \qquad 6.11$$

where A and B are constants. The value of B is 0.8704. If we drop T_g from Eq. (6.11), we get

$$E_B = A + B \log \frac{\varrho_v}{\varepsilon \tan \delta}. \qquad 6.12$$

Here the value of the constant B is 0.8721, which means that the effect of T_g on E_B was very weak.

Of course, Eq. (6.12) is only a rough empirical correlation, especially since we cannot measure the exact values of V_i for each polymer. Also, Eq. (6.11) is by no means a complete relationship as many other complicating factors are involved in dielectric breakdown of polymers. Yet the attempted correlation of the four fundamental parameters into one equation is a big step forward in seeking control over the electrical properties of polymers by chemical means.

TABLE 6.1 Measured Values of Electrical Properties of Some Polymers

Polymer	E_B (60 Hz), (V/mil)	ε (100 Hz)	tan δ (100 Hz)	ϱ_V (ohm cm)	T_g (K)
Polystyrene	890	2.31	0.00029	2.5×10^{16}	373
Butadiene-styrene rubber	816	2.46	0.00098	2.8×10^{15}	221
High-density polyethylene	811	2.30	0.00011	2.2×10^{16}	148
Cis-polybutadiene	810	2.05	0.00051	3.1×10^{15}	168
Trans-polyisoprene	782	2.27	0.00038	7.8×10^{16}	223
Low-density polyethylene	742	2.22	0.0039	2.5×10^{15}	148
Poly(phenylmethyl, diphenylsiloxane)	720	2.99	0.00024	4.4×10^{14}	176
Polycarbonate	683	2.72	0.00115	2.2×10^{13}	369
Cross-linked cis-polyisoprene	665	2.41	0.0024	1.1×10^{15}	210
Poly(phenylmethyl, dimethylsiloxane)	661	2.87	0.00010	3.0×10^{14}	149
Poly(diphenyl, dimethyl siloxane)	661	2.90	0.00041	9.8×10^{14}	151
Poly(methyl methacrylate)	608	3.03	0.057	1.2×10^{13}	382
Cis-polyisoprene	577	2.26	0.0094	7.1×10^{16}	210
Polydimethyl siloxane	552	2.86	0.00025	5.3×10^{14}	150
Chlorosulfonyl polyethylene	476	5.63	0.138	2.6×10^{13}	257
Polyethyl acrylate	463	5.56	0.013	1.4×10^{13}	258
Viton(copolymer of vinylidene fluoride and hexafluoropropy- lene)	351	8.55	0.0403	4.1×10^{11}	255
Polytrifluoropropyl methyl siloxane	342	6.85	0.109	2.7×10^{11}	199
Polychloroprene	236	7.83	0.639	8.2×10^{9}	230

6.3   DIELECTRIC BREAKDOWN

6.3.1   Introduction

In practical situations, insulation usually fails by processes such as treeing, internal discharges, tracking, and other impurity- and imperfection-dominated events. This being the case, the largest industrial gains probably lie in the informed dielectric design of components, careful attention to materials processing, and a better understanding of the solid/gas or solid/liquid interface. Thus, two points must be made concerning dielectric breakdown: the one has to do with treeing, and the other with the complexities of the fundamental processes underlying the breakdown.

6.3.2   Treeing

The more we learn about treeing phenomena, the more likely it becomes that tree initiation and growth will provide the basis for an explanation of nonintrinsic electrical breakdown of dielectrics.

We know that electrical breakdown must commence in regions of the highest and most divergent electric stress. We also know that only the idealized insulation system is perfect, consisting of absolutely smooth electrodes, perfect electrode-insulation interfaces, and pure, uniform, isotropic dielectrics containing no contaminant particles or cavities. Practical and commercial insulation systems contain stress concentrations resulting from such defects. Since these are the con ditions that can initiate treeing, it seems that treeing is a reasonable mechanism to explain breakdown. This does not mean that all insulations containing any stress concentration, or even some kinds of trees, must fail in less than very extended periods of time. In fact, reports of long lifetimes of solid electrical insulations suggest that a well-designed and well-constructed insulation system operated within its limits of electrical, mechanical, and thermal stresses may have a long life. Considering the current level of scientific interest in treeing, it seems certain that further improvements in materials, constructions, test methods, and understanding will come.

6.3.3   Complexities of Dielectric Breakdown

The fundamental processes underlying the electrical failure of a solid are very complex (Table 6.2), and only in extreme cases can the mechanism be predicted with any certainty. Fundamental changes, such as the nature of the predominant charge carrier, can occur as electric stress or temperature is raised, making a priori prediction very difficult. For this reason, conduction studies at fields below breakdown often cannot generate accurate enough parameters for breakdown models.

TABLE 6.2 Fundamental Processes of Dielectric Breakdown[5]

I. Electronic breakdown process
   1. Intrinsic breakdown ($\partial E_B/\partial d = 0$, where d is sample thickness)
     A. Theories based on the single-electron approximation ($\partial E_B/\partial T \geqq 0$)
       (1) high-energy criterion
       (2) low-energy criterion
     B. Collective critical field theories
       (1) single crystal ($\partial E_B/\partial T > 0$)
       (2) amorphous materials ($\partial E_B/\partial T < 0$)
   2. Electron avalanche breakdown ($\partial E_B/\partial d > 0$, $\partial E_B/\partial T \geqq 0$)
     A. Single-avalanche model
     B. Collective-avalanche model
   3. Field-emission breakdown ($\partial E_B/\partial d = 0$, $\partial E_B/\partial T = 0$)
   4. Free-volume breakdown ($\partial E_B/\partial T < 0$)

II. Thermal breakdown process
   1. Steady-state thermal breakdown ($\partial E_B/\partial T < 0$)
   2. Impulse thermal breakdown

III. Mechanical breakdown process
   Electromechanical breakdown ($\partial E_B/\partial T < 0$)

IV. Chemical breakdown process
   Gas-discharge electrochemical breakdown

Since dielectric breakdown is associated with localized imperfections of some kind in the polymer, the values of the dielectric strength will usually exhibit a very large degree of statistical deviation. This behavior is entirely different from the behavior of dielectric constant, Young's modulus, density, and other properties determined by the mean value of the molecular behavior of the polymer. Structural defects within a material usually occupy only a very small part of the total structure, hence their influence on many materials' properties is very small, or their statistical deviations are very small. However, in the case of dielectric breakdown the experimentally observed values are determined by just such structural defects. Since the formation and distribution of defects in general are highly statistically dispersive, the values of dielectric strength then also deviate rather strongly from their statistical mean.[6]

6.4 EFFECT OF MOLECULAR WEIGHT, MORPHOLOGY, AND PLASTICIZATION ON CONDUCTIVITY IN INSULATING POLYMERS

6.4.1 Molecular Weight

The molecular weight and molecular weight distribution are fundamental properties of polymers. As such, they affect a polymer's bulk density, crystallinity, morphology, and therefore, volume conductivity. Generally speaking, the molecular weight effect is very evident in the low-molecular-weight region and much less so in the high-molecular-weight region. The general trend is that conductivity decreases with increasing molecular weight, which is related to a decrease in free volume and an increase of viscosity and intermolecular forces. This generalization is true only if such other factors as crystallinity content and morphology are not drastically changed.

6.4.2 Morphology

In general, the study of the effect of morphology on conductivity has been mainly one of spherulite structure effects. The following correlations have been observed: (1) conductivity increases with spherulite formation, (2) conductivity increases with the number of spherulites per unit volume, (3) conductivity decreases with increasing spherulite diameter, (4) in semicrystalline polymers regularity of structure leads to a decrease in ionic conductivity, and (5) in general terms, ionic conductivity decreases with increasing crystallinity content.

6.4.3 Plasticization

One generalization can be made about the effect of molecular plasticization on conductivity: conductivity increases with plasticizer addition. This observation is strictly empirical. What is needed here is a theoretical investigation of the connection between free volume and conductivity. It would also help in the effort to develop more definitive tests for distinguishing between electronic and ionic conduction. These developments would be of special value in the study of plasticized polymers.

6.5 MATERIALS WITH SELECTED VALUES

In this section we list the top five materials from each property category for quick reference. The selection was made from the information collected in this book.

6.5.1 Dielectric Constant

Highest Values

Material	ε	Temp (°C)	Freq (Hz)	Ref.
Thiokol PRI Compound [100 pts bis(2-chloroethyl)formal and ethylene dichloride polysulfide, 60 pts carbon black, other compounding ingredients]	17,900	25	10^3	a
Thiokol ST Compoundl [100 pts polysulfide polymer of bis(2-chloroethyl) formal, 60 pts carbon black, other compounding ingredients]	17,300	25	10^3	a
Thiokol Type FA Compound [100 pts bis(1-chloroethyl)formal and ethylene dichloride polysulfide, 10 pts ZnO, 60 pts carbon black, 1 pt. stearic acid, 0.5 pt diphenylguanidine, 0.35 pt Altax]	2,260	23	10^3	a
80% Teflon, 20% carbon (Chemelac M 1406)	170	25	10^3	a
Teflon, 25% graphite (Chemelac M 1414)	150	25	10^7	a

Lowest Values

Material	Density (g/cm³)	ε	Temp (°C)	Freq (Hz)	Ref.
Polyimide	0.010–0.016	1.0	23	10^6	b
Polyurethane, flexible	0.014–0.128	1.0–1.5	23	10^6	b
Polypropylene, low density	0.010	1.02	23	10^4	b
Polyvinyl Chloride expanded (Plasticell)	–	1.04	25	10^3	a
Polystyrene, extruded	0.022–0.080	<1.05	23	10^2–10^8	b

6.5.2   Dissipation Factor

Lowest Values

Material	Density (g/cm³)	Tan δ	Temp (°C)	Freq (Hz)	Ref.
Polypropylene, low density	0.010	0.00006	23	10^4	b
Poly(Methyl-l-Pentene)	–	0.00007	25	60	c
Poly(α-Methyl Styrene)	–	0.00007	25	100	a
Polytetrafluoro-ethylene	–	<0.0001	25	10^3	b
Polystyrene, molded	0.016–0.080	0.0001–0.0007	23	10^2–10^6	b

6.5.3   Dielectric Strength

Highest Values

Material	V/mil.	Ref.
Biaxially oriented polypropylene	8000	b
Polyethylene terephthalate	7500	b
Polysulfone	7500	b
Polyimide	7000	b
Fluorinated ethylene propylene copolymer	6500	b

6.5.4   Arc Resistance

Highest Values

Material	Time (s)	Ref.
Acrylics	No track	d
Poly(chlorotrifluoroethylene)	>360	d
Cellulose acetate	310	c
Celcon	240	d
Polyethylene, medium density	235	c

6.5.5   Electrical Conductivity

Highest Values

Material	Conductivity $(\Omega \, cm)^{-1}$	Dopant Species	Ref.
Poly(sulfur nitride)	40,000	Br_2	k
Polyaceytlene, aligned	3,200	AsF_5	l
Polyacetylene	970	AsF_5	m
Poly(p-phenylene)	3,000	Na	n
Poly(p-phenylene)	500	AsF_5	o
Poly(p-phenylene vinylene)	500	AsF_5	p
Polypyrrole, layered structure	160	Sulfonate	q

6.5.6   Water Vapor Permeability

Lowest Values

Material	Temp (°C)	$P \times 10^{10}$	Ref.
Poly(trifluorochlorethylene) (Kel-F)	25	0.29	e
Poly(vinylidene chloride) (Saran)	25	0.5	f
Polyethylene, d = 0.964	25	12.0	f
Polyisoprene hydrochloride (Pliofilm)	25	16.0	g
Polypropylene	25	51.0	f

Highest Values

Material	Temp (°C)	$P \times 10^{10}$	Ref.
Poly(oxydimethylsilylene), filler 10%, vulcanized	35	43,000	h
Ethyl cellulose	20	12,000	g
Cellulose nitrate	25	6,300	i
Cellulose acetate	25	5,500	f
Poly(1,3-butadiene)	37.5	5,070	j

6.5.7 Water Absorption

Highest Values
Plastics

Material	%	Ref.
Regenerated cellulose (cellophane)	45–115	b
Nylon 6, extruded	9.5	b
Cellulose acetate	3–8.5	b
Ethyl cellulose	2.5–7.5	b
Cellulose triacetate	2.0–4.5	b

Plastic Foams

Material	Density (g/cm^3)	Vol%	Ref.
Phenolic, liquid resin	0.032–0.080	13–51	b
Cellulose acetate, board and rods	0.096–0.128	13–17	b
Acrylic, boards	0.041–0.099	11.8–13.3	b
Polystyrene, boards	0.016	2–6	b
Polyurethane	0.020–0.048	1–5	b

Lowest Values
Plastics

Material	%	Ref.
Poly(chlorotrifluoroethylene)	0.00	c
Poly(tetrafluoroethylene)	0.00	c
Polyethylene, medium density	~0	b
Polyethylene, high density	~0	b
Polypropylene	<0.005	b

Plastic Foams

Material	Density (g/cm^3)	Vol%	Ref.
Polyvinyl chloride, flexible, closed cell	0.064–0.176	~0	b
Styrene-acrylonitrile	0.013	~0	b
Polypropylene, low density	0.010	0.02	b
Polyethylene, low density	0.026–0.038	0.1	b
Silicone, liquid, closed cell	0.336–0.497	0.1	b

References to the Tables

a. A. von Hippel, Ed., *Dielectric Materials and Applications,* The Technology Press, M.I.T. and John Wiley & Sons, N.Y. (1958).

b. J. Agranoff, Ed., *Modern Plastics Encyclopedia,* Vol. 60, No. 10A, McGraw-Hill, New York, (1983 bis 1984).

c. J. Brandrup and E. H. Immergut, Eds., *Polymer Handbook,* Wiley-Interscience, New York (1977).

d. V. Shah, *Handbook of Plastics Testing Technology,* Wiley Interscience, New York (1984).

e. A. W. Myers, V. Tammela, V. Stannett, and M. Swarc, Modern Plastics *37,* No. 10, 193 (1960).

f. A. W. Myers, J. A. Myer, C. E. Rogers, V. T. Stannett, and M. Swarc, Tappi *44,* 58 (1961).

g. H. Yasuda and V. Stannett, J. Poly. Sci. *57,* 907 (1962).

h. J. A. Barrie and B. Plott, Polymer *4,* 303 (1963).

i. V. Stannett and J. L. Williams, J. Poly. Sci. *C10,* 45 (1966).

j. Y. Iyenger, J. Poly. Sci. *B3,* 663 (1965).

k. W. D. Gill, T. C. Clarke, G. B. Street, Appl. Phys. Comm. *2* (4), 211 (1982–83).

l. M. A. Druy, C. H. Tansg, N. Brown, A. J. Heeger, A. G. MacDiarmid, J. Polym. Sci., Poly. Phys. Edn. *18,* 429 (1980).

m. P. J. Nigrey, A. G. MacDiarmid, A. J. Heeger, J. Chem. Soc., Chem. Comm. 594 (1979).

n. L. W. Shacklette, R. R. Chance, D. M. Ivory, G. G. Miller, R. H. Baughman, Synth. Met. *1,* 307 (1979).

o. D. M. Ivory, G. G. Miller, J. M. Sowa, L. W. Shacklette, R. R. Chance, R. H. Baughman, J. Chem. Phys. *71,* 1506 (1979).

p. D. R. Gagnon, J. O. Capistran, F. E. Karasz, R. W. Lenz, Polymer Prep. Am. Chem. Soc. Div. Poly. Chem. *25*(2), 284 (1984).

q. W. Werner, M. Monkenbush, G. Wegner, Makromol. Chem., Rapid Commun. *5,* 157 (1984).

6.6   REFERENCES

1. S. Saito, Macromolecules *17,* 672 (1968) (Japanese).
2. S. Saito, Cellulose Industry *3*(3), 182 (1970) (Japanese).
3. S. Saito, and H. Sasabe, Rep. Prop. Polymer Phys. Japan *12,* 405 (1969) (Japanese).
4. S. N. Kolesov, *Structural Electrophysics of the Polymer Dielectrics,* Izd. Uzbekistan, Tashkent (1975) (Russian).
5. M. Ieda, J. Electrochem. Soc. Japan *95,* 36 (1975).
6. J. J. O'Dwyer, *The Theory of Dielectric Breakdown of Solids,* Oxford University Press, London (1964).

APPENDICES

APPENDIX 1
DIELECTRIC CONSTANTS
OF POLYMERS, POLYMER ALLOYS, PLASTICS, AND RESINS; FILLED PLASTICS AND
RESINS; PLASTIC AND RESIN COMPOSITES; RUBBERS; FILLED RUBBERS; FOAMED
PLASTICS AND RUBBERS; AND NATURAL PRODUCTS

POLYMERS, POLYMER ALLOYS, PLASTICS, AND RESINS

Material	ε^a	Temp (°C)	Frequency (Hz)	Ref.
ABS (Acrylonitrile-Butadiene-Styrene), low impact	2.5–3.5	25	60	1
ABS, medium impact	2.8–3.2	25	60	1
ABS, very high impact	2.8–3.5	25	60	1
ABS, heat resistant	2.7–3.5	25	60	1
ABS, Cycolac T	2.9	25	60	2
ABS/polycarbonate	3.2–3.6	25	10^4	1
ABS/polysulfone (polyaryl ether)	3.1	25	10^4	1
Acetal(polyoxymethylene), Delrin	3.7	25	60	1
Acetal, Celcon	3.7	25	100	1
Acrylonitrile/methyl acrylate, rubber modified	4.8	25	10^3	3
Allyl diglycol carbonate	3.5–3.9	25	10^4	1
Aniline-formaldehyde (Cibanite E)	3.57	25	10^3	4
Aniline-formaldehyde (Dilectene 100)	3.68	25	10^3	4
Aromatic polyamide-imides	3.32	25	10^3	2
Aromatic polyester-imides	3.50	25	10^3	2
Aromatic polyethers	3.14	25	60	5
Aromatic polyimides	3.5	25	10^3	2
Aromatic polysulfone	3.13	23	10^3	2
Poly(butyl methacrylate)	2.62	24	10^3	4
Poly(butylene terephthalate)	3.2–3.3	25	100	1
Poly(butylene terephthalate), high impact	3.2–3.64	25	100	1
Polycarbonate	2.99	25	10^3	3

Material	ε^a	Temp (°C)	Frequency (Hz)	Ref.
Polycarbonate/ABS alloy	2.4	25	60	5
Cellulose, regenerated (cellophane)	3.2	25	10^3	3
Cellulose acetate, LL-1, 55.4% acetyl	3.77	25	10^3	4
Cellulose acetate, LL-1, Lumarith XFA-H4, 28% plasticizer	4.51	25	10^3	4
Cellulose acetate, LL-1, Fibestos 2050 TVA, C1686, 26% plasticizer	4.53	26	10^3	4
Cellulose acetate butyrate	3.2–6.2	25	10^6	1
Cellulose acetate propionate	3.4–3.7	25	10^6	1
Cellulose nitrate	7.0–7.5	25	60	5
Cellulose nitrate, Pyralin, 25% camphor	8.4	27	10^3	4
Cellulose propionate	3.2	25	10^6	3
Cellulose propionate, Forticel, 8% plasticizer	3.48	25	10^3	4
Cellulose triacetate	3.2–4.5	25	10^3	3
O- and p-Chlorostyrene copolymer, (Plastic Q-409)	2.60	24	10^3	4
Poly(chlorotrifluoroethylene), Kel-F	2.63	26	10^3	4
Poly(chlorotrifluoroethylene), Kel-F Grade 300-P25, plasticized	2.75	25	10^3	4
Poly(chlorotrifluoroethylene), 80% crystalline	2.646	23	10^3	7
Poly(chlorotrifluoroethylene), 12% crystalline	2.492	23	10^3	7
Cycloaliphatic epoxy resin	3.2	25	60	5
Poly(cyclohexyl methacrylate)	2.52	25	10^3	4
Poly(diallyl phthalate)	3.57	26.8	10^3	4
Poly(diallyl phenyl phosphonate), Phoresin	3.84	25	10^3	4
Poly(2,5-dichlorostyrene), Plastic CY-8	2.61	24	10^3	4
Poly(3,4-dichlorostyrene)	2.93	25	10^3	4
Polymer of 50% 2,4-, 25% 2,5-, 25% 2,3-, 2,6-, and 3,4-dichlorostyrenes; Plastic CQ-10DM	2.70	25	10^3	4
Polymer of 53.5% 2,5-dichlorostyrene, 32.5% styrene, 0.5% divinylbenzene, and 13% hydrogenated terphenyl; Bureau of Standards Casting Resin	2.62	25	10^3	4
Poly(2,6-dimethyl-1,4-phenylene ether)	2.6	25	10^4	6
Epoxy, standard (Bisphenol A)	4.02	25	60	1
Epoxy, rigid, (Novolacs)	3.96–4.02	25	60	1
Poly(ether sulfone)	3.5	25	10^3	3
Ethyl cellulose, Ethocel LT-5	3.09	25	10^3	4
Poly(ethyl methacrylate)	2.75	22	10^3	4
Polyethylene, low density	2.2	25	10^3	3
Polyethylene, medium density	2.2	25	10^3	3
Polyethylene, high density	2.3	25	10^3	3

Material	ε^a	Temp (°C)	Frequency (Hz)	Ref.
Polyethylene, ultra high mol. weight	2.3	25	10^3	3
Ethylene/chlorotrifluoroethylene copolymer	2.6	25	10^3	3
Ethylene/ethyl acrylate copolymer	2.8	25	60	1
Poly(ethylene terephthalate), thermoplastic	3.2	25	10^3	3
Ethylene/tetrafluoroethylene copolymer	2.6	25	10^3	3
Ethylene/vinyl acetate copolymer	3.16	25	60	1
Fluorinated ethylene/propylene copolymer (FEP)	2.0–2.5	25	10^3	3
Polyfumaronitrile	8.5	26	10^3	8
Ionomer	2.4	25	10^3	3
Poly(isobutyl methacrylate)	2.68	25	10^3	4
Poly(isobutylene)	2.23	25	10^3	4
Melamine/formaldehyde resin	7.9	25	60	5
Melamine/phenol resin	7.0	25	60	5
Methyl cellulose (Methocel)	6.8	22	10^3	4
Poly(methyl methacrylate), Plexiglas	3.12	27	10^3	4
Poly(methyl methacrylate), Lucite HM-119	2.84	23	10^3	4
Poly(methyl methacrylate/α-methyl-styrene)	3.4	25	60	5
Poly(methyl methacrylate/25–30 mol% tributyltin methacrylate)	3.3–5.0	25	10^3	9
Poly(methyl methacrylate)/poly-(vinyl chloride) alloy	4.0	25	60	5
Poly(methyl-l-pentene)	2.12	25	60	5
Poly(α-methyl styrene)	2.60	25	10^3	4
Nomex paper (m-phenylene-diamine/isophthaloyl chloride)	2.8	25	10^3	2
Nylon 6	3.7	25	10^3	3
Nylon 66	4.0	25	60	1
Nylon 11	3.3	25	10^3	1
Nylon 12	3.6	25	10^3	1
Nylon 610	3.5	25	10^3	4
Nylon 610, 90% relative humidity	4.2	25	10^3	4
Nylon 6/6, high impact	3.2	25	60	1
Nylon 6/9, high impact	3.6	25	60	1
Nylon 6/12	4.0	25	60	1
Perfluoroalkyl (PFA)	2.0–2.1	25	10^3	3
Phenol/aniline/formaldehyde	4.50	25	10^3	10
Phenol/formaldehyde (Bakelite BT-48–306)	7.15	24	10^3	4
Phenol/furfuraldehyde (Durite No. 221X)	5.70	24	10^3	4
Phenoxy resins (Epichlorohydrin/bisphenol A)	4.10	25	60	2
Poly(2,6-dimethyl phenylene oxide) (PPO C-1001)	2.55	23	10^3	2
Poly(phenylene sulfide)	3.2	25	10^4	1
Polypropylene	2.2	25	10^3	3

Material	ε^a	Temp (°C)	Frequency (Hz)	Ref.
Polypyromellitimide (Kapton H film; Vespel)	3.4	23	10^5	11
Polysiloxane resin (methyl, phenyl, and methylphenyl)	3.04	25	10^3	4
Polystyrene	2.4–2.7	25	10^3	3
Polystyrene, cross-linked	2.51	22	10^3	4
Polystyrene, high heat stability	2.45	25	60	5
Polystyrene, high impact	2.45	25	60	5
Poly(styrene/acrylonitrile) (SAN)	2.6–3.0	25	10^4	1
Poly(styrene/10% butadiene) (Marbon S)	2.62	25	10^3	4
Poly(styrene/15% butadiene) (Marbon 8000)	2.56	25	10^3	4
50% Polystyrene/50% chlorinated biphenyl (Styramic No.18)	2.66	22	10^3	4
Poly(styrene/2,4-dimethylstyrene)	2.53	25	10^3	4
1:1 Poly(styrene/1,4-divinyl-2,3,5,6-tetrachlorobenzene)	2.70	26	10^3	4
Poly(styrene/ethylene oxide) block copolymers (50–70 wt% polystyrene)	2.0–3.9	20	10^3	6
Poly(styrene/α-methylstyrene) (Picolastic D-125)	2.58	25	10^3	4
1:1 Poly(styrene/1,3,5-trivinyl-2,4,6-trichlorobenzene)	2.70	25	10^3	4
Polytetrafluoroethylene	2.0–2.1	25	10^3	3
Poly(urea/formaldehyde)	6.7	24	10^3	10
Polyurethane (polyethylene oxide 600)	10	18	10	6
Poly(vinyl acetal) (Alvar 11/90)	3.14	25	10^3	4
Poly(vinyl acetate) (Elvacet 42A-900)	3.07	25	10^3	4
Poly(vinyl alcohol/acetate), 0–1.5% acetate (Elvanol 50A-42)	10.4	25	10^3	4
Poly(vinyl alcohol/acetate), 11–14% acetate, (Elvanol 51A-05)	7.8	23	10^3	4
Poly(vinyl butyral) (Butvar, low OH)	2.67	27	10^3	4
Poly(N-vinyl carbazole), 1.3% HB-40 oil, (Polectron No. 24)	2.95	25	10^3	4
Poly(vinyl chloride) (Vinylite QYNA)	3.10	20	10^3	4
Poly(vinyl chloride), chlorinated	3.08	25	60	1
Poly(vinyl chloride/vinyl acetate), 5% vinyl acetate (Vinylite VYNW)	3.15	20	10^3	4
Poly(vinyl chloride/vinyl acetate), 9% vinyl acetate (Vinylite VYNS)	3.08	20	10^3	4
Poly(vinyl chloride/vinyl acetate), 13% vinyl acetate (Vinylite VYHH)	3.12	22	10^3	4

Material	ε^a	Temp (°C)	Frequency (Hz)	Ref.
64.5% [95% Poly(vinyl chloride/5% vinyl acetate)], 32% dioctyl phthalate, 3.5% Misc. (Vinylite VU-1900)	5.65	24	10^3	4
87.8% Poly(vinyl chloride), 10.5% stabilizer, 1.7% misc. (Geon 80384)	3.34	25	10^3	4
65% Poly(vinyl chloride) (Geon 101), 35% Paraplex G-25	4.77	25	10^3	4
65% Poly(vinyl chloride) (Geon 101), 35% Paraplex G-50	5.20	15	100	4
65% Poly(vinyl chloride) (Geon 101), 35% Paraplex G-60	5.52	25	10^3	4
Poly(vinyl chloride/propylene)	3.1	25	60	5
Poly(vinyl cyclohexane) (Hydrogenated Polystyrene)	2.25	24	10^3	4
Poly(vinyl fluoride)	8.5	25	10^3	3
Poly(vinyl formal) (Formvar, Type E)	3.12	26	10^3	4
Poly (α-vinyl naphthalene)	2.6	24	10^3	4
Poly (2-vinyl pyridine)	4.64	22	10^3	4
Poly(2-vinyl pyridiene/styrene)	3.38	23	10^3	4
Poly (vinyl toluene)	2.59	25	10^3	4
Poly(vinylidene chloride/vinyl chloride) (Saran B-115)	4.65	23	10^3	4
Poly (vinylidene fluoride)	8.4	25	10^3	3
Poly (p-xylylene)	2.65	25	10^3	2
Poly (chloro-p-xylylene)	3.1	25	10^3	2
Poly (dichloro-p-xylylene)	2.82	25	10^3	2
Poly (methyl-p-xylylene)	2.48	25	10^3	2

FILLED PLASTICS AND RESINS

Material	ε^a	Temp (°C)	Frequency (Hz)	Ref.
Cellulose acetate, 23–31% plasticizer, pigments, dyes (Tenite I 008AH₂)	4.55	26	10^3	4
Cellulose acetate, 5–15% plasticizer, pigments, dyes (Tenite II 205AH₂)	3.50	26	10^3	4
Cresylic acid-formaldehyde, 50% α-cellulose (Micarta No. 254)	4.95	25	10^3	4
Cresylic acid-formaldehyde, 50% cotton drillings (Micarta No. 496)	7.00	25	10^3	4

Material	ε^a	Temp (°C)	Frequency (Hz)	Ref.
Poly(2,5-dichlorostyrene) (58.1%) + TiO$_2$ (41.9%)	5.30	23	10^3	4
Poly(2,5-dichlorostyrene) (34.7%) + TiO$_2$ (65.3%)	10.2	24	10^3	4
Poly(2,5-dichlorostyrene) (18.6%) + TiO$_2$ (81.4%)	23.4	23	10^3	4
Poly(2,5-dichlorostyrene) (38.2%) + MgTiO$_3$ (61.8%)	6.10	23	10^3	4
Poly(2,5-dichlorostryene) (63.0%) + SrTiO$_3$ (37.0%)	5.20	25	10^3	4
Poly(2,5-dichlorostyrene) (40.5%) + SrTiO$_3$ (59.5%)	9.65	24	10^3	4
Poly(2,5-dichlorostyrene) (25.2%) + SrTiO$_3$ (74.8%)	17.4	23	10^3	4
Poly(2,5-dichlorostyrene) (14.4%) + SrTiO$_3$ (80.6%)	22.8	23	10^3	4
Poly (2,5-dichlorostyrene) (66.6%) + BaTiO$_3$ (33.4%)	4.08	23	10^3	4
Poly(2,5-dichlorostyrene) (32.8%) + BaTiO$_3$ (67.2%)	9.72	5	10^3	4
Poly(2,5-dichlorostyrene) (23.5%) + BaTiO$_3$ (76.5%)	15.8	23	10^3	4
Poly(2,5-dichlorostyrene) (21.0%) + BaTiO$_3$ (79.0%)	19.3	23	10^3	4
Poly(2,5-dichlorostyrene) (94%) + Fe (6%, minus 200mesh)	2.78	25	3×10^9	4
Poly(2,5-dichlorostyrene) (60%) + Fe (40%, minus 200 mesh)	5.3	25	3×10^9	4
Poly(2,5-dichlorostyrene) (49.3%) + Fe (50.7%, minus 200 mesh)	6.93	25	3×10^9	4
Poly(2,5-dichlorostyrene) (40.7%) + Fe (59.3%, minus 200 mesh)	10	25	3×10^9	4
Poly(2,5-dichlorostyrene) (92%) + Fe$_3$O$_4$ (8%)	2.76	25	3×10^9	4
Poly(2,5-dichlorostyrene) (83.7%) + Fe$_3$O$_4$ (16.3%)	3.2	25	3×10^9	4
Poly(2–5-dichlorostyrene) (75%) + Fe$_3$O$_4$ (25%)	3.44	25	3×10^9	4
Poly(2–5,dichlorostyrene) (65.9%) + Fe$_3$O$_4$ (34.1%)	4.07	25	3×10^9	4
Poly(2,5-dichlorostyrene) (56.2%) + Fe$_3$O$_4$ (43.8%)	4.98	25	3×10^9	4
Poly(2,5-dichlorostyrene) (46.0%) + Fe$_3$O$_4$ (54.0%)	7.3	25	3×10^9	4
Poly(2,5-dichlorostyrene) (35.7%) + Fe$_3$O$_4$ (64.3%)	9.5	25	3×10^9	4
Poly(2,5-dichlorostryene) (24.5%) + Fe$_3$O$_4$ (75.5%)	18	25	3×10^9	4
Poly(2,5-dichlorostryene) (38.55%) + (Mn,Fe)$_3$O$_4$ (61.45%)	16.9	25	10^3	4
Poly(2,5-dichlorostyrene) (21.3%) + (Mn,Fe)$_3$O$_4$ (78.7%)	99	25	10^3	4

Material	ε^a	Temp (°C)	Frequency (Hz)	Ref.
Melamine-formaldehyde, 25% α-pulp, An stearate (Melmac Type 1077)	6.90	28	10^3	4
Melamine-formaldehyde, 40% wood fluor, 18% plasticizer (Melmac Molding Compound 1500)	6.31	25	10^3	4
Melamine-formaldehyde-aniline, 40% wood flour (Melmac Molding Compound 1502)	6.95	25	10^3	4
Phenol-formaldehyde, 40% wood flour, 8% misc. (Bakelite BM-120)	4.74	25	10^3	4
Phenol-formaldehyde, 67% mica filled (Durez 1601, natural)	4.94	26	10^3	4
Phenol-formaldehyde, 65% mica filled, 4% lubricant (Durite 500)	5.03	24	10^3	4
Phenol-formaldehyde, 35% mica filled, 18% other filler (Resinox 10900)	4.64	25	10^3	4
Phenol-aniline-formaldehyde, 62% mica filled (Bakelite BM-262)	4.80	25	10^3	4
Phenol-aniline-formaldehyde, 59.5% mica filled, 8.5% misc. (Bakelite BM-1895)	4.72	25	10^3	4
Phenol-aniline-formaldehyde, 60% mica filled (Resinox 7934)	4.46	25	10^3	4
Polystyrene, 9% carbon	3.85	26	10^3	4
Polystryene, 30% carbon	11	25	10^9	4
Polystyrene, 50% carbon	25.9	25	10^9	4
75% Teflon, 25% CaF_2 (Chemelac M1405)	2.50	25	10^3	4
80% Teflon, 20% carbon (Chemelac M1406)	170	25	10^5	4
88% Teflon, 12% ceramic (Chemelac M 1407)	3.02	25	10^3	4
80% Teflon, 20% TiO_2 (Chemelac M1422)	2.72	25	10^3	4
Teflon, ceramic filled	2.9–3.6	25	60	1
59% Poly(vinyl chloride), 30% dioctyl phosphate, 6% stabilizer, 5% filler (Geon 2046)	6.10	23	10^3	4
71% Poly(vinyl chloride), 10.5% filler, 5% plasticizer, 8.5% stabilizer (Geon 80365)	3.65	25	10^3	4
63.7% Poly(vinyl chloride), 33.1% di-2-ethylhexyl phthalate, 3.2% lead silicate (Koroseal 5CS-243)	5.65	27	10^3	4
57.5% Poly(vinyl chloride), 12.6% fillers, 28.7% plasticizers (PVC 1006)	4.55	25	10^4	4
52.3% Poly(vinylchloride), 15.1% fillers 31.4% plasticizers (PVC 1018)	4.95	25	10^4	4

Material	ε^a	Temp (°C)	Frequency (Hz)	Ref.
57.5% Poly(vinyl chloride), 10.4% fillers, 31.6% plasticizers (PVC 1216)	4.4	25	10^4	4
59.4% Poly(vinyl chloride), 10.7% fillers, 29.7% plasticizers (PVC 1406)	4.5	25	10^4	4
64.7% Poly(vinyl chloride), 2% filler, 32.5% plasticizers, (Ultron Wire Compound UL 1004)	4.65	25	10^4	4
60.1% Poly(vinyl chloride), 7.8% fillers, 31.2% plasticizers (Ultron Wire Compound UL2 4001)	4.7	25	10^4	4

PLASTIC AND RESIN COMPOSITES

Material	ε^a	Temp (°C)	Frequency (Hz)	Ref.
Acetal (Celcon), 25% glass fiber	4.12	25	100	1
Acetal (Delrin), 20% glass fiber	4.0	25	60	1
Poly(benzimidazole), glass laminate (Imidite 1850)	4.7	25	9.4×10^6	2
Benzoguanamine-formaldehyde, 28% α-paper (benzoguanamine resin)	4.58	25	10^3	4
Poly(butylene terephthalate), 30% glass fiber	3.7	25	10^4	1
Poly(butylene terephthalate), 15–40% glass fiber	3.6–3.8	25	100	1
Poly(butylene terephthalate), 10–30% mineral fiber	3.1–4.3	25	100	1
Polycarbonate, 20% glass fiber	3.17	25	60	1
Polycarbonate, 30% glass fiber	3.35	25	60	1
Polycarbonate, 40% glass fiber	3.53	25	60	1
84% Corning's 790 Glass Powder, 16% cross-linked organo-siloxane (Polyglass 5)	3.59	24	10^3	4
81.1% Corning's 790 Glass Powder, 18.6% polystyrene (Dow C-244) 0.25% paraffin, 0.1% Dow Corning's ignition sealing cpd. (Polyglass P^+)	3.36	24	10^3	4
64.9% Corning's 790 Glass Powder, 34.9% poly(2,5-dichlorostyrene), 0.1% paraffin wax, 0.1% Dow				

Material	ε^a	Temp (°C)	Frequency (Hz)	Ref.
Corning's ignition sealing cpd. (Polyglass D⁺)	3.22	24	10^3	4
45% Cresol-phenol-formaldehyde, 15% tung oil, 15% nylon fabric (Diletco; Mecoboard)	3.98	25	10^3	4
45% Cresol-phenol-formaldehyde, 15% Tung oil, 40% α-paper (Dilecto XXX-P-26)	8.61	25	10^3	4
Cresylic acid-formaldehyde, 60–65% glass fabric (Micarta No. 299)	5.29	24	10^3	4
Poly(ethylene terephthalate), 30–45% glass fiber	4.21–4.22	25	100	1
Poly(ethylene terephthalate/butylene terephthalate) 15–30% glass fiber	3.6	25	100	1
55% Fiberglass, ECC-261, 45% methyl and phenyl polysiloxane (DC 2103 Laminate)	3.92	25	10^3	4
65% Fiberglass, ECC-181, 35% methyl and phenyl polysiloxane (DC 2104 Laminate)	4.14	25	10^3	4
50–55% Glass cloth, 45–50% polysiloxane, DC 2103 (Taylor Grade GSC)	4.14	25	10^3	4
45% Glass fiber, 35% methyl and phenyl polysiloxane, 19% silica filler (Molding Compound XM-3)	4.00	25	10^3	4
56.5% Melamine resin, Melmac 7278, 43.5% Owens-Corning's Glass E (Polyglass M)	5.53	24	10^3	4
Melamine-formaldehyde, 65–70% fiberglass (Micarta No. 259)	6.07	24	10^3	4
Nylon 6, 30% glass fiber	4.6–5.6	25	60	1
Phenol-aniline-formaldehyde, 40% glass mat (Formica Grade MF-66)	4.50	25	10^3	4
Phenol-Formaldehdyde, 66% asbestos fiber (Bakelite BM-250)	22	25	10^3	4
Phenol-formaldehyde, 50% paper laminate (Formica XX)	5.15	26	10^3	4
Phenol-formaldehyde, 40% cotton fabric (Formica LE)	5.70	26	10^3	4
Phenol-formaldehyde, 50% nylon fabric (Formica Grade YN-25)	3.65	25	10^3	4
Phenol-formaldehyde, 40% random glass mat (Taylor Grade GGG)	6.08	25	10^3	4
Poly(phenylene oxide), 20% glass fiber	2.93	25	60	1
Poly(phenylene sulfide), 40% glass fiber	3.79	25	60	1
Polysulfone, 30% glass fiber	3.55	25	60	1
Polystyrene, 30% fiberglass	3.04	25	10^3	4

Material	ε^a	Temp (°C)	Frequency (Hz)	Ref.
Poly(styrene/acrylonitrile), 30% glass fiber (SAN)	3.5	25	10^4	1
Teflon, 32–35% continuous filament glass (Teflon Laminate GB-112-T)	2.74	25	10^3	4
Teflon, 25% fiberglass (Chemelac M1411)	2.14	25	10^3	4
Teflon, 25% graphite (Chemelac M 1414)	150	25	10^7	4
Teflon, 10% quartz (Chemelac M1418–2)	2.20	25	10^3	4
Teflon, 25% quartz (Chemelac M1418–5)	2.23	25	10^3	4

RUBBERS

Material	ε^a	Temp (°C)	Frequency (Hz)	Ref.
Balata, precipitated (Minusops Globosa)	2.50	25	10^3	4
Poly(butadiene)	3.3	25	10^6	1
Poly (75% butadiene/25% styrene), uncured (GR-S; Buna-S)	2.50	26	10^3	4
Poly(2-chlorobutadiene), stabilized with tetraethylthiuram disulfide (Neoprene GN)	6.5	26	10^3	4
Chlorosulfonated polyethylene	7.0	25	60	1
Cyclized rubber (Pliolite)	2.50	27	10^3	4
Depolymerized rubber (Permo Potting Compound No. 49)	3.39	25	10^3	4
Poly(ethylene/propylene), Poly-(allomer)	2.25–3.0	25	6	1
Gutta Percha (Palaquium Oblongifolium)	2.60	25	10^3	4
Hevea rubber, pale crepe	2.4	25	10^3	4
Hevea rubber, vulcanized, 6 pts sulfur	2.94	27	10^3	4
Poly (98–99% isobutylene/1–2% isoprene) (GR-I; butyl rubber)	2.38	25	10^3	4
Methyl and methylphenyl polysiloxane (DC 550)	2.90	25	10^3	4
Poly(styrene/acrylonitrile) and poly-(butadiene/acrylonitrile) alloy (Royalite 149–11)	5.20	25	10^3	4
Polysulfide	7.3	25	60	1
Polyurethanes	4.7–9.53	25	60	1

FILLED RUBBERS

Material	ε^a	Temp (°C)	Frequency (Hz)	Ref.
100 pts Poly (75% butadiene/25% styrene),5 pts Kadox, 5 pts Captax, 1 pt. stearic acid, and 3 pts sulfur (GR-S Compound; Buna S)	2.66	26	10^3	4
Hevea rubber compound (100 pts Hevea, 10 pts carbon black, 5 pts Kadox, 3 pts sulfur, 1 pt stearic acid, 0.5 pt Captax)	4.01	27	10^3	4
50% Siloxane elastomer, 50% TiO_2 (Silastic 120)	5.76	25	10^3	4
35% Siloxane elastomer, 35% ZnO, 30% $CaCO_3$ (Silastic 150)	5.85	25	10^3	4
33% Siloxane elastomer, 33% ZnO, 33% TiO_2 (Silastic 160)	9.27	25	10^3	4
33% Siloxane elastomer, 67% TiO_2 (Silastic 167)	8.6	25	10^3	4
35% Siloxane elastomer, 35% SiO_2, 30% TiO_2 (Silastic 180)	4.60	25	10^3	4
45% Siloxane elastomer, 55% SiO_2 (Silastic 181)	3.30	25	10^3	4
70% Siloxane elastomer, 30% SiO_2 (Silastic 250)	3.18	25	10^3	4
50% Siloxane elastomer, 50% SiO_2 (Silastic 342)	3.18	25	10^3	4
33% Siloxane elastomer, 67% TiO_2 (Silastic 6167)	10.1	25	10^3	4
45% Siloxane elastomer, 55% SiO_2 (Silastic 6181)	3.53	25	10^3	4
70% Siloxane elastomer, 30% SiO_2 (Silastic X-6734)	3.12	25	10^3	4
Thiokol PRI Compound [100 pts bis(2-chloroethyl)formal and ethylene dichloride polysulfide, 60 pts carbon black, other compounding ingredients]	17,900	25	10^3	4
Thiokol Type FA Compound [100 pts bis(1-chlorethyl) formal and ethylene dichloride polysulfide, 10 pts ZnO, 60 pts carbon black, 1 pt. stearic acid, 0.5 pt diphenylguanidine, 0.35 pt Altax]	2,260	23	10^3	4
Thiokol ST Compound [100 pts polysulfide polymer of bis(2-chloroethyl) formal, 60 pts carbon black, other compounding ingredients]	17,300	25	10^3	4

FOAMED PLASTICS AND RUBBER

	Density (g/cm³)	ε^a	Temp (°C)	Freq (Hz)	Ref.
Acrylic boards	0.042–0.099	1.90	23	10^6	3
Cellulose acetate, rigid, closed cell	0.096–0.128	1.12	23	10^6	3
Epoxy, rigid, closed cell	0.080	1.19	23	10^6	3
Poly(ethylene), low density	0.021–0.042	1.5	23	10^6	3
Poly(ethylene), interm. density	0.058–0.071	1.06	23	10^6	3
Poly(ethylene), cross-linked	0.144–0.200	1.1–1.55	23	10^6	3
Polyimide	0.010–0.016	1.0	23	10^6	3
Ionomer	0.032–0.320	1.5	23	10^6	3
Phenol-formaldehyde (Corfoam 114)	0.003	1.36	25	10^{10}	4
Polyphenylene oxide, modified	0.800	2.16	23	10^6	3
Polypropylene, low density	0.010	1.02	23	10^4	3
Rubber, foamed	–	1.31	25	3×10^9	4
Polystyrene, molded	0.010–0.080	1.06	23	$10^3 - 10^6$	3
Polystyrene, extruded	0.022–0.080	<1.05	23	$10^2 - 10^8$	3
Polystyrene, extruded film	0.096	1.27	23	10^6	3
Teflon, air filled	–	1.308	25	10^3	4
Polyurethane, rigid, closed cell	0.021–0.048	1.05	23	10^6	3
Polyurethane, flexible	0.014–0.128	1.0–1.5	23	10^6	3
Poly(vinyl chloride), expanded (Plasticell)	–	1.04	25	10^3	4
Silicone, liquid, closed cell	0.336–0.497	1.3–1.4	23	10^6	3

NATURAL PRODUCTS

Amber		2.7	25	10^3	4
Natural bitumen		2.66	26	10^3	4
Shellac, garnet, dewaxed		3.56	26	10^3	4
Shellac, natural, 3.5% wax		3.81	28	10^3	4

(a) The values reported in Ref. 4 are $\varepsilon'/\varepsilon_o$.

REFERENCES

1. Vishn Shah, *Handbook of Plastics Testing Technology*, Wiley-Interscience, New York (1984).
2. H. Lee, D. Stoffey, K. Neville, *New Linear Polymers*, McGraw-Hill, New York (1967).
3. J. Agranoff, Ed., *Modern Plastics Encyclopedia*, Vol. 60, No. 10A, McGraw-Hill, New York (1983–1984).
4. A. R. von Hippel, Ed., *Dielectric Materials and Applications*, The Technology Press of M.I.T. and John Wiley and Sons, New York (1958).
5. J. Brandrup and E. H. Immergut, Eds., *Polymer Handbook*, Wiley-Interscience, New York (1977).
6. F. E. Karasz, Ed., *Dielectric Properties of Polymers*, Plenum, New York (1972).
7. A. H. Scott, D. J. Scheiber, A. J. Curtis, J. A. Lauritzen, Jr., and J. O. Hoffman, J. Research NBS *66A* 269 (1962).
8. R. Liepins, D. Campbell, and C. Walker, J. Poly. Sci., Part A-1 *6*, 3059 (1968).
9. R. Liepins, M. L. Timmons, and N. Morosoff, J. Polym. Sci., Poly. Chem. Ed. *21*, 751 (1983).
10. R. C. Weast, and M. J. Astle, Eds., *CRC Handbook of Chemistry and Physics*, 62nd ed., CRC Press, Inc., Boca Raton, Florida (1981–1982).
11. R. E. Schramm, A. F. Clark, and R. P. Reed, NBS Monograph 132, National Bureau of Standards, Washington, DC (1973).

APPENDIX 2
DISSIPATION FACTOR

OF POLYMERS, POLYMER ALLOYS, PLASTICS AND RESINS; FILLED PLASTICS AND
RESINS; PLASTIC AND RESIN COMPOSITES; RUBBERS; FILLED RUBBERS, FOAMED
PLASTICS AND RUBBERS; AND NATURAL PRODUCTS

POLYMERS, POLYMER ALLOYS, PLASTICS, AND RESINS

Material	Tan δ	Temp (°C)	Freq (Hz)	Ref.
ABS (Acrylonitrile-Butadiene-Styrene), low impact	0.005–0.010	25	60	1
ABS, medium impact	0.003–0.006	25	60	1
ABS, very high impact	0.005–0.010	25	60	1
ABS, heat resistant	0.030–0.040	25	60	1
ABS, Cycolac T	0.005	25	60	2
ABS/polycarbonate	0.019–0.021	25	60	1
ABS/polysulfone (polyaryl ether)	0.006	25	60	1
Acetal (polyoxymethylene), Delrin	0.0048	25	60	1
Acetal, Celcon	0.001	25	100	1
Acrylonitrile/methylacrylate, rubber modified	0.036	25	10^3	3
Allyl diglycol carbonate	0.03–0.04	25	60	1
Aniline-formaldehyde (Cibanite E)	0.0029	25	100	4
Aniline-formaldehyde (Dilectene 100)	0.0033	22	100	4
Aromatic polyamide-imides	0.006	25	60	2
Aromatic polyester-imides	0.0064	25	10^3	2
Aromatic polyethers	0.006	25	60	5
Aromatic polyimides	0.003	25	10^3	2
Aromatic polysulfone	0.008	25	60	2
Poly(butyl methacrylate)	0.0605	24	100	4
Poly(butylene terephthalate)	0.002	25	100	1
Poly(butylene terephthalate), high impact	0.002–0.004	25	100	1
Polycarbonate	0.0015	25	10^3	3
Polycarbonate/ABS alloy	0.003–0.007	25	60	5
Cellulose, regenerated (cellophane)	0.015	25	10^3	3
Cellulose acetate, LL-1, 55.4% acetyl	0.0095	25	100	4
Cellulose acetate, LL-1, Lumarith XFA-H4, 28% plasticizer	0.052	25	100	4
Cellulose acetate, LL-1 Fibestos, 2050 TVA, C-1686-26% plasticizer	0.0180	25	100	4
Cellulose acetate butyrate	0.02–0.05	25	10^6	1
Cellulose acetate propionate	0.02–0.05	25	10^6	1
Cellulose nitrate	0.09–0.12	25	60	5
Cellulose nitrate, Pyralin, 25% camphor	0.6400	27	100	4
Cellulose propionate	0.015	25	10^6	3
Cellulose propionate, Forticel, 8% plasticizer	0.0060	25	100	4
Cellulose triacetate	0.016	25	10^3	3

Material	Tan δ	Temp (°C)	Freq (Hz)	Ref.
o- and p-Chlorostyrene copolymer, Plastic Q-409	0.0010	24	100	4
Poly(chlorotrifluoroethylene), Kel-F	0.0210	26	100	4
Poly(chlorotrifluoroethylene), Del-F Grade 300-P25,plasticized	0.0126	25	100	4
Poly(chlorotrifluoroethylene), 80% crystalline	0.0315	23	100	7
Poly(chlorotrifluoroethylene), 12% crystalline	0.0622	23	100	7
Cycloaliphatic epoxy resin	0.005	25	60	5
Poly(cyclohexyl methacrylate)	0.0046	25	100	4
Poly(diallyl phthalate)	0.0104	27	100	4
Poly(diallyl phenyl phosphonate), Phoresin	0.0260	25	100	4
Poly(2,5-dichlorostyrene), Plastic CY-8	<0.0002	24	100	4
Poly(3,4-dichlorostyrene)	0.0085	25	100	4
Polymer of 50% 2,4-, 25% 2,5-, 25% 2,3-, 2,6-, and 3,4-dichlorostyrenes; Plastic CQ-10DM	0.0005	25	100	4
Polymer of 53.5% 2,5-dichlorostyrene, 32.5%styrene, 0.5% divinylbenzene and 13% hydrogenated terphenyl; Bureau ofStandards Casting Resin	0.0020	25	100	4
Poly(2,6-dimethyl-1,4-phenylene ether)	0.0004	25	100	6
Epoxy, standard (Bisphenol A)	0.0074	25	60	1
Epoxy, rigid (Novolacs)	0.0074–0.0855	25	60	1
Poly(ether sulfone)	0.0035	25	10^3	3
Ethyl cellulose, Ethocel LT-5	0.0075	25	100	4
Poly(ethyl methacrylate)	0.0420	22	100	4
Polyethylene, low density	0.0003	25	10^3	3
Polyethylene, medium density	0.0003	25	10^3	3
Polyethylene, high density	0.0005	25	10^3	3
Polyethylene, ultra high mol. wt.	0.0023	25	10^3	3
Ethylene/chlorotrifluoroethylene copolymer	0.002	25	10^3	3
Ethylene/ethyl acrylate copolymer	0.001	25	60	1
Poly(ethylene/propylene)(Polyallomer)	<0.0005	25	60	5
Poly(ethylene terephthalate), thermoplastic	0.005	25	10^3	3
Ethylene/tetrafluoroethylene copolymer	0.0008	25	10^3	3
Ethylene/vinyl acetate copolymer	0.003	25	60	1
Fluorinated ethylene/propylene copolymer (FEP)	<0.0002	25	10^3	3
Ionomer	0.002	25	10^3	3
Poly(isobutyl methacrylate)	0.0111	25	100	4
Polyisobutylene	0.0004	25	100	4
Melamine/formaldehyde resin	0.048–0.162	25	60	5
Methyl cellulose (Methocel)	0.1280	22	100	4

Material	Tan δ	Temp (°C)	Freq (Hz)	Ref.
Poly(methyl methacrylate), Plexiglas	0.0605	27	100	4
Poly(methyl methacrylate), Lucite HM-119	0.0620	23	100	4
Poly(methyl methacrylate/α-methyl-styrene)	0.006	25	60	5
Poly(methyl methacrylate)/poly-(vinyl chloride) alloy	0.04	25	60	5
Poly(methyl-l-pentene)	0.00007	25	60	5
Poly(α-methylstyrene)	0.00007	25	100	4
Nomex paper(m-phenylenediamine/ iso phthaloyl chloride)	0.005	40	100	2
Nylon 6	0.016	25	10^3	3
Nylon 66	0.014	25	60	1
Nylon 11	0.03	25	60	1
Nylon 12	0.04	25	10^3	1
Nylon 610	0.0155	25	100	4
Nylon 610, 90% humidity	0.0650	25	100	4
Nylon 6/6, high impact (Zytel ST-801)	0.013	25	60	1
Nylon 6/9, high impact	0.02	25	60	1
Nylon 6/12	0.02	25	10^6	1
Perfluoroalkyl (PFA)	0.0002	25	20^3	3
Phenol/formaldehyde (Bakelite BT-48–306)	0.1350	24	100	4
Phenol/furfuraldehyde (Durite No. 221X)	0.2000	24	100	4
Phenoxy resins (epichlorohydrin/ bisphenol A)	0.0012	25	60	2
Poly(2,6-dimethylphenylene oxide) (PPO C1001)	0.0002	25	60	2
Poly(phenylene oxide)	0.00035	25	60	5
Polypropylene	0.0003	25	10^3	3
Polypyromellitimide (Kapton H film, Vespel)	0.005	22	10^5	8
Polysiloxane resin (methyl, phenyl, and methylphenyl)	0.0083	25	100	4
Polystyrene	0.0005	25	10^3	3
Polystyrene, cross-linked	0.0004	22	100	4
Polystyrene, high heat stable	0.0005–0.003	25	60	5
Polystyrene, high impact	0.0004–0.002	25	60	5
Poly(styrene/acrylonitrile) (SAN)	>0.006	25	60	1
Poly(styrene/10% butadiene) (Marbon S)	0.00174	25	100	4
Poly(styrene/15% butadiene) (Marbon 8000)	0.00054	25	100	4
50% Polystyrene/50% chlorinated-biphenyl (Styramic No. 18)	0.0029	22	100	4
Poly(styrene/2,4-dimethylstyrene)	0.00016	25	100	4
1:1 Poly(styrene/1,4-divinyl-2,3,5,6-tetrachlorobenzene)	0.0006	26	100	4
Poly(styrene/α-methylstyrene) (Piccolastic D-125)	0.0002	25	100	4

Material	Tan δ	Temp (°C)	Freq (Hz)	Ref.
1:1 Poly(styrene/1,3,5-trivinyl-2,4,6-trichlorobenzene)	0.00085	25	100	4
Poly(sulfone)	0.0008	25	60	5
Polytetrafluoroethylene	<0.0001	25	10^3	3
Poly(tetrafluoroethylene/hexa-fluoropropylene)	<0.0003	25	60	5
Poly(urethane), thermoplastic elastomer	0.015–0.048	25	60	5
Poly(vinyl acetal) (Alvar 11/90)	0.0065	25	100	4
Poly(vinyl acetate) (Elvacet 42A-900)	0.0049	25	100	4
Poly(vinyl alcohol/acetate), 0–1.5T acetate(Elvanol 50A-42)	0.4050	23	100	4
Poly(vinyl butyral) (Butvar, low OH)	0.0038	27	100	4
Poly(n-vinyl carbazole), 1.3% HB-40 Oil(Polectron No. 24)	0.0013	25	100	4
Poly(vinyl chloride) (Vinylite QYNA)	0.0130	20	100	4
Poly(vinyl chloride), chlorinated	0.019–0.021	25	60	1
Poly(vinyl chloride/vinyl acetate), 50% vinyl acetate(Vinylite VYNW)	0.0135	20	100	4
Poly(vinyl chloride/vinyl acetate), 9% vinyl acetate(Vinylite VYNS)	0.0115	20	100	4
Poly(vinyl chloride/vinyl acetate), 13% vinyl acetate(Vinylite VYHH)	0.0100	22	100	4
64.5% [Poly(95% vinyl chloride/5% vinyl acetate)], 32%dioctyl phthalate, 3.5% misc. (Vinylite VU-1900)	0.1000	24	100	4
87.8% Poly(vinyl chloride), 10.5% stabilizer, 1.7% misc. (Geon 80384)	0.0120	25	100	4
65% Poly(vinyl chloride) (Geon 101), 35% Paraplex G-25	0.0815	25	100	4
65% Poly(vinyl chloride) (Geon 101), 35% Paraplex G-50	0.0840	25	100	4
65% Poly(vinyl chloride) (Geon 101), 35% Paraplex G-60	0.0730	25	100	4
Poly(vinyl chloride/propylene)	0.008–0.010	25	50	5
Poly(vinyl cyclohexane) (hydrogenated polystyrene)	0.0015	24	—	4
Poly(vinyl fluoride)	1.6	25	10^3	3
Poly(vinyl formal) (Formvar, Type E)	0.0054	26	100	4
Poly(α-vinyl naphthalene)	0.00095	24	10^3	4
Poly(2-vinyl pyridine)	0.0360	22	100	4
Poly(2-vinyl pyridine/styrene)	0.0168	23	100	4
Poly(vinyl toluene)	0.00073	25	100	4
Poly(vinylidene chloride)	0.003–0.045	25	60	5
Poly(vinylidene chloride/vinyl chloride)(Saran B-115)	0.0450	23	100	4

Material	Tan δ	Temp (°C)	Freq (Hz)	Ref.
Poly(vinylidene fluoride)	0.016	25	10^3	3
Poly(p-xylylene)	0.0002	25	10^3	2
Poly(chloro-p-xylylene)	0.02	25	10^3	2
Poly (dichloro-p-xylylene)	0.003	25	10^3	2
Poly(methyl-p-xylylene)	0.0025	25	10^3	2

FILLED PLASTICS AND RESINS

Material	Tan δ	Temp (°C)	Freq (Hz)	Ref.
Cellulose acetate, 23–31% plasticizer, pigments, dyes (Tenite I 008AH$_2$)	0.010	26	100	4
Cellulose acetate, 5–15% plasticizer, pigments, dyes(Tenite II 205 AH$_2$)	0.0078	26	100	4
Cresylic acid-formaldehyde, 50% α-cellulose (Micarta No. 254)	0.0760	25	100	4
Cresylic acid-formaldehyde, 50% cotton drillings(Micarta No. 496)	0.2200	25	100	4
Poly(2,5-dichlorostyrene) (58.1%), + TiO$_2$ (41.9%)	0.0026	23	100	4
Poly(2,5-dichlorostyrene) (34.7%) + TiO$_2$ (65.3%)	0.0016	24	100	4
Poly(2,5-dichlorostyrene) (18.6%) + TiO$_2$ (81.4%)	0.0060	23	100	4
Poly(2,5-dichlorostyrene) (38.2%) + MgTiO$_3$ (61.8%)	0.0035	23	100	4
Poly(2,5-dichlorostyrene) (63.0%) + SrTiO$_3$ (37.0%)	0.0020	25	100	4
Poly(2,5-dichlorostyrene) (40.5%) + SrTiO$_3$ (59.5%)	0.0041	24	100	4
Poly(2,5-dichlorostyrene) (25.2%) + SrTiO$_3$ (74.8%)	0.0220	23	100	4
Poly(2,5-dichlorostyrene) (14.4%) + SrTiO$_3$ (80.6%)	0.0780	23	100	4
Poly(2,5-dichlorostyrene) (66.6%) + BaTiO$_3$ (33.4%)	0.0024	23	100	4
Poly(2,5-dichlorostyrene) (32.8%) + BaTiO$_3$ (67.2%)	0.0060	25	100	4
Poly(2,5-dichlorostyrene) (23.5%) + BaTiO$_3$ (76.5%)	0.0030	23	100	4
Poly(2,5-dichlorostyrene) (21.0%) + BaTiO$_3$ (79.0%)	0.0052	23	100	4
Poly(2,5-dichlorostyrene) (94%) + Fe (6% minus 200 mesh)	0.0250	25	3×10^9	4
Poly(2,5-dichlorostyrene) (60%) + Fe (40% minus 200 mesh)	0.2300	25	3×10^9	4
Poly(2,5-dichlorostyrene) (49.3%) + Fe (50.7% minus200 mesh)	0.3170	25	3×10^9	4
Poly(2,5-dichlorostyrene) (40.7%) + Fe (59.3% minus 200 mesh)	0.4500	25	3×10^9	4
Poly(2,5-dichlorostyrene) (92%) + Fe$_3$O$_4$ (8%)	0.0200	25	3×10^9	4

Material	Tan δ	Temp (°C)	Freq (Hz)	Ref.
Poly(2,5-dichlorostyrene) (83.7%) Fe$_3$O$_4$ (16.3%)	0.0420	25	3 × 10^9	4
Poly(2,5-ichlorostyrene) (75%) Fe$_3$O$_4$ (25%)	0.0590	25	3 × 10^9	4
Poly(2,5-dichlorostyrene) (65.9%) + Fe$_3$O$_4$ (34.1%)	0.1010	25	3 × 10^9	4
Poly(2,5-dichlorostyrene) (56.2%) + Fe$_3$O$_4$ (43.8%)	0.1720	25	3 × 10^9	4
Poly(2,5-dichlorostyrene) (46.0%) + Fe$_3$O$_4$ (54.0%)	0.2400	25	3 × 10^9	4
Poly(2,5-dichlorostyrene) (35.7%) + Fe$_3$O$_4$ (64.3%)	0.3000	25	3 × 10^9	4
Poly(2,5-dichlorostyrene) (24.5%) + Fe$_3$O$_4$ (75.5%)	0.3700	25	3 × 10^9	4
Poly(2,5-dichlorostyrene) (38.55%) (Mn$_1$,Fe)$_3$O$_4$ (61.45%)	0.4000	25	3 × 10^9	4
Poly(2,5-dichlorostyrene) (21.3%) + (M$_n$,Fe)$_3$ (78.7%)	0.4900	25	3 × 10^9	4
Melamine-formaldehyde, 25% α-pulp, zinc stearate (Melmac Type 1077)	0.0240	28	100	4
Melamine-Formaldehyde, 40% wood flour, 18% plasticizer Melmac Molding Compd. 1500)	0.0308	25	100	4
Melamine-formaldehyde-aniline, 40% wood flour (Melmac Molding Compd. 1502)	0.2020	25	100	4
Phenol-formaldehyde, 40% wood flour, 8% misc. (Bakelite BM-120)	0.0300	25	100	4
Phenol-formaldehyde, 67% mica filled (Durez 1601, Natural)	0.0270	26	100	4
Phenol-formaldehyde, 65% mica filled, 4% lubricant (Durite 500)	0.0130	24	100	4
Phenol-formaldehyde, 35% mica filled, 18% other filler (Resinox 10900)	0.0275	25	100	4
Phenol-aniline-formaldehyde, 62% mica filled (Bakelite BM-262)	0.0098	25	100	4
Phenol-aniline-formaldehyde, 59.5% mica filled, 8.5% misc. (Bakelite BM-1895)	0.0087	25	100	4
Phenol-aniline-formaldehyde, 60% mica filled (Resinox 7934)	0.0220	25	100	4
Polystyrene, 9% carbon	0.0017	26	100	4
Polystyrene, 30% carbon	0.2500	25	3 × 10^9	4
Polystyrene, 50% carbon	0.5600	25	3 × 10^9	4
75% Teflon, 25% CaF$_2$ (Chemelac M1405)	0.0018	25	100	4
80% Teflon, 20% carbon (Chemelac M1406)	2400	25	10^5	4
88% Teflon, 12% ceramic (Chemelac M 1407)	0.0917	25	100	4

Material	Tan δ	Temp (°C)	Freq (Hz)	Ref.
80% Teflon, 20% TiO$_2$ (Chemelac M1422)	0.00119	25	100	4
Teflon, ceramic filled	0.0005–0.0015	25	60	1
59% Poly(vinyl chloride), 30% dioctyl phosphate, 6% stabilizer, 5% filler (Geon 2406)	0.0820	23	100	4
71% Poly(vinyl chloride), 10.5% filler, 5% plasticizer, 8.5% stabilizer (Geon 80365)	0.0068	25	100	4
63.7% Poly(vinyl chloride), 33.1% di-2-ethylhexyl phthalate, 3.2% lead silicate (Koroseal 5CS-243)	0.0790	27	100	4
57.5% Poly(vinyl chloride), 12.6% filler, 28.7% plasticizers (PVC 1006)	0.0760	25	100	4
52.4% Poly(vinyl chloride), 15.1% fillers, 31.4% plasticizers (PVC 1018)	0.0630	25	100	4
57.5% Poly(vinyl chloride), 10.4% fillers, 31.6% plasticizers (PVC 1216)	0.1170	25	100	4
59.4% Poly(vinyl chloride), 20.7% fillers, 29.7% plasticizers (PVC 1406)	0.0870	25	100	4
64.7% Poly(vinyl chloride), 2% filler, 32.5% plasticizers (Ultron Wire Compd UL 1004)	0.0810	25	100	4
60.1% Poly(vinyl chloride), 7.8% fillers, 31.2% plasticizers (Ultron Wire Compd UL2 4001)	0.1100	25	100	4

PLASTIC AND RESIN COMPOSITES

Material	Tan δ	Temp (°C)	Freq (Hz)	Ref.
Acetal (Celcon), 25% glass fiber	0.003	25	100	1
Acetla (Delrin), 20% glass fiber	0.0047	25	100	1
Poly(benzimidazole), glass laminate (Imidite 1850)	0.007	25	9.4×10^6	2
Benzoguanamine-formaldehyde, 28% α-paper (Benzoguanamie Resin)	0.0348	25	100	4
Poly(butylene terephthalate), 15–40% glass fiber	0.002–0.003	25	100	1
Poly(butylene terephthalate), 10–30% mineral fiber	0.002	25	100	1
Polycarbonate, 20% glass fiber	0.0009	25	60	1
Polycarbonate, 30% glass fiber	0.0011	25	60	1
Polycarbonate, 40% glass fiber	0.0013	25	60	1
84% Corning's 790 Glass Powder, 16% cross-linked organo-siloxane (Polyglass S)	0.0011	24	100	4

Material	Tan δ	Temp (°C)	Freq (Hz)	Ref.
81.1% Corning's 790 Glass Powder, 18.6% polystyrene (Dow C-244) 0.25% paraffin, 0.1% Dow Corning's ignition sealing compound (Polyglass P⁺)	0.0008	24	100	4
64.9% Corning's 790 Glass Powder, 34.9% poly(2,5-dichlorostyrene), 0.1% paraffin wax, 0.1% Dow Corning's ignition sealing compound (Polyglass ⁺2)	0.0007	24	100	4
45% Cresol-phenol-formaldehyde, 15% tung oil, 15% nylon fabric (Dielecto, Mecoboard)	0.0400	25	100	4
45% Cresol-phenol-formaldehyde, 15% tung oil, 40% α-paper (Dielector XXX-P-26)	0.6420	25	100	4
Cresylic acid-formaldehyde, 60–56% glass fabric (Micarta No. 299)	0.0270	24	100	4
Poly(ethylene terephthalate), 30–45% glass fiber	0.0024–0.0096	25	100	1
Poly(ethylene terephthalate/butylene terephthalate), 15–30% glass fiber	0.0018	25	100	1
55% Fiberglass, ECC-261, 45% methyl and phenyl polysiloxane (DC 2103 Laminate)	0.0018	25	100	4
65% Fiberglass, ECC-181, 35% methyl and phenyl polysiloxane (DC 2104 Laminate)	0.0032	25	100	4
50–55% Glass Cloth, 45–50% polysiloxane, DC 2103 (Taylor Grade GSC)	0.0099	25	100	4
45% Glass fiber, 35% methyl and phenyl polysiloxane, 19% silica filler (Molding Compd XM-3)	0.0051	25	100	4
56.5% Melamine resin, Melmac 7278, 43.5% Owens-Corning's Glass E (Polyglass M)	0.0140	24	100	4
Melamine-formaldehyde, 65–70% fiberglass (Micarta No. 259)	0.0190	24	100	4
Nylon 6, 30% glass fiber	0.008–0.022	25	60	1
Phenol-aniline-formaldehyde, 40% glass mat (Formica Grade MF-66)	0.0106	25	100	4
Phenol-formaldehyde, 66% asbestos fiber (Bakelite BM-250)	0.3000	25	100	4
Phenol-formaldehyde, 50% paper laminate (Formica XX)	0.0230	26	100	4
Phenol-formaldehyde, 40% cotton fabric (Formica LE)	0.1350	26	100	4
Phenol-formaldehyde, 50% nylon fabric (Formica Grade YN-25)	0.0121	25	100	4

Material	Tan δ	Temp (°C)	Freq (Hz)	Ref.
Phenol-formaldehyde, 40% random glass mat (Taylor Grade GGG)	0.1300	25	100	4
Poly(phenylene oxide), 20% glass fiber (Noryl)	0.0009	25	60	1
Poly(phenylene sulfide), 40% glass fiber	0.0037	25	60	1
Polysulfone, 30% glass fiber	0.0019	25	60	1
Polystyrene, 30% fiberglass	0.00138	25	100	4
Poly(styrene/acrylonitrile), 30% glass fiber (SAN)	0.005	25	60	1
Teflon, 32–35% continuous filament glass (Teflon Laminate GB-112T)	0.00089	25	100	4
Teflon, 25% fiberglass (Chemelac M1411)	0.00185	25	100	4
Teflon, 25% graphite (Chemelac M1414)	11.8	25	10^7	4
Teflon, 10% quartz (Chemelac M1418–2)	0.0600	25	100	4
Teflon, 25% quartz (Chemelac M1418–5)	0.0450	25	100	4

RUBBERS

Material	Tan δ	Temp (°C)	Freq (Hz)	Ref.
Balata, precipitated (Minusops Globosa)	0.0009	25	100	4
Poly (75% butadiene/25% styrene), uncured (GR-S; Buna S)	0.0006	26	100	4
Poly (2-chlorobutadiene), stabilized with tetraethylthiuram disulfide (Neoprene GN)	0.6000	26	100	4
Cyclized rubber (Pliolite)	0.0052	27	100	4
Depolymerized rubber (Permo Potting Compd No. 49)	0.0169	25	100	4
Gutta-Percha (Palaquium Oblongiofolium)	0.0005	25	100	4
Hevea rubber, pale crepe	0.0028	25	100	4
Hevea rubber, vulcanized 6 pts sulfur	0.0048	27	100	4
Poly (98–99% isobutylene/1–2% isoprene) (GR-I; Butyl rubber)	0.0034	25	100	4
Poly(stryene/acrylonitrile) and poly-(butadiene/acrylonitrile) alloy (Royalite 149–11)	0.0320	25	100	4

FILLED RUBBERS

Material	Tan δ	Temp (°C)	Freq (Hz)	Ref.
100 pts Poly(75% butadiene/25% styrene), 5 pts Kadox, 5 pts Captox, 3 pts sulfur, 1 pt. stearic acid (GR-S Compound; Buna S)	0.0007	26	100	4
Hevea Rubber Compound (100 pts Hevea, 10 pts carbon black, 5 pts Kadox, 3 pts sulfur, 1 pt. stearic acid, 0.5 pt Captax)	0.0130	27	100	4
50% Siloxane elastomer, 50% TiO_2 (Silastic 120)	0.0051	25	100	4
35% Siloxane elastomer, 35% ZnO, 30% $CaCO_3$ (Silastic 150)	0.0043	25	100	4
33% Siloxane elastomer, 33% ZnO, 33% TiO_2 (Silastic 160)	0.0047	25	100	4
33% Siloxane elastomer, 67% TiO_2 (Silastic 167)	0.0052	25	100	4
35% Siloxane elastomer, 35% SiO_2, 30% TiO_2 (Silastic 180)	0.0062	25	100	4
45% Siloxane elastomer, 55% SiO_2 (Silastic 181)	0.0062	25	100	4
70% Siloxane elastomer, 30% SiO_2 (Silastic 250)	0.005	25	100	4
50% Siloxane elastomer, 50% SiO_2 (Silastic 4342)	0.0051	25	100	4
33% Siloxane elastomer, 67% TiO_2 (Silastic 6167)	0.0041	25	100	4
45% Siloxane elastomer, 55% SiO_2 (Silastic 6168)	0.0200	25	100	4
70% Siloxane elastomer, 30% SiO_2 (Silastic X-6734)	0.0028	25	100	4
Thiokol PRI Compound [200 pts bis(2-Chloroethyl) formal and ethylene dichloride polysulfide, 60 pts carbon black and other compounding ingredients]	3.6300	25	10^3	4
Thiokol Type FA Compound [100 pts bis(2-chloroethyl) formal and ethylene dichloride polysulfide, 60 pts carbon black, 10 pts ZnO, 1 pt stearic acid, 0.5 pt diphenylguanidine, 0.35 pt Altax]	1.2900	23	10^3	4
Thiokol ST Compound [100 pts polysulfide polymer of bis(2-chloroethyl) formal, 60 pts carbon black, other compounding ingredients]	1.0000	25	10^3	4

FOAMED PLASTICS AND RUBBERS

	Density (g/cm)	Tan δ	Temp (°C)	Freq (Hz)	Ref.
Acrylic boards	0.042	0.0036	23	10^6	3
Poly(ethylene), low density	0.021–0.042	0.0002	23	10^9	3
Poly(ethylene), intermediate density	0.058–0.071	0.0002	23	10^9	3
Poly(ethylene), cross-linked	0.144–0.200	0.0002–0.0007	23	10^6	3
Ionomer	0.032–0.320	0.003	23	10^6	3
Phenol-formaldehyde (Corfoam 114)	0.003	0.0750	25	10^{10}	4
Polyphenylene oxide, modified	0.801	0.0017	23	10^6	3
Polypropylene, low density	0.010	0.00006	23	10^4	3
Rubber, foamed	–	0.0075	25	3×10^9	4
Polystyrene, molded	0.016–0.080	0.0001–0.0007	23	10^2–10^6	3
Polystyrene, extruded	0.032–0.128	< 0.0004	23	10^3–10^8	3
Polystyrene, extruded film	0.100	0.00011	23	10^6	3
Teflon, air filled	–	0.000181	25	20^3	4
Polyurethane, rigid, closed cell	0.064–0.128	0.0018	23	10^6	3
Poly(vinyl chloride), expanded (Plasticell)	–	0.0021	25	100	4
Silicone, liquid, closed cell	0.336–0.497	< 0.01	23	10^6	3

NATURAL PRODUCTS

		Tan δ	Temp (°C)	Freq (Hz)	Ref.
Amber		0.00125	25	100	4
Beeswax, white		0.0140	23	100	4
Natural bitumen		0.0058	26	100	4
Natural paraffin (Ozokerite)		0.0006	20	100	4
Shellac, garnet, dewaxed		0.0058	26	100	4
Shellac, natural, 3.5% wax		0.0065	28	100	4

REFERENCES

1. Vishn Shah, *Handbook of Plastics Testing Technology*, Wiley-Interscience, New York (1984).
2. H. Lee, D. Stoffey, and K. Neville, *New Linear Polymers*, McGraw-Hill, New York (1967).
3. J. Agranoff, Ed., *Modern Plastics Encyclopedia*, Vol. 60, No. 10A, McGraw-Hill, New York (1983–1984).
4. A. von Hippel, Ed., *Dielectric Materials and Applications*, The Technology Press of M.I.T. and John Wiley and Sons, New York, (1958).
5. J. Brandrup and E. H. Immergut, Eds., *Polymer Handbook*, Wiley-Interscience, New York (1977).
6. F. E. Karasz, Ed., *Dielectric Porperties of Polymers*, Plenum, New York (1972).
7. A. H. Scott, D. J. Scheiber, A. J. Curtis, J. A. Lauritzen, Jr., and J. O. Hoffman, J. Research NBS *66A*, 269 (1962).
8. R. E. Schramm, A. F. Clark, and R. P. Reed, NBS Monograph 132, National Bureau of Standards, Washington DC (1973).

APPENDIX 3
DIELECTRIC STRENGTH
SHORT TIME ASTM D149

Material	V/Mil	Ref.
ABS, medium impact	385	1
ABS, very high impact	300–375	1
ABS, low temp. impact	300–415	1
ABS, heat resistant	360–400	1
ABS, Polyaryl ether sulfone	430	1
ABS/Polycarbonate alloy	1250–1550	1
ABS/PVC rigid alloy	600	1
Acrylics, general purpose, cast	450–530	1
Acrylics, moldings	400	1
Acrylics, high impact	400–500	1
Acrylics, modified	400–500	1
Acrylic/PVC alloy	430–670	1
Poly(acrylonitrile/methyl acrylate), rubber modified	400	2
Alkyds, encapsulating putty	300–350	1
Alkyds, general purpose	290	1
Alkyds, high-speed molding	300–350	1
Alkyds, glass reinforced	300–350	1
Polyallomer	500–650	1
Allyl diglycol carbonate	290	1
Poly(amide-imide), high impact	600	1
Aromatic polyester	400	1
Polybutadiene	400–600	1
Poly(butylene terephthalate), thermo-plastic, unreinforced	400–420	1
Poly(butylene terephthalate), flame retardant	350–470	
Poly(butylene terephthalate), 15–40% glass reinforced	450–560	1
Poly(butylene terephthalate), 15–30% glass reinforced, flame retardant	410–570	1
Poly(butylene terephthalate), mineral filled	390–600	1
Poly(butylene terephthalate), mineral/glass reinforced	500–600	1
Poly(butylene terephthalate), high impact	350–400	1
PBT/PET, 15–30% glass reinforced	470–530	1
Polycarbonates, unfilled	380–425	1
Polycarbonates, 20% glass reinforced	490	1
Polycarbonates, 30% glass reinforced	475	1
Polycarbonates, 40% glass reinforced	450	1
Polycarbonates, ABS alloy	356–508	3
Celcon, standard	500	1
Celcon, 25% glass reinforced	600	1
Celcon, high flow	500	1
Cellulose acetate	250–600	1
Cellulose acetate butyrate	250–400	1
Cellulose acetate propionate	300–450	1
Cellulose nitrate	305–610	3
Cellulose propionate	305–457	3
Chlorinated PVC	1220–1500	1
Delrin, standard	500	1
Delrin, 20% glass reinforced	500	1
Diallyl phthalate, Orlon filled	400	1
Diallyl phthalate, Dacron filled	376–390	1
Diallyl phthalate, asbestos filled	350–450	1

Material	V/Mil	Ref.
Diallyl phthalate, glass-fiber filled	350–430	1
Epoxies, standard Bisphenol A, cast rigid	>400	1
Epoxies, standard Bisphenol A, cast flexible	400–410	1
Epoxies, standard Bisphenol A, molded	360–400	1
Epoxies, Novolac, molded	280–400	1
Epoxies, cycloaliphatic	444	1
Polyesters, thermoset, cast, rigid	300–400	1
Polyesters, thermoset, cast, flexible	300–400	1
Polyesters, thermoset, glass-fiber reinforced	200–400	1
Polyesters, thermoset, asbestos reinforced	350	1
Polyesters, thermoset, general purpose	400–440	1
Polyether sulfone	400	1
Ethyl cellulose	356–508	3
Polyethylene/(ethyl acrylate)	550	1
Polyethylenes, low density (0.9l0–0.925), melt index 0.3–3.6	480	1
Polyethylenes, low density, melt index 6–26	480	1
Polyethylenes, low density, melt index 200	480	1
Polyethylenes, medium density, (0.926–0.940), melt index 20	480	1
Polyethylenes, medium density, melt index 1.0–4.0	480	1
Polyethylenes, high density (0.94l-0.965), melt index 0.2–0.9	480	1
Polyethylenes, high density, melt index 0.1-2	480	1
Polyethylenes, high density, melt index 1.5–15	480	1
Poly(ethylene terephthalate), 30–45% glass reinforced	403–550	1
Poly(ethylene/tetrafluoroethylene)	490	1
Poly(ethylene/trifluorochloroethylene)	490	1
Poly(ethylene/vinyl acetate)	525	1
Fluorinated ethylene/propylene	500–600	1
Polyfluoro alkoxy	2000	1
Polyimides, unreinforced	310–560	1
Polyimides, glass reinforced	300	1
Ionomer	1000	1
Melamine/phenol resin	229–330	3
Polymethylpentene	700	1
Poly(α-methylstyrene/methyl methacrylate)	457	3
Nylon 6, general purpose	385	1
Nylon 6, 30% glass-fiber reinforced	400–450	1
Nylon 6, cast	380	1
Nylon 6, flexible copolymers	440	1
Nylon 11	425	1
Nylon 12	840	1
Nylon, transparent	371–670	1
Nylon 66, general purpose	385	1
Nylon 66, glass-fiber reinforced	400	1
Nylon 66, glass-fiber, molybdenum disulfide filled	300–400	1
Nylon 66, high impact	390	1
Nylon 69	540	1
Phenolics, general purpose, woodflour filled	200–425	1
Phenolics, shock, paper, flock, or pulp filled	250–350	1
Phenolics, high shock, chopped-fabric or cord filled	200–350	1
Phenolics, very high shock, glass-fiber filled	200–370	1
Phenolics, arc resistant, mineral filled	200–370	1
Phenolics, rubber, woodflour, or flock filled	250–375	1
Phenolics, rubber, chopped-fabric filled	250	1
Phenolics, rubber, asbestos filled	350	1

Material	V/Mil	Ref.
Poly(phenylene oxides), Noryl, SE-100	400 (1/8 in.)	1
Poly(phenylene oxides), Noryl, SE-1	500 (1/8 in.)	1
Poly(phenylene oxides), Noryl, 20% glass-fiber reinforced	1020 (1/32 in.)	1
Polyphenylene sulfide, glass and mineral filled	340–521	1
Polyphenylene sulfide, 40% glass reinforced	450	1
Polyphenyl sulfone	371 (1/8 in.)	1
Polypropylene, general purpose	650	1
Polypropylene, high impact	450–650	1
Polypropylene, glass reinforced	317–475	1
Polypropylene, flame retardant	485–700	1
Polystyrenes, general purpose	>500	1
Polystyrenes, medium impact	>425	1
Polystyrenes, high impact	300–650	1
Polystyrenes, 30% glass fiber-reinforced	396	1
Poly(styrene/acrylonitrile) (SAN)	400–500	1
Poly(styrene/acrylonitrile) (SAN), 30% glass-fiber reinforced	515	1
Poly(styrene/butadiene)	432–508	3
Polysulfones, standard	425	1
Polysulfones, 30% glass-fiber reinforced	480	1
Poly(tetrafluoroethylene) (Teflon)	400–500	1
Poly(tetrafluoroethylene), ceramic reinforced	300–400	1
Poly(trifluorochloroethylene)	530–600	1
Poly(vinyl butyral)	356	3
Poly(vinyl chloride), nonrigid electrical	240–500	1
Poly(vinyl chloride), rigid normal impact	725–1400	1
Poly(vinyl chloride/methyl methacrylate)	406	3
Poly(vinyl chloride/vinyl acetate), nonrigid electrical	240–500	1
Poly(vinyl chloride/vinyl acetate), rigid, normal impact	725–1400	1
Poly(vinyl formal)	508	3
Poly(vinylidene chloride)	406–610	3
Poly(vinylidene fluoride)	260	1

RUBBERS

Polyacrylates	800	1
Polybutadiene	400–600	1
Chloroprene	400–600	1
Chlorosulfonated polyethylene	650	1
Ethylene/acrylic	730	1
Ethylene/propylene	500–1000	1
Fluorocarbon	500	1
Isobutylene/isoprene	600–900	1
Natural isoprene	400–600	1
Nitrile	250	1
Silicone	400–700	1
Styrene/butadiene	600–800	1
Polyurethanes	330–700	1

Material	V/Mil	Ref.

THERMOPLASTIC ELASTOMERS

Material	V/Mil	Ref.
Polyester urethanes	330–460	1
Polyether esters	525–900	1
Polyether urethanes	440–730	1
Olefinics	600	1
Styrenics	400–510	1

REFERENCES

1. Vishn Shah, *Handbook of Plastics Testing Technology*, Wiley-Interscience, New York (1984).
2. J. Agranoff, Ed., *Modern Plastics Encyclopedia* Vol. 60, No. 10A, McGraw-Hill, New York, 1983 to 1984.
3. J. Brandrup and E. H. Immergut, Eds., *Polymer Handbook*, Wiley Interscience, New York (1977).

APPENDIX 4
ARC RESISTANCE
ASTM D-495

Material	Seconds	Ref.
ABS, medium impact	50–85	1
ABS, high impact	50–85	1
ABS/Polyaryl ether sulfone	180	2
ABS/Polycarbonate	70–120	1
Acrylics	No track	2
Acrylic/PVC alloy	42–80	2
Alkyd	180	2
Allyl Diglycol Carbonate	185	2
Poly(amide-imide)	125	2
Poly(aryl ether)	> 180	1
Poly(butylene terephthalate), unreinforced	75–190	2
Poly(butylene terephthalate), 15–40% glass reinforced	125–146	2
Poly(butylene terephthalate), glass reinforced, flame retardant	85–130	2
Poly(butylene terephthalate), 10–30% mineral filled	125–130	2
Poly(butylene terephthalate), high impact	129–146	2
PBT/PET, 15–30% glass reinforced	68–136	2
Polycarbonate, unfilled	120	2
Polycarbonate, 20% glass reinforced	120	2
Celcon, standard	240	2
Celcon, 25% glass reinforced	142	2
Cellulose acetate	310	1
Cellulose propionate	190	1
Poly(chlorotrifluoroethylene)	> 360	1
Delrin, standard	129	2
Delrin, 20% glass reinforced	188	2
Diallyl phthalate, Orlon filled	85–115	2
Diallyl phthalate, Dacron filled	105–125	2
Diallyl phthalate, asbestos filled	125–140	2
Diallyl phthalate, glass-fiber filled	125–135	2
Epoxies, Bisphenol A, cast rigid	100	2
Epoxies, Bisphenol A, cast flexible	75–98	2
Epoxies, Bisphenol A, molded	135–190	2
Epoxies, Novolac, molded, mineral filled	180–185	2
Epoxies, Cycloaliphatic, cast, rigid	120	2
Polyesters, cast, rigid	115–135	2
Polyesters, cast, flexible	125–145	2
Polyesters, high strength, glass-fiber reinforced	130–170	2
Poly(ether sulfone)	116	2
Ethyl cellulose	60–80	1
Polyethylene, low density	160	1
Polyethylene, medium density	235	1
Poly(ethylene terephthalate), glass reinforced	81–126	2
Fluorinated ethylene propylene	> 165	2
Polyimide, unreinforced	152–230	2
Polyimide, glass reinforced	50–180	2
Ionomers	90	1
Melamine/formaldehyde resin	145	1
Melamine/phenol resin	180	1
Poly(methyl methacrylate)/Poly(vinyl chloride) alloy	25	1
Poly(α-methylstyrene/methyl methacrylate)	> 165	1

Material	Seconds	Ref.
Nylon 6, 30% glass-fiber reinforced	81–92	2
Nylon 66, general purpose	120	2
Nylon 66, 30% glass-fiber reinforced	148	2
Nylon 66, 40% glass-fiber reinforced	100	2
Nylon 66, 30% glass-fiber, molybdenum disulfide filled	135	2
Nylon 66, high impact	72–77	2
Phenolics, general purpose, woodflour filled	5–60	2
Phenolics, very high shock, glass-fiber filled	60	2
Phenolics, arc resistant, mineral filled	180	2
Phenolics, rubber, woodflour filled	7–20	2
Poly(phenylene oxides), Noryl, SE-100	75	2
Poly(phenylene oxides), Noryl, SE-1	75	2
Poly(phenylene oxides), Noryl, 30% glass-fiber reinforced	120	2
Polyphenylene sulfide, glass and mineral filled	182–200	2
Polyphenylene sulfide, 40% glass reinforced	34	2
Polyphenyl sulfone	41	2
Polypropylene, general purpose	126–136	2
Polypropylene, high impact	123–140	2
Polypropylene, glass reinforced	73–77	2
Polypropylene, flame retardant	15–40	2
Polysilicone, cast resin	60–130	1
Polystyrenes, general purpose	60–135	2
Polystyrenes, medium impact	20–135	2
Polystyrenes, high impact	20–100	2
Polystyrenes, 30% glass-fiber reinforced	28	2
Poly(styrene/acrylonitrile) (SAN)	100–150	2
Poly(styrene/acrylonitrile), 30% glass reinforced	65	2
Poly(styrene/butadiene)	95	1
Polysulfones, standard	122	2
Polysulfones, 30% glass-fiber reinforced	114	2
Poly(tetrafluoroethylene)	> 200	2
Poly(tetrafluoroethylene/hexafluoropropylene)	> 165	1
Poly(trifluorochloroethylene)	> 360	2
PVC	60–80	1
Poly(vinylidene fluoride)	50–60	2

REFERENCES

1. J. Brandrup and E. H. Immergut, Eds., *Polymer Handbook*, Wiley-Interscience, New York (1977).
2. Vishn Shah, *Handbook of Plastics Testing Technology*, Wiley-Interscience, New York (1984).

APPENDIX 5
ELECTRICAL CONDUCTIVITY

Polymer	Conductivity $(\Omega \text{ cm})^{-1}$	Dopant Species	Ref.
Polyacene (from β-chlorovinyl ketone)	100	–	1
Polyacene quinones (PAQR polymers)	300	–	2
Polyacetylene	970	AsF_5	3
Polyacetylene, aligned	3,200	AsF_5	4
Poly(acetylene/bromoacetylene)	10	I_2	5
Poly(acetylene/methylacetylene)	40	AsF_5	6
Poly(acetylene/isoprene) (AB blocks)	10	I_2	7
Poly(acetylene/styrene) (AB blocks)	10	I_2	7
Polyacrylonitrile, pyrolyzed	20	–	8
Polyacrylonitrile/Ag salt, pyrolyzed	100	–	9
Polyalkyl, aryl silanes	10	AsF_5	10
Polyaniline	10	BF_4^-	11
Polyazulene	1	BF_4^-	12
BBB(benzimidazobenzophenanthroline), Pyrrone	1	H_2SO_4	13
BBL, Pyrrone	20	H_2SO_4	13
Poly(copper octacyanophthalocyanine)	8	–	15
Poly(3,7-dibenzothiophene sulfide)	18.5	AsF_5	16
Poly(divinylbenzene), pyrolyzed	100	–	17
Ion exchange resins containing Ni, Al, Na, Ca, Th; pyrolyzed	100	–	18
Polyfuran	50	CF_3SO_3-	19
Kapton, pyrolyzed	20	–	20
Poly(metal phthalocyanines)	100	–	21
Poly(metal tetrathiooxalates)	20	–	22
Poly(3,3'-N-methyl carbazoyl)	5	I_2	23
Poly(3-methyl thiophene)	100	CF_3SO_3-	24
Poly(p-phenylene)	500	AsF_5	25
Polyphenothiazine type (PTL)	1	naphthalide	37
Poly(p-phenylene)	3,000	Na	26
Poly(p-phenylene-1,3,4-oxadiazole), pyrolyzed	510	–	27
Poly(p-phenylene oxide)	100	AsF_5	28
Poly(p-phenylene sulfide)	200	AsF_5	29
Poly(p-phenylene vinylene), aligned	500	AsF_5	30
Polypyrene	1	ClO_4	12
Polypyrrole	100	BF_4^-	31
Polypyrrole, layered structure	160	SO_3-	32
Pyrrone I	20	Cs electride	14
Pyrrone II	2	Cs electride	14
Polyquinoline	50	naphthalide	33
Polyquinoline	20	Cs electride	14
Polyquinoxalines	20	Cs electride	14
Polysulfur nitride	1,730	–	34
Polysulfur nitride	40,000	Br_2	35
Poly(tetrachlorophenyl thioether)	1	–	9
Poly(thiophene)	20	$CF_3SO_3^-$	24
Polyynes, pyrolyzed	2	–	36

REFERENCES

1. A. Rembaum, J. Moacanin, H. A. Pohl, Prog. Dielectr. *6*, 41 (1965); A. N.Nesmeyanov, M. I. Rybinskaia, G. L. Slonimskii, Vysokomol. Soedin. *2*, 526(1960).
2. J. W. Mason, H. A. Pohl, R. D. Hartman, J. Polym. Sci., Part C *17*, 187 (1967); R. D. Hartman, H. A. Pohl, J. Polym. Sci., Part A-1 *6*, 1135 (1968).
3. P. J. Nigrey, A. G. MacDiarmid, A. J. Heeger, J. Chem. Soc., Chem. Comm. 594 (1979).
4. M. A. Druy, C. H. Tansg, N. Brown, A. J. Heeger, A. G. MacDiarmid, J. Polym. Sci., Polym. Phys. Ed. *18*, 429 (1980).
5. M. J. Kletter, A. G. McDiarmid, A. J. Heeger, E. Faulques, S. Lefant, P.Bernier, J. Polym. Sci., Polym. Lett. Ed. *20*, 211 (1982).
6. G. E. Wnek, J. C. W. Chien, F. E. Karasz, Org. Coat. Plast. Chem. *43*, 88 (1980).
7. M. Aldissi, J. Chem. Soc., Chem. Comm. 1347 (1984).
8. N. Grassie, J. C. McHeill, J. Polym. Sci. *17*, 707 (1958).
9. H. A. Pohl in *Modern Aspects of the Vitreous State*, J. D. Mackenzie, Ed., Butterworths, London (1962), Vol. 2, p. 72.
10. R. West, L. D. David, P. I. Djurovich, K. L. Stearley, K. S. U. Srinivasan, H. Yu, J. Am. Chem. Soc. *103*, 7352 (1981); John Ziegler, personal communication, October 1985.
11. A. G. MacDiarmid, J. C. Chiang, M. Halpern, W. S. Huang, S. L. Mu, N. L. D. Somasiri, W. Wu, S. I. Yaniger, Mol. Cryst. Liq. Cryst. *121*, 173 (1985).
12. J. Bargon, S. Mohmand, R. J. Waltman, IBM J. Res. Dev. *27*, 330 (1983).
13. O. K. Kim, J. Polym. Sci., Polym. Lett. Ed. *20*, 663 (1982).
14. R. Liepins, M. Aldissi, Mol. Cryst. Liq. Cryst. *105*, 151 (1984).
15. J. W-P. Lin, L. P. Dudek, J. Polym. Sci., Polym. Chem Ed. *23*, 1589 (1985).
16. R. L. Elsenbaumer, L. W. Shacklette, J. Polym. Sci., Polym. Phys. Ed. *20*, 1781 (1982).
17. F. H. Winslow, W. O. Baker, W. A. Yager, J. Am. Chem. Soc. *77*, 4751 (1955).
18. H. A. Pohl, in *Proceedings of the Fourth Conference on Carbon*, Pergamon, London (1960), p. 241; H. A. Pohl, J. P. Laherre, ibid, p. 259; H. A. Pohl, J. P. Laherre, in *Proceedings of the Princeton University Conference on Semiconduction in Molecular Solids*, Ivy-Curtie Press, Princeton, N.J. (1960), p. 93.
19. G. Taurillon, F. Garnier, J. Electroanal. Chem. *135*, 173 (1982).
20. A. Rembaum, J. Polym. Sci., Part C (29), 157 (1970).
21. T. J. Marks, Science *227*, 881 (1985).
22. J. R. Reynolds, J. C. W. Chien, F. E. Karasz, C. P. Lillya, Polymer Preprints *25*(2), 242 (1984).
23. S. T. Wellinghoff, Z. Deng, J. Reed, and J. Racchini, Polymer Preprints *25*(2), 238 (1984); J. W. P. Lin, L. Dudek, J. Polym. Sci., Polym. Chem.Ed. *18*, 2689 (1980); T. Yamamoto, K. Sanechika, A. Yamamoto, J. Polym. Sci.,Polym. Lett. Ed. *18*, 9 (1980).
24. G. Tourillion, F. Garnier, J. Phys. Chem. *87*, 2289 (1983).
25. D. M. Ivory, G. G. Miller, J. M. Sowa, L. W. Shacklette, R. R. Chance, R. H. Baughman, J. Chem. Phys. *71*, 1506 (1979).
26. L. W. Shacklette, R. R. Chance, D. M. Ivory, G. G. Miller, R. H. Baughman, Synth. Met. *1*, 307 (1979).
27. M. Murakami, H. Yasujima, Y. Yumoto, S. Mizogami, S. Yoshimura, Solid StateComm. *45*, 1085 (1983).
28. J. E. Frommer, R. L. Elsenbaumer, personal communication.
29. J. E. Frommer, R. L. Elsenbaumer, R. R. Chance, ACS Symposium Ser *242*, 447 (1984).
30. D. R. Gagnon, J. O. Capistran, F. E. Karasz, R. W. Lenz, Polymer Preprints,Am. Chem. Soc. Div. Polym. Chem. *25*(2), 284 (1984).
31. A. F. Diaz, K. K. Kanazawa, G. P. Gardini, J. Chem. Soc., Chem. Commun. 635 (1979); K. K. Kanazawa, A. F. Diaz, W. D. Gill, P. M. Grant, G. B. Street, G. P. Gardini, J. F. Kwak, Syn. Metals *1*, 329 (1980).
32. W. Werner, M. Monkenbusch, G. Wegner, Makromol. Chem. Rapid Commun. *5*, 157 (1984).
33. Y. S. Papir, V. P. Kurkov, S. P. Current, "Synthesis and Chemical Doping of New Tractable Electrically Conducting Polymers," Abstract No. 543, The Electrochemical Soc. Inc., Annual Meeging, San Francisco, May 8-13, 1983; S. E.Tunney, J. Suenaga, J. K. Stille, Macromolecules *16*, 1398 (1983).
34. V. V. Walatka, M. M. Labes, J. H. Perlstein, Phys. Rev. Lett. *31*, 1139 (1973).
35. W. D. Gill, T. C. Clarke, G. B. Street, Appl. Phys. Commun. *2*(4), 211 (1982-83).

36. L. I. Kotlyarevskii, L. B. Fisher, A. A. Dulov, A. A. Slinkin, A. M. Rubinstein, High Mol. Comp. USSR *4*, 174 (1962); M. Hatano, S. Kambara, S. Okamoto, J. Chem. Soc. Japan, Ind. Chem. Sec. *65*, 716 (1962); A. V. Topchiev, J. Polym. Sci. Part A-1, 591 (1963); V. V. Korshak, V. I. Kasatochkin,A. M. Sladkov, J. P. Kudrjawzew, K. Usenbaev, Dokl. Akad. Nauk, SSSR *136*, 1342 (1961).
37. O. K. Kim, Mol. Cryst. Liq. Cryst. *105*, 161 (1984).

APPENDIX 6
WATER VAPOR PERMEABILITY

Polymer	$P \times 10^{10}$ [cm^3 (STP)cm cm^{-2}s^{-1} (cm HG)$^{-1}$]	Temp. (C°)	Ref.
Poly(acrylonitrile)	300	25	1
Poly(acrylonitrile/methylacrylate/ butadiene), 79/15/6	1,300	25	1
Poly(acrylonitrile/styrene), 86/14	850	25	1
Poly(acrylonitrile/styrene), 66/34	2,000	25	1
Poly(acrylonitrile/styrene), 57/43	2,500	25	1
Barex (Sohio)	660	25	1
Poly(butadiene)	5,070	37.5	2
Polycarbonate (Lexan)	1,400	25	9
Cellulose (Cellophane)	1,900	25	4
Cellulose acetate	5,500	25	3
Cellulose nitrate	6,300	25	5
Poly(chloroprene) (Neoprene G)	910	25	6
Ethyl cellulose	12,000	20	7
Poly(dimethylsiloxane), 100% filler, vulcanized	43,000	35	12
Poly(ethyl methacrylate)	3,200	25	8
Polyethylene, d 0.964	12	25	3
Poly(ethylene/propylene), 60/40	450	37.5	2
Poly(ethylene terephthalate), crystalline	130	25	3
Gutta Percha	510	25	3
Poly(isobutene/isoprene), 98/2 (butyl rubber)	110	37.5	2
Polyisoprene (natural rubber)	2,290	25	6
Polyisoprene hydrochloride (Pliofilm)	16	25	7
Lopac (Monsanto)	340	25	1
Poly(methacrylonitrile)	410	25	1
Poly(methacrylonitrile/styrene), 97/3	490	25	1
Poly(methacrylonitrile/styrene), 82/18	930	25	1
Poly(methacrylonitrile/styrene), 61/39	1,700	25	1
Poly(methacrylonitrile/styrene), 53/47	1,900	25	1
Poly(methacrylonitrile/styrene), 38/62	2,100	25	1
Poly(methacrylonitrile/styrene), 18/82	2,000	25	1
Poly(methylacrylonitrile/styrene butadiene), 88/7/5	600	25	1
Poly(methylacrylonitrile/styrene butadiene), 83/7/10	670	25	1
Poly(methylacrylonitrile/styrene butadiene), 78/7/15	770	25	1
Nylon 6	177	25	10
Poly(oxy–2,6–dimethyl–1,4–phenylene)	4,060	25	11
Poly(oxymethylene)	910	25	13
Polypropylene	51	25	3
Polystyrene	1,200	25	10
Poly(trifluorochloroethylene) (Kel–F)	0.29	25	10
Poly(vinyl chloride)	275	25	14
Poly(vinylidene chloride) (Saran)	0.5	25	3

REFERENCES

1. M. Salame, Polymer Symposia *41*, 46 (1973).
2. Y. Iyengar, J. Polymer Sci. B *3*, 663 (1965).
3. A. W. Myers, J. A. Myers, C. E. Rogers, V. Stannett, and M. Szwarc, TAPPI *44*, 58 (1961).
4. P. M. Hauser and A. D. Mclaren, Ind. Eng. Chem., Intern. Ed. *40*, 112 (1948).
5. P. Y. Hsieh, J. Appl. Polymer Sci. *1*, 1743 (1963).
6. R. L. Taylor, D. B. Herrmann, and A. R. Kemp, Ind. Eng. Chem. Intern. Ed. *28*, 1255 (1936).
7. H. Yasuda and V. Stannett, J. Polym. Sci. *57*, 907 (1962).
8. V. Stannett and J. L. Williams, J. Polym. Sci. C *10*, 45 (1966).
9. F. J. Norton, J. Appl. Polymer Sci. *7*, 1649 (1963).
10. A. W. Myers, V. Tammela, V. Stannett, and M. Szwarc, Modern Plastics *37*, No. 10, 139 (1960).
11. H. Yasuda and V. Stannett, J. Macromol. Sci. Phys. B *3*(4), 589 (1969).
12. J. A. Barrie and B. Plott, Polymer *4*, 303 (1963).
13. J. L. Williams and V. Stannett, J. Appl. Polym. Sci. *14*, 1949 (1970).
14. B. P. Tikhomirov, H. B. Hopfenberg, V. T. Stannett, and J. L. Williams, Makromol. Chem. *118*, 177 (1968).

APPENDIX 7
WATER ABSORPTION
ASTM D570

Material	Wt%	Ref.
ABS	0.6–1.0	1
ABS, high impact	0.20	2
Poly(acrylonitrile/methyl acrylate), rubber modified	0.28	1
Poly(aryl ether)	0.25	2
Poly(l-butene)	< 0.1	2
Poly(carbonate)	0.35	1
Polycarbonate/ABS alloy	0.20	2
Cellulose, regenerated (Cellophane)	45–115	1
Cellulose acetate	3–8.5	1
Cellulose acetate butyrate	1–2	1
Cellulose nitrate	1–2	1
Cellulose propionate	1.5–2.5	1
Cellulose triacetate	2–4.5	1
Poly(chlorotrifluoroethylene)	0	2
Epoxy cast resins	0.08	2
Polyester, rigid, cast	0.15	2
Poly (ether sulfone)	2.1	1
Ethyl cellulose	2.5–7.5	1
Polyethylene, low density	< 0.01	1
Polyethylene, medium density	< 0.01	1
Polyethylene, high density	< 0.01	1
Polyethylene, ultra high mol. wt.	nil	1
Poly(ethylene/chlorotrifluoroethylene)	< 0.02	1
Poly(ethylene/ethyl acrylate)	0.04	2
Poly(ethylene/propylene)	< 0.01	2
Poly(ethylene terephthalate)	< 0.8	1
Poly(ethylene/tetrafluoroethylene)	< 0.02	1
Poly(ethylene/vinyl acetate)	< 0.01	1
Fluorinated ethylene/propylene copolymer	< 0.01	1
Polyimide	2.9	1
Ionomer	0.4	1
Melamine-formaldehyde resin	0.30–0.50	2
Melamine-phenol resin	0.30–0.65	2
Poly(methyl methacrylate), standard	0.3–0.4	1
Poly(methyl methacrylate), Type A (Korad acrylic)	1.4–1.6	1
Poly(methyl methacrylate/PVC)	0.13	2
Poly(methylpentene)	0.005	1
Poly(α-methyl styrene/methyl methacrylate)	0.20	2
Nylon 6, extruded	9.5	1
Nylon 11	0.27	1
Nylon 12	0.25	1
Nylon 66	1.5	2
Poly(oxymethylene)	0.22–0.25	2
Perfluoroalkyl	< 0.03	1
Phenol-formaldehyde resin	0.10–0.20	2
Poly(phenylene oxide)	0.06	2
Polypropylene, extruded	< 0.005	1
Polypropylene, biaxially oriented	< 0.005	1
Polystyrene	0.04–0.10	1

Material	Wt%	Ref.
Polystyrene, high impact	0.05–0.20	2
Polystyrene, high heat stable	0.05–040	2
Poly(styrene/acrylonitrile)	0.20–0.30	2
Poly(styrene/butadiene)	0.19–0.39	2
Polysulfone	0.30	1
Polytetrafluoroethylene (Teflon)	0	2
Poly(tetrafluoroethylene/ hexafluoropropylene)	0.01	2
Polyurethane, elastomer	0.55–0.77	1
Poly(vinyl butyral)	1.0–2.0	2
Poly(vinyl chloride), nonplasticized	nil	1
Poly(vinyl chloride), plasticized	nil	1
Poly(vinyl chloride), chlorinated	0.02–0.15	2
Poly(vinyl chloride), ABS modified	0.20	2
Poly(vinyl chloride/vinyl acetate)	nil	1
Poly(vinyl chloride/propylene)	0.07–0.40	2
Poly(vinyl fluoride)	< 0.50	1
Poly(vinyl formal)	1.0–1.3	2
Vinyl nitrile rubber	nil	1
Poly(vinylidene chloride)	0.10	2
Poly(vinylidene fluoride)	0.04	1

REFERENCES

1. J. Agrannof, Ed., *Modern Plastics Encyclopedia* Vol. 60, No. 10A, McGraw-Hill, New York, 1983 to 1984.
2. J. Brandrup and E. H. Immergut, Eds., *Polymer Handbook*, Wiley Interscience, New York (1977).

AUTHOR INDEX

SUBJECT INDEX